A Charlton Standard Catalogue

CW00794740

CAITHNESS PAPERWEIGHTS

Second Edition

By

COLIN TERRIS

W. K. CROSS

Publisher

The Charlton Press

TORONTO, ONTARIO • PALM HARBOR, FLORIDA

Canadian Catalogue in Publication Data

The National Library of Canada has catalogued this publication as follows:

Main entry under title:

The Charlton standard catalogue of Caithness Glass paperweights

Biennial
1st ed.-
ISSN 1481-8051
ISBN 0-88968-244-5 (2nd edition)

1. Caithness Glass Ltd. Catalogs. 2. Paperweights Scotland Catalogs.

NK5440.P3C4   748.840294411   C99-900175-2

EDITORIAL

Editor	Jean Dale
Pricing Editor	W. K. Cross
Editorial Assistant	Susan Cross
Graphic Technician	Davina Rowan

ACKNOWLEDGEMENTS

The Charlton Press wishes to thank those who have helped with the second edition of *The Charlton Standard Catalogue of Caithness Glass Paperweights*. Also we would like to thank the author, Colin Terris, for his work on the second edition. Colin, now retired, headed the design department at Caithness Glass and is not in anyway connected with the pricing in this guide.

Contributors to the Second Edition

Rhona Burns, The Caithness Glass Company Limited, Scotland; Sam Welsh, Paperweight Collectors' Society, Scotland

A SPECIAL NOTE TO COLLECTORS

We welcome and appreciate any comments or suggestions in regard to *The Charlton Standard Catalogue of Caithness Glass Paperweights*. If any errors or omissions come to your attention, please write to us, or if you would like to participate in pricing or supply previously unavailable data or information, please contact Jean Dale at (416) 488-1418 or e-mail us at chpress@charltonpress.com.

**Printed in Canada
in the Province of Ontario**

The Charlton Press

Editorial Office
P.O. Box 820, Station Willowdale B
North York, Ontario M2K 2R1 Canada
Telephone: (416) 488-1418 Fax: (416) 488-4656
Telephone: (800) 442-6042 Fax: (800) 442-1542
www.charltonpress.com;
e-mail: chpress@charltonpress.com

HOW TO USE THIS GUIDE

THE PURPOSE

This publication has been designed to serve two specific purposes: first, to furnish collectors with accurate and detailed listings that will provide the information needed to build a rich and rewarding collection; second, to provide collectors and dealers with an indication of the current market prices of Caithness Glass paperweights.

THE LISTINGS

The Charlton Standard Catalogue of Caithness Glass Paperweights, 2nd edition is divided into two chapters, the first being devoted to the general collection of Caithness Glass weights and the second, to specially commissioned and exclusive weights.

In the first chapter, designs are listed in numerical order to 1997, and beginning in 1998 alphabetically within the year. In the second chapter, the companies that commissioned the weights are listed alphabetically, and the weights for these companies are listed in alphabetical order.

STYLES AND VERSIONS

All listings include the name of the weight, designer, type (i.e. shape), date of issue and edition size, status, series, original issue price and current value. Two points should be noted. First, if only a year is given for the edition, this means that the edition is unlimited. Second, American issue prices do not appear for weights issued prior to 1978, when Caithness began to expand its global distribution and to market its products more intensively in the U.S.

Styles: A change in style occurs when a design is altered or modified by a deliberate change that will result in a new design carrying the same name.

Versions: Versions are modifications in a major style element.

Variations: Variations are modifications in a minor style element. A change in colour is a variation.

PRICING AND THE INTERNET

Over the past thirty years we have gathered pricing information from auctions, dealer submissions, direct mail catalogues and newsletters, all contributed prices on one of two levels, wholesale or retail. We, at the Charlton Press, consider auctions basically a dealer affair, while price lists, naturally retail. To equate both prices, we needed to adjust the auction results upward, by a margin of 30% to 40%, allowing for dealer markups, before comparing and then looking for a consensus on a retail price.

The marketplace has changed, the Internet and on-line auctions are growing at such a rate that all other pricing sources we used are being completely overwhelmed by the sheer weight of the items being offered.

At a moment in time, on July 26, 2004 under the Caithness Glass category on e-Bay over 125 individual items were posted for sale. Assuming this is an average day, then for the week, 875 items are offered and for the year nearly 46,000 will be offered for sale. The "Economists" put the on-line auctions with now over 100,000,000 registered users.

The impact the Internet will have on collectables has yet to be appreciated by collectors and dealers alike. All the old avenues such as fairs, shows, dealer stores, retail outlets, direct mail houses and auction rooms are being forced to change due to the extreme pressure of this new marketing force. Margins have come under pressure, wholesale and retail prices are starting to blend, and competition for the Collectors' budget will intensify. However, through it all one point remains, a price guide is just that, a guide, the final say is between the buyer and the seller.

TABLE OF CONTENTS

INTRODUCTION

How Caithness Glass Entered the Paperweight Field   vi
The Author   vi
The Designer Team   vi
Collecting Caithness Paperweights   viii

CAITHNESS GLASS PAPERWEIGHT COLLECTORS' SOCIETY   ix

CAITHNESS GLASS VISITOR CENTRES   ix

CAITHNESS GLASS FACTORY SHOPS   ix

INTERNET AND CUSTOMER ENQUIRIES   ix

FURTHER READING   x

PART ONE
Caithness Collection   1

PART TWO
Commissioned and Exclusive Weights   323

ALPHABETICAL INDEX   373

INTRODUCTION

HOW CAITHNESS GLASS ENTERED THE PAPERWEIGHT FIELD

In 1961, Robin Sinclair founded Caithness Glass in Wick, in north eastern Scotland. The company's artglass output did not originally include paperweights, but this would change with the arrival in 1962 of Paul Ysart, who was interested in making millefiori paperweights. When Colin Terris joined Caithness in 1968 to establish an engraving studio, he met Paul, the company's training officer, and soon began to experiment with ideas, techniques and designs far removed from the conventional style of paperweight design. In 1969, Colin designed the first modern-style Caithness Glass paperweights, the Planets set, which was an instant success.

At the time the first weights were released, the paperweight team consisted of two people working in a corner of the Wick factory. In 1969, Caithness established a second factory in Oban and in 1979 opened the Perth factory. In 1992, new glassworks and visitors centres were opened in both Wick and Oban. By 1993, fourty-four people were involved in the paperweight-production process. Caithness centralized paperweight production in Perth in September 1995.

Over time, Caithness also expanded its roster of designers to include Alastair MacIntosh and Helen MacDonald, among others. This has translated into a diverse range of paperweight designs, from double magnum to miniature weights and from modern to traditional ones, more than 2,300 in total. Caithnesss paperweight output has developed a following among collectors the world over and has brought the company from its small beginnings to its current status as the world's leading producer of fine-quality glass paperweights.

THE AUTHOR

Colin Terris

Colin Terris

Colin Terris was born in Kirkcaldy in the Kingdom of Fife, Scotland, in 1937. A graduate of the Edinburgh College of Art, he specialised in glass design and, in 1960, went to Norway to further his skills in the intricate art of copperwheel glass engraving. He spent a year there, and on his return to Scotland he taught art for eight years before joining Caithness Glass to establish an engraving studio in 1968. Colin met the company's training officer, the legendary Paul Ysart, and was soon experimenting with paperweight design. His Planets series weights, the first modern-style Caithness Glass paperweights, were an instant success and marked the creation of a new category of artglass: the modern or contemporary paperweight. His work includes the Colin Terris Designer Collection, launched in 1997; and the Colin Terris Water Lily Collection, produced in 1998; and the Colin Terris Rose Collection, issued in 1999.

Colin was made a Member of the Order of the British Empire (MBE) in 1991 in recognition of his contribution to British glass, and his work can be seen in most major paperweight collections. He is recognized internationally as The Father of Modern Paperweight Design.

THE DESIGN TEAM

Helen MacDonald

Helen MacDonald

Helen was born in Caithness, Scotland, in 1958. She joined Caithness Glass in Wick as a trainee glass engraver in 1974 and, by 1979, had attained the highest skill rating in the engraving studios.

In 1985, she transferred to the Perth factory and engraved many prestige presentation pieces, including a number for members of the Royal Family. The year 1991 saw Helens first paperweight designs, and since that time her main design effort has been channelled in this direction. Her biblical theme series, which began with Covenant in 1995, is ongoing and is a great favourite with collectors, including those in the U.S., where she has been known mainly for her satin-finished weights and the engraving of the Studio Collection.

Each year, the designers attend a number of paperweight promotions at various locations in the U.K. and the U.S. Collectors have the opportunity to meet the designers and view a large selection of weights from that years collection.

Alastair MacIntosh

Alastair MacIntosh was born in Falkirk, Scotland, in 1951. A graduate of the Edinburgh College of Art, he specialised in glass design and was taught by master glassmakers Ken Wainwright and Andrew Scott.

From 1981 to 1987, he ran his own small glassworks, MacIntosh Glass, where he produced and made bowls, vases, perfume bottles and paperweights. He joined Caithness Glass in 1987 and since then has been actively involved in all aspects of product design and development. His first paperweight design for Caithness was Jamboree, issued in 1988 in a limited edition of 500. The Alastair MacIntosh Collection, a series of weights that illustrate his distinctive style, was released in 1999.

Alastair MacIntosh

OTHER MEMBERS OF THE DESIGN TEAM

Gordon Hendry

Sarah Peterson

Sarah Cable

Allan Scott

Linda Campbell

COLLECTING CAITHNESS PAPERWEIGHTS

Production over the years has evolved into three major groups, modern, traditional and Whitefriars. Each group may then be subdivided into limited or unlimited editions depending upon the group. For example, modern weights have always been issued in limited and unlimited editions. Given the range of weights produced, collectors should focus their collections on a particular aspect of Caithnesss output, as the following outline illustrates.

Modern Design

For this collection, designers and glassmakers use new colours, facetting, styles and making techniques to create original designs, often referred to by some as "abstract design."

These innovative weights are issued both in limited and unlimited editions. Caithness Glass, which has produced these weights since 1969, is considered the world leader in the design of modern weights.

Traditional Design

These limited-edition weights are produced in the traditional style of paperweights manufactured. Lampworked designs are first formed and then embedded in glass to form a great variety of weights. They will feature designs from the sea and wildlife themes to animals, insects and flowers.

Whitefriars Design

These limited-edition weights in the classical style illustrate floral themes using traditional millefiori and lampwork techniques combined with vibrant colours and new facetting styles. All weights in this collection contain the famous friar or monk signature cane.

FORMING A COLLECTION

A collector may choose to focus on a particular collection, such as Modern, Traditional or Whitefriars and then within these groups to further focus on design charactersitics which may be of interest.

Whatever the method by which a collection is built, the collector will surely find it satisfying to acquire and view these skilfullly crafted works of art.

With the entensive range or weights available it is only sensible to centre on one style of weight. To vary at the early stages can only lead to confusion of tastes, ending later with weights in the "will I buy that" category.

Choose one of three major style groups, modern, traditional or White Friars. Now within these groups you may further subdivide into the minor style groupings, engraved, smooth or facetted, or possibly a little of each.

By Style

A collector may wish to collect only engraved weights, or only smooth or facetted weights, for example.

By Colourway

A collector may concentrate on acquiring weights of a certain colour, such as heather or green.

Again the colourway theme can be carried into similar weights that differ only in colour.

By Shape

Collecting weights in a particular shape is another option. Weights are produced in spherical, domed egg and teardrop shapes, among others.

By Size

Acquiring weights of a particular size such as miniature, medium or magnum may appeal to a collector.

Medium and Miniature: This collection of distinctive weights in medium and miniature sizes was introduced in 1985. The weights are available in limited and unlimited editions.

Millefiori Miniatures: These weights in the classical style feature canes surrounding a lampworked design, They are available in limited and unlimited editions.

By Theme

In the Traditional weights, for example, one may collect the sea creatures that are embedded in glass, or possibly insects or the beautiful butterflies. The theme collection favours the lampwork design weight.

By Designer

The work of a particular designer such as Colin Terris, Alastair MacIntosh or Helen MacDonald may interest a collector. Of course you may have the designer within that special group that you have chosen.

INSURING YOUR PAPERWEIGHTS

As with any other of your valuables, making certain your paperweights are protected is a very important concern. It is paramount that you display or store any glass items in a secure place - preferably one safely away from traffic in the home.

Your paperweights are most often covered under your basic homeowner's policy and there are generally three kinds of such policies - standard, broad and comprehensive. Each has its own specific deductible and terms.

Under a general policy, your paperweights are considered 'contents' and are covered for all of the perils covered under the contractual terms of your policy (fire, theft, water damage and so on).

However, since glass paperweights are delicate, breakage is treated differently by most insurance companies. There is usually an extra premium attached to insure glass against accidental breakage or carelessness by the owner. This is sometimes referred to as 'fine arts' rider. You are advised to contact your insurance professional to get all the answers.

In order to help you protect yourself, it is critical that you take inventory of your paperweights and have colour photographs taken of all your pieces. This is the surest method of clearly establishing, for the police and your insurance company, the items lost or destroyed. It is also the easiest way to establish their replacement value in the event of a tragedy

CAITHNESS GLASS PAPERWEIGHT COLLECTORS' SOCIETY

In 1976, the Caithness Glass Paperweight Collectors' Society was formed, and the International Society was created in 1995 to serve collectors in countries where there is no national Caithness Glass Society.

The Society is the clearing-house for all information on Caithness paperweights. Members are entitled to receive Reflections, the magazine published twice a year by the Society, as well as catalogues and a personal tour of the Paperweight Studios in Perth, Scotland, if they are ever in the area.

New members receive a free paperweight upon joining, and all members receive advance notice of new or specially commissioned weights and have an opportunity to purchase the Collectors Paperweights for the year, available exclusively to Society members. The Society holds a biennial international convention in Scotland in October.

To join the Caithness Glass Paperweight Collectors' Society, please contact the Society at one of the addresses or telephone numbers opposite:

In the U.K. and International:
Caithness Glass Paperweight Collectors' Society
The Caithness Glass Company Ltd
Inveralmond, Perth PH1 3TZ, Scotland
Tel: (44) (0) 1738 492329
Fax: (44) (0) 1738 492300
E-mail: collector@caithnessglass.co.uk

In the U.S.A.:
Caithness Glass Paperweight Collectors' Society
The Royal China & Porcelain Companies Inc.
1265 Glen Avenue
Moorestown, NJ 08057 U.S.A.
Tel: (856) 866-2900
Fax: (856) 866-2499
E-mail: caithness@royalchina.com

CAITHNESS GLASS VISITOR CENTRES

Perth Factory and Visitor Centre

Opened in 1979 in Perth, Scotland, the Visitor Centre is home to the largest public display of Caithness paperweights with over 1,200 designs. There is a resident engraver, and a spacious viewing gallery enables visitors to watch the paperweight-making process from start to finish. In addition, there is a large, well-stocked factory shop with lots of bargains. There is a large restaurant, a childrens play area, and ample free parking.

The Visitor Centre is open seven days a week all year, but the glassmaking section is in operation Monday to Friday all year. Admission to the Visitor Centre is free and no booking is required.

Inveralmond, Perth PH1 3TZ, Scotland
Tel.: (01738) 492320
Fax: (01738) 492300

Caithness Crystal Visitor Centre, Kings Lynn, Norfolk, England

At this centre, visitors can view demonstrations by Creative Glass glassmakers and browse in the well-stocked factory shop. There is also a spacious restaurant.

The factory shop and restaurant are open seven days a week all year. The glassmaking demonstrations can be seen Monday to Friday all year, and Saturday and Sunday from mid-June to mid-September. Admission to the Visitor Centre is free and no booking is required.

Paxman Road
Hardwick Industrial Estate
Kings Lynn, Norfolk, PE30 4NE, England
Tel.: (01553) 765111
Fax: (01553) 767628

Factory Shops

Caithness Glass Visitor Centre
Inveralmond
Perth PH1 3TZ, Scotland
Tel: (01738) 492320

Caithness Crystal Visitor Centre
Paxman Road
Hardwick Industrial Estate
Kings Lynn, Norfolk, PE30 4NE, England
Tel.: (01553) 765111
Fax: (01553) 767628

Internet and Customer Enquiries

Site: www.caithnessglass.co.uk
E-mail: collector@caithnessglass.co.uk

FURTHER READING

Books

All About Paperweights by Lawrence H. Selman
The Annual Bulletin of the Paperweight Collectors Association published by Collector Books
The Art of the Paperweight by Lawrence H. Selman
The Caithness Collection, 1981 by Glenn S. Johnson
Collectors Guide to Paperweights by Sara Rossi
The Dictionary of Paperweight Signature Canes — Identification and Dating by Andrew H. Dohan
The Encyclopedia of Glass Paperweights by Paul Hollister
The Glass Menagerie — A Study of Silhouette Canes in Antique Paperweights by John D. Hawley
Glass Paperweights, 2nd ed., by Patricia McCawley
Glass Paperweights by James MacKay
Identifying Antique Paperweights — Lampwork by George N. Kulles and Jean Kusy Kulles
Identifying Antique Paperweights — Millefiori by George N. Kulles
Old English Paperweights by Robert G. Hall
Paperweights by Sibylle Jargstorf
Paperweights: The Collector's Guide to Selecting and Enjoying New and Antique Paperweights by Pat Reilly
Paperweights of the World, 2nd ed., by Monika Flemming and Peter Pommerencke
Sotheby's Concise Encyclopedia of Glass by David Battie and Simon Cottle
Sulphides — The Art of Cameo Incrustation by Paul Jokelson

Magazines and Newsletters

Collecting Doulton Magazine, Contact Doug Pinchin, P.O. Box 310, Richmond, Surrey TW9 1FS England

Collect It! Contact subscription department at P.O. Box 3658, Bracknell, Berkshire RG12 7XZ, England.
Tel.: (1344) 868280 E-mail: collectit@dialpipex.com

Doulton News, published by Thorndon Antiques & Fine China Ltd., edited by David Harcourt
P.O. Box 12-076 (109 Molesworth Street), Wellington, New Zealand

Glass Collectors Digest, Contact subscription department at P.O. Box 553, Marietta, Ohio 45750, U.S.A.
Tel.: (800) 533-3433 E-mail: 102552.726@CompuServe.co

Reflections, published by the Caithness Glass Paperweight Collectors' Society: Inveralmond, Perth
PH1 3TZ, Scotland

Videos

Reflections — The Magic of Caithness Glass Paperweights, In the U.S., contact the Secretary of the Caithness Glass
Paperweight Collectors Society by phone at (973) 340-3330; in the U.K. and international, contact the
Secretary of the Caithness Glass Paperweight Collectors' Society by phone at (44) (0) 1738 492329.

CAITHNESS WEIGHTS

ISSUES OF 1969

CT-1A
MARS
Style One

Designer: Colin Terris
Type: Weight – Spherical
Issued: 1969 in a limited
edition of 500
Status: Fully subscribed
Series: Planets, Set One
O.I.P.: £40.00/set

	Mars	Set
U.K.:	£ 600.	2,500.
U.S.:	$1,000.	4,500.
Can.:	$1,300.	5,750.

Note: CT-1a,b, c and d were
issued and sold as a set.

CT-1B
MERCURY
Style One

Designer: Colin Terris
Type: Weight – Spherical
Issued: 1969 in a limited
edition of 500
Status: Fully subscribed
Series: Planets, Set One
O.I.P.: £40.00/set

U.K.:	£ 600.00
U.S.	$1,000.00
Can.:	$1,300.00

CT-1C
SATURN
Style One

Designer: Colin Terris
Type: Weight – Spherical
Issued: 1969 in a limited
edition of 500
Status: Fully subscribed
Series: Planets, Set One
O.I.P.: £40.00/set

U.K.:	£ 600.00
U.S.:	$1,000.00
Can.:	$1,300.00

CT-1D
VENUS
Style One

Designer: Colin Terris
Type: Weight – Spherical
Issued: 1969 in a limited
edition of 500
Status: Fully subscribed
Series: Planets, Set One
O.I.P.: £40.00/set

U.K.:	£ 600.00
U.S.:	$1,000.00
Can.:	$1,300.00

ISSUES OF 1970

CT-2
MOONFLOWER
First Variation

Designer: Colin Terris
Type: Weight – Spherical
Colour: Many colour variations
Issued: 1970
Status: Closed
Series: Unlimited – Modern Design
O.I.P.: £8.00

U.K.: £ 30.00
U.S.: $ 75.00
Can.: $100.00

CT-3
ORBIT

Designer: Colin Terris
Type: Weight – Spherical
Issued: 1970 in a limited edition of 500
Status: Fully subscribed
O.I.P.: £12.00

U.K.: £225.00
U.S.: $400.00
Can.: $525.00

CT-4A
URANUS

Designer: Colin Terris
Type: Weight – Spherical
Issued: 1970 in a limited edition of 500
Status: Fully subscribed
Series: Planets, Set Two
O.I.P.: £45.00/set

	Uranus	Set
U.K.:	£350.	1,500.
U.S.:	$625.	2,500.
Can.:	$800.	3,200.

Note: CT4a, b, c and d were issued and sold as a set.

CT-4B
JUPITER
Style One

Designer: Colin Terris
Type: Weight – Spherical
Issued: 1970 in a limited edition of 500
Status: Fully subscribed
Series: Planets, Set Two
O.I.P.: £45.00/set

U.K.: £350.00
U.S.: $625.00
Can.: $800.00

CT-4C
NEPTUNE

Designer: Colin Terris
Type: Weight – Spherical
Issued: 1970 in a limited edition of 500
Status: Fully subscribed
Series: Planets, Set Two
O.I.P.: £45.00/set

U.K.: £350.00
U.S.: $625.00
Can.: $800.00

CT-4D
EARTH
Style One

Designer: Colin Terris
Type: Weight – Spherical
Issued: 1970 in a limited edition of 500
Status: Fully subscribed
Series: Planets, Set Two
O.I.P.: £45.00/set

U.K.: £350.00
U.S.: $625.00
Can.: $800.00

ISSUES OF 1971

CT-5A
SUN

Designer: Colin Terris
Type: Weight – Spherical
Issued: 1971 in a limited
edition of 500
Status: Fully subscribed
Series: Planets, Set Three
O.I.P.: £40.00/set

	Sun	Set
U.K.:	£325.	975.
U.S.:	$575.	1,700.
Can.:	$750.	2,250.

Note: CT5a, b and c were
issued and sold as a set.

CT-5B
MOON

Designer: Colin Terris
Type: Weight – Spherical
Issued: 1971 in a limited
edition of 500
Status: Fully subscribed
Series: Planets, Set Three
O.I.P.: £40.00/set

U.K.:	£325.00
U.S.:	$575.00
Can.:	$750.00

CT-5C
PLUTO

Designer: Colin Terris
Type: Weight – Spherical
Issued: 1971 in a limited
edition of 500
Status: Fully subscribed
Series: Planets, Set Three
O.I.P.: £40.00/set

U.K.:	£325.00
U.S.:	$575.00
Can.:	$750.00

CT-6
SPIRAL

Designer: Colin Terris
Type: Weight – Spherical
Colour: 1. Purple/yellow
2. Purple/red
Issued: 1971 in a limited
edition of 500 for
each colourway
Status: 1. closed at 120
2. closed at 150
O.I.P.: £12.00

U.K.:	£200.00
U.S.:	$350.00
Can.:	$450.00

CT-7
STARBASE

Designer: Colin Terris
Type: Weight – Spherical
Issued: 1971 in a limited
edition of 500
Status: Fully subscribed
O.I.P.: £12.00

U.K.:	£350.00
U.S.:	$625.00
Can.:	$800.00

ISSUES OF 1972

CT-8
CORAL

Designer:	Colin Terris		
Type:	Weight – Spherical		
Colour:	1. Blue		
	2. Damson		
	3. Orange		
Issued:	1972 in a limited edition of 500 for each colourway		
Status:	Fully subscribed		
O.I.P.:	£15.00		

	Blue	Damson	Orange
U.K.:	£250.00	250.00	250.00
U.S.:	$450.00	450.00	450.00
Can.:	$575.00	575.00	575.00

CT-9
CASED CORAL

Designer:	Colin Terris		
Type:	Weight – Spherical		
Colour:	1. Blue		
	2. Damson		
	3. Orange		
Issued:	1972 in a limited edition of 100 for each colourway		
Status:	Fully subscribed		
O.I.P.:	£21.00		

	Blue	Damson	Orange
U.K.:	£150.00	150.00	150.00
U.S.:	$275.00	275.00	275.00
Can.:	$350.00	350.00	350.00

CT-10
HARLEQUIN SINGLE
Style One

Designer:	Paul Ysart
Type:	Weight – Spherical
Cane:	1. PH (Peter Holmes, 1972–75)
	2. CG (Caithness Glass, 1976)
Issued:	1972
Status:	Closed
O.I.P.:	£10.00

	PH	CG
U.K.:	£ 60.	60.
U.S.:	$100.	100.
Can.:	$125.	125.

CT-11
HARLEQUIN DOUBLE
Style One

Designer:	Paul Ysart
Type:	Weight – Domed
Cane:	1. PH (Peter Holmes, 1972–75)
	2. CG (Caithness Glass, 1976)
Issued:	1972
Status:	Closed
O.I.P.:	£14.00

	PH	CG
U.K.:	£125.	125.
U.S.:	$225.	225.
Can.:	$300.	300.

CT-12
INK BOTTLE

Designer:	Peter Holmes
Type:	Weight – Ink Bottle
Cane:	1. PH (Peter Holmes in stopper, 1972)
	2. CG (Caithness Glass in stopper, 1976)
Issued:	1972
Status:	Closed
O.I.P.:	£19.00

	PH	CG
U.K.:	£150.	150.
U.S.:	$275.	275.
Can.:	$350.	350.

CT-13
SUNFLOWER
Style One

Designer:	Colin Terris
Type:	Weight – Spherical
Issued:	1972 in a limited edition of 500
Status:	Fully subscribed
O.I.P.:	£12.00

U.K.:	£250.00
U.S.:	$450.00
Can.:	$575.00

CT-14
TROPICANA
Style One

Designer:	Peter Holmes
Type:	Weight – Spherical
Colour:	1. Pink
	2. Purple
	3. Yellow
Issued:	1972 in a limited edition of 500 for each colourway
Cane:	PH (Peter Holmes)
Status:	1. Fully subscribed
	2. Fully subscribed
	3. Closed at No. 487
O.I.P.:	£17.00

	Pink	Purple	Yellow
U.K.:	£125.00	125.00	125.00
U.S.:	$225.00	225.00	225.00
Can.:	$300.00	300.00	300.00

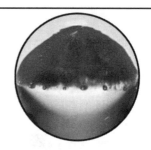

CT-15
JELLYFISH

Designer:	Colin Terris
Type:	Weight – Spherical
Colour:	1. Red
	2. Purple
	3. Green
Issued:	1972 in a limited edition of 500 for each colourway
Status:	1. Fully subscribed
	2. Fully subscribed
	3. Closed at No. 444
O.I.P.:	£9.00

	Red	Purple	Green
U.K.:	£40.00	40.00	40.00
U.S.:	$75.00	75.00	75.00
Can.:	$95.00	95.00	95.00

CT-16
SEA URCHIN

Designer:	Colin Terris
Type:	Weight – Spherical
Issued:	1972 in a limited edition of 500
Status:	Fully subscribed
O.I.P.:	£10.00
U.K.:	£ 65.00
U.S.:	$120.00
Can.:	$150.00

CT-17
SHIPWRECK

Designer:	Peter Holmes
Type:	Weight – Spherical
Issued:	1972 in a limited edition of 50
Status:	Fully subscribed
O.I.P.:	£30.00
U.K.:	£1,200.00
U.S.:	$2,100.00
Can.:	$2,800.00

CT-18
FISH

Designer:	Colin Terris
Type:	Weight – Spherical (Engraved)
Issued:	1972 in a limited edition of 500
Status:	Fully subscribed
O.I.P.:	£10.00
U.K.:	£ 75.00
U.S.:	$135.00
Can.:	$225.00

Note: This was the first engraved paperweight issued by Caithness.

CT-19
ARIEL

Designer:	Colin Terris
Type:	Weight – Spherical
Issued:	1972 in a limited edition of 500
Status:	Fully subscribed
O.I.P.:	£10.00
U.K.:	£ 75.00
U.S.:	$135.00
Can.:	$225.00

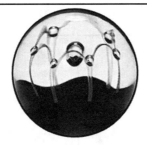

CT-20
MAY DANCE

Designer:	Colin Terris
Type:	Weight – Spherical
Colour:	1. Red
	2. Purple
	3. Green
Issued:	1972
Status:	Closed
O.I.P.:	£8.00

	Red	Purple	Green
U.K.:	£30.00	30.00	30.00
U.S.:	$55.00	55.00	55.00
Can.:	$70.00	70.00	70.00

ISSUES OF 1973

CT-21A
EARTH
Style Two

Designer: Colin Terris
Type: Weight – Spherical
Issued: 1973 in a limited
         edition of 1,000
Status: Fully subscribed
Series: Elements, Set One
O.I.P.: £52.00/set

	Earth	Set
U.K.:	£250.	1,000.
U.S.:	$450.	1,750.
Can.:	$575.	2,250.

Note: CT-21a, b, c and d were
issued and sold as a set.

CT-21B
AIR
Style One

Designer: Colin Terris
Type: Weight – Spherical
Issued: 1973 In a limited
         edition of 1,000
Status: Fully subscribed
Series: Elements, Set One
O.I.P.: £52.00/set

U.K.:	£250.00
U.S.:	$450.00
Can.:	$575.00

CT-21C
FIRE
Style One

Designer: Colin Terris
Type: Weight – Spherical
Issued: 1973 in a limited
         edition of 1,000
Status: Fully subscribed
Series: Elements, Set One
O.I.P.: £52.00/set

U.K.:	£250.00
U.S.:	$450.00
Can.:	$575.00

CT-21D
WATER
Style One

Designer: Colin Terris
Type: Weight – Spherical
Issued: 1973 in a limited
         edition of 1,000
Status: Fully subscribed
Series: Elements, Set One
O.I.P.: £52.00/set

U.K.:	£250.00
U.S.:	$450.00
Can.:	$575.00

CT-22
GENESIS

Designer: Colin Terris
Type: Weight – Spherical
Issued: 1973 in a limited
         edition of 500
Status: Fully subscribed
O.I.P.: £15.00

U.K.:	£325.00
U.S.:	$575.00
Can.:	$750.00

CT-23
SCULPTURE

Designer: Peter Holmes
Type: Weight – Spherical
Issued: 1973 in a limited
         edition of 500
Status: Fully subscribed
O.I.P.: £17.00

U.K.:	£325.00
U.S.:	$575.00
Can.:	$750.00

CT-24
STARDUST

Designer: Colin Terris
Type: Weight – Spherical
Issued: 1973 in a limited
         edition of 500
Status: Fully subscribed
Series: Limited – Modern
         Design
O.I.P.: £20.00

U.K.:	£250.00
U.S.:	$450.00
Can.:	$575.00

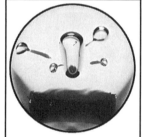

CT-25
FIRE DANCE

Designer: Colin Terris
Type: Weight – Spherical
Issued: 1973
Status: Closed
O.I.P.: £11.00

U.K.:	£ 50.00
U.S.:	$ 90.00
Can.:	$125.00

CT-26
FULMAR

Designer:	Colin Terris
Type:	Weight — Spherical, engraved
Issued:	1973 in a limited edition of 500
Status:	Fully subscribed
Series:	Sea Birds
O.I.P.:	£13.00
U.K.:	£ 50.00
U.S.:	$ 90.00
Can.:	$125.00

ISSUES OF 1974

CT-27
FLOWER IN THE RAIN
Style One

Designer:	Jack Allan
Type:	Weight – Spherical
Colour:	1. Red
	2. Blue
	3. Purple
	4. Yellow
Issued:	1974
Status:	Closed
O.I.P.:	£16.00

	Red	Blue	Purple	Yellow
U.K.:	£40.00	40.00	40.00	40.00
U.S.:	$75.00	75.00	75.00	75.00
Can.:	$95.00	95.00	95.00	95.00

CT-28
CROWN
Style One

Designer:	Colin Terris
Type:	Weight – Spherical
Cane:	A & M (Anne and Mark)
Issued:	1974 in a limited edition of 100
Status:	Fully subscribed
O.I.P.:	£35.00
U.K.:	£1.000.00
U.S.:	$1,750.00
Can.:	$2,250.00

Note: This paperweight was issued to commemorate the Royal Wedding of Princess Anne and Captain Mark Phillips.

CT-29
SPACE ROSE

Designer:	Colin Terris
Type:	Weight – Spherical
Colour:	1. Ruby
	2. Sienna
	3. White
Issued:	1974 in a limited edition of 1,000 for each colourway
Status:	1. Ruby closed at No. 631
	2. Sienna closed at No. 320
	3. White closed at No. 273
O.I.P.:	£19.50

	Ruby	Sienna	White
U.K.:	£ 50.00	50.00	50.00
U.S.:	$ 90.00	90.00	90.00
Can.:	$125.00	125.00	125.00

CT-30
SEA CRAB

Designer:	Colin Terris
Type:	Weight – Spherical
Issued:	1974 in a limited edition of 1,500
Status:	Fully subscribed
O.I.P.:	£18.00
U.K.:	£100.00
U.S.	$175.00
Can.:	$225.00

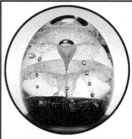

CT-31
CASCADE
Style One

Designer:	Peter Holmes
Type:	Weight – Domed
Colour:	Silver
Cane:	1. PH (Peter Holmes, 1974/5)
	2. CG (Caithness Glass, 1975)
Issued:	1974
Status:	Closed
O.I.P.:	£17.00

	PH	CG
U.K.:	£ 65.	65.
U.S.:	$120.	120.
Can.:	$150.	150.

  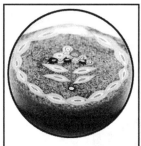 

CT-32
CASCADE RAINBOW

Designer:	Peter Holmes
Type:	Weight – Domed
Colour:	Yellow, ruby, blue and green
Cane:	1. PH (Peter Holmes, 1974/5)
	2. CG (Caithness Glass, 1975)
Issued:	1974
Status:	Closed
O.I.P.:	1. £17.00
	2. £19.50

	PH	CG
U.K.:	£100.	100.
U.S.:	$175.	175.
Can.:	$225.	225.

CT-33
BUTTERFLY
Style One

Designer:	Colin Terris
Type:	Weight – Spherical
Cane:	CG (Caithness Glass)
Issued:	1974 in a limited edition of 100
Status:	Fully subscribed
O.I.P.:	£35.00
U.K.:	£ 500.00
U.S.	$ 900.00
Can.:	$1,200.00

CT-34
BULLSEYE MILLEFIORI

Designer:	Colin Terris
Type:	Weight – Spherical
Cane:	CG (Caithness Glass)
Issued:	1974
Status:	Closed
O.I.P.:	£25.00
U.K.:	£100.00
U.S.:	$175.00
Can.:	$225.00

CT-35
ARCTIC TERN

Designer:	Colin Terris
Type:	Weight – Spherical, engraved
Issued:	1974 in a limited edition of 500
Status:	Fully subscribed
Series:	Sea Birds
O.I.P.:	£14.00
U.K.:	£40.00
U.S.	$75.00
Can.:	$95.00

ISSUES OF 1975

CT-36
SPACE BEACON

Designer:	Colin Terris	
Type:	Weight – Spherical	
Colour:	1. Damson	
	2. Green	
	3. Purple	
Issued:	1975 in a limited edition of 500 for each colourway	
Status:	Fully subscribed	
O.I.P.:	£17.00	

	Damson	Green	Purple
U.K.:	£ 75.00	75.00	75.00
U.S.:	$135.00	135.00	135.00
Can.:	$175.00	175.00	175.00

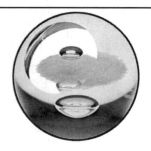

CT-37
REFLECTIONS

Designer:	Colin Terris	
Type:	Weight – Spherical	
Colour:	1. Blue	
	2. Damson	
	3. Green	
Issued:	1975 in a limited edition of 500 for each colourway	
Status:	Fully subscribed	
O.I.P.:	£15.00	

	Blue	Damson	Green
U.K.:	£ 65.00	65.00	65.00
U.S.:	$120.00	120.00	120.00
Can.:	$150.00	150.00	150.00

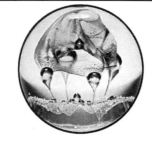

CT-38
VORTEX

Designer:	Colin Terris	
Type:	Weight – Spherical	
Colour:	1. Blue	
	2. Green	
	3. Red	
Issued:	1975 in a limited edition of 1,000 for each colourway	
Status:	1. Blue Fully subscribed	
	2. Green Closed at No. 803	
	3. Red Closed at No. 778	
O.I.P.:	£20.00	

	Blue	Green	Red
U.K.:	£35.00	35.00	35.00
U.S.:	$65.00	65.00	65.00
Can.:	$85.00	85.00	85.00

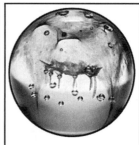

CT-39
SEA KELP

Designer:	Colin Terris
Type:	Weight – Spherical
Issued:	1975 in a limited edition of 1,500
Status:	Fully subscribed
O.I.P.:	£16.00
U.K.:	£ 75.00
U.S.:	$135.00
Can.:	$175.00

CT-40
SENTINEL
Style One

Designer:	Colin Terris		
Type:	Weight – Spherical		
Colour:	1. Green		
	2. Purple		
	3. Red		
Issued:	1975		
Status:	Closed		
O.I.P.:	£12.00		
	Green	Purple	Red
U.K.:	£40.00	40.00	40.00
U.S.:	$75.00	75.00	75.00
Can.:	$95.00	95.00	95.00

CT-41
DRAGONFLY
Style One

Designer:	Colin Terris
Type:	Weight – Spherical
Issued:	1975 in a limited edition of 1,500
Status:	Fully subscribed
O.I.P.:	£17.00
U.K.;	£350.00
U.S.:	$625.00
Can.:	$800.00

ISSUES OF 1976

CT-42
SEABASE
Designer: Colin Terris
Type: Weight – Spherical
Issued: 1976 in a limited edition of 400
Status: Fully subscribed
O.I.P.: £44.00

U.K.:	£325.00
U.S.:	$575.00
Can.:	$750.00

CT-43
SPACE FLOWER
Designer: Colin Terris
Type: Weight – Spherical
Issued: 1976 in a limited edition of 1,000
Status: Fully subscribed
O.I.P.: £24.00

U.K.:	£100.00
U.S.:	$175.00
Can.:	$225.00

CT-44
SEA ORCHID
Designer: Colin Terris
Type: Weight – Spherical
Issued: 1976 in a limited edition of 1,000
Status: Fully subscribed
O.I.P.: £24.00

U.K.:	£150.00
U.S.:	$275.00
Can.:	$350.00

CT-45
SEA PEARL
Designer: Peter Holmes
Type: Weight – Spherical
Cane: PH (Peter Holmes)
Issued: 1976 in a limited edition of 500
Status: Fully subscribed
O.I.P.: £30.00

U.K.:	£150.00
U.S.:	$275.00
Can.:	$350.00

CT-46A
SPRING
Style One
Designer: Colin Terris
Type: Weight – Spherical
Cane: WM (William Manson)
Issued: 1976 in a limited edition of 500
Status: Closed at No. 473
Series: Four Seasons
O.I.P.: £250.00/set

	Spring	Set
U.K.:	£300.	1,200.
U.S.:	$550.	2,200.
Can.:	$700.	2,800.

Note: CT-46a, b, c and d were issued and sold as a set.

CT-46B
SUMMER
Style One
Designer: Colin Terris
Type: Weight – Spherical
Cane: WM (William Manson)
Issued: 1976 in a limited edition of 500
Status: Closed at No. 473
Series: Four Seasons
O.I.P.: £250.00/set

U.K.:	£300.00
U.S.:	$550.00
Can.:	$700.00

CT-46C
AUTUMN
Style One
Designer: Colin Terris
Type: Weight – Spherical
Cane: WM (William Manson)
Issued: 1976 in a limited edition of 500
Status: Closed at No. 473
Series: Four Seasons
O.I.P.: £250.00/set

U.K.:	£300.00
U.S.:	$550.00
Can.:	$700.00

CT-46D
WINTER
Style One
Designer: Colin Terris
Type: Weight – Spherical
Cane: WM (William Manson)
Issued: 1976 in a limited edition of 500
Status: Closed at No. 473
Series: Four Seasons
O.I.P.: £250.00/set

U.K.:	£300.00
U.S.:	$550.00
Can.:	$700.00

CT-47A
TRIO WEIGHT – ONE
Designer: Colin Terris
Type: Weight – Spherical
Issued: 1976 in a limited edition of 750
Status: Closed at No. 646
Series: Trio Set
O.I.P.: £70.00/set

	Trio One	Set
U.K.:	£150.	450.
U.S.:	$300.	900.
Can.:	$375.	1,100.

Note: CT47a, b and c were issued and sold as a set.

CT-47B
TRIO WEIGHT – TWO
Designer: Colin Terris
Type: Weight – Spherical
Issued: 1976 in a limited edition of 750
Status: Closed at No. 646
Series: Trio Set
O.I.P.: £70.00/set

U.K.:	£150.00
U.S.:	$300.00
Can.:	$375.00

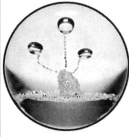

CT-47C
TRIO WEIGHT – THREE
Designer: Colin Terris
Type: Weight – Spherical
Issued: 1976 in a limited edition of 750
Status: Closed at No. 646
Series: Trio Set
O.I.P.: £70.00/set

U.K.:	£150.00
U.S.:	$300.00
Can.:	$375.00

CT-48
PUFFIN
Style One
Designer: Colin Terris
Type: Weight – Spherical, engraved
Issued: 1976 in a limited edition of 500
Status: Fully subscribed
Series: Sea Birds
O.I.P.: £17.00

U.K.:	£ 65.00
U.S.:	$130.00
Can.:	$175.00

CT-49
CORMORANT
Designer: Colin Terris
Type: Weight – Spherical, engraved
Issued: 1976 in a limited edition of 500
Status: Fully subscribed
Series: Sea Birds
O.I.P.: £17.00

U.K.:	£ 65.00
U.S.:	$120.00
Can.:	$150.00

CT-50
GANNET
Designer: David Gulland
Type: Weight – Spherical, copperwheel engraved
Issued: 1976 in a limited edition of 100
Status: Fully subscribed
O.I.P.: £60.00

U.K.:	£325.00
U.S.:	$575.00
Can.:	$750.00

CT-51
DIVING TERN
Designer: Denis Mann
Type: Weight – Spherical, copperwheel engraved
Issued: 1976 in a limited edition of 100
Status: Fully subscribed
O.I.P.: £60.00

U.K.:	£325.00
U.S.:	$575.00
Can.:	$750.00

CT-52
SEAL
Style One
Designer: Christine Beaton
Type: Weight – Spherical, copperwheel engraved
Issued: 1976 in a limited edition of 100
Status: Fully subscribed
O.I.P.: £60.00

U.K.:	£325.00
U.S.:	$575.00
Can.:	$750.00

CT-53
DOLPHIN
Style One
Designer: David Gulland
Type: Weight – Spherical,
           copperwheel
           engraved
Issued: 1976 in a limited
           edition of 100
Status: Fully subscribed
O.I.P.:   £60.00

U.K.:   £325.00
U.S.: $575.00
Can.: $750.00

CT-54
SPECTRE
Designer: Colin Terris
Type: Weight – Spherical
Issued: 1976 in a limited
           edition of 1,000
Status: Fully subscribed
O.I.P.:   £17.00

U.K.:   £ 75.00
U.S.: $135.00
Can.: $175.00

CT-55
SUN DANCE
Designer: Colin Terris
Type: Weight – Spherical
Issued: 1976 in a limited
           edition of 3,000
Status: Fully subscribed
O.I.P.:   £19.50

U.K.:   £100.00
U.S.: $175.00
Can.: $225.00

CT-56
ALIEN
Designer: Peter Holmes
Type: Weight – Spherical
Cane: CG (Caithness Glass)
Issued: 1976 in a limited
           edition of 2,000
Status: Fully subscribed
O.I.P.:   £20.50

U.K.:   £ 75.00
U.S.: $135.00
Can.: $175.00

CT-57
FIRST QUARTER
Designer: Peter Holmes
Type: Weight – Spherical
Cane: PH (Peter Holmes)
Issued: 1976 in a limited
           edition of 1,500
Status: Fully subscribed
O.I.P.:   £20.50

U.K.:   £ 75.00
U.S.: $135.00
Can.: $175.00

CT-58
RHAPSODY
Designer: Colin Terris
Type: Weight – Spherical
Issued: 1976 in a limited
           edition of 400
Status: Closed at No. 378
O.I.P.:   £30.00

U.K.:   £100.00
U.S.: $175.00
Can.: $225.00

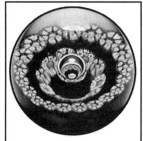

CT-59
MILLEFIORI REFLECTIONS
Designer: William Manson
Type: Weight – Spherical
Cane: CG (Caithness Glass)
Issued: 1976
Status: Closed
O.I.P.:   £20.00

U.K.:   £100.00
U.S.: $175.00
Can.: $225.00

CT-60
LATTICINO
Designer: William Manson
Type: Weight – Spherical
Cane: CG (Caithness Glass)
Issued: 1976
Status: Closed
O.I.P.:   £24.00

U.K.:   £100.00
U.S.: $175.00
Can.: $225.00

CT-62
POLAR BEAR
Designer: Christine Beaton
Type: Weight – Spherical, copperwheel engraved
Issued: 1976 in a limited edition of 100
Status: Closed at No. 46
O.I.P.: £74.40

U.K.: £ 425.00
U.S.: $ 775.00
Can.: $1,000.00

CT-63
OTTER
Designer: Denis Mann
Type: Weight – Spherical, copperwheel engraved
Issued: 1976 in a limited edition of 100
Status: Fully subscribed
O.I.P.: £74.40

U.K.: £325.00
U.S.: $575.00
Can.: $750.00

CT-64
OSPREY
Designer: Denis Mann
Type: Weight – Spherical, copperwheel engraved
Issued: 1976 in a limited edition of 100
Status: Fully subscribed
O.I.P.: £74.40

U.K.: £325.00
U.S.: $575.00
Can.: $750.00

CT-65
EIDER DUCK
Style One
Designer: Denis Mann
Type: Weight – Spherical, engraved
Issued: 1976 in a limited edition of 500
Status: Fully subscribed
Series: Sea Birds
O.I.P.: £19.50

U.K.: £ 65.00
U.S.: $120.00
Can.: $150.00

CT-66
BLACK HEADED GULL
Designer: Denis Mann
Type: Weight – Spherical, engraved
Issued: 1976 in a limited edition of 500
Status: Fully subscribed
Series: Sea Birds
O.I.P.: £19.50

U.K.: £ 60.00
U.S.: $110.00
Can.: $145.00

ANGLER DOME   EAGLE DOME   GOLFING DOME   YACHTING DOME

Designer: Caithness Design Studio
Type: Weight – Domed
Issued: 1976 – Unlimited
Status: Closed
Series: Sports
O.I.P.: £8.50

	Angler	Eagle	Golfing	Yachting
U.K.:	£ 65.00	65.00	65.00	65.00
U.S.:	$125.00	125.00	125.00	125.00
Can.:	$150.00	150.00	150.00	150.00

ISSUES OF 1977

CT-67
STORMY PETREL

Designer:	Denis Mann
Type:	Weight – Spherical, engraved
Issued:	1977 in a limited edition of 500
Status:	Fully subscribed
Series:	Sea Birds
O.I.P.:	£21.40
U.K.:	£ 50.00
U.S.:	$ 90.00
Can.:	$125.00

CT-68
GUILLEMOT

Designer:	Denis Mann
Type:	Weight – Spherical, engraved
Issued:	1977 in a limited edition of 500
Status:	Fully subscribed
Series:	Sea Birds
O.I.P.:	£21.40
U.K.:	£ 50.00
U.S.:	$ 90.00
Can.:	$125.00

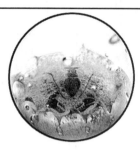

CT-69
LOBSTER

Designer:	Colin Terris
Type:	Weight – Spherical
Issued:	1977 in a limited edition of 1,500
Status:	Closed at No. 1,245
O.I.P.:	£25.00
U.K.:	£ 45.00
U.S.:	$ 80.00
Can.:	$100.00

CT-70
JUBILEE MOONFLOWER

Designer:	Colin Terris
Type:	Weight – Spherical
Colour:	Silver
Issued:	1977 in a limited edition of 3,000
Status:	Fully subscribed
Series:	HM Queen Elizabeth II Silver Jubilee Collection
O.I.P.:	£15.00
U.K.:	£ 65.00
U.S.:	$120.00
Can.:	$150.00

Note: CT70 and the following three weights were issued to commemorate the 25th anniversary of the coronation of Queen Elizabeth II.

CT-71
JUBILEE CROWN BUBBLE

Designer:	Colin Terris
Type:	Weight – Spherical
Issued:	1977 in a limited edition of 3,000
Status:	Fully subscribed
Series:	HM Queen Elizabeth II Silver Jubilee Collection
O.I.P.:	£17.00
U.K.:	£ 60.00
U.S.:	$110.00
Can.:	$135.00

CT-72
JUBILEE FLOATING CROWN

Designer:	Colin Terris
Type:	Weight – Spherical
Issued:	1977 in a limited edition of 1,000
Status:	Fully subscribed
Series:	HM Queen Elizabeth II Silver Jubilee Collection
O.I.P.:	£45.00
U.K.:	£150.00
U.S.:	$275.00
Can.:	$350.00

CT-73
JUBILEE MILLEFIORI CROWN

Designer:	Colin Terris
Type:	Weight – Spherical
Cane:	EIIR (Queen Elizabeth II)
Issued:	1977 in a limited edition of 500
Status:	Fully subscribed
Series:	HM Queen Elizabeth II Silver Jubilee Collection
O.I.P.:	£70.00
U.K.:	£250.00
U.S.:	$450.00
Can.:	$575.00

CT-75
COMET

Designer:	Colin Terris
Type:	Weight – Spherical
Issued:	1977 in a limited edition of 3,000
Status:	Fully subscribed
O.I.P.:	£25.00
U.K.:	£ 75.00
U.S.:	$135.00
Can.:	$175.00

CT-76
PLOUGH

Designer:	Colin Terris
Type:	Weight – Spherical
Issued:	1977 in a limited edition of 3,000
Status:	Closed at No. 2,332
O.I.P.:	£25.40
U.K.:	£ 65.00
U.S.:	$120.00
Can.:	$150.00

Note: This is the constellation known in North America as the Big Dipper.

CT-77
INTRUDER

Designer:	Colin Terris
Type:	Weight – Spherical
Issued:	1977 in a limited edition of 2,000
Status:	Closed at No. 904
O.I.P.:	£26.00
U.K.:	£100.00
U.S.:	$175.00
Can.:	$225.00

CT-78
ZEPHYR

Designer:	Colin Terris
Type:	Weight – Spherical
Issued:	1977 in a limited edition of 400
Status:	Fully subscribed
O.I.P.:	£35.00
U.K.:	£150.00
U.S.:	$275.00
Can.:	$350.00

CT-79
PETAL PERFUME BOTTLE

Designer:	Colin Terris
Type:	Perfume Bottle
Issued:	1977
Status:	Closed
O.I.P.:	£50.00
U.K.:	£150.00
U.S.:	$275.00
Can.:	$350.00

CT-80
CHRISTMAS WEIGHT

Designer:	Colin Terris
Type:	Weight – Spherical
Issued:	1977 in a limited edition of 500
Status:	Fully subscribed
Series:	Collectors' Society
O.I.P.:	£50.00
U.K.:	£400.00
U.S.:	$725.00
Can.:	$950.00

ISSUES OF 1978

CT-81
ANGEL FISH
Style One

Designer: Jennie Robertson
Type: Weight – Spherical,
          engraved
Issued: 1978 in a limited
          edition of 1,500
Status: Closed at No. 1,347
Series: Exotic Fishes
O.I.P.:   £25.00

U.K.:   £ 50.00
U.S.: $100.00
Can.: $130.00

CT-82
KITTIWAKE

Designer: Denis Mann
Type: Weight – Spherical,
          engraved
Issued: 1978 in a limited
          edition of 500
Status: Closed at No. 473
Series: Sea Birds
O.I.P.:   £23.50

U.K.:   £ 55.00
U.S.: $100.00
Can.: $130.00

CT-83
SKUA

Designer: Denis Mann
Type: Weight – Spherical,
          engraved
Issued: 1978 in a limited
          edition of 500
Status: Closed at No. 460
Series: Sea Birds
O.I.P.:   £23.50

U.K.:   £ 55.00
U.S.: $100.00
Can.: $130.00

CT-84
EIDER DUCK
Style Two

Designer: Denis Mann
Type: Weight   Spherical,
          copperwheel
          engraved
Issued: 1978 in a limited
          edition of 100
Status: Fully subscribed
O.I.P.:   £80.00

U.K.:   £375.00
U.S.: $675.00
Can.: $875.00

CT-85
MERMAID

Designer: Ann Robertson
Type: Weight – Spherical,
          copperwheel
          engraved
Issued: 1978 in a limited
          edition of 100
Status: Fully subscribed
O.I.P.:   £80.00

U.K.:   £375.00
U.S.: $675.00
Can.: $875.00

CT-86
AQUILA

Designer: Colin Terris
Type: Weight – Spherical
Issued: 1978 in a limited
          edition of 3,000
Status: Closed at No. 1,029
Series: Stars and
          Constellations
O.I.P.:   £25.50

U.K.:   £ 55.00
U.S.: $100.00
Can.: $130.00

CT-87
SAGITTARIUS
Style One

Designer: Colin Terris
Type: Weight – Spherical
Issued: 1978 in a limited
          edition of 3,000
Status: Closed at No. 1,949
Series: Stars and
          Constellations
O.I.P.:   £25.50

U.K.:   £ 55.00
U.S.: $100.00
Can.: $130.00

CT-88
ASTEROID

Designer: Colin Terris
Type: Weight – Spherical
Issued: 1978 in a limited
          edition of 3,000
Status: Closed at No. 995
O.I.P.:   £25.00

U.K.:   £ 55.00
U.S.: $100.00
Can.: $130.00

CT-89
SPINDRIFT
Designer: Colin Terris
Type: Weight – Spherical
Issued: 1978 in a limited edition of 3,000
Status: Fully subscribed
O.I.P.: £19.00

U.K.: £ 75.00
U.S.: $135.00
Can.: $175.00

CT-90
SUNFLARE
Designer: Colin Terris
Type: Weight – Spherical
Issued: 1978 in a limited edition of 3,000
Status: Closed at No. 1,387
O.I.P.: £27.00

U.K.: £ 55.00
U.S.: $100.00
Can.: $130.00

CT-91
MYRIAD
Style One
Designer: Oban Studios
Type: Weight – Spherical
Colour: Many colour variations
1. Blue
2. Green
3. Purple
4. Red
Issued: 1978
Status: Closed
Series: Unlimited – Modern Design
O.I.P.: U.K. £11.00, U.S. $50.00

	Blue	Green	Purple	Red
U.K.:	£30.00	30.00	30.00	30.00
U.S.:	$55.00	55.00	55.00	55.00
Can.:	$70.00	70.00	70.00	70.00

CT-92
MORNING DEW
Designer: Colin Terris
Type: Weight – Spherical
Colour: 1. Blue
2. Green
3. Orange
4. Red
5. Silver
6. Yellow
Issued: 1978
Status: Closed
O.I.P.: U.K. £13.00
U.S. $50.00

	Blue	Green	Orange	Red	Silver	Yellow
U.K.:	£35.00	35.00	35.00	35.00	35.00	35.00
U.S.:	$65.00	65.00	65.00	65.00	65.00	65.00
Can.:	$85.00	85.00	85.00	85.00	85.00	85.00

CT-93
MAROONED
Designer: Colin Terris
Type: Weight – Spherical
Issued: 1978 in a limited edition of 3,000
Status: Closed at No. 1,454
O.I.P.: U.K. £27.50
U.S. $95.00

U.K.: £ 50.00
U.S.: $ 90.00
Can.: $125.00

CT-94
PEGASUS
Designer: Colin Terris
Type: Weight – Spherical
Issued: 1978 in a limited edition of 1,500
Status: Closed at No. 655
O.I.P.: U.K. £27.00
U.S. $125.00

U.K.: £ 65.00
U.S.: $120.00
Can.: $150.00

CT-95
SPACE PEARL
Designer: Colin Terris
Type: Weight – Spherical
Issued: 1978 in a limited
edition of 3,000
Status: Closed at No. 1,648
O.I.P.: U.K. £27.00
U.S. $125.00

U.K.: £ 50.00
U.S.: $100.00
Can.: $130.00

CT-96
ICE PETAL PERFUME BOTTLE
Designer: Colin Terris
Type: Perfume Bottle
Issued: 1978
Status: Closed
O.I.P.: U.K. £55.00
U.S. $235.00

U.K.: £125.00
U.S.: $225.00
Can.: $300.00

CT-97
SEA GRASS PERFUME BOTTLE
Designer: Colin Terris
Type: Perfume Bottle
Issued: 1978
Status: Closed
O.I.P.: U.K. £55.00
U.S. $235.00

U.K.: £125.00
U.S.: $225.00
Can.: $300.00

CT-98
QUARTET PERFUME BOTTLE
Designer: Colin Terris
Type: Perfume Bottle
Issued: 1978
Status: Closed
Series: Limited – Modern
Design
O.I.P.: U.K. £55.00
U.S. $235.00

U.K.: £125.00
U.S.: $225.00
Can.: $300.00

CT-99
SNOWFLOWER
Designer: Colin Terris
Type: Weight – Spherical
Issued: 1978 in a limited
edition of 3,000
Status: Fully subscribed
O.I.P.: U.K. £30.00
U.S. $135.00

U.K.: £ 85.00
U.S.: $150.00
Can.: $200.00

CT-100
COBRA
Style One
Designer: Colin Terris and
William Manson
Type: Weight – Spherical
Cane: 78 (in base)
Issued: 1978 in a limited
edition of 50
Status: Fully subscribed
O.I.P.: U.K. £200.00
U.S. $850.00

U.K.: £ 700.00
U.S.: $1,250.00
Can.: $1,650.00

Note: See CT-135 for the 1979
issue and CT-190 for the
1980 issue.

CT-101
SALAMANDER
Style One
Designer: Colin Terris and
William Manson
Type: Weight – Spherical
Cane: 78 (in base)
Issued: 1978 in a limited
edition of 50
Status: Fully subscribed
O.I.P.: U.K. £200.00
U.S. $850.00

U.K.: £ 700.00
U.S.: $1,250.00
Can.: $1,650.00

Note: See CT-136 for the 1979
issue and CT-187 for the
1980 issue.

CT-102
OCTOPUS
First Version
Designer: William Manson
Type: Weight – Spherical
Cane: 78 (in base)
Issued: 1978 in a limited
edition of 50
Status: Fully subscribed
O.I.P.: U.K. £200.00
U.S. $850.00

U.K.: £ 700.00
U.S.: $1,250.00
Can.: $1,650.00

Note: See CT-138 for the
1979 issue.

CT-103
MANTA RAY
Style One, First Version

Designer: Colin Terris and
William Manson
Type: Weight – Spherical
Cane: 78 (in base)
Issued: 1978 in a limited
edition of 50
Status: Fully subscribed
O.I.P.: U.K. £200.00
U.S. $850.00

U.K.: £ 700.00
U.S.: $1,250.00
Can.: $1,650.00

Note: See CT-137 for the 1979
issue and CT189 for the
1980 issue.

CT-104
EL DORADO

Designer: Colin Terris and
William Manson
Type: Weight – Spherical
Cane: 78 (in base)
Issued: 1978 in a limited
edition of 100
Status: Fully subscribed
O.I.P.: U.K. £100.00
U.S. $450.00

U.K.: £ 500.00
U.S.: $ 900.00
Can.: $1,200.00

CT-105
LADYBIRD
Style One, First Version

Designer: Colin Terris
Type: Weight – Spherical
Cane: 78 (in base)
Issued: 1978 in a limited
edition of 100
Status: Fully subscribed
O.I.P.: U.K. £100.00
U.S. $450.00

U.K.: £325.00
U.S.: $575.00
Can.: $750.00

Note: See CT-139 for the 1979
issue.

CT-106
SWAN
Style One, First Version

Designer: Colin Terris and
William Manson
Type: Weight – Spherical
Cane: 78 (in base)
Issued: 1978 in a limited
edition of 100
Status: Fully subscribed
O.I.P.: U.K. £100.00
U.S. $450.00

U.K.: £325.00
U.S.: $575.00
Can.: $750.00

Note: See CT-144 for the 1979
issue.

CT-107
BUTTERFLY and FLOWER
First Version

Designer: Colin Terris
Type: Weight – Spherical
Cane: 78 (in base)
Issued: 1978 in a limited
edition of 250
Status: Fully subscribed
O.I.P.: U.K. £130.00
U.S. $565.00

U.K.: £350.00
U.S.: $625.00
Can.: $800.00

Note: See CT-140 for the 1979
issue.

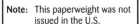

CT-108
SILVER LIZARD

Designer: Colin Terris and
David Hodge
Type: Weight – Spherical
Issued: 1978 in a limited
edition of 50
Status: Closed at No. 45
O.I.P.: £200.00

U.K.: £1,000.00
U.S.: $1,750.00
Can.: $2,250.00

Note: This paperweight was not
issued in the U.S.

CT-109
MISTLETOE
Style One

Designer: Colin Terris
Type: Weight – Spherical
Issued: 1978 in a limited
edition of 500
Status: Fully subscribed
O.I.P.: £75.00

U.K.: £175.00
U.S.: $325.00
Can.: $400.00

Note: This paperweight was not
issued in the U.S.

CT-110
JOURNEY OF THE WISE MEN

Designer: Helen MacDonald
Type: Weight – Spherical,
engraved
Issued: 1978 in a limited
edition of 2,000
Status: Closed at No. 1,583
Series: Nativity
O.I.P.: U.K. £50.00
U.S. $195.00

U.K.: £ 85.00
U.S.: $175.00
Can.: $225.00

CT-111
CORONATION SILVER JUBILEE

Designer:	Colin Terris
Type:	Weight – Spherical
Issued:	1978 in a limited edition of 1,000
Status:	Closed at No. 156
Series:	Limited – Modern Design
O.I.P.:	£25.00
U.K.:	£100.00
U.S.:	$175.00
Can.:	$225.00

Note: This paperweight was issued to commemorate the 25th anniversary of the Coronation of Queen Elizabeth II. It was not issued in the U.S.

CT-113
ARCTIC NIGHT

Designer:	Colin Terris
Type:	Weight – Spherical
Issued:	1978 in a limited edition of 1,500
Status:	Closed at No. 839
Series:	Collectors' Society
O.I.P.:	£30.00
U.K.:	£40.00
U.S.:	$75.00
Can.:	$95.00

Note: This weight was offered to U.K. Club members only.

ISSUES OF 1979

CT-114
KING NEPTUNE
Designer: Ann Robertson
Type: Weight – Spherical, copperwheel engraved
Issued: 1979 in a limited edition of 100
Status: Fully subscribed
O.I.P.: U.K. £80.00
U.S. $400.00

U.K.:	£225.00
U.S.:	$400.00
Can.:	$525.00

CT-115
VEIL TAIL
Designer: Colin Terris
Type: Weight – Spherical, engraved
Issued: 1979 in a limited edition of 1,500
Status: Closed at No. 1,145
O.I.P.: U.K. £26.00
U.S. $130.00

U.K.:	£ 60.00
U.S.:	$120.00
Can.:	$150.00

CT-116
HUMMING BIRD
Style One
Designer: Colin Terris
Type: Weight – Spherical, engraved
Issued: 1979 in a limited edition of 1,000
Status: Fully subscribed
Series: Exotic Birds
O.I.P.: U.K. £35.00
U.S. $120.00

U.K.:	£ 60.00
U.S.:	$120.00
Can.:	$150.00

CT-117
LIBRA
Style One
Designer: Colin Terris
Type: Weight – Spherical
Issued: 1979 in a limited edition of 1,500
Status: Closed at No. 450
O.I.P.: U.K. £25.00
U.S. $125.00

U.K.:	£ 50.00
U.S.:	$100.00
Can.:	$130.00

CT-118
ARIES
Style One
Designer: Colin Terris
Type: Weight – Spherical
Issued: 1979 in a limited edition of 1,500
Status: Closed at No. 447
O.I.P.: U.K. £25.00
U.S. $125.00

U.K.:	£ 50.00
U.S.:	$100.00
Can.:	$130.00

CT-119A
SEA LACE
Designer: Colin Terris
Type: Weight – Spherical
Issued: 1979 in a limited edition of 100
Status: Fully subscribed
O.I.P.: U.K. £90.00/set
U.S. $450.00/set

U.K.:	£225.00
U.S.:	$400.00
Can.:	$525.00

Note: CT-119a and b were issued and sold as a set.

CT-119B
SEA LACE PERFUME BOTTLE
Designer: Colin Terris
Type: Perfume Bottle
Issued: 1979 in a limited edition of 100
Status: Fully subscribed
O.I.P.: U.K. £90.00/set
U.S. $450.00/set

	Bottle	Set
U.K.:	£400.	650.
U.S.:	$725.	1,175.
Can.:	$950.	1,500.

CT-120
BLUE PETAL PERFUME BOTTLE
Designer: Colin Terris
Type: Perfume Bottle
Issued: 1979
Status: Closed
Series: Unlimited – Modern Design
O.I.P.: U.K. £55.00
U.S. $265.00

U.K.:	£100.00
U.S.:	$200.00
Can.:	$260.00

CT-121
SILVER SENTINEL
Designer: Colin Terris
Type: Weight – Spherical
Issued: 1979
Status: Closed
O.I.P.: U.K. £15.00
         U.S. $75.00

U.K.:   £35.00
U.S.: $70.00
Can.: $90.00

CT-122A
DAWN
Designer: Colin Terris
Type: Weight – Spherical
Issued: 1979 in a limited
         edition of 750
Status: Fully subscribed
O.I.P.; U.K. £60.00/set
         U.S. $295.00/set

	Dawn	Set
U.K.:	£125.	250.
U.S.:	$225.	450.
Can.:	$300.	600.

Note: CT-122a and b were
issued and sold as a set.

CT-122B
DUSK
Designer: Colin Terris
Type: Weight – Spherical
Issued: 1979 in a limited
         edition of 750
Status: Fully subscribed
O.I.P.: U.K. £60.00/sct
         U.S. $295.00/set

U.K.:   £125.00
U.S.: $225.00
Can.: $300.00

CT-123
ICE FLAME
Designer: Colin Terris
Type: Weight – Spherical
Issued: 1979 in a limited
         edition of 1,000
Status: Closed at No. 905
Series: Limited – Modern
         Design
O.I.P.: U.K. £27.00
         U.S. $135.00

U.K.:   £ 55.00
U.S.: $110.00
Can.: $150.00

CT-124
STAR FLOWER
Designer: Colin Terris
Type: Weight – Spherical
Issued: 1979 in a limited
         edition of 1,000
Status: Fully subscribed
Series: Limited – Modern
         Design
O.I.P.: U.K. £27.00
         U.S. $135.00

U.K.:   £ 60.00
U.S.: $125.00
Can.: $165.00

CT-125
NOMAD
Designer: Colin Terris
Type: Weight – Spherical
Issued: 1979 in a limited
         edition of 1,000
Status: Fully subscribed
Series: Limited – Modern
         Design
O.I.P.: U.K. £27.00
         U.S. $135.00

U.K.:   £ 75.00
U.S.: $150.00
Can.: $200.00

CT-126
TRIAD
Designer: Colin Terris
Type: Weight – Spherical
Issued: 1979 in a limited
         edition of 1,500
Status: Closed at No. 815
Series: Limited – Modern
         Design
O.I.P.: U.K. £25.00
         U.S. $125.00

U.K.:   £ 45.00
U.S.: $ 90.00
Can.: $125.00

CT-127
CAROUSEL
Designer: Colin Terris
Type: Weight – Spherical
Issued: 1979 in a limited
         edition of 1,000
Status: Fully subscribed
Series: Limited – Modern
         Design
O.I.P.: U.K. £27.00
         U.S. $135.00

U.K.:   £ 55.00
U.S.: $120.00
Can.: $150.00

CT-128
ICE FOUNTAIN

Designer: Colin Terris
Type: Weight – Spherical
Issued: 1979 in a limited
edition of 1,500
Status: Fully subscribed
Series: Limited – Modern
Design
O.I.P.: U.K. £25.00
U.S. $125.00

U.K.: £ 45.00
U.S.: $ 90.00
Can.: $125.00

CT-129
FLOWER FORM

Designer: Colin Terris
Type: Weight – Spherical
Issued: 1979 in a limited
edition of 1,500
Status: Closed at No. 1,484
Series: Limited – Modern
Design
O.I.P.: U.K. £25.00
U.S. $125.00

U.K.: £ 55.00
U.S.: $110.00
Can.: $150.00

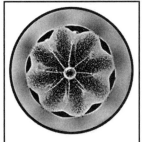

CT-130
ICE BLOSSOM

Designer: Colin Terris
Type: Weight – Spherical
Issued: 1979 in a limited
edition of 1,000
Status: Closed at No. 854
Series: Limited – Modern
Design
O.I.P.: U.K. £30.00
U.S. $150.00

U.K.: £ 75.00
U.S.: $135.00
Can.: $175.00

CT-131
ATLANTIS

Designer: Colin Terris
Type: Weight – Spherical
Issued: 1979 in a limited
edition of 1,500
Status: Fully subscribed
Series: Limited – Modern
Design
O.I.P.: U.K. £25.00
U.S. $125.00

U.K.: £100.00
U.S.: $175.00
Can.: $225.00

CT-132
OCTET

Designer: Colin Terris
Type: Weight – Spherical
Issued: 1979 in a limited
edition of 500
Status: Fully subscribed
Series: Limited – Modern
Design
O.I.P.: U.K. £37.00
U.S. $185.00

U.K.: £ 85.00
U.S.: $160.00
Can.: $200.00

CT-133
ILLUSION

Designer: Colin Terris
Type: Weight – Spherical
Issued: 1979 in a limited
edition of 1,000
Status: Fully subscribed
Series: Limited – Modern
Design
O.I.P.: U.K. £27.00
U.S. $135.00

U.K.: £ 75.00
U.S.: $135.00
Can.: $175.00

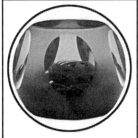

CT-134
MYSTIQUE

Designer: Colin Terris
Type: Weight – Spherical
Issued: 1979 in a limited
edition of 750
Status: Closed at No. 630
Series: Limited – Modern
Design
O.I.P.: U.K. £45.00
U.S. $225.00

U.K.: £ 85.00
U.S.: $175.00
Can.: $225.00

CT-135
COBRA
Style Two

Designer: Colin Terris and
William Manson
Type: Weight – Spherical
Cane: 79 (in base)
Issued: 1979 in a limited
edition of 50
Status: Fully subscribed
O.I.P.: U.K. £215.00
U.S. $950.00

U.K.: £ 550.00
U.S.: $1,000.00
Can.: $1,300.00

Note: See CT-100 for the 1978
issue and CT-190 for the
1980 Issue.

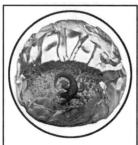

CT-136
SALAMANDER
Style Two

Designer:	Colin Terris and William Manson
Type:	Weight – Spherical
Cane:	79 (in base)
Issued:	1979 in a limited edition of 50
Status:	Fully subscribed
O.I.P.:	U.K. £215.00
	U.S. $950.00
U.K.:	£ 550.00
U.S.:	$1,000.00
Can.:	$1,300.00

Note: See CT-101 for the 1978 issue and CT-187 for the 1980 issue.

CT-137
MANTA RAY
Style One, Second Version

Designer:	Colin Terris and William Manson
Type:	Weight – Spherical
Cane:	79 (in base)
Issued:	1979 in a limited edition of 50
Status:	Fully subscribed
O.I.P.:	U.K. £215.00
	U.S. $950.00
U.K.:	£ 550.00
U.S.:	$1,000.00
Can.:	$1,300.00

Note: See CT-103 for the 1978 issue and CT-189 for the 1980 issue.

CT-138
OCTOPUS
Second Version

Designer:	William Manson
Type:	Weight – Spherical
Cane:	79 (in base)
Issued:	1979 in a limited edition of 50
Status:	Fully subscribed
O.I.P.:	U.K. £215.00
	U.S. $950.00
U.K.:	£ 550.00
U.S.:	$1,000.00
Can.:	$1,300.00

Note: See CT-102 for the 1978 issue.

CT-139
LADYBIRD
Style One, Second Version

Designer:	Colin Terris
Type:	Weight – Spherical
Cane:	79 (in base)
Issued:	1979 in a limited edition of 100
Status:	Closed at No. 51
O.I.P.:	U.K. £100.00
	U.S. $495.00
U.K.:	£350.00
U.S.:	$625.00
Can.:	$800.00

Note: See CT-105 for the 1978 issue.

CT-140
BUTTERFLY and FLOWER
Second Version

Designer:	Colin Terris
Type:	Weight – Spherical
Cane:	79 (in base)
Issued:	1979 in a limited edition of 250
Status:	Closed at No. 104
O.I.P.:	U.K. £130.00
	U.S. $220.00
U.K.:	£300.00
U.S.:	$550.00
Can.:	$700.00

Note: See CT-107 for the 1978 issue.

CT-141
HEATHER BELL

Designer:	William Manson
Type:	Weight – Spherical
Issued:	1979 in a limited edition of 100
Status:	Closed at No. 91
O.I.P.:	U.K. £100.00
	U.S. $465.00
U.K.:	£300.00
U.S.:	$550.00
Can.:	$700.00

CT-142
ROSEBUD
First Version

Designer:	William Manson
Type:	Weight – Spherical
Cane:	79 (in base)
Issued:	1979 in a limited edition of 50
Status:	Fully subscribed
O.I.P.:	U.K. £200.00
	U.S. $950.00
U.K.:	£ 550.00
U.S.:	$1,000.00
Can.:	$1,300.00

Note: See CT-188 for the 1980 issue.

CT-143
FLORAL FOUNTAIN

Designer:	Colin Terris
Type:	Weight – Spherical
Colour:	Red
Cane:	CG (Caithness Glass)
Issued:	1979 in a limited edition of 750
Status:	Closed at No. 636
O.I.P.:	U.K. £45.00
	U.S. $225.00
U.K.:	£100.00
U.S.:	$200.00
Can.:	$250.00

CT-144
SWAN
Style One, Second Version
Designer: Colin Terris and
William Manson
Type: Weight – Spherical
Cane: 79 (in base)
Issued: 1979 in a limited
edition of 100
Status: Fully subscribed
O.I.P.: U.K. £100.00
U.S. $495.00

U.K.: £300.00
U.S.: $550.00
Can.: $700.00

CT-145
HOLLY WREATH
Designer: Colin Terris
Type: Weight – Spherical
Issued: 1979 in a limited
edition of 500
Status: Closed at No. 495
O.I.P.: U.K. £89.00
U.S. $395.00

U.K.: £125.00
U.S.: $250.00
Can.: $325.00

CT-146
SHEPHERDS
Designer: Helen MacDonald
Type: Weight – Spherical,
engraved
Issued: 1979 in a limited
edition of 2,000
Status: Closed at No. 864
Series: Nativity
O.I.P.: U.K. £55.00
U.S. $195.00

U.K.: £ 85.00
U.S.: $170.00
Can.: $220.00

CT-147
CHRISTMAS ROSE
Style One
Designer: Colin Terris
Type: Weight – Spherical,
sulphide and
lampwork
Issued: 1979 in a limited
edition of 1,000
Status: Closed at No. 507
O.I.P.: U.K. £70.00
U.S. $375.00

U.K.: £100.00
U.S.: $200.00
Can.: $260.00

CT-148
HENRY VIII
First Version, Large
Designer: Colin Terris
Type: Weight – Spherical,
sulphide
Issued: 1979 in a limited
edition of 1,000
Status: Closed at No. 502
O.I.P.: U.K. £70.00
U.S. $375.00

U.K.: £100.00
U.S.: $200.00
Can.: $250.00

CT-149
KALEIDOSCOPE
Designer: Colin Terris
Type: Weight – Spherical
Issued: 1979
Status: Closed
O.I.P.: U.K. £10.00
U.S. $15.00

U.K.: £35.00
U.S.: $65.00
Can.: $85.00

CT-150
NUCLEUS
Designer: Colin Terris
Type: Weight – Spherical
Issued: 1979 in a limited
edition of 1,500
Status: Closed at No. 383
Series: Limited - Modern
Design
O.I.P.: U.K. £30.90
U.S. $135.00

U.K.: £ 40.00
U.S.: $ 80.00
Can.: $100.00

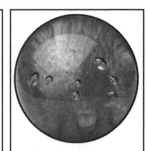

CT-151
OCEAN SPRING
Designer: Colin Terris
Type: Weight – Spherical
Issued: 1979 in a limited
edition of 1,500
Status: Closed at No. 630
Series: Limited - Modern
Design
O.I.P.: U.K. £30.90
U.S. $135.00

U.K.: £ 55.00
U.S.: $110.00
Can.: $150.00

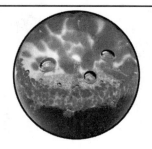

CT-152
EMBRYO

Designer:	Colin Terris
Type:	Weight – Spherical
Issued:	1979 in a limited edition of 1,500
Status:	Closed at No. 649
Series:	Limited - Modern Design
O.I.P.:	U.K. £30.90
	U.S. $135.00
U.K.:	£ 45.00
U.S.:	$100.00
Can.:	$130.00

ISSUES OF 1980

CT-157
DREAM FLOWER

Designer:	Colin Terris
Type:	Weight – Spherical
Issued:	1980 in a limited edition of 750
Status:	Fully subscribed
Series:	Limited - Modern Design
O.I.P.:	U.K. £41.55 U.S. $185.00
U.K.:	£ 75.00
U.S.:	$150.00
Can.:	$200.00

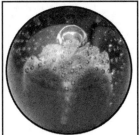

CT-158
NIGHT VENTURE

Designer:	Colin Terris
Type:	Weight – Spherical
Issued:	1980 in a limited edition of 1,500
Status:	Closed at No. 827
Series:	Limited - Modern Design
O.I.P.:	U.K. £30.90 U.S. $135.00
U.K.:	£ 45.00
U.S.:	$ 90.00
Can.:	$125.00

CT-159
SPACE ORCHID

Designer:	Colin Terris
Type:	Weight – Spherical
Issued:	1980 in a limited edition of 1,000
Status:	Fully subscribed
Series:	Limited - Modern Design
O.I.P.:	U.K. £35.00 U.S. $155.00
U.K.:	£ 65.00
U.S.:	$125.00
Can.:	$165.00

CT-160
SPACE TRAVELLER

Designer:	Colin Terris
Type:	Weight – Spherical
Issued:	1980 in a limited edition of 1,000
Status:	Closed at No. 571
Series:	Limited - Modern Design
O.I.P.:	U.K. £35.15 U.S. $155.00
U.K.:	£ 45.00
U.S.:	$ 90.00
Can.:	$125.00

CT-161
COSMIC RAIN

Designer:	Colin Terris
Type:	Weight – Spherical
Issued:	1980 in a limited edition of 750
Status:	Closed at No. 394
Series:	Limited - Modern Design
O.I.P.:	U.K. £55.40 U.S. $250.00
U.K.:	£ 85.00
U.S.:	$175.00
Can.:	$225.00

CT-162
BLUE FLORAL FOUNTAIN

Designer:	Colin Terris
Type:	Weight – Spherical
Issued:	1980 in a limited edition of 750
Status:	Fully subscribed
O.I.P.:	U.K. £58.60 U.S. $265.00
U.K.:	£ 85.00
U.S.:	$175.00
Can.:	$225.00

CT-163
BAUBLE, BANGLE and BEADS

Designer:	Colin Terris
Type:	Weight – Spherical
Issued:	1980 in a limited edition of 1,500
Status:	Closed at No. 1,054
Series:	Limited - Modern Design
O.I.P.:	U.K. £30.90 U.S. $135.00
U.K.:	£ 40.00
U.S.:	$ 80.00
Can.:	$100.00

CT-164
BLUE SPIRAL

Designer:	Colin Terris
Type:	Weight – Spherical
Issued:	1980 in a limited edition of 750
Status:	Closed at No. 724
Series:	Limited - Modern Design
O.I.P.:	U.K. £39.40 U.S. $175.00
U.K.:	£ 65.00
U.S.:	$135.00
Can.:	$175.00

CT-165
MOONPROBE
Designer: Colin Terris
Type: Weight – Spherical
Issued: 1980 in a limited
edition of 1,000
Status: Closed at No. 398
Series: Limited - Modern
Design
O.I.P.: U.K. £33.55
U.S. $150.00

U.K.: £ 55.00
U.S.: $110.00
Can.: $145.00

CT-166
VERTIGO
Designer: Colin Terris
Type: Weight – Spherical
Issued: 1980 in a limited
edition of 1,500
Status: Closed at No. 571
Series: Limited - Modern
Design
O.I.P.: U.K. £30.90
U.S. $135.00

U.K.: £ 50.00
U.S.: $100.00
Can.: $130.00

CT-167
DOUBLE SPIRAL
Designer: Colin Terris
Type: Weight – Spherical
Issued: 1980 in a limited
edition of 1,000
Status: Closed at No. 643
Series: Limited - Modern
Design
O.I.P.: U.K. £33.55
U.S. $150.00

U.K.: £ 45.00
U.S.: $ 90.00
Can.: $125.00

CT-168
SANCTUARY
Designer: Colin Terris
Type: Weight – Spherical
Issued: 1980 in a limited
edition of 500
Status: Fully subscribed
Series: Limited - Modern
Design
O.I.P.: U.K. £55.45
U.S. $250.00

U.K.: £125.00
U.S.: $250.00
Can.: $325.00

CT-169
NIGHT FLOWER
Designer: Colin Terris
Type: Weight – Spherical
Issued: 1980 in a limited
edition of 1,500
Status: Fully subscribed
Series: Limited - Modern
Design
O.I.P.: U.K. £30.90
U.S. $135.00

U.K.: £ 60.00
U.S.: $120.00
Can.: $150.00

CT-170
FIRE FLOWER
Designer: Colin Terris
Type: Weight – Spherical
Issued: 1980 in a limited
edition of 1,500
Status: Closed at No. 406
Series: Limited - Modern
Design
O.I.P.: U.K. £30.90
U.S. $135.00

U.K.: £ 40.00
U.S.: $ 80.00
Can.: $100.00

CT-171
SATELLITE
Designer: Colin Terris
Type: Weight – Spherical
Issued: 1980 in a limited
edition of 1,000
Status: Closed at No. 948
Series: Limited - Modern
Design
O.I.P.: U.K. £35.15
U.S. $165.00

U.K.: £ 65.00
U.S.: $135.00
Can.: $175.00

CT-172
TIME ZONE
Designer: Colin Terris
Type: Weight – Spherical
Issued: 1980 in a limited
edition of 1,500
Status: Closed at No. 426
Series: Limited - Modern
Design
O.I.P.: U.K. £30.90
U.S. $135.00

U.K.: £ 50.00
U.S.: $100.00
Can.: $130.00

CT-173
CONTRAST

Designer: Colin Terris
Type: Weight – Spherical
Issued: 1980 in a limited
edition of 1,500
Status: Closed at No. 769
Series: Limited - Modern
Design
O.I.P.: U.K. £30.90
U.S. $135.00

U.K.: £ 45.00
U.S.: $ 90.00
Can.: $125.00

CT-174
FIREWORKS

Designer: Colin Terris
Type: Weight – Spherical
Issued: 1980 in a limited
edition of 1,000
Status: Fully subscribed
Series: Limited - Modern
Design
O.I.P.: U.K. £30.90
U.S. $165.00

U.K.: £100.00
U.S.: $175.00
Can.: $225.00

CT-175
PARASOL

Designer: Colin Terris
Type: Weight – Spherical
Issued: 1980 in a limited
edition of 1,000
Status: Closed at No. 956
Series: Limited - Modern
Design
O.I.P.: U.K. £35.15
U.S. $165.00

U.K.: £ 50.00
U.S.: $100.00
Can.: $130.00

CT-176
TWILIGHT

Designer: Colin Terris
Type: Weight – Spherical
Issued: 1980 in a limited
edition of 750
Status: Closed at No. 539
Series: Limited - Modern
Design
O.I.P.: U.K. £39.40
U.S. $175.00

U.K.: £ 55.00
U.S.: $110.00
Can.: $150.00

CT-177
FLAMENCO
Style One

Designer: Alistair Ross
Type: Weight – Spherical
Issued: 1980
Status: Closed
Series: Unlimited - Modern
Design
O.I.P.: U.K. £23.95
U.S. $115.00

U.K.: £ 40.00
U.S.: $ 80.00
Can.: $100.00

CT-178
METEOR

Designer: Colin Terris
Type: Weight – Spherical
Issued: 1980 in a limited
edition of 1,000
Status: Closed at No. 518
Series: Limited - Modern
Design
O.I.P.: U.K. £31.95
U.S. $145.00

U.K.: £ 45.00
U.S.: $ 90.00
Can.: $125.00

CT-179
SUNSET

Designer: Colin Terris
Type: Weight – Spherical
Issued: 1980 in a limited
edition of 1,000
Status: Closed at No. 434
Series: Limited - Modern
Design
O.I.P.: U.K. £31.95
U.S. $145.00

U.K.: £ 45.00
U.S.: $ 90.00
Can.: $125.00

CT-180
WINTER MOON

Designer: Colin Terris
Type: Weight – Spherical
Issued: 1980 in a limited
edition of 1,000
Status: Closed at No. 418
Series: Limited - Modern
Design
O.I.P.: U.K. £31.95
U.S. $145.00

U.K.: £ 50.00
U.S.: $100.00
Can.: $130.00

CT-181
SKYLINE

Designer:	Colin Terris
Type:	Weight – Spherical
Issued:	1980 in a limited edition of 1,000
Status:	Closed at No. 404
Series:	Limited - Modern Design
O.I.P.:	U.K. £31.95
	U.S. $145.00
U.K.:	£ 45.00
U.S.:	$ 90.00
Can.:	$125.00

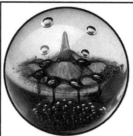

CT-182
SPACEPORT

Designer:	Colin Terris
Type:	Weight – Spherical
Issued:	1980 in a limited edition of 1,500
Status:	Closed at No. 723
Series:	Limited - Modern Design
O.I.P.:	U.K. £30.90
	U.S. $135.00
U.K.:	£ 45.00
U.S.:	$ 90.00
Can.:	$125.00

CT-183
BLACK GEM

Designer:	Colin Terris
Type:	Weight – Spherical
Issued:	1980 in a limited edition of 1,000
Status:	Closed at No. 857
Series:	Collectors' Society
O.I.P.:	£27.50
U.K.:	£ 55.00
U.S.:	$100.00
Can.:	$130.00

Note: This weight was offered to U.K. Club Members only.

CT-184
NATIVITY
Style One

Designer:	Helen MacDonald
Type:	Weight – Spherical, engraved
Issued:	1980 in a limited edition of 2,000 (1,000 in the U.K. and 1,000 in the US)
Status:	Closed at No. 557
Series:	Nativity
O.I.P.:	U.K. £63.90
	U.S. $275.00
U.K.:	£ 85.00
U.S.:	$175.00
Can.:	$225.00

CT-185
SIAMESE FIGHTING FISH

Designer:	Caithness Design Studio
Type:	Weight – Spherical, engraved
Issued:	1980 in a limited edition of 1,500
Status:	Closed at No. 367
Series:	Exotic Fishes
O.I.P.:	U.K. £31.95
	U.S. $145.00
U.K.:	£ 50.00
U.S.:	$100.00
Can.:	$130.00

CT-186
SEAL
Style Two

Designer:	Ray Gannon
Type:	Weight – Spherical
Issued:	1980 in a limited edition of 50
Status:	Closed at No. 27
O.I.P.:	£215.00
U.K.:	£ 650.00
U.S.:	$1,175.00
Can.:	$1,500.00

Note: This paperweight was not issued in the U.S.

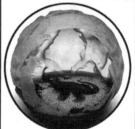

CT-187
SALAMANDER
Style Three

Designer:	Caithness Paperweight Studio
Type:	Weight – Spherical
Cane:	80 (in base)
Issued:	1980 in a limited edition of 50
Status:	Closed at No. 39
O.I.P.:	U.K. £215.00
	U.S. $950.00
U.K.:	£ 400.00
U.S.:	$ 800.00
Can.:	$1,000.00

Note: See CT-101 for the 1978 issue and CT-136 for the 1979 issue.

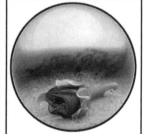

CT-188
ROSEBUD
Second Version

Designer:	Caithness Paperweight Studio
Type:	Weight – Spherical
Issued:	1980 in a limited edition of 50
Status:	Fully subscribed
O.I.P.:	U.K. £215.00
	U.S. $950.00
U.K.:	£350.00
U.S.:	$700.00
Can.:	$950.00

Note: See CT-142 for the 1979 issue.

CT-189
MANTA RAY
Style Two

Designer	Caithness Paperweight Studio
Type:	Weight – Spherical
Cane:	80 (in base)
Issued:	1980 in a limited edition of 50
Status:	Closed at No. 30
O.I.P.:	U.K. £215.00
	U.S. $950.00
U.K.:	£275.00
U.S.:	$550.00
Can.:	$700.00

Note: See CT-103 for the 1978 issue and CT-137 for the 1979 issue.

CT-190
COBRA
Style Three

Designer:	Caithness Paperweight Studio
Type:	Weight – Spherical
Cane:	80 (in base)
Issued:	1980 in a limited edition of 50
Status:	Closed at No. 27
O.I.P.:	U.K. £215.00
	U.S. $950.00
U.K.:	£300.00
U.S.:	$600.00
Can.:	$800.00

Note: See CT-100 for the 1978 issue and CT-135 for the 1979 issue.

CT-191A
BLUE ROSE

Designer:	Colin Terris
Type:	Weight – Spherical
Issued:	1980 in a limited edition of 100
Status:	Fully subscribed
O.I.P.:	U.K. £124.60/set
	U.S. $550.00/set
U.K.:	£200.00
U.S.:	$400.00
Can.:	$525.00

Note: CT-191A and B were issued and sold as a set.

CT-191B
BLUE ROSE PERFUME BOTTLE

Designer:	Colin Terris	
Type:	Perfume bottle	
Issued:	1980 in a limited edition of 100	
Status:	Fully subscribed	
O.I.P.:	U.K. £124.60/set	
	U.S. $550.00/set	
	Blue	**Set**
U.K.:	£400.	600.
U.S.:	$725.	1,125.
Can.:	$950.	1,500.

CT-192A
BLACK and GOLD

Designer:	James MacBeath
Type:	Weight – Spherical
Issued:	1980 in a limited edition of 100
Status:	Fully subscribed
O.I.P.:	U.K. £124.60/set
	U.S. $550.00/set
U.K.:	£200.00
U.S.:	$350.00
Can.:	$450.00

Note: CT-192A and B were issued and sold as a set.

CT-192B
BLACK and GOLD PERFUME BOTTLE

Designer:	James MacBeath	
Type:	Perfume bottle	
Issued:	1980 in a limited edition of 100	
Status:	Fully subscribed	
O.I.P.:	U.K. £124.60/set	
	U.S. $550.00/set	
	Black/Gold	**Set**
U.K.:	£400.	600.
U.S.:	$725.	1,100.
Can.:	$950.	1,400.

CT-195
GOLD THROAT

Designer:	Colin Terris
Type:	Weight – Spherical, engraved
Issued:	1980 in a limited edition of 1,000
Status:	Closed at No. 545
Series:	Exotic Birds
O.I.P.:	U.K. £42.60
	U.S. $195.00
U.K.:	£ 60.00
U.S.:	$125.00
Can.:	$165.00

CT-196
SILENT WATCHER

Designer:	Ray Gannon
Type:	Weight – Domed
Issued:	1980 in a limited edition of 50
Status:	Closed at No. 23
O.I.P.:	£225.60
U.K.:	£ 500.00
U.S.:	$ 900.00
Can.:	$1,200.00

Note: This paperweight was not issued in the U.S.

CT-197
QUEEN ELIZABETH I

Designer:	Colin Terris
Type:	Weight – Spherical, sulphide
Issued:	1980 in a limited edition of 1,000
Status:	Closed at No. 390
O.I.P.:	U.K. £81.75
	U.S. $395.00
U.K.:	£125.00
U.S.:	$250.00
Can.:	$325.00

CT-198
ROYAL BIRTHDAY

Designer:	Colin Terris
Type:	Weight – Spherical, engraved
Issued:	1980 in a limited edition of 1,000
Status:	Closed at No. 188
O.I.P.:	£30.00
U.K.:	£ 50.00
U.S.:	$100.00
Can.:	$130.00

Note: Weights CT-198, 199, 200 and 201 were issued to commemorate the 80th birthday of HM Queen Elizabeth The Queen Mother. They were not issued in the U.S.

CT-199
QUEEN MOTHER

Designer:	Colin Terris
Type:	Weight – Spherical, sulphide
Cane:	1980
Issued:	1980 in a limited edition of 1,000
Status:	Closed at No. 310
O.I.P.:	£85.00
U.K.:	£100.00
U.S.:	$200.00
Can.:	$260.00

CT-200
ROYAL ARMS

Designer:	Jennie Robertson
Type:	Weight – Spherical, engraved
Issued:	1980 in a limited edition of 80
Status:	Fully subscribed
O.I.P.:	£99.00
U.K.:	£150.00
U.S.:	$300.00
Can.:	$400.00

CT-201
THISTLE AND ROSE

Designer:	Helen MacDonald
Type:	Weight – Spherical
Issued:	1980 in a limited edition of 1,000
Status:	Closed at No. 796
O.I.P.:	£39.50
U.K.:	£ 55.00
U.S.:	$100.00
Can.:	$130.00

Note: This paperweight was not issued in the U.S.

CT-202
PIROUETTE

Designer:	Colin Terris
Type:	Weight – Spherical
Issued:	1980 in a limited edition of 1,000
Status:	Closed at No. 527
Series:	Collectors' Society
O.I.P.:	£35.00
U.K.:	£ 75.00
U.S.:	$135.00
Can.:	$175.00

Note: This weight was offered to U.K. Club members only.

ISSUES OF 1981

CT-203
SPRINGTIME
Designer: Andrew Lawson
Type: Weight – Spherical
Issued: 1981 in a limited
          edition of 750
Status: Fully subscribed
Series: Limited – Modern
          Design
O.I.P.:   U.K. £44.75
          U.S. $195.00

U.K.:   £ 65.00
U.S.: $130.00
Can.: $175.00

CT-204
ELEGANCE
Designer: Colin Terris
Type: Weight – Spherical
Issued: 1981 in a limited
          edition of 250
Status: Fully subscribed
Series: Limited – Modern
          Design
O.I.P.:   U.K. £63.00
          U.S. $295.00

U.K.:   £150.00
U.S.: $275.00
Can.: $350.00

CT-205
PEACH FLORAL FOUNTAIN
Designer: Colin Terris
Type: Weight – Spherical
Issued: 1981 in a limited
          edition of 750
Status: Fully subscribed
O.I.P.:   U.K. £63.00
          U.S. $265.00

U.K.:   £100.00
U.S.: $200.00
Can.: $260.00

CT-206
FANTASIA
Designer: Colin Terris
Type: Weight – Spherical
Issued: 1981 in a limited
          edition of 750
Status: Closed at No. 592
O.I.P.:   U.K. £50.00
          U.S. $225.00

U.K.:   £ 60.00
U.S.: $125.00
Can.: $165.00

CT-207
TRISTAR
Designer: Colin Terris
Type: Weight – Spherical
Issued: 1981 in a limited
          edition of 750
Status: Closed at No. 711
O.I.P.:   U.K. £50.00
          U.S. $225.00

U.K.:   £ 60.00
U.S.: $125.00
Can.: $165.00

CT-208
SPACE SHUTTLE
Designer: Colin Terris
Type: Weight – Spherical
Issued: 1981 in a limited
          edition of 1,000
Status: Fully subscribed
Series: Limited – Modern
          Design
O.I.P.:   U.K. £32.00
          U.S. $135.00

U.K.:   £ 50.00
U.S.: $100.00
Can.: $130.00

CT-209
TOUCHDOWN
Designer: Colin Terris
Type: Weight – Spherical
Issued: 1981 in a limited
          edition of 1,000
Status: Closed at No. 988
O.I.P.:   U.K. £32.00
          U.S. $135.00

U.K.:   £ 75.00
U.S.: $135.00
Can.: $175.00

CT-210
LUNAR III
Designer: Colin Terris
Type: Weight – Spherical
Issued: 1981 in a limited
          edition of 750
Status: Fully subscribed
O.I.P.:   U.K. £41.00
          U.S. $175.00

U.K.:   £ 85.00
U.S.: $150.00
Can.: $200.00

CT-211
STAR PAVILION

Designer: Colin Terris
Type: Weight – Spherical
Issued: 1981 in a limited
edition of 750
Status: Closed at No. 246
Series: Limited – Modern
Design
O.I.P.: U.K. £41.50
U.S. $175.00

U.K.: £ 50.00
U.S.: $100.00
Can.: $130.00

CT-212
JESTER

Designer: Caithness
Paperweight Studios
Type: Weight – Spherical
Issued: 1981 in a limited
edition of 1,000
Status: Closed at No. 961
Series: Limited – Modern
Design
O.I.P.: U.K. £32.00
U.S. $135.00

U.K.: £ 50.00
U.S.: $100.00
Can.: $130.00

CT-213
CORONET

Designer: Colin Terris
Type: Weight – Spherical
Issued: 1981 in a limited
edition of 750
Status: Closed at No. 120
Series: Limited – Modern
Design
O.I.P.: U.K. £41.50
U.S. $175.00

U.K.: £ 60.00
U.S.: $120.00
Can.: $150.00

CT-214
GAZEBO

Designer: Caithness
Paperweight Studios
Type: Weight – Spherical
Issued: 1981 in a limited
edition of 1,000
Status: Fully subscribed
Series: Limited – Modern
Design
O.I.P.: U.K. £32.00
U.S. $135.00

U.K.: £ 45.00
U.S.: $ 90.00
Can.: $125.00

CT-215
VIKING FLAME

Designer: Colin Terris
Type: Weight – Spherical
Issued: 1981 in a limited
edition of 750
Status: Closed at No. 390
Series: Limited – Modern
Design
O.I.P.: U.K. £41.50
U.S. $175.00

U.K.: £ 45.00
U.S.: $ 90.00
Can.: $125.00

CT-216
MIDAS

Designer: Colin Terris
Type: Weight – Spherical
Issued: 1981 in a limited
edition of 750
Status: Closed at No. 738
Series: Limited – Modern
Design
O.I.P.: U.K. £41.50
U.S. $175.00

U.K.: £ 55.00
U.S.: $110.00
Can.: $150.00

CT-217
ZENITH PERFUME BOTTLE

Designer: Colin Terris
Type: Perfume bottle
Issued: 1981 in a limited
edition of 150
Status: Closed at No. 125
O.I.P.: U.K. £85.00
U.S. $375.00

U.K.: £250.00
U.S.: $450.00
Can.: $575.00

CT-218A
FAITH

Designer: Colin Terris
Type: Weight – Spherical
Issued: 1981 in a limited
edition of 250
Status: Closed at No. 237
Series: Limited – Modern
Design
O.I.P.: U.K. £127.50/set
U.S. $575.00/set

	Weight	Set
U.K.:	£150.	450.
U.S.:	$300.	800.
Can.:	$400.	1,050.

Note: CT-218A, B and C were
issued and sold as a set.

CT-218B
HOPE

Designer: Colin Terris
Type: Weight – Spherical
Issued: 1981 in a limited
edition of 250
Status: Closed at No. 237
Series: Limited – Modern
Design
O.I.P.: U.K. £127.50/set
U.S. $575.00/set

U.K.: £150.00
U.S.: $300.00
Can.: $400.00

CT-218C
CHARITY

Designer: Colin Terris
Type: Weight – Spherical
Issued: 1981 in a limited
edition of 250
Status: Closed at No. 237
Series: Limited – Modern
Design
O.I.P.: U.K. £127.50/set
U.S. $575.00/set

U.K.: £150.00
U.S.: $300.00
Can.: $400.00

CT-219
SAND SPRITE

Designer: Colin Terris
Type: Weight – Spherical
Issued: 1981 in a limited
edition of 750
Status: Closed at No. 743
Series: Limited – Modern
Design
O.I.P.: U.K. £41.50
U.S. $175.00

U.K.: £ 65.00
U.S.: $130.00
Can.: $175.00

CT-220
ETERNA

Designer: Colin Terris
Type: Weight – Spherical
Issued: 1981 in a limited
edition of 500
Status: Closed at No. 334
Series: Limited – Modern
Design
O.I.P.: U.K. £59.50
U.S. $275.00

U.K.: £100.00
U.S.: $200.00
Can.: $260.00

CT-221
SAMARKAND PERFUME
BOTTLE

Designer: Colin Terris
Type: Perfume bottle
Issued: 1981 in a limited
edition of 150
Status: Fully subscribed
Series: Limited – Modern
Design
O.I.P.: U.K. £85.00
U.S. $375.00

U.K.: £200.00
U.S.: $400.00
Can.: $525.00

CT-222
AQUAFLORA PERFUME
BOTTLE

Designer: Colin Terris
Type: Perfume bottle
Issued: 1981
Status: Closed
O.I.P.: U.K. £55.00
U.S. $245.00

U.K.: £ 85.00
U.S.: $175.00
Can.: $225.00

CT-223
ENCHANTED FOREST

Designer: Colin Terris
Type: Weight – Spherical
Issued: 1981 in a limited
edition of 1,000
Status: Closed at No. 227
O.I.P.: U.K. £28.75
U.S. $125.00

U.K.: £ 75.00
U.S.: $150.00
Can.: $200.00

CT-224
COQUETTE

Designer: Douglas Cowie
Type: Weight – Spherical,
engraved
Issued: 1981 in a limited
edition of 1,000
Status: Closed at No. 254
Series: Exotic Birds
O.I.P.: U.K. £45.75
U.S. $195.00

U.K.: £ 65.00
U.S.: $130.00
Can.: $175.00

CT-225
WHIRLYGIG

Designer: Colin Terris
Type: Weight – Spherical
Colour: Silver
Issued: 1981
Status: Closed
Series: Unlimited - Modern Design
O.I.P.: U.K. £12.75
 U.S. $57.50

U.K.: £30.00
U.S.: $60.00
Can.: $75.00

CT-226
NOVA

Designer: Colin Terris
Type: Weight – Conical
Colour: Many colour variations
Issued: 1981
Status: Closed
Series: Unlimited - Modern Design
O.I.P.: U.K. £10.75
 U.S. $49.50

U.K.: £30.00
U.S.: $60.00
Can.: $75.00

CT-227
POLKA

Designer: Colin Terris
Type: Weight – Spherical
Colour: Many colour variations
Issued: 1981
Status: Closed
Series: Unlimited - Modern Design
O.I.P.: U.K. £13.75
 U.S. $62.50

U.K.: £30.00
U.S.: $60.00
Can.: $75.00

CT-228
TIGER

Designer: Douglas Cowie
Type: Weight – Spherical, engraved
Issued: 1981 in a limited edition of 1,500
Status: Closed at No. 105
O.I.P.: U.K. £28.75
 U.S. $125.00

U.K.: £100.00
U.S.: $200.00
Can.: $250.00

CT-229
WHITE RHINO

Designer: Caithness Engraving Studios
Type: Weight – Spherical, engraved
Issued: 1981 in a limited edition of 1,500
Status: Closed at No. 138
O.I.P.: U.K. £28.75
 U.S. $125.00

U.K.: £ 75.00
U.S.: $150.00
Can.: $200.00

CT-230
PANDA

Designer: Douglas Cowie
Type: Weight – Spherical, engraved
Issued: 1981 in a limited edition of 1,500
Status: Closed at No. 185
O.I.P.: U.K. £28.75
 U.S. $125.00

U.K.: £ 60.00
U.S.: $120.00
Can.: $160.00

CT-231
SHIP'S WHEEL

Designer: Colin Terris
Type: Weight – Spherical
Issued: 1981 in a limited edition of 1,000
Status: Closed at No. 891
O.I.P.: U.K. £35.00
 U.S. $135.00

U.K.: £ 45.00
US: $ 90.00
Can.: $125.00

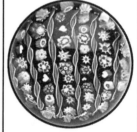

CT-232
REGENCY STRIPE

Designer: Colin Terris
Type: Weight – Spherical
Issued: 1981 in a limited edition of 1,000
Status: Closed at No. 749
O.I.P.: U.K. £35.00
 U.S. $135.00

U.K.: £ 45.00
U.S.: $ 90.00
Can.: $125.00

CT-233
INITIAL

Designer:	Colin Terris
Type:	Weight – Spherical
Cane:	Initial
Issued:	1981
Status:	Closed
O.I.P.:	U.K. £33.20
	U.S. $125.00
U.K.:	£35.00
U.S.:	$70.00
Can.:	$95.00

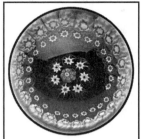

CT-234
AMETHYST LACE

Designer:	Colin Terris
Type:	Weight – Spherical
Cane:	CG (Caithness Glass)
Issued:	1981 in a limited
	edition of 1,000
Status:	Closed at No. 831
O.I.P.:	U.K. £35.00
	U.S. $135.00
U.K.:	£ 45.00
U.S.:	$ 90.00
Can.:	$125.00

CT-235
GLASSMAKER, THE

Designer:	Colin Terris
Type:	Weight – Spherical
Cane:	CG (Caithness
	Glass – in base)
Issued:	1981 in a limited
	edition of 1,000
Status:	Closed at No. 995
O.I.P.:	U.K. £35.00
	U.S. $135.00
U.K.:	£ 50.00
U.S.:	$100.00
Can.:	$130.00

CT-236
HEART
Style One

Designer:	Colin Terris
Type:	Weight – Spherical
Cane:	CG (Caithness Glass)
Issued:	1981 in a limited
	edition of 1,000
Status:	Closed at No. 998
O.I.P.:	U.K. £35.00
	U.S. $135.00
U.K.:	£ 40.00
U.S.:	$ 80.00
Can.:	$100.00

CT-237
ROMANCE PERFUME BOTTLE

Designer:	Colin Terris
Type:	Perfume bottle
Issued:	1981
Status:	Closed
Series:	Unlimited - Modern
	Design
O.I.P.:	U.K. £63.00
	U.S. $295.00
U.K.:	£ 85.00
U.S.:	$175.00
Can.:	$225.00

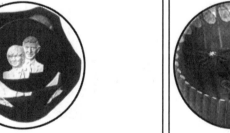

CT-238
ROYAL WEDDING
Style One

Designer:	Colin Terris
Type:	Weight – Spherical, sulphide
Issued:	1981 in a limited edition of 750
Status:	Closed at No. 131
Series:	Royal Wedding Collection
O.I.P.:	£81.75
U.K.:	£200.00
U.S.:	$350.00
Can.:	$450.00

Note: This paperweight and the following twelve were issued to commemorate the wedding of Prince Charles and Lady Diana Spencer. It was not issued in the U.S.

CT-239
FLORAL TRIBUTE

Designer:	Colin Terris
Type:	Weight – Spherical
Canes:	C & D (Charles
	and Diana)
Issued:	1981 in a limited
	edition of 100
Status:	Fully subscribed
Series:	Royal Wedding
	Collection
O.I.P.:	£150.00
U.K.:	£ 500.00
U.S.:	$ 900.00
Can.:	$1,200.00

Note: This paperweight was not issued in the U.S.

CT-240
WEDDING BELL

Designer: Colin Terris
Type: Weight – Spherical
Cane: C & D (Charles and Diana)
Issued: 1981 in a limited edition of 250
Status: Fully subscribed
Series: Royal Wedding Collection
O.I.P.: U.K. £96.00
U.S. $450.00

U.K.: £125.00
U.S.: $250.00
Can.: $350.00

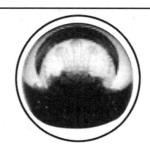

CT-241A
DUET – ONE

Designer: Caithness Engraving Studios
Type: Weight – Spherical, engraved
Issued: 1981 in a limited edition of 500
Status: Fully subscribed
Series: Royal Wedding Collection
O.I.P.: U.K. £75.00/set
U.S. $350.00/set

	Duet One	Set
U.K.:	£ 60.00	120.00
U.S.:	$120.00	250.00
Can.:	$150.00	350.00

Note: This paperweight forms a set with CT-241B, Duet Weight Two.

CT-241B
DUET – TWO

Designer: Caithness Engraving Studios
Type: Weight – Spherical, engraved
Issued: 1981 in a limited edition of 500
Status: Fully subscribed
Series: Royal Wedding Collection
O.I.P.: U.K. £75.00/set
U.S. $350.00/set

U.K.: £ 60.00
U.S.: $120.00
Can.: $150.00

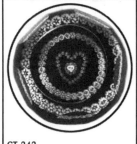

CT-242
HEART
Style Two

Designer: Colin Terris
Type: Weight – Spherical
Cane: C & D (Charles and Diana)
Issued: 1981 in a limited edition of 250
Status: Fully subscribed
Series: Royal Wedding Collection
O.I.P.: U.K. £75.00
U.S. $375.00

U.K.: £125.00
U.S.: $250.00
Can.: $350.00

CT-243
CROWN
Style Two

Designer: Colin Terris
Type: Weight – Spherical
Cane: C & D (Charles and Diana)
Issued: 1981 in a limited edition of 250
Status: Fully subscribed
Series: Royal Wedding Collection
O.I.P.: U.K. £58.50
U.S. $295.00

U.K.: £200.00
U.S.: $400.00
Can.: $525.00

CT-244
CELEBRATION

Designer: Colin Terris
Type: Weight – Spherical
Cane: C & D (Charles and Diana)
Issued: 1981 in a limited edition of 750
Status: Closed at No. 425
Series: Royal Wedding Collection
O.I.P.: U.K. £50.00
U.S. $235.00

U.K.: £ 60.00
U.S.: $120.00
Can.: $150.00

CT-245
GARLAND

Designer: Colin Terris
Type: Weight – Spherical
Cane: C & D (Charles and Diana)
Issued: 1981 in a limited edition of 750
Status: Closed at No. 420
Series: Royal Wedding Collection
O.I.P.: U.K. £44.75
U.S. $210.00

U.K.: £ 55.00
U.S.: $110.00
Can.: $150.00

CT-246
ST. PAUL'S

Designer: Caithness Engraving
Studios
Type: Weight – Spherical,
engraved
Issued: 1981 in a limited
edition of 750
Status: Fully subscribed
Series: Royal Wedding
Collection
O.I.P.: U.K. £39.50
U.S. $185.00

U.K.: £ 45.00
U.S.: $ 90.00
Can.: $125.00

CT-247
ROYAL PORTRAIT

Designer: Caithness Engraving
Studios
Type: Weight – Spherical,
engraved
Issued: 1981 in a limited
edition of 750
Status: Closed at No. 734
Series: Royal Wedding
Collection
O.I.P.: U.K. £39.50
U.S. $185.00

U.K.: £ 45.00
U.S.: $ 90.00
Can.: · $125.00

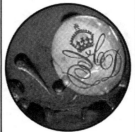

CT-248
ROYAL WEDDING
MOONFLOWER

Designer: Colin Terris
Type: Weight – Spherical
Issued: 1981 in a limited
edition of 1,500
Status: Fully subscribed
Series: Royal Wedding
Collection
O.I.P.: U.K. £30.00
U.S. $135.00

U.K.: £ 45.00
U.S.: $ 90.00
Can.: $125.00

CT-249
CONGRATULATIONS
Style One

Designer: Colin Terris
Type: Weight – Spherical
Issued: 1981
Status: Closed
Series: Royal Wedding
Collection
O.I.P.: U.K. £20.00
U.S. $95.00

U.K.: £ 50.00
U.S.: $100.00
Can.: $130.00

CT-252
I SAW THREE SHIPS

Designer: John Taylor
Type: Weight – Spherical,
engraved
Issued: 1981 in a limited
edition of 500
Status: Closed at No. 263
Series: Limited – Modern
Design
O.I.P.: U.K. £50.00
U.S. $195.00

U.K.: £ 70.00
U.S.: $150.00
Can.: $200.00

CT-253
ENIGMA

Designer: Colin Terris
Type: Weight – Spherical
Issued: 1981 in a limited
edition of 1,000
Status: Closed at No. 558
Series: Collectors Club
O.I.P.: £35.00

U.K.: £ 65.00
U.S.: $120.00
Can.: $150.00

Note: This weight was offered to
U.K. Club members only.

CT-254
ROBIN

Designer: Colin Terris and
William Manson
Type: Weight – Spherical
Issued: 1981 in a limited
edition of 500
Status: Closed at No. 489
O.I.P.: U.K. £96.00
U.S. $395.00

U.K.: £135.00
U.S.: $275.00
Can.: $350.00

CT-255
SNOWFLAKE CROWN

Designer: Colin Terris
Type: Weight – Spherical
Issued: 1981 in a limited
edition of 250
Status: Fully subscribed
Series: Traditional
Collection
O.I.P.: U.K. £63.95
U.S. $275.00

U.K.: £135.00
U.S.: $270.00
Can.: $350.00

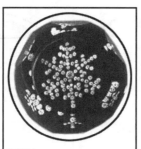

**CT-256
SNOW CRYSTAL**

Designer: Colin Terris
Type: Weight – Spherical,
        facets
Issued: 1981 in a limited
        edition of 1,000
Status: Closed at No. 280
Series: Whitefriars
        Collection
O.I.P.: U.K. £63.00
        U.S. $250.00

U.K.:   £100.00
U.S.: $200.00
Can.: $250.00

**HMS KELLY
40th ANNIVERSARY**

Designer: Unknown
Type: Weight – Spherical
Issued: 1981 in a limited
        edition of 500
Status: Closed
Series: Unknown
O.I.P.: U.K. £39.00

U.K.:   £ 50.00
U.S.: $100.00
Can.: $125.00

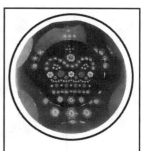

**ROYAL WEDDING MILLEFIORI
CROWN**

Designer: Colin Terris
Type: Weight – Spherical,
        facets
Issued: 1981 in a limited
        edition of 250
Status: Closed
Series: Royal Wedding
        Collection
O.I.P.: Unknown

U.K.:   £ 75.00
U.S.: $150.00
Can.: $225.00

ISSUES OF 1982

CT-257
APRIL PERFUME FLASK

Designer: Colin Terris
Type: Perfume flask
Issued: 1982
Status: Closed
O.I.P.: £44.75

U.K.: £ 55.00
U.S.: $110.00
Can.: $145.00

Note: This perfume flask was
not issued in the U.S.

CT-258
BIANCA PERFUME FLASK

Designer: Colin Terris
Type: Perfume flask
Issued: 1982
Status: Closed
O.I.P.: £50.00

U.K.: £ 55.00
U.S.: $110.00
Can.: $145.00

Note: This perfume flask was
not issued in the U.S.

CT-259
CORDELIA PERFUME FLASK

Designer: Colin Terris
Type: Perfume flask
Issued: 1982
Status: Closed
O.I.P.: £44.75

U.K.: £ 50.00
U.S.: $100.00
Can.: $130.00

Note: This perfume flask was
not issued in the U.S.

CT-260
DANIELLE PERFUME FLASK

Designer: Colin Terris
Type: Perfume flask
Issued: 1982
Status: Closed
O.I.P.: £55.00

U.K.: £ 85.00
U.S.: $150.00
Can.: $200.00

Note: This perfume flask was
not issued in the U.S.

CT-261
ERICA PERFUME FLASK

Designer: Colin Terris
Type: Perfume flask
Issued: 1982
Status: Closed
O.I.P.: £39.95

U.K.: £ 85.00
U.S.: $150.00
Can.: $200.00

Note: This perfume flask was
not issued in the U.S.

CT-262A
CURIO

Designer: Colin Terris
Type: Weight – Spherical
Issued: 1982 in a limited
edition of 150
Status: Closed at No. 124
O.I.P.: U.K. £150.00/set
U.S. $625.00/set

U.K.: £150.00
U.S.: $300.00
Can.: $400.00

Note: CT-262A and B were
issued and sold as a set.

CT-262B
CURIO PERFUME BOTTLE

Designer: Colin Terris
Type: Perfume bottle
Issued: 1982 in a limited
edition of 150
Status: Closed at No. 124
O.I.P.: U.K. £150.00/set
U.S. $625.00/set

	Perfume	Set
U.K.:	£300.	450.
U.S.:	$550.	850.
Can.:	$700.	1,100.

CT-263A
FROST

Designer: Colin Terris
Type: Weight – Spherical
Issued: 1982 in a limited
edition of 150
Status: Fully subscribed
Series: Limited – Modern
Design
O.I.P.: U.K. £115.00/set
U.S. $475.00/set

	Frost	Set
U.K.:	£150.	300.
U.S.:	$300.	600.
Can.:	$400.	800.

Note: CT-263A and B were
issued and sold as a set.

CT-263B
FIRE
Designer: Colin Terris
Type: Weight – Spherical
Issued: 1982 in a limited
edition of 150
Status: Fully subscribed
Series: Limited – Modern
Design
O.I.P.: U.K. £115.00/set
U.S. $475.00/set

U.K.: £150.00
U.S.: $300.00
Can.: $400.00

CT-264
ENCHANTÉ PERFUME BOTTLE
Designer: Colin Terris
Type: Perfume bottle
Issued: 1982 in a limited
edition of 250
Status: Fully subscribed
O.I.P.: U.K. £75.00
U.S. $315.00

U.K.: £100.00
U.S.: $200.00
Can.: $260.00

CT-265
SPLASHDOWN
Designer: Colin Terris
Type: Weight – Spherical
Issued: 1982
Status: Closed
Series: Unlimited – Modern
Design
O.I.P.: U.K. £15.95
U.S. $67.50

U.K.: £25.00
U.S.: $50.00
Can.: $65.00

CT-266
WHIRLYGIG AMETHYST
Designer: Colin Terris
Type: Weight – Spherical
Issued: 1982
Status: Closed
Series: Unlimited – Modern
Design
O.I.P.: U.K. £13.85
U.S. $57.50

U.K.: £25.00
U.S.: $50.00
Can.: $65.00

CT-267
VERMILION
Designer: Colin Terris
Type: Weight – Spherical
Issued: 1982 in a limited
edition of 500
Status: Closed at No. 178
Series: Limited – Modern
Design
O.I.P.: U.K. £37.50
U.S. $165.00

U.K.: £ 75.00
U.S.: $150.00
Can.: $200.00

CT-268
TERRA NOVA
Designer: Colin Terris
Type: Weight – Spherical
Issued: 1982 in a limited
edition of 1,000
Status: Closed at No. 862
Series: Limited – Modern
Design
O.I.P.: U.K. £36.75
U.S. $165.00

U.K.: £ 50.00
U.S.: $100.00
Can.: $130.00

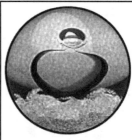

CT-269
HARMONY
Designer: Colin Terris
Type: Weight – Spherical
Issued: 1982 in a limited
edition of 1,000
Status: Fully subscribed
Series: Limited – Modern
Design
O.I.P.: U.K. £35.00
U.S. $145.00

U.K.: £30.00
U.S.: $60.00
Can.: $80.00

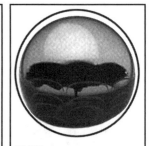

CT-270
NOCTURNE
Designer: Colin Terris
Type: Weight – Spherical
Issued: 1982 in a limited
edition of 1,000
Status: Closed at No. 260
Series: Limited – Modern
Design
O.I.P.: U.K. £35.00
U.S. $145.00

U.K.: £ 45.00
U.S.: $ 90.00
Can.: $125.00

CT-271
POPPIES
Style One

Designer: Colin Terris
Type: Weight – Spherical
Issued: 1982 in a limited
edition of 750
Status: Closed at No. 423
Series: Limited – Modern
Design
O.I.P.: U.K. £36.75
U.S. $150.00

U.K.: £ 45.00
U.S.: $ 90.00
Can.: $125.00

CT-272
DAMSON FLORAL FOUNTAIN

Designer: Colin Terris
Type: Weight – Spherical
Issued: 1982 in a limited
edition of 750
Status: Closed at No. 228
O.I.P.: U.K. £63.00
U.S. $265.00

U.K.: £125.00
U.S.: $250.00
Can.: $325.00

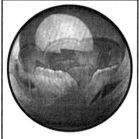

CT-273
FRAGRANCE

Designer: Colin Terris
Type: Weight – Spherical
Issued: 1982 in a limited
edition of 250
Status: Fully subscribed
Series: Limited – Modern
Design
O.I.P.: U.K. £63.00
U.S. $265.00

U.K.: £125.00
U.S.: $250.00
Can.: $325.00

CT-274
CHERRIES
Style One

Designer: William Manson
Type: Weight – Spherical
Issued: 1982 in a limited
edition of 150
Status: Fully subscribed
Series: Traditional Collection
O.I.P.: U.K. £110.00
U.S. $350.00

U.K.: £150.00
U.S.: $300.00
Can.: $375.00

CT-275
WHITE ROSE
Style One

Designer: William Manson
Type: Weight – Spherical
Issued: 1982 in a limited
edition of 150
Status: Closed at No. 108
O.I.P.: U.K. £125.00
U.S. $525.00

U.K.: £150.00
U.S.: $300.00
Can.: $375.00

CT-276
DRAGONFLY AND FLOWERS

Designer: William Manson
Type: Weight – Spherical
Issued: 1982 in a limited
edition of 500
Status: Closed at No. 436
Series: Traditional Collection
O.I.P.: U.K. £90.00
U.S. $295.00

U.K.: £100.00
U.S.: $200.00
Can.: $260.00

CT-277
FIONA

Designer: Caithness
Paperweight Studios
Type: Weight – Spherical
Issued: 1982 in a limited
edition of 500
Status: Closed at No. 151
O.I.P.: U.K. £75.00
U.S. $295.00

U.K.: £100.00
U.S.: $200.00
Can.: $260.00

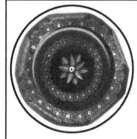

CT-278
HEATHER

Designer: Caithness
Paperweight Studios
Type: Weight – Spherical
Issued: 1982 in a limited
edition of 500
Status: Closed at No. 126
Series: Traditional Collection
O.I.P.: U.K. £75.00
U.S. $250.00

U.K.: £100.00
U.S.: $200.00
Can.: $260.00

CT-279
RONA

Designer: Caithness
Paperweight Studios
Type: Weight – Spherical
Issued: 1982 in a limited
edition of 500
Status: Closed at No. 163
O.I.P.: U.K. £75.00
U.S. $295.00

U.K.: £ 85.00
U.S.: $170.00
Can.: $225.00

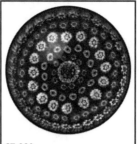

CT-280
RINGS OF ROSES

Designer: Colin Terris
Type: Weight – Spherical
Issued: 1982
Status: Closed
Series: Whitefriars Collection
O.I.P.: U.K. £39.50
U.S. $150.00

U.K.: £ 55.00
U.S.: $110.00
Can.: $150.00

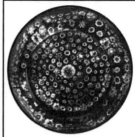

CT-281
BED OF ROSES

Designer: Colin Terris
Type: Weight – Spherical
Cane: 82
Issued: 1982 in a limited
edition of 750
Status: Closed at No. 246
Series: Whitefriars Collection
O.I.P.: U.K. £55.00
U.S. $195.00

U.K.: £ 60.00
U.S.: $120.00
Can.: $150.00

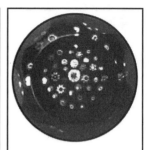

CT-282
SPREAD OF ROSES

Designer: Colin Terris
Type: Weight – Spherical
Issued: 1982 in a limited
edition of 750
Status: Closed at No. 275
Series: Whitefriars Collection
O.I.P.: U.K. £55.00
U.S. $195.00

U.K.: £ 70.00
U.S.: $150.00
Can.: $200.00

CT-283
GARLAND OF ROSES

Designer: Colin Terris
Type: Weight – Spherical
Issued: 1982 in a limited
edition of 750
Status: Closed at No. 217
Series: Whitefriars Collection
O.I.P.: U.K. £55.00
U.S. $195.00

U.K.: £ 75.00
U.S.: $150.00
Can.: $200.00

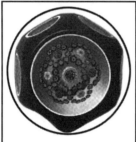

CT-284
ROSE GARDEN

Designer: Colin Terris
Type: Weight – Spherical,
double overlay
Issued: 1982 in a limited
edition of 100
Status: Fully subscribed
Series: Whitefriars Collection
O.I.P.: U.K. £150.00
U.S. $595.00

U.K.: £200.00
U.S.: $400.00
Can.: $525.00

CT-285
STAR OF ROSES

Designer: Colin Terris
Type: Weight – Spherical,
double overlay
Issued: 1982 in a limited
edition of 100
Status: Closed at No. 83
Series: Whitefriars Collection
O.I.P.: U.K. £150.00
U.S. $650.00

U.K.: £200.00
U.S.: $400.00
Can.: $525.00

CT-286
BUTTERFLY
Style Two

Designer: Colin Terris
Type: Weight – Spherical
Issued: 1982 in a limited
edition of 750
Status: Closed at No. 312
Series: Whitefriars Collection
O.I.P.: U.K. £55.00
U.S. $195.00

U.K.: £ 75.00
U.S.: $150.00
Can.: $200.00

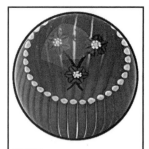

CT-287
ROYAL BIRTHDAY TRIBUTE
Style One
Designer: Colin Terris
Type: Weight – Spherical
Issued: 1982 in a limited edition of 100
Status: Fully subscribed
O.I.P.: U.K. £150.00
U.S. $550.00

U.K.: £225.00
U.S.: $450.00
Can.: $500.00

Note: CT-287, 288 and 289 were issued to commemorate the birth of HRH Prince William on June 21, 1982.

CT-288
ROYAL BIRTHDAY MOONFLOWER
Style One
Designer: Colin Terris
Type: Weight – Spherical
Issued: 1982 in a limited edition of 750
Status: Fully subscribed
O.I.P.: U.K. £29.95
U.S. $135.00

U.K.: £ 40.00
U.S.: $ 80.00
Can.: $100.00

CT-289
ROYAL BIRTHDAY CROWN
Style One
Designer: Colin Terris
Type: Weight – Spherical
Issued: 1982 in a limited edition of 250
Status: Fully subscribed
O.I.P.: £75.00

U.K.: £135.00
U.S.: $270.00
Can.: $350.00

Note: This paperweight was not issued in the U.S.

CT-290
CAULDRON
Designer: Innes Burns
Type: Weight – Spherical
Colour: 1. Aqua
2. Emerald
3. Sable
Issued: 1982
Status: Closed
Series: Unlimited – Modern Design
O.I.P.: U.K. £14.95
U.S. $49.50

U.K.: £30.00
U.S.: $60.00
Can.: $80.00

CT-291
CAULDRON RUBY
Designer: Innes Burns
Type: Weight – Spherical
Issued: 1982
Status: Active
Series: Unlimited – Modern Design
O.I.P.: U.K. £14.95
U.S. $49.50

U.K.: £34.95
U.S.: $87.50
Can.: –

CT-292
MAGIC CIRCLE
Designer: Colin Terris
Type: Weight – Spherical
Issued: 1982
Status: Closed
Series: Unlimited – Modern Design
O.I.P.: U.K. £14.95
U.S. $49.50

U.K.: £30.00
U.S.: $60.00
Can.: $80.00

CT-293
CREATION
Designer: Colin Terris
Type: Weight – Spherical, iridescent overlay
Issued: 1982 in a limited edition of 500
Status: Fully subscribed
Series: Limited – Modern Design
O.I.P.: U.K. £39.95
U.S. $135.00

U.K.: £ 60.00
U.S.: $120.00
Can.: $160.00

CT-294
STARBURST
Designer: Colin Terris
Type: Weight – Spherical
Issued: 1982 in a limited edition of 500
Status: Fully subscribed
O.I.P.: U.K. £35.00
U.S. $115.00

U.K.: £ 55.00
U.S.: $110.00
Can.: $145.00

CT-295
SEAFORM

Designer: Innes Burns
Type: Weight – Spherical
Issued: 1982
Status: Closed
Series: Unlimited – Modern Design
O.I.P.: U.K. £15.95
U.S. $57.50

U.K.: £30.00
U.S.: $60.00
Can.: $80.00

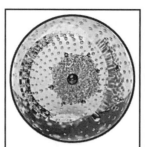

CT-296
SPACE COURIER

Designer: Colin Terris
Type: Weight – Spherical
Issued: 1982 in a limited edition of 750
Status: Closed at No. 500
Series: Limited – Modern Design
O.I.P.: U.K. £29.75
U.S. $97.50

U.K.: £ 45.00
U.S.: $ 90.00
Can.: $125.00

CT-297
SPACE TRAIL

Designer: Colin Terris
Type: Weight – Spherical
Issued: 1982
Status: Closed
Series: Unlimited – Modern Design
O.I.P.: U.K. £16.95
U.S. $49.50

U.K.: £30.00
U.S.: $60.00
Can.: $80.00

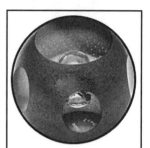

CT-298
SPACE VISTA

Designer: Colin Terris
Type: Weight – Spherical, iridescent overlay
Issued: 1982 in a limited edition of 500
Status: Closed at No. 333
Series: Limited – Modern Design
O.I.P.: U.K. £39.95
U.S. $135.00

U.K.: £ 65.00
U.S.: $130.00
Can.: $170.00

CT-300
PERSEPHONE

Designer: David Green
Type: Weight – Spherical
Issued: 1982 in a limited edition of 1,000
Status: Closed at No. 474
Series: Limited – Modern Design
O.I.P.: £35.00

U.K.: £ 60.00
U.S.: $120.00
Can.: $150.00

CT-301
CHRISTMAS ROSE
Style Two

Designer: Colin Terris
Type: Weight – Spherical
Issued: 1982 in a limited edition of 500
Status: Closed at No. 307
O.I.P.: U.K. £75.00
U.S. $345.00

U.K.: £100.00
U.S.: $200.00
Can.: $260.00

CT-302
CHRISTMAS TREE

Designer: Colin Terris
Type: Weight – Spherical
Issued: 1982 in a limited edition of 1,000
Status: Closed at No. 310
Series: Whitefriars Collection
O.I.P.: U.K. £58.75
U.S. $250.00

U.K.: £100.00
U.S.: $200.00
Can.: $260.00

Note: The winning entry in a design competition run by the Collectors' Club, this was the 1982 Collectors' Weight. It was not issued in the U.S.

ISSUES OF 1983

CT-303
ANTENNAE

Designer: Colin Terris
Type: Weight – Spherical
Issued: 1983 in a limited
edition of 750
Status: Fully subscribed
Series: Limited – Modern
Design
O.I.P.: U.K. £41.50
U.S. $150.00

U.K.: £ 75.00
U.S.: $150.00
Can.: $200.00

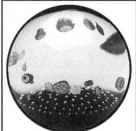

CT-304
HELTER SKELTER

Designer: Colin Terris
Type: Weight – Spherical
Issued: 1983
Status: Closed
Series: Unlimited – Modern
Design
O.I.P.: U.K. £19.75
U.S. $75.00

U.K.: £30.00
U.S.: $60.00
Can.: $80.00

CT-305
FIREBALL

Designer: Colin Terris
Type: Weight – Spherical
Issued: 1983
Status: Closed
Series: Unlimited – Modern
Design
O.I.P.: U.K. £15.95
U.S. $72.50

U.K.: £30.00
U.S.: $60.00
Can.: $80.00

CT-306
ANDROMEDA

Designer: Colin Terris
Type: Weight – Spherical
Issued: 1983 in a limited
edition of 500
Status: Fully subscribed
Series: Limited – Modern
Design
O.I.P.: U.K. £45.75
U.S. $175.00

U.K.: £ 85.00
U.S.: $170.00
Can.: $225.00

CT-307
CAMELOT

Designer: Colin Terris
Type: Weight – Spherical
Issued: 1983 in a limited
edition of 750
Status: Fully subscribed
Series: Limited – Modern
Design
O.I.P.: U.K. £35.00
U.S. $135.00

U.K.: £100.00
U.S.: $200.00
Can.: $260.00

CT-308
MOONSCAPE

Designer: Colin Terris
Type: Weight – Spherical
Issued: 1983 in a limited
edition of 750
Status: Fully subscribed
Series: Limited – Modern
Design
O.I.P.: U.K. £35.00
U.S. $135.00

U.K.: £ 85.00
U.S.: $170.00
Can.: $225.00

CT-309
HONESTY

Designer: Colin Terris
Type: Weight – Spherical
Issued: 1983 in a limited
edition of 250
Status: Fully subscribed
Series: Limited – Modern
Design
O.I.P.: U.K. £50.00
U.S. $195.00

U.K.: £135.00
U.S.: $270.00
Can.: $350.00

CT-310
FUGUE

Designer: Colin Terris
Type: Weight – Spherical
Colour: Orange, ruby,
green and blue
Issued: 1983 in a limited
edition of 750
Status: Fully subscribed
Series: Limited – Modern
Design
O.I.P.: U.K. £39.95
U.S. $175.00

U.K.: £ 60.00
U.S.: $120.00
Can.: $150.00

CT-311
WHIRLWIND
Style One

Designer: Colin Terris
Type: Weight — Spherical
Issued: 1983
Status: Closed
Series: Unlimited — Modern
          Design
O.I.P.:   U.K. £13.85
          U.S. $55.00

U.K.:   £30.00
U.S.: $60.00
Can.: $80.00

CT-312
SYMPHONY

Designer: Andrew Lawson
Type: Weight — Spherical
Issued: 1983 in a limited
          edition of 750
Status: Fully subscribed
Series: Limited — Modern
          Design
O.I.P.:   U.K. £47.95
          U.S. $195.00

U.K.:   £ 65.00
U.S.: $130.00
Can.: $175.00

CT-313
JOURNEY'S END

Designer: Colin Terris
Type: Weight — Spherical
Issued: 1983 in a limited
          edition of 750
Status: Fully subscribed
Series: Limited — Modern
          Design
O.I.P.:   U.K. £33.50
          U.S. $125.00

U.K.:   £ 45.00
U.S.: $ 90.00
Can.: $125.00

CT-314
CAPRICE

Designer: Colin Terris
Type: Weight — Spherical
Issued: 1983 in a limited
          edition of 750
Status: Fully subscribed
Series: Limited — Modern
          Design
O.I.P.:   U.K. £39.95
          U.S. $150.00

U.K.:   £ 50.00
U.S.: $100.00
Can.: $130.00

CT-315
HENRY VIII
Second Version, Miniature

Designer: Colin Terris
Type: Weight — Spherical,
          sulphide
Issued: 1983 in a limited
          edition of 250
Status: Closed at No. 51
O.I.P.:   U.K. £50.00
          U.S. $175.00

U.K.:   £ 60.00
U.S.: $120.00
Can.: $150.00

Note: The miniature sulphide is
set in a millefiori cane
circle.

CT-316
ELIZABETH I

Designer: Colin Terris
Type: Weight — Spherical,
          sulphide
Issued: 1983 in a limited
          edition of 250
Status: Closed at No. 69
O.I.P.:   U.K. £50.00
          U.S. $175.00

U.K.:   £ 60.00
U.S.: $120.00
Can.: $150.00

Note: The miniature sulphide is
set in a millefiori cane
circle.

CT-317
ROYAL WEDDING
Style Two

Designer: Colin Terris
Type: Weight — Spherical,
          sulphide
Issued: 1983 in a limited
          edition of 500
Status: Closed at No. 69
O.I.P.:   U.K. £50.00
          U.S. $175.00

U.K.:   £150.00
U.S.: $275.00
Can.: $350.00

Note: The miniature sulphide is
set in a millefiori cane
circle.

CT-318
FLOWER IN THE SNOW

Designer: Colin Terris
Type: Weight — Spherical
Issued: 1983
Status: Closed
Series: Unlimited — Modern
          Design
O.I.P.:   U.K. £29.75
          U.S. $99.50

U.K.:   £ 40.00
U.S.: $ 80.00
Can.: $100.00

CT-319A
SONATA
Designer: Colin Terris
Type: Weight – Spherical
Issued: 1983 in a limited
edition of 150
Status: Closed at No. 120
Series: Limited – Modern
Design
O.I.P.: U.K. £125.00/set
U.S. $495.00/set

U.K.: £100.00
U.S.: $200.00
Can.: $260.00

Note: CT-319A and B were
issued and sold as a set.

CT-319B
SONATA PERFUME BOTTLE
Designer: Colin Terris
Type: Perfume bottle
Issued: 1983 in a limited
edition of 150
Status: Closed at No. 120
Series: Limited – Modern
Design
O.I.P.: U.K. £125.00/set
U.S. $495.00/set

	Perfume	Set
U.K.:	£200.	300.
U.S.:	$400.	600.
Can.:	$525.	775.

CT-320
CORRYVRECKAN PERFUME BOTTLE
Designer: Colin Terris
Type: Perfume bottle
Issued: 1983
Status: Closed
Series: Unlimited – Modern
Design
O.I.P.: U.K. £39.95
U.S. $135.00

U.K.: £ 50.00
U.S.: $100.00
Can.: $130.00

CT-321
MISTY PERFUME BOTTLE
Designer: Colin Terris
Type: Perfume bottle
Issued: 1983
Status: Closed
Series: Unlimited – Modern
Design
O.I.P.: U.K. £39.95
U.S. $135.00

U.K.: £ 50.00
U.S.: $100.00
Can.: $130.00

CT-322
DOUBLE MAGNUM RUBY
Designer: Colin Terris
Type: Weight – Spherical
Size: Double magnum
Issued: 1983
Status: Closed
Series: Unlimited – Modern
Design
O.I.P.: U.K. £125.00
U.S. $450.00

U.K.: £175.00
U.S.: $350.00
Can.: $450.00

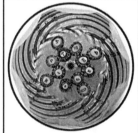

CT-323
THE ZODIAC
Designer: Colin Terris
Type: Weight – Spherical
Issued: 1983 in a limited
edition of 250
Status: Closed at No. 155
Series: Whitefriars Collection
O.I.P.: U.K. £96.00
U.S. $350.00

U.K.: £175.00
U.S.: $350.00
Can.: $450.00

CT-324
WINTER FLOWER
Designer: William Manson
Type: Weight – Spherical
Issued: 1983 in a limited
edition of 500
Status: Closed at No. 415
Series: Traditional Collection
O.I.P.: U.K. £56.50
U.S. $225.00

U.K.: £ 60.00
U.S.: $125.00
Can.: $165.00

CT-325
MARGUERITE
Style One
Designer: William Manson
Type: Weight – Spherical
Issued: 1983 in a limited
edition of 500
Status: Closed at No. 474
Series: Traditional Collection
O.I.P.: U.K. £50.00
U.S. $195.00

U.K.: £ 60.00
U.S.: $125.00
Can.: $165.00

CT-326
CROCUS
Style One

Designer: William Manson
Type: Weight – Spherical
Issued: 1983 in a limited
edition of 500
Status: Closed at No. 450
Series: Traditional Collection
O.I.P.: U.K. £50.00
U.S. $195.00

U.K.: £ 60.00
U.S.: $125.00
Can.: $165.00

CT-327
HIGHLAND FLING

Designer: William Manson
Type: Weight – Spherical
Issued: 1983 in a limited
edition of 250
Status: Fully subscribed
Series: Traditional Collection
O.I.P.: U.K. £69.50
U.S. $275.00

U.K.: £110.00
U.S.: $225.00
Can.: $300.00

CT-328
PARTRIDGE IN A PEAR TREE

Designer: William Manson
Type: Weight – Spherical
Issued: 1983 in a limited
edition of 500
Status: Closed at No. 382
Series: Traditional Collection
O.I.P.: U.K. £69.50
U.S. $250.00

U.K.: £ 75.00
U.S.: $150.00
Can.: $200.00

CT-329
FLORA

Designer: William Manson
Type: Weight – Spherical
Issued: 1983 in a limited
edition of 500
Status: Closed at No. 165
Series: Traditional Collection
O.I.P.: U.K. £50.00
U.S. $185.00

U.K.: £ 60.00
U.S.: $125.00
Can.: $165.00

CT-330
BLUE CORAL

Designer: Colin Terris
Type: Weight – Domed
Issued: 1983 in a limited
edition of 250
Status: Fully subscribed
Series: Limited – Modern
Design
O.I.P.: U.K. £52.95
U.S. $175.00

U.K.: £125.00
U.S.: $225.00
Can.: $300.00

CT-331
DARK ISLAND

Designer: Colin Terris
Type: Weight – Spherical
Issued: 1983 in a limited
edition of 500
Status: Fully subscribed
Series: Limited – Modern
Design
O.I.P.: U.K. £48.00
U.S. $175.00

U.K.: £ 90.00
U.S.: $160.00
Can.: $200.00

CT-332
FREE SPIRIT

Designer: Colin Terris
Type: Weight – Spherical
Issued: 1983 in a limited
edition of 750
Status: Fully subscribed
Series: Limited – Modern
Design
O.I.P.: U.K. £36.95
U.S. $135.00

U.K.: £ 55.00
U.S.: $110.00
Can.: $145.00

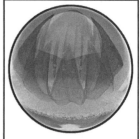

CT-333
OCTAVIA

Designer: Colin Terris
Type: Weight – Spherical
Colour: Fuchsia
Issued: 1983 in a limited
edition of 500
Status: Fully subscribed
Series: Limited – Modern
Design
O.I.P.: U.K. £41.95
U.S. $175.00

U.K.: £ 55.00
U.S.: $110.00
Can.: $145.00

CT-334
RICHARD III

Designer: Colin Terris
Type: Weight – Spherical, sulphide
Issued: 1983 in a limited edition of 500
Status: Closed at No. 81
O.I.P.: U.K. £50.00
U.S. $175.00

U.K.: £ 75.00
U.S.: $150.00
Can.: $200.00

Note: The sulphide is set in a millefiori cane circle. This paperweight, while originally created exclusively for the Richard III Society, was later offered on general release within the U.K. only.

CT-335
ROBIN and KETTLE

Designer: Colin Terris
Type: Weight – Spherical
Issued: 1983 in a limited edition of 1,000
Status: Closed at No. 536
Series: 1 Traditional Collection
2. Collectors Club
O.I.P.: U.K. £55.00
U.S. $200.00

U.K.: £ 65.00
U.S.: $130.00
Can.: $175.00

CT-336
WHITE FUGUE
Style Two

Designer: Colin Terris
Type: Weight – Spherical
Issued: 1983 in a limited edition of 500
Status: Fully subscribed
Series: Limited – Modern Design
O.I.P.: U.S. $175.00

U.K.: £125.00
U.S.: $225.00
Can.: $300.00

Note: White Fugue, Style One, was issued by Gump's; see page 337.

CT-337
SEA DANCE

Designer: Colin Terris
Type: Weight – Spherical
Colour: Gold
Issued: 1983
Status: Closed
Series: Unlimited – Modern Design
O.I.P.: U.K. £23.50
U.S. $85.00

U.K.: £35.00
U.S.: $70.00
Can.: $95.00

CT-338
SPINAWAY

Designer: Colin Terris
Type: Weight – Spherical
Issued: 1983
Status: Closed
Series: Unlimited – Modern Design
O.I.P.: U.K. £16.95
U.S. $62.50

U.K.: £30.00
U.S.: $60.00
Can.: $80.00

ISSUES OF 1984

CT-339
BLUE OCTAVIA
Designer: Colin Terris
Type: Weight – Spherical
Issued: 1984 in a limited
edition of 500
Status: Fully subscribed
Series: Limited – Modern
Design
O.I.P.: U.K. £43.95
U.S. $150.00

U.K.: £ 60.00
U.S.: $120.00
Can.: $150.00

CT-340
CHANTILLY
Designer: Jeneo Lewis
Type: Weight – Spherical
Issued: 1984 in a limited
edition of 500
Status: Fully subscribed
Series: Limited – Modern
Design
O.I.P.: U.K. £43.95
U.S. $150.00

U.K.: £ 75.00
U.S.: $135.00
Can.: $175.00

CT-341
DILEMMA
Designer: Colin Terris
Type: Weight – Spherical
Issued: 1984 in a limited
edition of 750
Status: Fully subscribed
Series: Limited – Modern
Design
O.I.P.: U.K. £39.95
U.S. $150.00

U.K.: £ 55.00
U.S.: $110.00
Can.: $150.00

CT-342
GRACE
Designer: Colin Terris
Type: Weight – Domed
Issued: 1984 In a limited
edition of 500
Status: Fully subscribed
Series: Limited – Modern
Design
O.I.P.: U.K. £60.00
U.S. $225.00

U.K.: £ 90.00
U.S.: $175.00
Can.: $225.00

CT-343
MOUNTAINS OF MARS
Designer: Colin Terris
Type: Weight – Spherical
Issued: 1984 in a limited
edition of 750
Status: Fully subscribed
Series: Limited – Modern
Design
O.I.P.: U.K. £39.95
U.S. $150.00

U.K.: £ 95.00
U.S.: $170.00
Can.: $225.00

CT-344
NAUTILUS
Designer: Colin Terris
Type: Weight – Domed
Issued: 1984 in a limited
edition of 500
Status: Fully subscribed
Series: Limited – Modern
Design
O.I.P.: U.K. £60.00
U.S. $225.00

U.K.: £ 85.00
U.S.: $170.00
Can.: $225.00

CT-345
THREE WITCHES
Designer: Colin Terris
Type: Weight – Spherical
Issued: 1984 in a limited
edition of 500
Status: Fully subscribed
Series: Limited – Modern
Design
O.I.P.: U.K. £43.95
U.S. $150.00

U.K.: £ 65.00
U.S.: $120.00
Can.: $150.00

CT-346
BLUEBIRDS
Designer: William Manson
Type: Weight – Spherical
Issued: 1984 in a limited
edition of 250
Status: Fully subscribed
Series: Traditional Collection
O.I.P.: U.K. £85.00
U.S. $325.00

U.K.: £ 75.00
U.S.: $150.00
Can.: $200.00

CT-347
DOLPHIN
Style Two
Designer: William Manson
Type: Weight – Spherical
Issued: 1984 in a limited
         edition of 100
Status: Fully subscribed
Series: Traditional Collection
O.I.P.: U.K. £125.00
         U.S. $450.00

U.K.:   £150.00
U.S.: $300.00
Can.: $400.00

CT-348
FIRE LIZARD
Designer: William Manson
Type: Weight – Spherical
Issued: 1984 in a limited
         edition of 100
Status: Fully subscribed
Series: Traditional Collection
O.I.P.: U.K. £200.00
         U.S. $750.00

U.K.:   £275.00
U.S.: $550.00
Can.: $700.00

CT-349
MANTA RAY and CORAL
Designer: William Manson
Type: Weight – Spherical
Issued: 1984 in a limited
         edition of 100
Status: Fully subscribed
Series: Traditional Collection
O.I.P.: U.K. £125.00
         U.S. $450.00

U.K.:   £150.00
U.S.: $300.00
Can.: $400.00

CT-350
TROUT and MAYFLY
Designer: William Manson
Type: Weight – Spherical
Issued: 1984 in a limited
         edition of 100
Status: Fully subscribed
Series: Traditional Collection
O.I.P.: U.K. £250.00
         U.S. $900.00

U.K.:   £350.00
U.S.: $700.00
Can.: $900.00

CT-351
TROUT
Designer: William Manson
Type: Weight – Spherical
Issued: 1984 in a limited
         edition of 100
Status: Fully subscribed
Series: Traditional Collection
O.I.P.: U.K. £125.00
         U.S. $450.00

U.K.:   £150.00
U.S.: $300.00
Can.: $400.00

CT-352
TWO SALMON
Designer: William Manson
Type: Weight – Spherical
Issued: 1984 in a limited
         edition of 100
Status: Closed at No. 86
Series: Traditional Collection
O.I.P.: U.K. £200.00
         U.S. $750.00

U.K.:   £275.00
U.S.: $550.00
Can.: $700.00

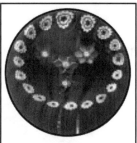

CT-353
ROYAL BIRTHDAY TRIBUTE
Style Two
Designer: Colin Terris
Type: Weight – Spherical
Issued: 1984 in a limited
         edition of 100
Status: Fully subscribed
O.I.P.: U.K. £175.00
         U.S. $600.00

U.K.:   £300.00
U.S.: $600.00
Can.: $775.00

Note: Weights CT-353, 354
       and 355 were issued to
       commemorate the birth
       of HRH Prince Harry.

CT-354
ROYAL BIRTHDAY CROWN
Style Two
Designer: Colin Terris
Type: Weight – Spherical
Issued: 1984 in a limited
         edition of 250
Status: Fully subscribed
O.I.P.: U.K. £85.00
         U.S. $300.00

U.K.:   £125.00
U.S.: $250.00
Can.: $325.00

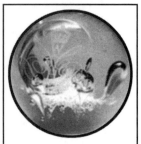

CT-355
ROYAL BIRTHDAY
MOONFLOWER
Style Two

Designer: Colin Terris
Type: Weight – Spherical
Issued: 1984 in a limited
edition of 750
Status: Fully subscribed
O.I.P.: U.K. £43.95
U.S. $165.00

U.K.: £ 45.00
U.S.: $ 90.00
Can.: $125.00

CT-356A
CANTATA

Designer: Colin Terris
Type: Weight – Spherical
Issued: 1984 in a limited
edition of 150
Status: Closed at No. 123
O.I.P.: U.K. £137.50/set
U.S. $495.00/set

U.K.: £100.00
U.S.: $200.00
Can.: $260.00

Note: CT-356A and B were
issued and sold as a set.

CT-356B
CANTATA PERFUME BOTTLE

Designer: Colin Terris
Type: Perfume bottle
Issued: 1984 in a limited
edition of 150
Status: Closed at No. 123
O.I.P.: U.K. £137.50/set
U.S. $495.00/set

	Perfume	Set
U.K.:	£200.	300.
U.S.:	$350.	525.
Can.:	$450.	675.

CT-357
FLORAL BASKET

Designer: Colin Terris
Type: Weight – Domed
Issued: 1984
Status: Closed
Series: Whitefriars Collection
O.I.P.: U.K. £39.50
U.S. $145.00

U.K.: £ 65.00
U.S.: $130.00
Can.: $170.00

CT-358
BLUE and PINK POSY

Designer: Allan Scott
Type: Weight – Spherical
Issued: 1984 in a limited
edition of 250
Status: Fully subscribed
Series: Whitefriars Collection
O.I.P.: U.K. £59.50
U.S. $235.00

U.K.: £ 65.00
U.S.: $125.00
Can.: $165.00

CT-359
BLUE FLOWER

Designer: Allan Scott
Type: Weight – Spherical
Issued: 1984 in a limited
edition of 250
Status: Closed at No. 117
Series: Whitefriars Collection
O.I.P.: U.K. £47.50
U.S. $150.00

U.K.: £ 75.00
U.S.: $150.00
Can.: $200.00

CT-360
FUCHSIA
Style One

Designer: Allan Scott
Type: Weight – Spherical
Issued: 1984 in a limited
edition of 250
Status: Fully subscribed
Series: Whitefriars Collection
O.I.P.: U.K. £59.50
U.S. $195.00

U.K.: £ 75.00
U.S.: $150.00
Can.: $200.00

CT-361
BOUQUET and FERNS

Designer: Allan Scott
Type: Weight – Spherical
Issued: 1984 in a limited
edition of 150
Status: Fully subscribed
Series: Whitefriars Collection
O.I.P.: U.K. £150.00
U.S. $595.00

U.K.: £150.00
U.S.: $300.00
Can.: $450.00

CT-362
AMETHYST BOUQUET

Designer: Allan Scott
Type: Weight – Spherical
Issued: 1984 in a limited
edition of 150
Status: Fully subscribed
Series: Whitefriars Collection
O.I.P.: U.K. £125.00
U.S. $475.00

U.K.: £225.00
U.S.: $450.00
Can.: $575.00

CT-363
FLORAL PINK

Designer: Allan Scott
Type: Weight – Spherical
Issued: 1984 in a limited
edition of 250
Status: Fully subscribed
Series: Whitefriars Collection
O.I.P.: U.K. £75.00
U.S. $275.00

U.K.: £ 95.00
U.S.: $200.00
Can.: $260.00

CT-364
WHITE and PINK SPRAY

Designer: Allan Scott
Type: Weight – Spherical
Issued: 1984 in a limited
edition of 250
Status: Fully subscribed
Series: Whitefriars Collection
O.I.P.: U.K. £69.50
U.S. $265.00

U.K.: £ 95.00
U.S.: $200.00
Can.: $260.00

CT-365
SEA DANCE BLUE

Designer: Colin Terris
Type: Weight – Spherical
Issued: 1984
Status: Closed
Series: Unlimited – Modern
Design
O.I.P.: U.K. £24.95
U.S. $85.00

U.K.: £35.00
U.S.: $70.00
Can.: $90.00

CT-366
BOLERO

Designer: Colin Terris
Type: Weight – Spherical
Issued: 1984 in a limited
edition of 750
Status: Fully subscribed
Series: Limited – Modern
Design
O.I.P.: U.K. £35.95
U.S. $125.00

U.K.: £ 55.00
U.S. $110.00
Can.: $150.00

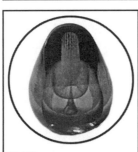

CT-367
CITADEL

Designer: Colin Terris
Type: Weight – Domed
Issued: 1984 in a limited
edition of 500
Status: Fully subscribed
Series: Limited – Modern
Design
O.I.P.: U.K. £60.00
U.S. $225.00

U.K.: £ 55.00
U.S.: $110.00
Can.: $150.00

CT-368
EVERGREEN

Designer: Colin Terris
Type: Weight – Spherical
Issued: 1984 in a limited
edition of 750
Status: Closed at No. 500
Series: Limited – Modern
Design
O.I.P.: U.K. £35.95
U.S. $135.00

U.K.: £35.00
U.S.: $70.00
Can.: $90.00

CT-369
GYRO

Designer: Colin Terris
Type: Weight – Spherical
Issued: 1984 in a limited
edition of 750
Status: Fully subscribed
Series: Limited – Modern
Design
O.I.P.: U.K. £35.95
U.S. $135.00

U.K.: £35.00
U.S.: $70.00
Can.: $90.00

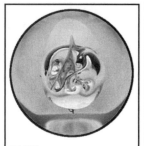

CT-370
LIFE FORCE

Designer: Colin Terris
Type: Weight – Spherical
Issued: 1984 in a limited
           edition of 750
Status: Fully subscribed
Series: Limited – Modern
           Design
O.I.P.:   U.K. £37.95
           U.S. $135.00

U.K.:   £ 45.00
U.S.: $ 90.00
Can.: $125.00

CT-371
MARINER 2

Designer: Colin Terris
Type: Weight – Spherical
Issued: 1984 in a limited
           edition of 750
Status: Fully subscribed
O.I.P.:   U.K. £39.95
           U.S. $125.00

U.K.   £ 55.00
U.S.: $110.00
Can.: $145.00

CT-372
NINETEEN EIGHTY-FOUR

Designer: Colin Terris
Type: Weight – Spherical
Issued: 1984 in a limited
           edition of 750
Status: Fully subscribed
Series: Limited – Modern
           Design
O.I.P.:   U.K. £42.25
           U.S. $135.00

U.K.:   £ 65.00
U.S.: $130.00
Can.: $175.00

CT-373
SOLITAIRE

Designer: Colin Terris
Type: Weight – Spherical
Issued: 1984 in a limited
           edition of 1,000
Status: Closed at No. 461
Series: Collectors Club
O.I.P.:   U.K. £39.95
           U.S. $175.00

U.K.:   £ 65.00
U.S.: $130.00
Can.: $175.00

CT-374
PAGODA

Designer: Colin Terris
Type: Weight – Domed
Issued: 1984 in a limited
           edition of 500
Status: Fully subscribed
Series: Limited – Modern
           Design
O.I.P.:   U.K. £60.00
           U.S. $195.00

U.K.:   £ 85.00
U.S.: $170.00
Can.: $225.00

CT-375
SPECTRUM

Designer: Colin Terris
Type: Weight – Spherical
Issued: 1984 in a limited
           edition of 750
Status: Fully subscribed
Series: Limited – Modern
           Design
O.I.P.:   U.K. £37.95
           U.S. $125.00

U.K.:   £ 40.00
U.S.: $ 80.00
Can.: $100.00

CT-376
STAR BEACON

Designer: Colin Terris
Type: Weight – Spherical
Issued: 1984 in a limited
           edition of 750
Status: Fully subscribed
Series: Limited – Modern
           Design
O.I.P.:   U.K. £39.95
           U.S. $150.00

U.K.:   £ 40.00
U.S.: $ 80.00
Can.: $100.00

CT-377
TRANQUILLITY

Designer: Colin Terris
Type: Weight – Spherical
Issued: 1984 in a limited
           edition of 750
Status: Fully subscribed
Series: Limited – Modern
           Design
O.I.P.:   U.K. £49.95
           U.S. $175.00

U.K.:   £ 55.00
U.S.: $110.00
Can.: $150.00

CT-378
WHISPERS

Designer:	Colin Terris
Type:	Weight – Spherical
Issued:	1984 in a limited edition of 500
Status:	Fully subscribed
Series:	Limited – Modern Design
O.I.P.:	U.K. £49.95
	U.S. $175.00
U.K.:	£ 65.00
U.S.:	$130.00
Can.:	$175.00

CT-379
SAFFRON

Designer:	Colin Terris
Type:	Weight – Spherical
Issued:	1984
Status:	Closed
Series:	Unlimited – Modern Design
O.I.P.:	U.K. £16.95
	U.S. $65.00
U.K.:	£30.00
U.S.:	$60.00
Can.:	$80.00

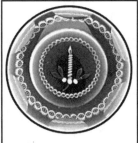

CT-380
CHRISTMAS CANDLE

Designer:	Colin Terris
Type:	Weight – Spherical
Issued:	1984 in a limited edition of 500
Status:	Closed at No. 268
Series:	Traditional Collection
O.I.P.:	U.K. £75.00
	U.S. $265.00
U.K.:	£ 75.00
U.S.:	$150.00
Can.:	$200.00

CT-381
BLACK SALAMANDER

Designer:	William Manson
Type:	Weight – Spherical
Issued:	1984 in a limited edition of 100
Status:	Fully subscribed
Series:	Traditional Collection
O.I.P.:	U.K. £200.00
	U.S. $750.00
U.K.:	£250.00
U.S.:	$500.00
Can.:	$650.00

CT-382
CROSSED HALBERDS

Designer:	William Manson
Type:	Weight – Spherical
Issued:	1984 in a limited edition of 250
Status:	Fully subscribed
Series:	Traditional Collection
O.I.P.:	U.K. £75.00
	U.S. $265.00
U.K.:	£ 85.00
U.S.:	$175.00
Can.:	$225.00

CT-383
KINGFISHER
Style One

Designer:	William Manson
Type:	Weight – Spherical
Issued:	1984 in a limited edition of 250
Status:	Fully subscribed
Series:	Traditional Collection
O.I.P.:	U.K. £75.00
	U.S. $265.00
U.K.:	£ 75.00
U.S.:	$150.00
Can.:	$200.00

CT-384
MOONDROP

Designer:	Colin Terris
Type:	Weight – Drawn teardrop
Colour:	Many colour variations
Issued:	1984
Status:	Closed
Series:	Unlimited – Modern Design
O.I.P.:	U.K. £12.95
	U.S. $39.50
U.K.:	£20.00
U.S.:	$40.00
Can.:	$50.00

CT-385
PEBBLE
Style One

Designer:	Colin Terris
Type:	Weight – Sculptural
Colour:	Many colour variations
Issued:	1984
Status:	Closed
Series:	Unlimited – Modern Design
O.I.P.:	U.K. £17.95
	U.S. $39.50
U.K.:	£20.00
U.S.:	$40.00
Can.:	$50.00

CT-386
DOUBLE MAGNUM AMETHYST
Designer: Colin Terris
Type: Weight – Spherical,
           double magnum
Issued: 1984
Status: Closed
O.I.P.:   U.K. £130.00
           U.S. $425.00

U.K.:   £150.00
U.S.: $300.00
Can.: $400.00

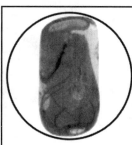

CT-387
FLOWER CRYSTAL PINK
CARNATIONS
Designer: Colin Terris
Type: Weight – Rectangular
           freeform
Issued: 1984
Status: Closed
O.I.P.:   U.K. £19.95
           U.S. $85.00

U.K.:   £30.00
U.S.: $60.00
Can.: $80.00

CT-388
FLOWER CRYSTAL BLACK
ORCHIDS
Designer: Colin Terris
Type: Weight – Rectangular
           freeform
Issued: 1984
Status: Closed
O.I.P.:   U.K. £19.95
           U.S. $85.00

U.K.:   £30.00
U.S.: $60.00
Can.: $80.00

CT-389
FLOWER CRYSTAL BLUE
PANSIES
Designer: Colin Terris
Type: Weight – Rectangular
           freeform
Issued: 1984
Status: Closed
O.I.P.:   U.K. £19.95
           U.S. $85.00

U.K.:   £30.00
U.S.: $60.00
Can.: $80.00

CT-390
FLOWER CRYSTAL RED
POPPIES
Designer: Colin Terris
Type: Weight – Rectangular
           freeform
Issued: 1984
Status: Closed
O.I.P.:   U.K. £19.95
           U.S. $85.00

U.K.:   £30.00
U.S.: $60.00
Can.: $80.00

ISSUES OF 1985

CT-391
CHIFFON

Designer: Colin Terris
Type: Weight – Spherical
Issued: 1985 in a limited
          edition of 750
Status: Fully subscribed
Series: Limited – Modern
          Design
O.I.P.:   U.K. £39.95
          U.S. $125.00

U.K.:   £ 55.00
U.S.: $110.00
Can.: $150.00

CT-392
DERVISH

Designer: Colin Terris
Type: Weight – Spherical
Issued: 1985 in a limited
          edition of 750
Status: Fully subscribed
Series: Limited – Modern
          Design
O.I.P.:   U.K. £41.95
          U.S. $125.00

U.K.:   £ 55.00
U.S.: $110.00
Can.: $150.00

CT-393
EVENSONG

Designer: Colin Terris
Type: Weight – Domed
Issued: 1985 in a limited
          edition of 250
Status: Fully subscribed
Series: Limited – Modern
          Design
O.I.P.:   U.K. £41.95
          U.S. $135.00

U.K.:   £ 65.00
U.S.: $130.00
Can.: $175.00

CT-394
GALACTICA

Designer: Colin Terris
Type: Weight – Spherical
Issued: 1985 in a limited
          edition of 750
Status: Fully subscribed
Series: Limited – Modern
          Design
O.I.P.:   U.K. £39.95
          U.S. $125.00

U.K.:   £ 55.00
U.S.: $110.00
Can.: $150.00

CT-395
ICE PRINCESS

Designer: Colin Terris
Type: Weight – Domed
Issued: 1985 in a limited
          edition of 500
Status: Fully subscribed
Series: Limited – Modern
          Design
O.I.P.:   U.K. £60.00
          U.S. $185.00

U.K.:   £ 85.00
U.S.: $170.00
Can.: $220.00

CT-396
LABYRINTH

Designer: Colin Terris
Type: Weight – Domed
Issued: 1985 in a limited
          edition of 500
Status: Fully subscribed
Series: Limited – Modern
          Design
O.I.P.:   U.K. £60.00
          U.S. $185.00

U.K.:   £ 65.00
U.S.: $130.00
Can.: $175.00

CT-397
MISTRAL

Designer: Colin Terris
Type: Weight – Spherical
Issued: 1985 in a limited
          edition of 750
Status: Fully subscribed
Series: Limited – Modern
          Design
O.I.P.:   U.K. £41.95
          U.S. $125.00

U.K.:   £ 70.00
U.S.: $140.00
Can.: $185.00

CT-398
SERENITY

Designer: Colin Terris
Type: Weight – Domed
Issued: 1985 in a limited
          edition of 500
Status: Fully subscribed
Series: Limited – Modern
          Design
O.I.P.:   U.K. £60.00
          U.S. $185.00

U.K.:   £ 85.00
U.S.: $170.00
Can.: $220.00

CT-399
SUMMER POOL
Designer: Colin Terris
Type: Weight – Spherical
Issued: 1985 in a limited edition of 250
Status: Fully subscribed
Series: Limited – Modern Design
O.I.P.: U.K. £50.00
U.S. $150.00

U.K.: £ 60.00
U.S.: $120.00
Can.: $160.00

CT-400
TELSTAR
Designer: Colin Terris
Type: Weight – Spherical
Issued: 1985 in a limited edition of 750
Status: Fully subscribed
Series: Limited – Modern Design
O.I.P.: U.K. £39.95
U.S. $125.00

U.K.: £ 45.00
U.S.: $ 90.00
Can.: $125.00

CT-401
TRITON
Designer: Colin Terris
Type: Weight – Spherical
Issued: 1985 in a limited edition of 750
Status: Fully subscribed
Series: Limited – Modern Design
O.I.P.: U.K. £41.95
U.S. $125.00

U.K.: £ 45.00
U.S.: $ 90.00
Can.: $125.00

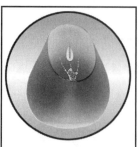

CT-402
VIRTUE
Designer: Colin Terris
Type: Weight – Domed
Issued: 1985 in a limited edition of 250
Status: Fully subscribed
Series: Limited – Modern Design
O.I.P.: U.K. £63.00
U.S. $195.00

U.K.: £ 85.00
U.S.: $170.00
Can.: $225.00

CT-403
WATER LILIES
Designer: Colin Terris
Type: Weight – Teardrop
Issued: 1985 in a limited edition of 250
Status: Fully subscribed
Series: Limited – Modern Design
O.I.P.: U.K. £65.00
U.S. $195.00

U.K.: £125.00
U.S.: $250.00
Can.: $325.00

CT-404
20,000 LEAGUES
Designer: Colin Terris
Type: Weight – Spherical
Issued: 1985 in a limited edition of 500
Status: Fully subscribed
Series: Limited – Modern Design
O.I.P.: U.K. £45.95
U.S. $150.00

U.K.: £ 55.00
U.S.: $110.00
Can.: $150.00

CT-405
CHANTILLY PERFUME BOTTLE
Designer: Jeneo Lewis
Type: Perfume bottle
Issued: 1985 in a limited edition of 250
Status: Fully subscribed
Series: Limited – Modern Design
O.I.P.: U.K. £75.00
U.S. $250.00

U.K.: £125.00
U.S.: $250.00
Can.: $325.00

CT-406A
LILAC TIME
Designer: Jeneo Lewis
Type: Weight – Spherical
Issued: 1985 in a limited edition of 150
Status: Fully subscribed
Series: Limited – Modern Design
O.I.P.: U.K. £150.00/set
U.S. $495.00/set

U.K.: £100.00
U.S.: $200.00
Can.: $260.00

Note: CT-406A and B were issued and sold as a set.

CT-406B
LILAC TIME PERFUME BOTTLE
Designer: Jeneo Lewis
Type: Perfume bottle
Issued: 1985 in a limited
edition of 150
Status: Fully subscribed
Series: Limited – Modern
Design
O.I.P.: U.K. £150.00/set
U.S. $495.00/set

	Perfume	Set
U.K.:	£200.	300.
U.S.:	$400.	600.
Can.:	$525.	775.

CT-407
HONEY BEE
Style One
Designer: William Manson
Type: Weight – Spherical
Issued: 1985 in a limited
edition of 100
Status: Fully subscribed
Series: Traditional Collection
O.I.P.: U.K. £175.00
U.S. $550.00

U.K.:	£200.00
U.S.:	$400.00
Can.:	$525.00

CT-408
TROPICAL FISH
Style One
Designer: William Manson
Type: Weight – Spherical
Issued: 1985 in a limited
edition of 100
Status: Closed at No. 80
Series: Traditional Collection
O.I.P.: U.K. £150.00
U.S. $500.00

U.K.:	£200.00
U.S.:	$400.00
Can.:	$525.00

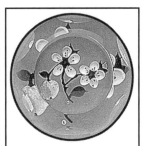

CT-409
APPLE BLOSSOM
Designer: Allan Scott
Type: Weight – Spherical
Issued: 1985 in a limited
edition of 250
Status: Fully subscribed
Series: Whitefriars Collection
O.I.P.: U.K. £69.50
U.S. $225.00

U.K.:	£ 75.00
U.S.:	$150.00
Can.:	$200.00

CT-410
PANSY
Style One
Designer: Allan Scott
Type: Weight – Spherical
Issued: 1985 in a limited
edition of 250
Status: Fully subscribed
Series: Whitefriars Collection
O.I.P.: U.K. £59.50
U.S. $210.00

U.K.:	£ 65.00
U.S.:	$130.00
Can.:	$170.00

CT-411
PRIMROSES
Style One
Designer: Allan Scott
Type: Weight – Spherical
Issued: 1985 in a limited
edition of 250
Status: Fully subscribed
Series: Whitefriars Collection
O.I.P.: U.K. £69.50
U.S. $225.00

U.K.:	£ 65.00
U.S.:	$130.00
Can.:	$170.00

CT-412
SUMMER MEADOW
BUTTERFLY
Designer: Allan Scott and
Harry McKay
Type: Weight – Spherical
Issued: 1985 in a limited
edition of 150
Status: Fully subscribed
Series: Whitefriars Collection
O.I.P.: U.K. £125.00
U.S. $395.00

U.K.:	£200.00
U.S.:	$400.00
Can.:	$525.00

CT-413
SUMMER MEADOW
DRAGONFLY
Designer: Allan Scott and
Harry McKay
Type: Weight – Spherical
Issued: 1985 in a limited
edition of 150
Status: Fully subscribed
Series: Whitefriars Collection
O.I.P.: U.K. £125.00
U.S. $395.00

U.K.:	£200.00
U.S.:	$400.00
Can.:	$525.00

CT-414
BOUQUET PERFUME BOTTLE

Designer: Allan Scott
Type: Perfume bottle
Issued: 1985 in a limited edition of 100
Status: Fully subscribed
Series: Traditional Collection
O.I.P.: U.K. £150.00
U.S. $495.00

U.K.: £175.00
U.S.: $350.00
Can.: $450.00

CT-415
CARNIVAL

Designer: Colin Terris
Type: Weight – Spherical
Colour: See below
Issued: 1985
Status: Closed
Series: Unlimited – Modern Design
O.I.P.: U.K. £19.95
U.S. $65.00

	Emerald	Ruby	Yellow
U.K.:	£25.00	25.00	25.00
U.S.:	$50.00	50.00	50.00
Can.:	$65.00	65.00	65.00

CT-416
DOUBLE MAGNUM EMERALD

Designer: Colin Terris
Type: Weight – Spherical, double magnum
Issued: 1985
Status: Closed
Series: Unlimited – Modern Design
O.I.P.: U.K. £131.00
U.S. $425.00

U.K.: £125.00
U.S.: $250.00
Can.: $325.00

CT-417
QUICKSILVER

Designer: Colin Terris
Type: Weight – Spherical
Issued: 1985
Status: Closed
Series: Unlimited – Modern Design
O.I.P.: U.K. £24.95
U.S. $75.00

U.K.: £30.00
U.S.: $60.00
Can.: $80.00

CT-418
STARWATCH

Designer: Colin Terris
Type: Weight – Spherical
Colour: 1. Emerald
2. Ruby
3. Yellow
Issued: 1985
Status: Closed
Series: Unlimited – Modern Design
O.I.P.: U.K. £29.95
U.S. $90.00

U.K.: £30.00
U.S.: $60.00
Can.: $80.00

CT-419
MOONCRYSTAL
Style One

Designer: Colin Terris
Type: Weight – Spherical
Size: Miniature
Colour: Many colour variations
Issued: 1985
Status: Closed
Series: Medium and Miniature Size
O.I.P.: U.K. £9.95
U.S. $30.00

U.K.: £20.00
U.S.: $40.00
Can.: $50.00

CT-420
HALLEY'S COMET
Style One

Designer: Colin Terris
Type: Weight – Spherical
Issued: 1985 in a limited edition of 750
Status: Fully subscribed
Series: Limited – Modern Design
O.I.P.: U.K. £37.95
U.S. $135.00

U.K.: £100.00
U.S.: $200.00
Can.: $260.00

CT-421
BLUE VELVET

Designer:	Colin Terris
Type:	Weight – Spherical
Issued:	1985 in a limited edition of 500
Status:	Fully subscribed
Series:	Limited – Modern Design
O.I.P.:	U.K. £41.95
	U.S. $150.00
U.K.:	£ 55.00
U.S.:	$110.00
Can.:	$150.00

CT-422
DAMASK

Designer:	Colin Terris
Type:	Weight – Spherical
Issued:	1985 in a limited edition of 250
Status:	Fully subscribed
Series:	Limited – Modern Design
O.I.P.:	U.K. £85.00
	U.S. $265.00
U.K.:	£ 85.00
U.S.:	$170.00
Can.:	$225.00

CT-423
ICE DANCE

Designer:	Colin Terris
Type:	Weight – Domed, single overlay
Issued:	1985 in a limited edition of 500
Status:	Fully subscribed
Series:	Limited – Modern Design
O.I.P.:	U.K. £65.00
	U.S. $225.00
U.K.:	£ 85.00
U.S.:	$170.00
Can.:	$225.00

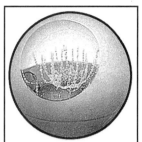

CT-424
AQUARELLE

Designer:	Colin Terris
Type:	Weight – Spherical
Issued:	1985 in a limited edition of 500
Status:	Fully subscribed
Series:	Limited – Modern Design
O.I.P.:	U.K. £50.00
	U.S. $175.00
U.K.:	£ 55.00
U.S.:	$110.00
Can.:	$150.00

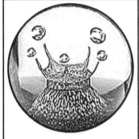

CT-425A
QUINTESSENCE

Designer:	Stuart Cumming
Type:	Weight – Spherical
Issued:	1985 in a limited edition of 250
Status:	Closed at No. 188
Series:	Limited – Modern Design
O.I.P.:	U.K. £150.00/set
	U.S. $550.00/set
U.K.:	£ 85.00
U.S.:	$170.00
Can.:	$225.00

CT-425B
QUINTESSENCE PERFUME BOTTLE

Designer:	Stuart Cumming
Type:	Perfume bottle
Issued:	1985 in a limited edition of 250
Status:	Closed at No. 188
Series:	Limited Edition – Modern Design
O.I.P.:	U.K. £150.00/set
	U.S. $550.00/set

	Perfume	Set
U.K.:	£125.00	200.00
U.S.:	$250.00	400.00
Can.:	$325.00	525.00

Note: CT-425A and B were issued and sold as a set.

CT-426
WINDFLOWER RUBY

Designer:	Colin Terris
Type:	Weight – Spherical
Issued:	1985 in a limited edition of 750
Status:	Closed at No. 506
O.I.P.:	U.K. £41.95
	U.S. $135.00
U.K.:	£ 40.00
U.S.:	$ 80.00
Can.:	$100.00

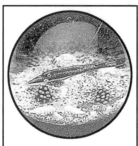

CT-427
BLUE MARLIN

Designer: William Manson
Type: Weight – Spherical
Issued: 1985 in a limited edition of 100
Status: Fully subscribed
O.I.P.: U.K. £150.00
U.S. $500.00

U.K.: £200.00
U.S.: $400.00
Can.: $525.00

CT-428
POND LIFE

Designer: William Manson
Type: Weight – Spherical
Issued: 1985 in a limited edition of 100
Status: Fully subscribed
Series: Traditional Collection
O.I.P.: U.K. £250.00
U.S. $750.00

U.K.: £275.00
U.S.: $550.00
Can.: $700.00

CT-429
MAYFLY and FLOWERS

Designer: William Manson
Type: Weight – Spherical
Issued: 1985 in a limited edition of 250
Status: Closed at No. 155
O.I.P.: U.K. £125.00
U.S. $425.00

U.K.: £150.00
U.S.: $300.00
Can.: $400.00

CT-430
PHEASANT

Designer: William Manson
Type: Weight – Domed
Issued: 1985 in a limited edition of 150
Status: Closed at No. 72
O.I.P.: U.K. £175.00
U.S. $550.00

U.K.: £250.00
U.S.: $500.00
Can.: $650.00

CT-431
ANEMONE
Style One

Designer: Jeneo Lewis
Type: Weight – Spherical
Issued: 1985 in a limited edition of 500
Status: Fully subscribed
Series: Limited – Modern Design
O.I.P.: U.K. £48.00
U.S. $165.00

U.K.: £ 55.00
U.S.: $110.00
Can.: $150.00

CT-432
PASTORALE

Designer: Colin Terris
Type: Weight – Domed
Issued: 1985 in a limited edition of 500
Status: Fully subscribed
Series: Limited – Modern Design
O.I.P.: U.K. £65.00
U.S. $200.00

U.K.: £ 65.00
U.S.: $130.00
Can.: $170.00

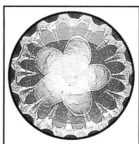

CT-433
FLORETTE

Designer: Colin Terris
Type: Weight – Disk, ribbed
Colour: Many colour variations
Issued: 1985
Status: Closed
O.I.P.: U.K. £9.50
U.S. $30.00

U.K.: £15.00
U.S.: $30.00
Can.: $40.00

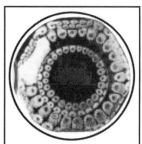

CT-434
THE FIREFLY

Designer: Colin Terris
Type: Weight – Spherical
Issued: 1985 in a limited edition of 500
Status: Closed at No. 154
O.I.P.: U.K. £54.95
U.S. $195.00

U.K.: £ 55.00
U.S.: $110.00
Can.: $150.00

Note: This paperweight was issued to commemorate the invention of the famous railway engine.

CT-435
MOON ORCHID

Designer:	Colin Terris
Type:	Weight – Spherical
Issued:	1985 in a limited edition of 1,000
Status:	Closed at No. 604
Series:	Collectors Club
O.I.P.:	U.K. £29.95
	U.S. $100.00
U.K.:	£ 55.00
U.S.:	$110.00
Can.:	$150.00

ISSUES OF 1986

CT-436
JUBILEE

Designer:	Colin Terris
Type:	Weight – Spherical
Issued:	1986 in a limited edition of 500
Status:	Fully subscribed
Series:	Limited – Modern Design
O.I.P.:	U.K. £50.00
	U.S. $175.00
U.K.:	£ 85.00
U.S.:	$170.00
Can.:	$225.00

Note: This paperweight was issued to celebrate Caithness's 25th anniversary.

CT-437
CABARET

Designer:	Colin Terris
Type:	Weight – Teardrop
Issued:	1986 in a limited edition of 650
Status:	Closed at No. 556
O.I.P.:	U.K. £53.00
	U.S. $185.00
U.K.:	£ 55.00
U.S.:	$110.00
Can.:	$150.00

CT-438
AQUAMARINE

Designer:	Colin Terris
Type:	Weight – Spherical, single overlay
Issued:	1986 in a limited edition of 350
Status:	Fully subscribed
O.I.P.:	U.K. £85.00
	U.S. $295.00
U.K.:	£ 85.00
U.S.:	$170.00
Can.:	$225.00

CT-439
CELESTE

Designer:	Colin Terris
Type:	Weight – Domed
Issued:	1986 in a limited edition of 500
Status:	Fully subscribed
Series:	Limited – Modern Design
O.I.P.:	U.K. £60.00
	U.S. $200.00
U.K.:	£ 65.00
U.S.:	$130.00
Can.:	$170.00

CT-440
FLYING FISH

Designer:	Colin Terris
Type:	Weight – Spherical
Issued:	1986 in a limited edition of 500
Status:	Closed at No. 455
Series:	Limited – Modern Design
O.I.P.:	U.K. £50.00
	U.S. $175.00
U.K.:	£ 50.00
U.S.:	$100.00
Can.:	$130.00

CT-441
THE WANDERER

Designer:	Colin Terris
Type:	Weight – Spherical
Issued:	1986 in a limited edition of 750
Status:	Closed at No. 232
Series:	Limited – Modern Design
O.I.P.:	U.K. £37.95
	U.S. $135.00
U.K.:	£ 45.00
U.S.:	$ 90.00
Can.:	$125.00

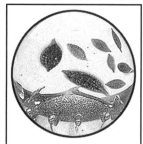

CT-442
AUTUMN LEAVES

Designer:	Colin Terris
Type:	Weight – Spherical
Issued:	1986 in a limited edition of 750
Status:	Closed at No. 250
Series:	Limited – Modern Design
O.I.P.:	U.K. £42.00
	U.S. $150.00
U.K.:	£ 45.00
U.S.:	$ 90.00
Can.:	$125.00

40th ANNIVERSARY OF CAITHNESS GLASS

Since he joined Caithness in 1968, Master Designer Colin Terris has literally designed thousands of paperweights and artglass pieces. Caithness celebrated its 40th Anniversary in 2001 and to commemorate this, Colin designed this collection of limited edition paperweights.

Golden Galaxy

Astral Celebration

Nostradamus
(Magnum)

2001: 40th ANNIVERSARY

Jubilation
(Magnum)

Mirror Image

Crystal
Chandelier

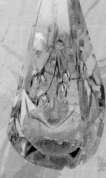

Winter Wonderland

COLIN TERRIS CLASSIC COLLECTION

In celebration of his 33 years with Caithness Glass, Colin Terris created his "Classic Collection". Reflecting back over those exciting years of paperweight design, Colin selected 12 of his favourites and reinterpreted them for release in 2002. Due to his retirement in 2001, this may be the last collection of paperweights by Colin Terris.

Floral Vision

Court Jester

Pagoda Orchid

Golden Renaissance

Arctic Twilight

Quintet

Coral Dream

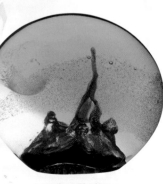

Martian Skyline

ALASTAIR MACINTOSH

Alastair MacIntosh ran his own glass studio
before joining Caithness Glass in 1987.

Delilah

Over the Hills
(Magnum)

SPACE 2001

Lunar Enigma

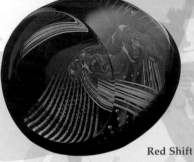

Red Shift

Return to Earth

Astronaut

Ringed Planet
(Magnum)

Lunar Quest

HELEN MACDONALD

The Last Tango

Hawaiian Harmony
(Magnum)

Helen MacDonald began her journey with Caithness Glass at the age of 16, when she joined the company as a trainee engraver, in the Wick Glass Studios.

She is now one of the top designers of Caithness Glass and is well known for her "Biblical" and "Once Upon a Time" series of paperweights.

Baptism

Blue Lotus

Flamenco Passions

ONCE UPON A TIME

Little Red
Riding Hood

Princess and
the Pea

The Glass Slipper
(Magnum)

PROMOTION EXCLUSIVES

Tranquil Oasis

Rhythm

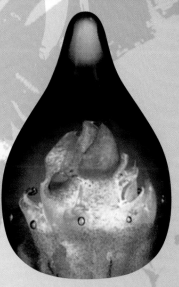

Perpetua

Dream World

Millennium Fanfare

COLLECTORS' SOCIETY COLLECTION

The Society offers members an opportunity to enter the world of Caithness Glass and keep in touch with other collectors around the world. The Society is a must for established collectors who want to know more about their paperweights and for new collectors looking to build up their collections.

Millennium Carousel
(2000)

Aquamarina
(1998)

Dignity
(2001)

Phoenix
(1989)

Shooting Star
(2003)

Floral Illusion
(1991)

COMMISSIONED WEIGHTS

Hadleigh China & Crystal

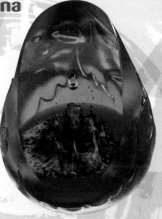

Lunar Seal

Peter Jones China

The Queen Mother's
Favourite Flowers

United States Collection

Alexandra

L.H. Selman Ltd.

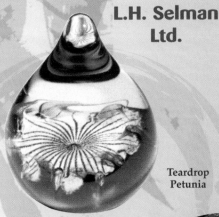

Teardrop
Petunia

Art Institute of Chicago

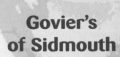

Govier's of Sidmouth

Festival of Colour

Unicorn, Twilight

PREMIER STOCKIST SERIES

Introduced in 1997 this collection was created for Caithness's most exclusive retailers. This Premier Stockist network covers the whole of the United Kingdom.

Knossos

Stella Maris

Gothic Splendour

Forest Flame

Elsinore

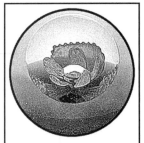

CT-443
RENAISSANCE
Designer: Colin Terris
Type: Weight – Spherical
Issued: 1986 in a limited
          edition of 500
Status: Fully subscribed
Series: Limited – Modern
          Design
O.I.P.:   U.K. £50.00
          U.S. $175.00

U.K.:   £ 75.00
U.S.: $150.00
Can.: $200.00

CT-444
NEPTUNE'S KINGDOM
Style One
Designer: Colin Terris
Type: Weight – Spherical
Issued: 1986 in a limited
          edition of 500
Status: Closed at No. 215
Series: Limited – Modern
          Design
O.I.P.:   U.K. £68.00
          U.S. $260.00

U.K.:   £100.00
U.S.: $200.00
Can.: $260.00

CT-445
STAR SHIP
Designer: Colin Terris
Type: Weight – Spherical
Issued: 1986 in a limited
          edition of 750
Status: Fully subscribed
Series: Limited – Modern
          Design
O.I.P.:   U.K. £44.95
          U.S. $150.00

U.K.:   £ 60.00
U.S.: $120.00
Can.: $150.00

CT-446
SEA SPRAY
Designer: Colin Terris
Type: Weight – Spherical
Issued: 1986 in a limited
          edition of 750
Status: Fully subscribed
Series: Limited – Modern
          Design
O.I.P.:   U.K. £47.95
          U.S. $165.00

U.K.:   £ 50.00
U.S.: $100.00
Can.: $130.00

CT-447
HELIX
Designer: Colin Terris
Type: Weight – Spherical
Issued: 1986 in a limited
          edition of 750
Status: Fully subscribed
Series: Limited Edition –
          Modern Design
O.I.P.:   U.K. £50.00
          U.S. $175.00

U.K.:   £ 50.00
U.S.: $100.00
Can.: $130.00

CT-448
ZEST
Designer: Colin Terris
Type: Weight – Spherical
Issued: 1986 in a limited
          edition of 750
Status: Fully subscribed
Series: Limited – Modern
          Design
O.I.P.:   U.K. £42.00
          U.S. $150.00

U.K.:   £ 60.00
U.S.: $120.00
Can.: $150.00

CT-449
GEMINI
Style One
Designer: Colin Terris
Type: Weight – Spherical
Issued: 1986 in a limited
          edition of 650
Status: Fully subscribed
Series: Limited – Modern
          Design
O.I.P.:   U.K. £55.00
          U.S. $195.00

U.K.:   £ 60.00
U.S.: $120.00
Can.: $150.00

CT-450
HONEYSUCKLE PERFUME
BOTTLE
Designer: Jeneo Lewis
Type: Perfume bottle
Issued: 1986 in a limited
          edition of 250
Status: Fully subscribed
Series: Limited – Modern
          Design
O.I.P.:   U.K. £85.00
          U.S. $295.00

U.K.:   £100.00
U.S.: $200.00
Can.: $260.00

CT-451
BLUE SPRAY

Designer:	Allan Scott
Type:	Weight – Spherical
Issued:	1986 in a limited edition of 250
Status:	Closed at No. 104
Series:	Whitefriars Collection
O.I.P.:	U.K. £85.00
	U.S. $295.00
U.K.:	£ 85.00
U.S.:	$170.00
Can.:	$225.00

CT-452
SPRING BOUQUET

Designer:	Allan Scott
Type:	Weight – Spherical
Issued:	1986 in a limited edition of 250
Status:	Closed at No. 230
Series:	Four Seasons, Whitefriars
O.I.P.:	U.K. £125.00
	U.S. $450.00
U.K.:	£125.00
U.S.:	$250.00
Can.:	$325.00

CT-453
SUMMER BOUQUET

Designer:	Allan Scott
Type:	Weight – Spherical
Issued:	1986 in a limited edition of 250
Status:	Closed at No. 215
Series:	Four Seasons, Whitefriars
O.I.P.:	U.K. £125.00
	U.S. $450.00
U.K.:	£125.00
U.S.:	$250.00
Can.:	$325.00

CT-454
AUTUMN BOUQUET

Designer:	Allan Scott
Type:	Weight – Spherical
Issued:	1986 in a limited edition of 250
Status:	Closed at No. 211
Series:	Four Seasons, Whitefriars
O.I.P.:	U.K. £125.00
	U.S. $450.00
U.K.:	£125.00
U.S.:	$250.00
Can.:	$325.00

CT-455
WINTER BOUQUET

Designer:	Allan Scott
Type:	Weight – Spherical
Issued:	1986 in a limited edition of 250
Status:	Closed at No. 211
Series:	Four Seasons, Whitefriars
O.I.P.:	U.K. £125.00
	U.S. $450.00
U.K.:	£125.00
U.S.:	$250.00
Can.:	$325.00

CT-456
PASTEL

Designer:	Colin Terris
Type:	Weight – Spherical, miniature
Colour:	Many colour variations
Issued:	1986
Status:	Closed
Series:	Medium and Miniature Size
O.I.P.:	U.K. £14.95
	U.S. $50.00
U.K.:	£15.00
U.S.:	$30.00
Can.:	$40.00

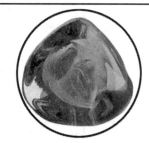

CT-457
PEBBLE
Style Two

Designer:	Colin Terris		
Type:	Weight – Pebble		
Size:	Medium		
Colour:	1. Black/Topaz	4.	Coral/White
	2. Blue/Topaz	5.	Green/Silver
	3. Blue/White	6.	Ruby/White
Issued:	1986		
Status:	Active		
Series:	Medium and Miniature Size		
O.I.P.:	U.K. £8.95		
	U.S. $30.00		
U.K.:	£12.95		
U.S.:	$30.00		
Can.:	–		

CT-458
VALENTINE PERFUME BOTTLE

Designer: Colin Terris
Type: Perfume bottle
Issued: 1986 in a limited
edition of 350
Status: Closed at No. 320
Series: Watercolours
O.I.P.: U.K. £65.00
U.S. $275.00

U.K.: £ 75.00
U.S.: $150.00
Can.: $200.00

CT-459
JULIET

Designer: Colin Terris
Type: Weight – Domed
Issued: 1986 in a limited
edition of 500
Status: Closed at No. 341
Series: Watercolours
O.I.P.: U.K. £37.95
U.S. $135.00

U.K.: £ 40.00
U.S.: $ 80.00
Can.: $100.00

CT-460
ORCHIDS
Style One

Designer: Colin Terris
Type: Weight – Spherical
Issued: 1986 in a limited
edition of 750
Status: Closed at No. 575
Series: Watercolours
O.I.P.: U.K. £37.95
U.S. $135.00

U.K.: £ 40.00
U.S.: $ 80.00
Can.: $100.00

CT-461
BUTTERFLIES
Style One

Designer: Colin Terris
Type: Weight – Spherical
Issued: 1986 in a limited
edition of 750
Status: Closed at No. 671
Series: Watercolours
O.I.P.: U.K. £37.95
U.S. $135.00

U.K.: £ 45.00
U.S.: $ 90.00
Can.: $125.00

CT-462
HEARTS

Designer: Colin Terris
Type: Weight – Spherical
Issued: 1986 in a limited
edition of 750
Status: Closed at No. 540
Series: Watercolours
O.I.P.: U.K. £37.95
U.S. $135.00

U.K.: £ 40.00
U.S.: $ 80.00
Can.: $100.00

CT-463
YULETIDE

Designer: Colin Terris
Type: Weight – Spherical
Issued: 1986 in a limited
edition of 500
Status: Closed at No. 118
Series: Traditional Collection
O.I.P.: U.K. £75.00
U.S. 250.00

U.K.: £ 85.00
U.S.: $170.00
Can.: $225.00

CT-464
SEAHORSE
Style One

Designer: William Manson
Type: Weight – Domed
Issued: 1986 in a limited
edition of 150
Status: Closed at No. 78
O.I.P.: U.K. £150.00
U.S. $550.00

U.K.: £300.00
U.S.: $600.00
Can.: $775.00

CT-465
CAMELIA

Designer: William Manson
Type: Weight – Spherical
Issued: 1986 in a limited
edition of 250
Status: Closed at No. 208
Series: Traditional Collection
O.I.P.: U.K. £100.00
U.S. $350.00

U.K.: £125.00
U.S.: $250.00
Can.: $325.00

CT-466
GOLDEN CORSAGE

Designer: William Manson
Type: Weight – Spherical
Issued: 1986 in a limited edition of 250
Status: Fully subscribed
Series: Traditional Collection
O.I.P.: U.K. £85.00
U.S. $295.00

U.K.: £ 85.00
U.S.: $170.00
Can.: $225.00

CT-467
FIELD STUDY BUTTERFLY

Designer: William Manson
Type: Weight – Spherical
Issued: 1986 in a limited edition of 250
Status: Closed at No. 228
Series: Traditional Collection
O.I.P.: U.K. £125.00
U.S. $450.00

U.K.: £150.00
U.S.: $300.00
Can.: $400.00

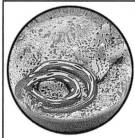

CT-468
RATTLESNAKE

Designer: William Manson
Type: Weight – Spherical
Issued: 1986 in a limited edition of 150
Status: Closed at No. 105
O.I.P.: U.K. £200.00
U.S. $695.00

U.K.: £225.00
U.S.: $450.00
Can.: $575.00

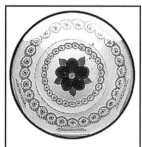

CT-469
RED ROSE
Style One

Designer: William Manson
Type: Weight – Spherical
Issued: 1986 in a limited edition of 500
Status: Closed at No. 159
Series: Traditional Collection
O.I.P.: U.K. £70.00
U.S. $250.00

U.K.: £ 75.00
U.S.: $150.00
Can.: $200.00

CT-470
INFERNO

Designer: Colin Terris
Type: Weight – Spherical
Issued: 1986
Status: Closed
Series: Unlimited – Modern Design
O.I.P.: U.K. £18.95
U.S. $65.00

U.K.: £25.00
U.S.: $50.00
Can.: $65.00

CT-471
BLUSH

Designer: Colin Terris
Type: Weight – Spherical
Issued: 1986
Status: Closed
Series: Unlimited – Modern Design
O.I.P.: U.K. £19.95
U.S. $65.00

U.K.: £25.00
U.S.: $50.00
Can.: $65.00

CT-472
DOUBLE MAGNUM VIOLET

Designer: Colin Terris
Type: Weight – Spherical
Size: Double magnum
Issued: 1986
Status: Closed
Series: Unlimited – Modern Design
O.I.P.: U.K. £136.00
U.S. $495.00

U.K.: £150.00
U.S.: $300.00
Can.: $400.00

CT-473
ROYAL WEDDING ANCHOR

Designer: Colin Terris
Type: Weight – Spherical
Canes: A & S (Andrew and Sarah)
Issued: 1986 in a limited edition of 500
Status: Closed at No. 362
O.I.P.: U.K. £75.00
U.S. $265.00

U.K.: £ 75.00
U.S.: $150.00
Can.: $200.00

Note: Weights CT-473 through 477 were issued to commemorate the wedding of Prince Andrew and Sarah Ferguson.

CT-474
ROYAL WEDDING HEART

Designer: Colin Terris
Type: Weight – Spherical
Cane: A & S (Andrew and Sarah)
Issued: 1986 in a limited edition of 500
Status: Closed at No. 329
O.I.P.: U.K. £65.00
U.S. $265.00

U.K.: £ 65.00
U.S.: $130.00
Can.: $165.00

CT-475
ROYAL WEDDING TRIBUTE

Designer: Colin Terris
Type: Weight – Spherical
Canes: A & S (Andrew and Sarah)
Issued: 1986 in a limited edition of 150
Status: Fully subscribed
O.I.P.: U.K. £150.00
U.S. $225.00

U.K.: £175.00
U.S.: $350.00
Can.: $450.00

CT-476
ROYAL WEDDING MONOGRAM

Designer: Colin Terris
Type: Weight – Spherical
Issued: 1986 in a limited edition of 1,500
Status: Closed at No. 751
O.I.P.: U.K. £39.95
U.S. $135.00

U.K.: £ 40.00
U.S.: $ 80.00
Can.: $100.00

CT-477
ROYAL BOUQUET PERFUME BOTTLE

Designer: Colin Terris
Type: Perfume bottle
Canes: A & S (Andrew and Sarah)
Issued: 1986 in a limited edition of 100
Status: Fully subscribed
O.I.P.: U.K. £150.00
U.S. $225.00

U.K.: £150.00
U.S.: $300.00
Can.: $400.00

CT-478
VIVAT REGINA

Designer: Colin Terris
Type: Weight – Spherical
Cane: 60
Issued: 1986 in a limited edition of 250
Status: Fully subscribed
O.I.P.: U.K. £85.00
U.S. $295.00

U.K.: £ 85.00
U.S.: $170.00
Can.: $225.00

Note: This paperweight was issued to commemorate the 60th birthday of HM Queen Elizabeth II.

CT-479
ASTRAL

Designer: Colin Terris
Type: Weight – Spherical
Issued: 1986 in a limited edition of 750
Status: Fully subscribed
Series: Limited – Modern Design
O.I.P.: U.K. £44.95
U.S. $150.00

U.K.: £ 45.00
U.S.: $ 90.00
Can.: $125.00

CT-480
OCEAN TREASURE
Designer: Colin Terris
Type: Weight – Domed
Issued: 1986 in a limited
edition of 650
Status: Closed at No. 597
Series: Limited – Modern
Design
O.I.P.: U.K. £60.00
U.S. $210.00

U.K.: £ 60.00
U.S.: $120.00
Can.: $150.00

CT-481
QUADRILLE
Designer: Colin Terris
Type: Weight – Spherical
Issued: 1986 in a limited
edition of 500
Status: Fully subscribed
Series: Limited – Modern
Design
O.I.P.: U.K. £55.00
U.S. $195.00

U.K.: £ 55.00
U.S.: $110.00
Can.: $150.00

CT-482
IMPULSE
Style One
Designer: Colin Terris
Type: Weight – Spherical
Issued: 1986 in a limited
edition of 750
Status: Fully subscribed
Series: Limited – Modern
Design
O.I.P.: U.K. £42.00
U.S. $150.00

U.K.: £ 45.00
U.S.: $ 90.00
Can.: $125.00

CT-483
KISMET
Designer: Colin Terris
Type: Weight – Spherical
Issued: 1986 in a limited
edition of 750
Status: Fully subscribed
Series: Limited – Modern
Design
O.I.P.: U.K. £47.95
U.S. $175.00

U.K.: £ 50.00
U.S.: $100.00
Can.: $130.00

CT-484
ENCOUNTER
Designer: Colin Terris
Type: Weight – Spherical
Issued: 1986 in a limited
edition of 750
Status: Fully subscribed
Series: Limited – Modern
Design
O.I.P.: U.K. £50.00
U.S. $175.00

U.K.: £ 50.00
U.S.: $100.00
Can.: $130.00

CT-485
MAGIC CARPET
Designer: Colin Terris
Type: Weight – Spherical
Issued: 1986 in a limited
edition of 750
Status: Fully subscribed
Series: Limited – Modern
Design
O.I.P.: U.K. £47.95
U.S. $175.00

U.K.: £ 50.00
U.S.: $100.00
Can.: $130.00

CT-486
JUBILEE ROSE
Style One
Designer: Colin Terris
Type: Weight – Spherical
Issued: 1986 in a limited
edition of 750
Status: Fully subscribed
Series: Limited – Modern
Design
O.I.P.: U.K. £50.00
U.S. $175.00

U.K.: £ 50.00
U.S.: $100.00
Can.: $130.00

Note: This paperweight was
issued to celebrate the
25th anniversary of
Caithness Glass.

CT-487
TRILOGY
Designer: Colin Terris
Type: Weight – Spherical
Issued: 1986 in a limited
edition of 750
Status: Fully subscribed
Series: Limited – Modern
Design
O.I.P.: U.K. £39.95
U.S. $150.00

U.K.: £ 40.00
U.S.: $ 80.00
Can.: $100.00

CT-488
IRIS
Style One
Designer: Colin Terris
Type: Weight – Spherical
Issued: 1986 in a limited
edition of 750
Status: Closed at No. 239
Series: Watercolours
O.I.P.: U.K. £37.95
U.S. $135.00

U.K.: £ 50.00
U.S.: $100.00
Can.: $130.00

CT-489
CAMILLA PERFUME BOTTLE
Designer: Colin Terris
Type: Perfume bottle
Issued: 1986 in a limited
edition of 350
Status: Closed at No. 250
Series: Watercolours
O.I.P.: U.K. £65.00
U.S. $275.00

U.K.: £ 85.00
U.S.: $170.00
Can.: $225.00

CT-490
MICHAELMAS DAISY
Designer: William Manson
Type: Weight – Spherical
Issued: 1986 in a limited
edition of 250
Status: Closed at No. 127
Series: Traditional Collection
O.I.P.: U.K. £100.00
U.S. $350.00

U.K.: £125.00
U.S.: $250.00
Can.: $325.00

CT-491
FLUTTER BY
Designer: William Manson
Type: Weight – Spherical
Issued: 1986 in a limited
edition of 250
Status: Closed at No. 157
Series: Traditional Collection
O.I.P.: U.K. £175.00
U.S. $595.00

U.K.: £200.00
U.S.: $400.00
Can.: $525.00

CT-492
SHARK
Designer: William Manson
Type: Weight – Spherical
Issued: 1986 in a limited
edition of 150
Status: Closed at No. 123
O.I.P.: U.K. £200.00
U.S. $695.00

U.K.: £200.00
U.S.: $400.00
Can.: $525.00

CT-493
THISTLE
Style One
Designer: William Manson
Type: Weight – Spherical
Issued: 1986 in a limited
edition of 750
Status: Closed at No. 429
Series: Traditional Collection
O.I.P.: U.K. £55.00
U.S. $195.00

U.K.: £ 55.00
U.S.: $110.00
Can.: $150.00

CT-494
FLOURISH
Designer: William Manson
Type: Weight – Spherical
Issued: 1986 in a limited
edition of 750
Status: Closed at No. 244
Series: Traditional Collection
O.I.P.: U.K. £50.00
U.S. $175.00

U.K.: £ 50.00
U.S.: $100.00
Can.: $130.00

CT-495
NOSEGAY
Designer: Allan Scott
Type: Weight – Spherical
Issued: 1986 in a limited
edition of 250
Status: Closed at No. 151
Series: Whitefriars Collection
O.I.P.: U.K. £85.00
U.S. $295.00

U.K.: £ 85.00
U.S.: $170.00
Can.: $225.00

CT-496
CANDIDA

Designer: Allan Scott
Type: Weight – Spherical
Issued: 1986 in a limited edition of 250
Status: Closed at No. 152
Series: Whitefriars Collection
O.I.P.: U.K. £85.00
U.S. $295.00

U.K.: £ 85.00
U.S.: $170.00
Can.: $225.00

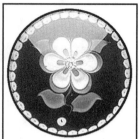

CT-497
ROSETTE

Designer: Allan Scott
Type: Weight – Spherical
Issued: 1986 in a limited edition of 500
Status: Closed at No. 164
Series: Whitefriars Collection
O.I.P.: U.K. £55.00
U.S. $195.00

U.K.: £ 55.00
U.S.: $110.00
Can.: $145.00

CT-498
DOMINO

Designer: Colin Terris
Type: Weight – Domed
Issued: 1986 in a limited edition of 1,000
Status: Closed at No. 792
O.I.P.: U.K. £35.00
U.S. $115.00

U.K.: £ 50.00
U.S.: $100.00
Can.: $130.00

Note: This is the 1986 Collectors' Weight.

CURLING
(Crossed Brooms)

Designer: Caithness Design Studios
Type: Weight – Spherical
Issued: 1986 Unlimited
Status: Closed
Series: Unknown
O.I.P.: £25.00

U.K.: £30.00
U.S.: $60.00
Can.: $80.00

Photograph not available at press time

CURLING
(Female)

Designer: Caithness Design Studios
Type: Weight –
Issued: 1986 Unlimited
Status: Closed
Series: Unknown
O.I.P.: £25.00

U.K.: £30.00
U.S.: $60.00
Can.: $80.00

Photograph not available at press time

CURLING
(Male)

Designer: Caithness Design Studios
Type: Weight –
Issued: 1986 Unlimited
Status: Closed
Series: Unknown
O.I.P.: £25.00

U.K.: £30.00
U.S.: $60.00
Can.: $80.00

GOLF
(Female)

Designer: Unknown
Type: Weight – Spherical
Issued: 1986 Unlimited
Status: Closed
Series: Unknown
O.I.P.: £42.00

U.K.: £ 45.00
U.S.: $ 90.00
Can.: $125.00

GOLF
(Male)

Designer: Unknown
Type: Weight – Spherical
Issued: 1986 Unlimited
Status: Closed
Series: Unknown
O.I.P.: £42.00

U.K.: £ 45.00
U.S.: $ 90.00
Can.: $125.00

HUMMINGBIRD

Designer:	Unknown
Type:	Weight – Spherical
Issued:	1986 in a limited edition of 500
Status:	Closed
Series:	Krystals
O.I.P.:	£26.50
U.K.:	£30.00
U.S.:	$60.00
Can.:	$80.00

Note: Others known in this series are Owl, Geese, Eagle, Butterfly, Honey Bee, Penguin, Polar Bear, Seal, Swans, Salmon and Otter (12 in total).

PLAYFUL AND WATCHFUL

Designer:	Unknown
Type:	Weight – Spherical
Issued:	1986 in a limited edition of 100
Status:	Closed
Series:	Krystals
O.I.P.:	£44.75
U.K.:	£ 45.00
U.S.:	$ 90.00
Can.:	$125.00

TENNIS (Female)

Designer:	Caithness Design Studio
Type:	Weight – Spherical
Issued:	1986 Unlimited
Status:	Closed
Series:	Unknown
O.I.P.:	U.K. £25.00
U.K.:	£25.00
U.S.:	$50.00
Can.:	$65.00

TENNIS (Male)

Designer:	Caithness Design Studios
Type:	Weight – Spherical
Issued:	1986 Unlimited
Status:	Closed
Series:	Unknown
O.I.P.:	U.K. £25.00
U.K.:	£25.00
U.S.:	$50.00
Can.:	$65.00

ISSUES OF 1987

CT-499
NIGHT OWL

Designer: Colin Terris
Type: Weight – Spherical
Issued: 1987 in a limited edition of 500
Status: Fully subscribed
Series: Limited – Modern Design
O.I.P.: U.K. £50.00
U.S. $175.00

U.K.: £ 60.00
U.S.: $120.00
Can.: $150.00

CT-500
VIGIL

Designer: Colin Terris
Type: Weight – Spherical
Issued: 1987 in a limited edition of 750
Status: Fully subscribed
Series: Limited – Modern Design
O.I.P.: U.K. £39.95
U.S. $135.00

U.K.: £ 40.00
U.S.: $ 80.00
Can.: $100.00

CT-501
SHANGRI-LA

Designer: Colin Terris
Type: Weight – Spherical
Issued: 1987 in a limited edition of 150
Status: Fully subscribed
Series: Limited – Modern Design
O.I.P.: U.K. £99.00
U.S. $350.00

U.K.: £175.00
U.S.: $350.00
Can.: $450.00

CT-502
ADAGIO

Designer: Val Coghlin
Type: Weight – Spherical
Issucd: 1987 in a limited edition of 750
Status: Fully subscribed
Series: Limited – Modern Design
O.I.P.: U.K. £54.00
U.S. $195.00

U.K.: £ 60.00
U.S.: $120.00
Can.: $150.00

CT-503
VAGABOND

Designer: Colin Terris
Type: Weight – Spherical
Issued: 1987 in a limited edition of 750
Status: Closed at No. 312
Series: Limited – Modern Design
O.I.P.: U.K. £42.00
U.S. $150.00

U.K.: £ 70.00
U.S.: $140.00
Can.: $180.00

CT-504
LOOP THE LOOP

Designer: Colin Terris
Type: Weight – Spherical
Issued: 1987 in a limited edition of 750
Status: Closed at No. 596
Series: Limited – Modern Design
O.I.P.: U.K. £54.00
U.S. $195.00

U.K.: £ 60.00
U.S.: $120.00
Can.: $150.00

CT-505
MAGENTA

Designer: Colin Terris
Type: Weight – Spherical
Issued: 1987 in a limited edition of 750
Status: Fully subscribed
Series: Limited – Modern Design
O.I.P.: U.K. £50.00
U.S. $175.00

U.K.: £ 55.00
U.S.: $110.00
Can.: $150.00

CT-506
MINUET

Designer: Colin Terris
Type: Weight – Spherical
Issued: 1987 in a limited edition of 750
Status: Fully subscribed
Series: Limited – Modern Design
O.I.P.: U.K. £45.00
U.S. $165.00

U.K.: £ 55.00
U.S.: $110.00
Can.: $150.00

CT-507
EMERALD

Designer:	Colin Terris
Type:	Weight – Spherical
Issued:	1987 in a limited edition of 250
Status:	Fully subscribed
Series:	Limited – Modern Design
O.I.P.:	U.K. £60.00
	U.S. $210.00
U.K.:	£ 75.00
U.S.:	$150.00
Can.:	$200.00

CT-508
ORACLE

Designer:	Colin Terris
Type:	Weight – Spherical
Issued:	1987 in a limited edition of 500
Status:	Closed at No. 468
Series:	Limited – Modern Design
O.I.P.:	U.K. £55.00
	U.S. $195.00
U.K.:	£ 55.00
U.S.:	$110.00
Can.:	$150.00

CT-509
MINARET

Designer:	Colin Terris
Type:	Weight – Domed
Issued:	1987 in a limited edition of 650
Status:	Fully subscribed
Series:	Limited – Modern Design
O.I.P.:	U.K. £53.00
	U.S. $195.00
U.K.:	£ 65.00
U.S.:	$130.00
Can.:	$170.00

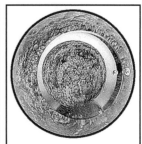

CT-510
JUPITER
Style Two

Designer:	Colin Terris
Type:	Weight – Spherical
Issued:	1987 in a limited edition of 750
Status:	Fully subscribed
Series:	Limited – Modern Design
O.I.P.:	U.K. £37.95
	U.S. $135.00
U.K.:	£ 45.00
U.S.:	$ 90.00
Can.:	$120.00

CT-511
FLIGHT

Designer:	Colin Terris
Type:	Weight – Spherical
Issued:	1987 in a limited edition of 750
Status:	Fully subscribed
Series:	Limited – Modern Design
O.I.P.:	U.K. £50.00
	U.S. $185.00
U.K.:	£ 85.00
U.S.:	$170.00
Can.:	$225.00

CT-512
RENDEZVOUS

Designer:	Colin Terris
Type:	Weight – Spherical
Issued:	1987 in a limited edition of 750
Status:	Fully subscribed
Series:	Limited – Modern Design
O.I.P.:	U.K. £45.00
	U.S. $165.00
U.K.:	£125.00
U.S.:	$250.00
Can.:	$325.00

CT-513
EIGHTY EIGHT

Designer:	Colin Terris
Type:	Weight – Spherical
Issued:	1987 in a limited edition of 150
Status:	Fully subscribed
Series:	Limited – Modern Design
O.I.P.:	U.K. £99.00
	U.S. $350.00
U.K.:	£125.00
U.S.:	$250.00
Can.:	$325.00

Note: There are 88 facets cut and polished on the surface of this paperweight

CT-514
BALLOON SELLER

Designer:	Colin Terris
Type:	Weight – Domed
Issued:	1987 in a limited edition of 650
Status:	Fully subscribed
Series:	Limited – Modern Design
O.I.P.:	U.K. £55.00
	U.S. $195.00
U.K.:	£ 60.00
U.S.:	$120.00
Can.:	$160.00

CT-515
SHAMAL

Designer:	Colin Terris
Type:	Weight – Spherical
Issued:	1987 in a limited edition of 750
Status:	Fully subscribed
Series:	Limited – Modern Design
O.I.P.:	U.K. £37.95 U.S. $135.00

U.K.:	£ 40.00
U.S.:	$ 80.00
Can.:	$100.00

CT-516
REVERIE

Designer:	Colin Terris
Type:	Weight – Spherical
Issued:	1987 in a limited edition of 750
Status:	Fully subscribed
Series:	Limited – Modern Design
O.I.P.:	U.K. £47.95 U.S. $165.00

U.K.:	£ 50.00
U.S.:	$100.00
Can.:	$130.00

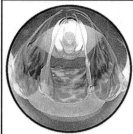

CT-517
SOLACE

Designer:	Colin Terris
Type:	Weight – Spherical
Issued:	1987 in a limited edition of 750
Status:	Fully subscribed
Series:	Limited – Modern Design
O.I.P.:	U.K. £42.00 U.S. $150.00

U.K.:	£ 45.00
U.S.:	$ 90.00
Can.;	$120.00

CT-518
ALPHA
Style One

Designer:	Colin Terris
Type:	Weight – Spherical
Issued:	1987 in a limited edition of 750
Status:	Closed at No. 692
Series:	Limited – Modern Design
O.I.P.:	U.K. £45.00 U.S. $165.00

U.K.:	£ 45.00
U.S.:	$ 90.00
Can.:	$120.00

CT-519
FLEUR
Style One

Designer:	Colin Terris
Type:	Weight – Spherical
Colour:	See below
Issued:	1987
Status:	Closed
O.I.P.:	U.K. £12.95 U.S. $45.00

	Blue	Pink	Violet
U.K.:	£20.00	20.00	20.00
U.S.:	$40.00	40.00	40.00
Can.:	$50.00	50.00	50.00

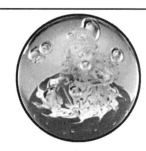

CT-520
TANGO

Designer:	Colin Terris
Type:	Weight – Spherical
Colour:	See below
Issued:	1987
Status:	Closed
Series:	Unlimited – Modern Design
O.I.P.:	U.K. £16.95 U.S. $49.50

	Crimson	Lapis	Sable	Topaz
U.K.:	£20.00	20.00	20.00	20.00
U.S.:	$40.00	40.00	40.00	40.00
Can.:	$50.00	50.00	50.00	50.00

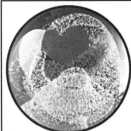

CT-521
SWEETHEART
Designer: Colin Terris
Type: Weight – Spherical
Issued: 1987
Status: Closed
Series: Romance
O.I.P.: U.K. £15.95
U.S. $49.50

U.K.: £20.00
U.S.: $40.00
Can.: $50.00

CT-522
DOUBLE MAGNUM CRIMSON
Designer: Colin Terris
Type: Weight – Spherical
Size: Double magnum
Issued: 1987
Status: Closed
Series: Unlimited – Modern
Design
O.I.P.: U.K. £136.00
U.S. $450.00

U.K.: £150.00
U.S.: $300.00
Can.: $400.00

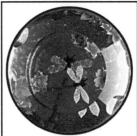

CT-523
DOUBLE DRAGONFLY
Designer: William Manson
Type: Weight – Spherical
Issued: 1987 in a limited
edition of 150
Status: Fully subscribed
Series: Traditional Collection
O.I.P.: U.K. £130.00
U.S. $450.00

U.K.: £150.00
U.S.: $300.00
Can.: $400.00

CT-524
AMETHYST SPRAY
Designer: Allan Scott
Type: Weight – Spherical
Issued: 1987 in a limited
edition of 350
Status: Closed at No. 160
Series: Traditional Collection
O.I.P.: U.K. £85.00
U.S. $295.00

U.K.: £ 85.00
U.S.: $170.00
Can.: $225.00

CT-525
WHITE HEATHER
Designer: William Manson
Type: Weight – Spherical
Issued: 1987 in a limited
edition of 500
Status: Closed at No. 93
Series: Traditional Collection
O.I.P.: U.K. £50.00
U.S. $175.00

U.K.: £ 75.00
U.S.: $150.00
Can.: $200.00

CT-526
SNOWDROPS
Designer: William Manson
Type: Weight – Spherical
Issued: 1987 in a limited
edition of 500
Status: Closed at No. 409
Series: Traditional Collection
O.I.P.: U.K. £55.00
U.S. $195.00

U.K.: £ 55.00
U.S.: $110.00
Can.: $145.00

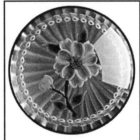

CT-527
ZINNIA
Designer: William Manson
Type: Weight – Spherical
Issued: 1987 in a limited
edition of 350
Status: Closed at No. 170
Series: Traditional Collection
O.I.P.: U.K. £85.00
U.S. $295.00

U.K.: £ 95.00
U.S.: $200.00
Can.: $260.00

CT-528
NATIONAL FLOWERS
Designer: William Manson
Type: Weight – Spherical
Issued: 1987 in a limited
edition of 250
Status: Closed at No. 184
Series: Traditional Collection
O.I.P.: U.K. £150.00
U.S. $495.00

U.K.: £150.00
U.S.: $300.00
Can.: $400.00

CT-529
DUCK POND
Designer: William Manson
Type: Weight – Spherical
Issued: 1987 in a limited edition of 150
Status: Fully subscribed
Series: Traditional Collection
O.I.P.: U.K. £150.00
U.S. $495.00

U.K.: £175.00
U.S.: $350.00
Can.: $450.00

CT-530
HEDGEHOG
Style One
Designer: William Manson
Type: Weight – Spherical
Issued: 1987 in a limited edition of 100
Status: Fully subscribed
Series: Traditional Collection
O.I.P.: U.K. £200.00
U.S. $695.00

U.K.: £200.00
U.S.: $400.00
Can.: $525.00

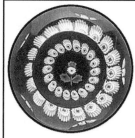

CT-531
MINIATURE SCOTS THISTLE
Designer: Allan Scott
Type: Weight – Spherical
Issued: 1987
Status: Closed
Series: Millefiori Miniatures
O.I.P.: U.K. £19.95
U.S. $65.00

U.K.: £30.00
U.S.: $60.00
Can.: $80.00

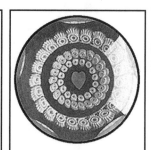

CT-532
MINIATURE HEART
Style One, First Version
Designer: Allan Scott
Type: Weight – Spherical
Issued: 1987
Status: Closed
Series: Millefiori Miniatures
O.I.P.: U.K. £19.95
U.S. $65.00

U.K.: £30.00
U.S.: $60.00
Can.: $80.00

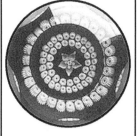

CT-533
MINIATURE FORGET-ME-NOT
Style One, First Version
Designer: Allan Scott
Type: Weight – Spherical
Issued: 1987
Status: Closed
Series: Millefiori Miniatures
O.I.P.: U.K. £19.95
U.S. $65.00

U.K.: £30.00
U.S.: $60.00
Can.: $80.00

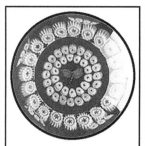

CT-534
MINIATURE DRAGONFLY
Designer: Allan Scott
Type: Weight – Spherical
Issued: 1987
Status: Closed
Series: Millefiori Miniatures
O.I.P.: U.K. £19.95
U.S. $65.00

U.K.: £30.00
U.S.: $60.00
Can.: $80.00

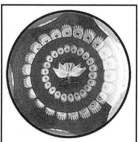

CT-535
MINIATURE NARCISSUS
Designer: Allan Scott
Type: Weight – Spherical
Issued: 1987
Status: Closed
Series: Millefiori Miniatures
O.I.P.: U.K. £19.95
U.S. $65.00

U.K.: £30.00
U.S.: $60.00
Can.: $80.00

CT-536
BUTTERFLY DUET
Designer: Allan Scott
Type: Weight – Spherical
Issued: 1987 in a limited edition of 250
Status: Closed at No. 165
Series: Whitefriars Collection
O.I.P.: U.K. £100.00
U.S. $350.00

U.K.: £100.00
U.S.: $200.00
Can.: $260.00

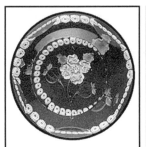

CT-537
OPIUM POPPY

Designer:	Allan Scott
Type:	Weight – Spherical
Issued:	1987 in a limited edition of 250
Status:	Closed at No. 218
Series:	Whitefriars Collection
O.I.P.:	U.K. £75.00
	U.S. $275.00
U.K.:	£100.00
U.S.:	$200.00
Can.:	$260.00

CT-538
BLUE and WHITE GARLAND

Designer:	Allan Scott
Type:	Weight – Spherical
Issued:	1987 in a limited edition of 250
Status:	Fully subscribed
Series:	Whitefriars Collection
O.I.P.:	U.K. £100.00
	U.S. $350.00
U.K.:	£100.00
U.S.:	$200.00
Can.:	$260.00

CT-539
SCARLET PIMPERNEL
Style One

Designer:	Allan Scott
Type:	Weight – Spherical
Issued:	1987 in a limited edition of 250
Status:	Closed at No. 227
Series:	Whitefriars Collection
O.I.P.:	U.K. £75.00
	U.S. $275.00
U.K.:	£100.00
U.S.:	$200.00
Can.:	$260.00

CT-540
REGATTA

Designer:	Margot Thomson
Type:	Weight – Domed
Issued:	1987 in a limited edition of 350
Status:	Closed at No. 333
Series:	Limited – Modern Design
O.I.P.:	U.K. £64.00
	U.S. $225.00
U.K.:	£ 65.00
U.S.:	$130.00
Can.:	$170.00

CT-541
WILL O' THE WISP

Designer:	Colin Terris
Type:	Weight – Spherical
Issued:	1987 in a limited edition of 150
Status:	Fully subscribed
Series:	Limited – Modern Design
O.I.P.:	U.K. £99.00
	U.S. $350.00
U.K.:	£175.00
U.S.:	$350.00
Can.:	$450.00

CT-542
VALHALLA

Designer:	Colin Terris
Type:	Weight – Domed
Issued:	1987 in a limited edition of 650
Status:	Fully subscribed
Series:	Limited – Modern Design
O.I.P.:	U.K. £55.00
	U.S. $195.00
U.K.:	£ 60.00
U.S.:	$120.00
Can.:	$160.00

CT-543
ODYSSEY

Designer:	Margot Thomson
Type:	Weight – Spherical
Issued:	1987 in a limited edition of 750
Status:	Closed at No. 718
Series:	Limited – Modern Design
O.I.P.:	U.K. £47.95
	U.S. $165.00
U.K.:	£ 50.00
U.S.:	$100.00
Can.:	$130.00

CT-544
SPRING BREEZE

Designer:	Colin Terris
Type:	Weight – Spherical
Issued:	1987 in a limited edition of 750
Status:	Fully subscribed
Series:	Limited – Modern Design
O.I.P.:	U.K. £39.95
	U.S. $135.00
U.K.:	£ 40.00
U.S.:	$ 80.00
Can.:	$100.00

CT-545
MARRAKESH

Designer: Colin Terris
Type: Weight – Spherical
Issued: 1987 in a limited edition of 500
Status: Fully subscribed
Series: Limited – Modern Design
O.I.P.: U.K. £50.00
U.S. $175.00

U.K.:	£ 55.00
U.S.:	$110.00
Can.:	$150.00

CT-546
NEBULA

Designer: Colin Terris
Type: Weight – Spherical
Issued: 1987 in a limited edition of 750
Status: Fully subscribed
Series: Limited – Modern Design
O.I.P.: U.K. £45.00
U.S. $165.00

U.K.:	£ 45.00
U.S.:	$ 90.00
Can.:	$120.00

CT-547
HOBGOBLIN

Designer: Margot Thomson
Type: Weight – Spherical
Issued: 1987 in a limited edition of 750
Status: Closed at No. 711
Series: Limited – Modern Design
O.I.P.: U.K. £42.00
U.S. $150.00

U.K.:	£ 45.00
U.S.:	$ 90.00
Can.:	$120.00

CT-548
SPACE FRONTIER

Designer: Colin Terris
Type: Weight – Spherical
Issued: 1987 in a limited edition of 750
Status: Fully subscribed
Series: Limited – Modern Design
O.I.P.: U.K. £47.95
U.S. $165.00

U.K.:	£ 50.00
U.S.:	$100.00
Can.:	$130.00

 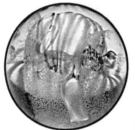

CT-549
ACROBAT

Designer: Margot Thomson
Type: Weight – Spherical
Colour: See below
Issued: 1987
Status: Closed
Series: Unlimited – Modern Design
O.I.P.: U.K. £19.95
U.S. $69.50

	Emerald	Jet	Sapphire
U.K.:	£20.00	20.00	20.00
U.S.:	$40.00	40.00	40.00
Can.:	$55.00	55.00	55.00

CT-550
PINK CHAMPAGNE

Designer: Colin Terris
Type: Weight – Spherical
Issued: 1987
Status: Active
Series: Unlimited – Modern Design
O.I.P.: U.K. £19.95
U.S. $69.50

U.K.:	£34.95
U.S.:	$95.00
Can.:	–

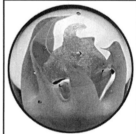

CT-551
STRAWBERRY FAYRE

Designer: Margot Thomson
Type: Weight – Spherical
Issued: 1987
Status: Closed
Series: Unlimited – Modern Design
O.I.P.: U.K. £19.95
U.S. $69.50

U.K.:	£30.00
U.S.:	$60.00
Can.:	$80.00

CT-552
TEMPEST
Designer: Margot Thomson
Type: Weight – Spherical
Colour: See below
Issued: 1987
Status: Closed
Series: Unlimited – Modern Design
O.I.P.: U.K. £21.95
U.S. $75.00

	Cobalt	Magenta
U.K.:	£30.	30.
U.S.:	$60.	60.
Can.:	$80.	80.

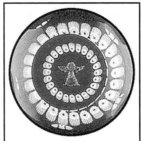

CT-553
MINIATURE ANGEL
Designer: Allan Scott
Type: Weight – Spherical
Issued: 1987
Status: Closed
Series: Millefiori Miniatures
O.I.P.: U.K. £22.50
U.S. $75.00

U.K.:	£30.00
U.S.:	$60.00
Can.:	$80.00

CT-554
MINIATURE CHRISTMAS TREE
Designer: Allan Scott
Type: Weight – Spherical
Issued: 1987
Status: Closed
Series: Millefiori Miniatures
O.I.P.: U.K. £22.50
U.S. $75.00

U.K.:	£30.00
U.S.:	$60.00
Can.:	$80.00

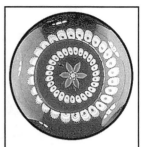

CT-555
MINIATURE POINSETTIA
First Version
Designer: Allan Scott
Type: Weight – Spherical
Issued: 1987
Status: Closed
Series: Millefiori Miniatures
O.I.P.: U.K. £22.50
U.S. $75.00

U.K.:	£30.00
U.S.:	$60.00
Can.:	$80.00

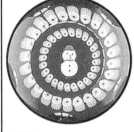

CT-556
MINIATURE SNOWMAN
Designer: Allan Scott
Type: Weight – Spherical
Issued: 1987
Status: Closed
Series: Millefiori Miniatures
O.I.P.: U.K. £22.50
U.S. $75.00

U.K.:	£30.00
U.S.:	$60.00
Can.:	$80.00

CT-557
CHRISTMAS DECORATION
Designer: William Manson
Type: Weight – Spherical
Issued: 1987 in a limited edition of 250
Status: Closed at No. 79
Series: Christmas Traditional Collection
O.I.P.: U.K. £70.00
U.S. $250.00

U.K.:	£ 85.00
U.S.:	$170.00
Can.:	$220.00

CT-558
CHRISTMAS STAR
Designer: William Manson
Type: Weight – Spherical
Issued: 1987 in a limited edition of 250
Status: Closed at No. 157
Series: Christmas Traditional Collection
O.I.P.: U.K. £80.00
U.S. $295.00

U.K.:	£ 80.00
U.S.:	$160.00
Can.:	$210.00

CT-559
NOEL
Designer: William Manson
Type: Weight – Spherical
Issued: 1987 in a limited edition of 250
Status: Closed at No. 97
Series: Christmas Traditional Collection
O.I.P.: U.K. £70.00
U.S. $250.00

U.K.:	£ 85.00
U.S.:	$170.00
Can.:	$220.00

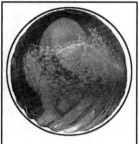

CT-560
CHORALE

Designer: Colin Terris
Type: Weight – Pyramid facets
Issued: 1987 in a limited edition of 1,000
Status: Closed at No. 816
Series: Collectors Club
O.I.P.: U.K. £50.00
U.S. $175.00

U.K.: £ 75.00
U.S.: $150.00
Can.: $200.00

MISTY LAVENDER MIST

Designer: Colin Terris
Type: Weight – Spherical
Issued: 1987 Unlimited
Status Closed
Series: Unknown
O.I.P.: £13.95

U.K.: £20.00
U.S.: $40.00
Can.: $50.00

MISTY ROSE MIST

Designer: Colin Terris
Type: Weight – Spherical
Issued: 1987 Unlimited
Status Closed
Series: Unknown
O.I.P.: £13.95

U.K.: £20.00
U.S.: $40.00
Can.: $50.00

ISSUES OF 1988

CT-561
NECTAR

Designer: Alastair MacIntosh
Type: Weight – Spherical
Issued: 1988 in a limited edition of 750
Status: Closed at No. 375
Series: Limited – Modern Design
O.I.P.: U.K. £50.00
U.S. $190.00

U.K.:	£ 60.00
U.S.:	$120.00
Can.:	$160.00

CT-562
READY STEADY GO

Designer: Colin Terris
Type: Weight – Spherical
Issued: 1988 in a limited edition of 150
Status: Fully subscribed
Series: Limited – Modern Design
O.I.P.: U.K. £120.00
U.S. $450.00

U.K.:	£150.00
U.S.:	$300.00
Can.:	$400.00

CT-563
ETHERIA

Designer: Colin Terris
Type: Weight – Spherical
Issued: 1988 in a limited edition of 750
Status: Closed at No. 726
Series: Limited – Modern Design
O.I.P.: U.K. £69.00
U.S. $275.00

U.K.:	£ 70.00
U.S.:	$140.00
Can.:	$180.00

CT-564
MERRY GO ROUND

Designer: Colin Terris
Type: Weight – Spherical
Issued: 1988 in a limited edition of 750
Status: Closed at No. 730
Series: Limited – Modern Design
O.I.P.: U.K. £60.00
U.S. $225.00

U.K.:	£ 60.00
U.S.:	$120.00
Can.:	$160.00

CT-565
WHEELSPIN

Designer: Colin Terris
Type: Weight – Spherical
Issued: 1988 in a limited edition of 750
Status: Closed at No. 372
Series: Limited – Modern Design
O.I.P.: U.K. £65.00
U.S. $250.00

U.K.:	£ 65.00
U.S.:	$130.00
Can.:	$170.00

CT-566
MAGIC LANTERN

Designer: Colin Terris
Type: Weight – Spherical
Issued: 1988 in a limited edition of 750
Status: Fully subscribed
Series: Limited – Modern Design
O.I.P.: U.K. £45.00
U.S. $175.00

U.K.:	£ 60.00
U.S.:	$120.00
Can.:	$160.00

CT-567
FIRECRACKER

Designer: Alastair MacIntosh
Type: Weight – Spherical
Issued: 1988 in a limited edition of 750
Status: Closed at No. 741
Series: Limited – Modern Design
O.I.P.: U.K. £50.00
U.S. $190.00

U.K.:	£ 50.00
U.S.:	$120.00
Can.:	$160.00

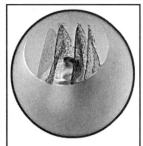

CT-568
CHAMELEON

Designer: Colin Terris
Type: Weight – Spherical
Issued: 1988 in a limited edition of 750
Status: Closed at No. 184
Series: Limited – Modern Design
O.I.P.: U.K. £65.00
U.S. $250.00

U.K.:	£ 75.00
U.S.:	$150.00
Can.:	$200.00

CT-569
AUTUMN BREEZE

Designer: Colin Terris
Type: Weight – Spherical
Issued: 1988 in a limited
edition of 750
Status: Closed at No. 723
Series: Limited – Modern
Design
O.I.P.: U.K. £43.00
U.S. $165.00

U.K.: £ 50.00
U.S.: $100.00
Can.: $130.00

CT-570
JAMBOREE

Designer: Alastair MacIntosh
Type: Weight – Spherical
Issued: 1988 in a limited
edition of 500
Status: Fully subscribed
Series: Limited – Modern
Design
O.I.P.: U.K. £65.00
U.S. $250.00

U.K.: £ 70.00
U.S.: $140.00
Can.: $180.00

CT-571
POINSETTIA PERFUME BOTTLE

Designer: Colin Terris
Type: Perfume bottle
Issued: 1988 in a limited
edition of 250
Status: Closed at No. 174
O.I.P.: U.K. £85.00
U.S. $350.00

U.K.: £ 85.00
U.S.: $170.00
Can.: $225.00

CT-572
EQUINOX

Designer: Alastair MacIntosh
Type: Weight – Spherical
Issued: 1988 in a limited
edition of 750
Status: Closed at No. 573
Series: Limited – Modern
Design
O.I.P.: U.K. £50.00
U.S. $190.00

U.K.: £ 70.00
U.S.: $140.00
Can.: $180.00

CT-573
REPOSE

Designer: Colin Terris
Type: Weight – Spherical
Issued: 1988 in a limited
edition of 750
Status: Closed at No. 725
Series: Limited – Modern
Design
O.I.P.: U.K. £50.00
U.S. $190.00

U.K.: £ 50.00
U.S.: $100.00
Can.: $130.00

CT-574
MERRY MAKER

Designer: Colin Terris
Type: Weight – Spherical
Issued: 1988 in a limited
edition of 750
Status: Fully subscribed
Series: Limited – Modern
Design
O.I.P.: U.K. £45.00
U.S. $175.00

U.K.: £ 50.00
U.S.: $100.00
Can.: $130.00

CT-575A
MERCURY
Style Two

Designer: Colin Terris
Type: Weight – Spherical
Issued: 1988 in a limited
edition of 150
Status: Closed at No. 142
Series: Limited – Modern
Design
O.I.P.: U.K. £175.00/set
U.S. $695.00/set

U.K.: £100.00
U.S.: $200.00
Can.: $260.00

Note: CT-575A and B were
issued and sold as a set.

CT-575B
MERCURY PERFUME BOTTLE

Designer: Colin Terris
Type: Bottle
Issued: 1988 in a limited
edition of 150
Status: Closed at No. 142
Series: Limited – Modern
Design
O.I.P.: U.K. £175.00/set
U.S. $695.00/set

	Perfume	Set
U.K.:	£150.	250.
U.S.:	$300.	500.
Can.:	$400.	660.

CT-576
AMMONITE

Designer: Margot Thomson
Type: Weight – Spherical
Issued: 1988 in a limited edition of 500
Status: Closed at No. 444
Series: Limited – Modern Design
O.I.P.: U.K. £50.00
U.S. $190.00

U.K.: £ 50.00
U.S.: $100.00
Can.: $130.00

CT-577
AURORA

Designer: Colin Terris
Type: Weight – Spherical
Issued: 1988 in a limited edition of 250
Status: Fully subscribed
Series: Limited – Modern Design
O.I.P.: U.K. £85.00
U.S. $350.00

U.K.: £100.00
U.S.: $200.00
Can.: $260.00

CT-578
COUNTERPOINT

Designer: Colin Terris
Type: Weight – Spherical
Issued: 1988 in a limited edition of 750
Status: Fully subscribed
Series: Limited – Modern Design
O.I.P.: U.K. £50.00
U.S. $190.00

U.K.: £ 60.00
U.S.: $125.00
Can.: $175.00

CT-579
CYCLONE

Designer: Colin Terris
Type: Weight – Spherical
Issued: 1988 in a limited edition of 750
Status: Fully subscribed
Series: Limited – Modern Design
O.I.P.: U.K. £43.00
U.S. $165.00

U.K.: £ 45.00
U.S.: $ 90.00
Can.: $120.00

CT-580
LISTENER

Designer: Colin Terris
Type: Weight – Spherical
Issued: 1988 in a limited edition of 750
Status: Fully subscribed
Series: Limited – Modern Design
O.I.P.: U.K. £45.00
U.S. $175.00

U.K.: £ 50.00
U.S.: $100.00
Can.: $130.00

CT-581
CRUSADER

Designer: Margot Thomson
Type: Weight – Spherical
Issued: 1988 in a limited edition of 750
Status: Fully subscribed
Series: Limited – Modern Design
O.I.P.: U.K. £60.00
U.S. $225.00

U.K.: £ 65.00
U.S.: $130.00
Can.: $170.00

CT-582
WOOD NYMPH

Designer: Margot Thomson
Type: Weight – Domed
Issued: 1988 in a limited edition of 650
Status: Closed at No. 452
Series: Limited – Modern Design
O.I.P.: U.K. £55.00
U.S. $210.00

U.K.: £ 60.00
U.S.: $120.00
Can.: $160.00

CT-583
ADVENTURE

Designer: Colin Terris
Type: Weight – Spherical
Issued: 1988 in a limited edition of 500
Status: Fully subscribed
Series: Limited – Modern Design
O.I.P.: U.K. £69.00
U.S. $275.00

U.K.: £ 75.00
U.S.: $150.00
Can.: $200.00

Note: This paperweight has basket facets and an opaque spatter overlay.

CT-584
SEA SPRITE
Designer: Colin Terris
Type: Weight – Spherical
Issued: 1988 in a limited
edition of 250
Status: Fully subscribed
Series: Limited – Modern
Design
O.I.P.: U.K. £85.00
U.S. $350.00

U.K.: £ 85.00
U.S.: $170.00
Can.: $220.00

CT-585
SPINNING TOP
Designer: Colin Terris
Type: Weight – Spherical
Issued: 1988 in a limited
edition of 750
Status: Fully subscribed
Series: Limited – Modern
Design
O.I.P.: U.K. £55.00
U.S. $210.00

U.K.: £ 55.00
U.S.: $110.00
Can.: $145.00

CT-586
MADRIGAL
Designer: Colin Terris
Type: Weight – Spherical
Issued: 1988 in a limited
edition of 350
Status: Fully subscribed
Series: Limited – Modern
Design
O.I.P.: U.K. £69.00
U.S. $275.00

U.K.: £ 75.00
U.S.: $150.00
Can.: $200.00

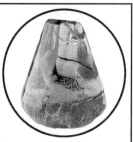

CT-587
MAELSTROM
Designer: Margot Thomson
Type: Weight – Conical
Issued: 1988 in a limited
edition of 650
Status: Closed at No. 501
Series: Limited – Modern
Design
O.I.P.: U.K. £55.00
U.S. $210.00

U.K.: £ 55.00
U.S.: $110.00
Can.: $145.00

CT-588
PINNACLE
Designer: Colin Terris
Type: Weight – Spherical,
facets
Issued: 1988 in a limited
edition of 150
Status: Fully subscribed
Series: Limited – Modern
Design
O.I.P.: U.K. £120.00
U.S. $450.00

U.K.: £150.00
U.S.: $300.00
Can.: $400.00

CT-589
BLITHE SPIRIT
Designer: Colin Terris
Type: Weight – Spherical
Issued: 1988 in a limited
edition of 150
Status: Fully subscribed
Series: Limited – Modern
Design
O.I.P.: U.K. £99.00
U.S. $395.00

U.K.: £150.00
U.S.: $300.00
Can.: $400.00

CT-590
FLIGHT OF FANCY
Designer: Colin Terris
Type: Weight – Domed
Issued: 1988 in a limited
edition of 650
Status: Fully subscribed
O.I.P.: U.K. £69.00
U.S. $275.00

U.K.: £ 85.00
U.S.: $170.00
Can.: $225.00

CT-591
**SPRING BREEZE PERFUME
BOTTLE**
Designer: Colin Terris
Type: Perfume bottle
Issued: 1988 in a limited
edition of 250
Status: Closed at No. 235
Series: Limited – Modern
Design
O.I.P.: U.K. £85.00
U.S. $350.00

U.K.: £ 85.00
U.S.: $170.00
Can.: $225.00

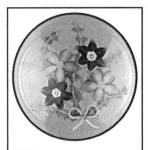

CT-592
VICTORIAN BOUQUET
Designer: Allan Scott
Type: Weight – Spherical
Issued: 1988 in a limited edition of 500
Status: Closed at No. 272
Series: Whitefriars Collection
O.I.P.: U.K. £70.00
U.S. $275.00

U.K.: £ 70.00
U.S.; $140.00
Can.: $180.00

CT-593
STILL LIFE
Designer: Allan Scott
Type: Weight – Spherical
Issued: 1988 in a limited edition of 100
Status: Fully subscribed
Series: Whitefriars Collection
O.I.P.: U.K. £125.00
U.S. $475.00

U.K.: £150.00
U.S.: $300.00
Can.: $400.00

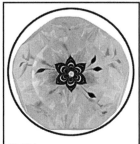

CT-594
SAPPHIRE STAR
Designer: Allan Scott
Type: Weight – Spherical, facets
Issued: 1988 in a limited edition of 100
Status: Fully subscribed
Series: Whitefriars Collection
O.I.P.: U.K. £125.00
U.S. $475.00

U.K.: £150.00
U.S.: $300.00
Can.: $400.00

CT-595
MIDNIGHT BOUQUET
Designer: Allan Scott
Type: Weight – Spherical
Issued: 1988 in a limited edition of 250
Status: Closed at No. 222
Series: Whitefriars Collection
O.I.P.: U.K. £90.00
U.S. $350.00

U.K.: £100.00
U.S.: $200.00
Can.: $260.00

CT-596
BROCADE BUTTERFLY
Designer: Allan Scott
Type: Weight – Spherical
Issued: 1988 in a limited edition of 250
Status: Closed at No. 206
Series: Whitefriars Collection
O.I.P.: U.K. £90.00
U.S. $350.00

U.K.: £100.00
U.S.: $200.00
Can.: $260.00

CT-597
LACE
Designer: Allan Scott
Type: Weight – Spherical
Issued: 1988 in a limited edition of 250
Status: Closed at No. 209
Series: Whitefriars Collection
O.I.P.: U.K. £90.00
U.S. $350.00

U.K.: £100.00
U.S.: $200.00
Can.: $260.00

CT-598
FLORAL WHIMSY
Designer: Allan Scott
Type: Weight – Spherical
Issued: 1988 in a limited edition of 500
Status: Closed at No. 121
Series: Whitefriars Collection
O.I.P.: U.K. £70.00
U.S. $275.00

U.K.: £100.00
U.S.: $200.00
Can.: $260.00

CT-599
SUMMER BLUE
Designer: Allan Scott
Type: Weight – Spherical
Issued: 1988 in a limited edition of 100
Status: Closed at No. 91
Series: Whitefriars Collection
O.I.P.: U.K. £125.00
U.S. $475.00

U.K.: £125.00
U.S.: $250.00
Can.: $325.00

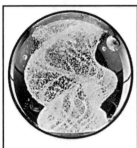

CT-600
CARNIVAL SILVER

Designer: Colin Terris
Type: Weight – Spherical
Issued: 1988
Status: Closed
Series: Unlimited – Modern Design
O.I.P.: U.K. £13.30
U.S. $69.50

U.K.: £25.00
U.S.: $50.00
Can.: $65.00

CT-601
FROG and LADYBIRD

Designer: William Manson
Type: Weight – Low Dome
Issued: 1988 in a limited edition of 150
Status: Fully subscribed
Series: Traditional Collection
O.I.P.: U.K. £200.00
U.S. $775.00

U.K.: £300.00
U.S.: $600.00
Can.: $775.00

CT-602
NESTING BLUEBIRD

Designer: William Manson
Type: Weight – Spherical
Issued: 1988 in a limited edition of 250
Status: Closed at No. 230
Series: Traditional Collection
O.I.P.: U.K. £150.00
U.S. $575.00

U.K.: £300.00
U.S.: $600.00
Can.: $775.00

CT-603
HARVEST MOUSE

Designer: William Manson
Type: Weight – Spherical
Issued: 1988 in a limited edition of 200
Status: Closed at No. 126
Series: Traditional Collection
O.I.P.: U.K. £175.00
U.S. $695.00

U.K.: £225.00
U.S.: $450.00
Can.: $575.00

CT-604
NATURE STUDY

Designer: William Manson
Type: Weight – Spherical
Issued: 1988 in a limited edition of 200
Status: Closed at No. 137
O.I.P.: U.K. £175.00
U.S. $695.00

U.K.: £300.00
U.S.: $600.00
Can.: $775.00

CT-605
BADGER

Designer: William Manson
Type: Weight – Spherical
Issued: 1988 in a limited edition of 100
Status: Closed at No. 41
Series: Traditional Collection
O.I.P.: U.K. £225.00
U.S. $850.00

U.K.: £ 400.00
U.S.: $ 800.00
Can.: $1,000.00

CT-606
OCEAN HUNTER

Designer: William Manson
Type: Weight – Spherical
Issued: 1988 in a limited edition of 250
Status: Closed at No. 80
Series: Traditional Collection
O.I.P.: U.K. £130.00
U.S. $495.00

U.K.: £200.00
U.S.: $400.00
Can.: $525.00

CT-607
SWAN LAKE

Designer: William Manson
Type: Weight – Spherical
Issued: 1988 in a limited edition of 250
Status: Closed at No. 241
Series: Traditional Collection
O.I.P.: U.K. £150.00
U.S. $575.00

U.K.: £150.00
U.S.: $300.00
Can.: $400.00

CT-608
CROCODILE

Designer: William Manson
Type: Weight – Spherical
Issued: 1988 in a limited edition of 150
Status: Closed at No. 104
Series: Traditional Collection
O.I.P.: U.K. £200.00
U.S. $775.00

U.K.: £250.00
U.S.: $500.00
Can.: $650.00

CT-609
STARWATCH SILVER

Designer: Colin Terris
Type: Weight – Spherical
Issued: 1988
Status: Active
Series: Unlimited – Modern Design
O.I.P.: U.K. £25.95
U.S. $99.50

U.K.: £ 39.95
U.S.: $125.00
Can.: –

CT-610
TIDAL WAVE

Designer: Margot Thomson
Type: Weight – Spherical
Issued: 1988
Status: Closed
Series: Unlimited – Modern Design
O.I.P.: U.K. £19.95
U.S. $79.50

U.K.: £ 50.00
U.S.: $100.00
Can.: $130.00

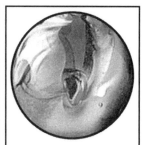

CT-611
NEON

Designer: Alastair MacIntosh
Type: Weight – Spherical
Colour: 1. Green, white and blue
2. Pink, white and blue
3. Purple, white and yellow
Issued: 1988
Status: Closed
Series: Unlimited – Modern Design
O.I.P.: U.K. £23.95
U.S. $95.00

U.K.: £35.00
U.S.: $70.00
Can.: $90.00

CT-612
PETALS

Designer: Colin Terris
Type: Weight – Spherical
Colour: See below
Issued: 1988
Status: Closed
Series: Unlimited – Modern Design
O.I.P.: U.K. £25.95
U.S. $99.50

	Blue	Gold	Red	Yellow
U.K.:	£30.00	30.00	30.00	30.00
U.S.:	$60.00	60.00	60.00	60.00
Can.:	$80.00	80.00	80.00	80.00

CT-613
SNOW TRAIL

Designer: Margot Thomson
Type: Weight – Spherical
Colour: See below
Issued: 1988
Status: Closed
Series: Unlimited – Modern Design
O.I.P.: U.K. £25.95
U.S. $99.50

	Amethyst	Clear
U.K.:	£ 40.	40.
U.S.:	$ 80.	80.
Can.:	$100.	100.

CT-614
CALYPSO

Designer: Margot Thomson
Type: Weight – Spherical
Colour: See below
Issued: 1988
Status: Closed
Series: Unlimited – Modern Design
O.I.P.: U.K. £21.95
U.S. $79.50

	Pink	Topaz
U.K.:	£30.	30.
U.S.:	$60.	60.
Can.:	$80.	80.

CT-615
DOUBLE MAGNUM SABLE
Designer: Colin Terris
Type: Weight – Spherical
Size: Double magnum
Issued: 1988
Status: Closed
Series: Unlimited – Modern Design
O.I.P.: U.K. £145.00
U.S. $495.00

U.K.: £150.00
U.S.: $300.00
Can.: $400.00

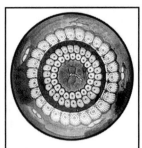

CT-616
MINIATURE DRAGONFLY
Style Two
Designer: Allan Scott
Type: Weight – Spherical
Issued: 1988
Status: Closed
Series: Millefiori Miniatures
O.I.P.: U.K. £23.95
U.S. $79.50

U.K.: £35.00
U.S.: $70.00
Can.: $90.00

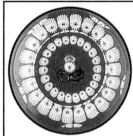

CT-617
MINIATURE THISTLE
First Version
Designer: Allan Scott
Type: Weight – Spherical
Issued: 1988
Status: Closed
Series: Millefiori Miniatures
O.I.P.: U.K. £23.95
U.S. $79.50

U.K.: £35.00
U.S.: $70.00
Can.: $90.00

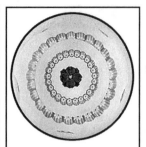

CT-618
MINIATURE ROSE
Style One, First Version
Designer: Allan Scott
Type: Weight – Spherical
Issued: 1988
Status: Closed
Series: Millefiori Miniatures
O.I.P.: U.K. £23.95
U.S. $79.50

U.K.: £35.00
U.S.: $70.00
Can.: $90.00

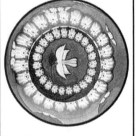

CT-619
MINIATURE DAFFODIL
Designer: Allan Scott
Type: Weight – Spherical
Issued: 1988
Status: Closed
Series: Millefiori Miniatures
O.I.P.: U.K. £23.95
U.S. $79.50

U.K.: £35.00
U.S.: $70.00
Can.: $90.00

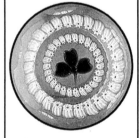

CT-620
MINIATURE SHAMROCK
Designer: Allan Scott
Type: Weight – Spherical
Issued: 1988
Status: Closed
Series: Millefiori Miniatures
O.I.P.: U.K. £23.95
U.S. $79.50

U.K.: £35.00
U.S.: $70.00
Can.: $90.00

CT-621
MINIATURE HEART
Style One, Second Version
Designer: Allan Scott
Type: Weight – Spherical
Issued: 1988
Status: Closed
Series: Millefiori Miniatures
O.I.P.: U.K. £23.95
U.S. $79.50

U.K.: £35.00
U.S.: $70.00
Can.: $90.00

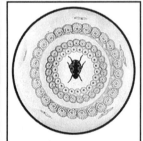

CT-622
MINIATURE LADYBIRD
First Version
Designer: Allan Scott
Type: Weight – Spherical
Issued: 1988
Status: Closed
Series: Millefiori Miniatures
O.I.P.: U.K. £23.95
U.S. $79.50

U.K.: £35.00
U.S.: $70.00
Can.: $90.00

CT-623
MINIATURE FORGET-ME-NOT
Designer: Allan Scott
Type: Weight − Spherical
Issued: 1988
Status: Closed
Series: Millefiori Miniatures
O.I.P.:   U.K. £23.95
          U.S. $79.50

U.K.:   £35.00
U.S.: $70.00
Can.: $90.00

CT-624
SERPENTINE
Designer: Stuart Cumming
Type: Weight − Spherical
Issued: 1988 in a limited
          edition of 750
Status: Closed at No. 733
Series: Limited − Modern
          Design
O.I.P.:   U.K. £43.00
          U.S. $165.00

U.K.:   £ 50.00
U.S.: $100.00
Can.: $130.00

CT-625
CALIPH
Designer: Margot Thomson
Type: Weight − Spherical
Issued: 1988 in a limited
          edition of 750
Status: Fully subscribed
Series: Limited − Modern
          Design
O.I.P.:   U.K. £45.00
          U.S. $175.00

U.K.:   £ 50.00
U.S.: $100.00
Can.: $130.00

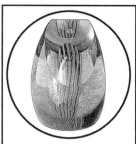

CT-626
MERIDIAN
Designer: Alastair MacIntosh
Type: Weight − Domed
Issued: 1988 in a limited
          edition of 500
Status: Fully subscribed
Series: Limited − Modern
          Design
O.I.P.:   U.K. £65.00
          U.S. $250.00

U.K.:   £ 65.00
U.S.: $130.00
Can.: $170.00

CT-627
VESUVIUS
Designer: Colin Terris
Type: Weight − Pyramid
          facets
Issued: 1988 in a limited
          edition of 650
Status: Closed at No. 462
Series: Limited − Modern
          Design
O.I.P.:   U.K. £59.00
          U.S. $225.00

U.K.:   £ 60.00
U.S.: $120.00
Can.: $160.00

CT-628
TIME WARP
Designer: Colin Terris
Type: Weight − Spherical
Issued: 1988 in a limited
          edition of 750
Status: Closed at No. 557
Series: Limited − Modern
          Design
O.I.P.:   U.K. £55.00
          U.S. $210.00

U.K.:   £ 55.00
U.S.: $110.00
Can.: $145.00

CT-629
ARGOSY
Designer: Colin Terris
Type: Weight − Spherical
Issued: 1988 in a limited
          edition of 250
Status: Fully subscribed
Series: Limited − Modern
          Design
O.I.P.:   U.K. £90.00
          U.S. $350.00

U.K.:   £100.00
U.S.: $200.00
Can.: $260.00

CT-630
SNOWFLAME
Designer: Margot Thomson
Type: Weight − Spherical
Issued: 1988 in a limited
          edition of 750
Status: Fully subscribed
Series: Limited − Modern
          Design
O.I.P.:   U.K. £45.00
          U.S. $175.00

U.K.:   £ 45.00
U.S.: $ 90.00
Can.: $125.00

CT-631
MISTS OF TIME

Designer:	Margot Thomson
Type:	Weight – Pyramid facets
Issued:	1988 in a limited edition of 500
Status:	Closed at No. 368
Series:	Limited – Modern Design
O.I.P.:	U.K. £75.00
	U.S. $295.00
U.K.:	£ 80.00
U.S.:	$160.00
Can.:	$210.00

CT-632
GALLEON

Designer:	Colin Terris
Type:	Weight – Spherical
Issued:	1988 in a limited edition of 750
Status:	Closed at No. 696
Series:	Limited – Modern Design
O.I.P.:	U.K. £50.00
	U.S. $190.00
U.K.:	£ 50.00
U.S.:	$100.00
Can.:	$130.00

CT-633
BRITANNIA

Designer:	Alastair MacIntosh
Type:	Weight – Spherical
Issued:	1988 in a limited edition of 250
Status:	Fully subscribed
Series:	Limited – Modern Design
O.I.P.:	U.K. £85.00
	U.S. $350.00
U.K.:	£ 85.00
U.S.:	$170.00
Can.:	$225.00

CT-634
PARROT

Designer:	William Manson
Type:	Weight – Spherical
Issued:	1988 in a limited edition of 150
Status:	Closed at No. 142
Series:	Whitefriars Collection
O.I.P.:	U.K. £200.00
	U.S. $775.00
U.K.:	£200.00
U.S.:	$400.00
Can.:	$525.00

CT-635
DRAGONFLY
Style Three

Designer:	William Manson
Type:	Weight – Spherical
Issued:	1988 in a limited edition of 200
Status:	Fully subscribed
Series:	Traditional Collection
O.I.P.:	U.K. £185.00
	U.S. $695.00
U.K.:	£200.00
U.S.:	$400.00
Can.:	$525.00

CT-636
ROSE and LADYBIRD

Designer:	William Manson
Type:	Weight – Spherical
Issued:	1988 in a limited edition of 250
Status:	Fully subscribed
Series:	Traditional Collection
O.I.P.:	U.K. £150.00
	U.S. $575.00
U.K.:	£150.00
U.S.:	$300.00
Can.:	$400.00

CT-637
SUMMER GARDEN

Designer:	Allan Scott
Type:	Weight – Spherical
Issued:	1988 in a limited edition of 250
Status:	Fully subscribed
Series:	Whitefriars Collection
O.I.P.:	U.K. £100.00
	U.S. $375.00
U.K.:	£125.00
U.S.:	$250.00
Can.:	$325.00

CT-638
HANGING BASKET

Designer:	Allan Scott
Type:	Weight – Spherical
Issued:	1988 in a limited edition of 250
Status:	Closed at No. 244
Series:	Whitefriars Collection
O.I.P.:	U.K. £100.00
	U.S. $395.00
U.K.:	£125.00
U.S.:	$250.00
Can.:	$325.00

CT-639
MAGNUM OPUS '88

Designer:	Colin Terris
Type:	Weight – Spherical
Size:	Treble magnum
Colour:	Pink flower with aqua and green leaves
Issued:	1988 in a limited edition of 100
Status:	Fully subscribed
Series:	Limited – Modern Design
O.I.P.:	U.K. £450.00
	U.S. $1,500
U.K.:	£ 650.00
U.S.:	$1,300.00
Can.:	$1,700.00

CT-640
FIESTA

Designer:	Alastair MacIntosh
Type:	Weight – Spherical
Colour:	See below
Issued:	1988
Status:	Closed
Series:	Unlimited – Modern Design
O.I.P.:	U.K. £23.95
	U.S. $90.00

	Aqua	Lime	Orange	Ruby
U.K.:	£ 40.00	40.00	40.00	40.00
U.S.:	$ 80.00	80.00	80.00	80.00
Can.:	$100.00	100.00	100.00	100.00

CT-641
SPINNAKER

Designer:	Alastair MacIntosh
Type:	Weight – Spherical
Colour:	See below
Issued:	1988
Status:	Closed
Series:	Unlimited – Modern Design
O.I.P.:	U.K. £14.95
	U.S. $55.00

	Cobalt	Lime	Orange	Ruby
U.K.:	£20.00	20.00	20.00	20.00
U.S.:	$40.00	40.00	40.00	40.00
Can.:	$50.00	50.00	50.00	50.00

CT-642
MINIATURE MISTLETOE

Designer:	Allan Scott
Type:	Weight – Spherical
Issued:	1988
Status:	Closed
Series:	Millefiori Miniatures
O.I.P.:	U.K. £24.95
	U.S. $79.50
U.K.:	£30.00
U.S.:	$60.00
Can.:	$80.00

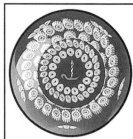

CT-643
MINIATURE CANDLE

Designer:	Allan Scott
Type:	Weight – Spherical
Issued:	1988
Status:	Closed
Series:	Millefiori Miniatures
O.I.P.:	U.K. £24.95
	U.S. $79.50
U.K.:	£30.00
U.S.:	$60.00
Can.:	$80.00

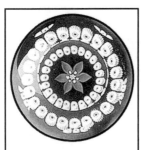

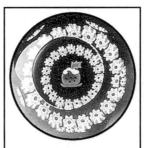

CT-644
MINIATURE POINSETTIA
Second Version

Designer:	Allan Scott
Type:	Weight – Spherical
Issued:	1988
Status:	Closed
Series:	Millefiori Miniatures
O.I.P.:	U.K. £24.95
	U.S. $79.50
U.K.:	£30.00
U.S.:	$60.00
Can.:	$80.00

CT-645
MINIATURE FESTIVE FARE

Designer:	Allan Scott
Type:	Weight – Spherical
Issued:	1988
Status:	Closed
Series:	Millefiori Miniatures
O.I.P.:	U.K. £24.95
	U.S. $79.50
U.K.:	£30.00
U.S.:	$60.00
Can.:	$80.00

CT-646
OPUS 88

Designer:	Colin Terris
Type:	Weight – Spherical
Colour:	Pink and white flower with blue leaves
Issued:	1988 in a limited edition of 1,000
Status:	Fully subscribed
Series:	Collectors' Society
O.I.P.:	U.K. £55.00
	U.S. $195.00
U.K.:	£150.00
U.S.:	$300.00
Can.:	$400.00

ISSUES OF 1989

CT-647
AFFINITY

Designer:	Margot Thomson
Type:	Weight – Spherical
Issued:	1989 in a limited edition of 750
Status:	Closed at No. 636
Series:	Limited – Modern Design
O.I.P.:	U.K. £55.00
	U.S. $275.00
U.K.:	£ 55.00
U.S.:	$110.00
Can.:	$145.00

CT-648
ALPINE WINTER

Designer:	Alastair MacIntosh
Type:	Weight – Domed
Issued:	1989 in a limited edition of 650
Status:	Fully subscribed
Series:	Limited – Modern Design
O.I.P.:	U.K. £60.00
	U.S. $250.00
U.K.:	£ 60.00
U.S.:	$120.00
Can.:	$155.00

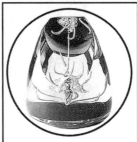

CT-649
BONSAI

Designer:	Alastair MacIntosh
Type:	Weight – Domed
Issued:	1989 in a limited edition of 500
Status:	Fully subscribed
Series:	Limited – Modern Design
O.I.P.:	U.K. £69.00
	U.S. $275.00
U.K.:	£ 70.00
U.S.:	$140.00
Can.:	$180.00

CT-650
BUTTERFLY ORCHID

Designer:	Colin Terris
Type:	Weight – Spherical
Issued:	1989 in a limited edition of 750
Status:	Closed at No. 602
Series:	Limited – Modern Design
O.I.P.:	U.K. £60.00
	U.S. $225.00
U.K.:	£ 60.00
U.S.:	$120.00
Can.:	$155.00

CT-651
CLEOPATRA

Designer:	Colin Terris
Type:	Weight – Pyramid facets
Issued:	1989 in a limited edition of 500
Status:	Closed at No. 465
Series:	Limited – Modern Design
O.I.P.:	U.K. £80.00
	U.S. $325.00
U.K.:	£ 80.00
U.S.:	$160.00
Can.:	$200.00

CT-652
CONFUSION

Designer:	Colin Terris
Type:	Weight – Spherical
Issued:	1989 in a limited edition of 750
Status:	Closed at No. 716
Series:	Limited – Modern Design
O.I.P.:	U.K. £55.00
	U.S. $210.00
U.K.:	£ 55.00
U.S.:	$110.00
Can.:	$145.00

CT-653A
EARTH
Style Three

Designer:	Colin Terris
Type:	Weight – Spherical
Issued:	1989 in a limited edition of 250
Status:	Fully subscribed
Series:	Elements, Set Two
O.I.P.:	U.K. £295.00/set
	U.S. $1,000.00/set

	Earth	Set
U.K.:	£100.	400.
U.S.:	$200.	800.
Can.:	$260.	1,050.

Note: CT-653a, b, c and d were issued and sold as a set.

CT-653B
AIR
Style Two

Designer:	Colin Terris
Type:	Weight – Spherical
Issued:	1989 in a limited edition of 250
Status:	Fully subscribed
Series:	Elements, Set Two
O.I.P.:	U.K. £295.00/set
	U.S. $1,000.00/set
U.K.:	£100.00
U.S.:	$200.00
Can.:	$260.00

CT-653C
FIRE
Style Three

Designer:	Colin Terris
Type:	Weight – Spherical
Issued:	1989 in a limited edition of 250
Status:	Fully subscribed
Series:	Elements, Set Two
O.I.P.:	U.K. £295.00/set U.S. $1,000/set
U.K.:	£100.00
U.S.:	$200.00
Can.:	$260.00

CT-653D
WATER
Style Two

Designer:	Colin Terris
Type:	Weight – Spherical
Issued:	1989 in a limited edition of 250
Status:	Fully subscribed
Series:	Elements, Set Two
O.I.P.:	U.K. £295.00/set U.S. $1,000/set
U.K.:	£100.00
U.S.:	$200.00
Can.:	$260.00

CT-654
EVOLUTION

Designer:	Alastair MacIntosh
Type:	Weight – Spherical
Issued:	1989 in a limited edition of 750
Status:	Closed at No. 651
Series:	Limited – Modern Design
O.I.P.:	U.K. £55.00 U.S. $225.00
U.K.:	£ 55.00
U.S.:	$110.00
Can.:	$145.00

CT-655
GLOBE TROTTER

Designer:	Margot Thomson
Type:	Weight – Spherical
Issued:	1989 in a limited edition of 650
Status:	Closed at No. 546
Series:	Limited – Modern Design
O.I.P.:	U.K. £65.00 U.S. $250.00
U.K.:	£ 65.00
U.S.:	$130.00
Can.:	$170.00

CT-656
HALLOWEEN

Designer:	Margot Thomson
Type:	Weight – Spherical
Issued:	1989 in a limited edition of 650
Status:	Closed at No. 602
Series:	Limited – Modern Design
O.I.P.:	U.K. £69.00 U.S. $275.00
U.K.:	£ 70.00
U.S.:	$140.00
Can.:	$180.00

CT-657
ICE FAIRY

Designer:	Margot Thomson
Type:	Weight – Teardrop
Issued:	1989 in a limited edition of 650
Status:	Fully subscribed
Series:	Limited – Modern Design
O.I.P.:	U.K. £80.00 U.S. $325.00
U.K.:	£ 80.00
U.S.:	$160.00
Can.:	$210.00

CT-658
INCANTATION

Designer:	Colin Terris
Type:	Weight – Domed
Issued:	1989 in a limited edition of 500
Status:	Fully subscribed
Series:	Limited – Modern Design
O.I.P.:	U.K. £69.00 U.S. $275.00
U.K.:	£ 70.00
U.S.:	$140.00
Can.:	$180.00

CT-659
INTRIGUE

Designer:	Colin Terris
Type:	Weight – Spherical
Issued:	1989 in a limited edition of 750
Status:	Closed at No. 529
Series:	Limited – Modern Design
O.I.P.:	U.K. £55.00 U.S. $225.00
U.K.:	£ 55.00
U.S.:	$110.00
Can.:	$145.00

CT-660
MARDI-GRAS

Designer: Margot Thomson
Type: Weight – Teardrop
Issued: 1989 in a limited
edition of 650
Status: Fully subscribed
Series: Limited – Modern
Design
O.I.P.: U.K. £65.00
U.S. $250.00

U.K.: £ 65.00
U.S.: $130.00
Can.: $170.00

CT-661
MAZOURKA

Designer: Colin Terris
Type: Weight – Spherical
Issued: 1989 in a limited
edition of 250
Status: Closed at No. 231
Series: Limited – Modern
Design
O.I.P.: U.K. £99.00
U.S. $395.00

U.K.: £100.00
U.S.: $200.00
Can.: $260.00

CT-662
MERCATOR

Designer: Alastair MacIntosh
Type: Weight – Spherical
Issued: 1989 in a limited
edition of 650
Status: Closed at No. 610
Series: Limited – Modern
Design
O.I.P.: U.K. £69.00
U.S. $275.00

U.K.: £ 70.00
U.S.: $140.00
Can.: $185.00

CT-663
MIDNIGHT

Designer: Colin Terris
Type: Weight – Spherical
Issued: 1989 in a limited
edition of 750
Status: Closed at No. 440
Series: Limited – Modern
Design
O.I.P.: U.K. £60.00
U.S. $250.00

U.K.: £ 60.00
U.S.: $120.00
Can.: $155.00

CT-664
MOONFLOWER CELEBRATION

Designer: Colin Terris
Type: Weight – Spherical
Colour: Blue and silver
Issued: 1989 in a limited edition of 500
Series: Limited – Modern Design
Status: Closed at No. 421
O.I.P.: U.K. £120.00
U.S. $475.00

U.K.: £100.00
U.S.: $200.00
Can.: $260.00

Note: This paperweight was issued to celebrate the 20th
anniversary of the Moonflower design (1969-1989).

CT-665
MOONLIGHT DANCER

Designer: Colin Terris
Type: Weight – Spherical
Issued: 1989 in a limited
edition of 750
Status: Fully subscribed
Series: Limited – Modern
Design
O.I.P.: U.K. £45.00
U.S. $175.00

U.K.: £ 55.00
U.S.: $110.00
Can.: $145.00

CT-666
MYSTERIA

Designer: Colin Terris
Type: Weight – Spherical
Issued: 1989 in a limited
edition of 750
Status: Closed at No. 496
Series: Limited – Modern
Design
O.I.P.: U.K. £55.00
U.S. $225.00

U.K.: £ 55.00
U.S.: $110.00
Can.: $145.00

CT-667
OASIS

Designer: Stuart Cumming
Type: Weight – Spherical, magnum size
Issued: 1989 in a limited edition of 350
Status: Fully subscribed
Series: Limited – Modern Design
O.I.P.: U.K. £85.00
U.S. $350.00

U.K.: £ 85.00
U.S.: $170.00
Can.: $220.00

CT-668
PETRONELLA

Designer: Alastair MacIntosh
Type: Weight – Spherical
Issued: 1989 in a limited edition of 250
Status: Closed at No. 244
Series: Limited – Modern Design
O.I.P.: U.K. £120.00
U.S. $475.00

U.K.: £125.00
U.S.: $250.00
Can.: $325.00

CT-669
PLANETARIUM

Designer: Colin Terris
Type: Weight – Spherical
Issued: 1989 in a limited edition of 750
Status: Fully subscribed
Series: Limited – Modern Design
O.I.P.: U.K. £50.00
U.S. $210.00

U.K.: £ 50.00
U.S: $100.00
Can.: $130.00

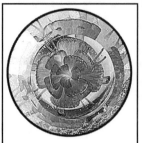

CT-670
PRINCESS

Designer: Colin Terris
Type: Weight – Spherical
Issued: 1989 in a limited edition of 250
Status: Fully subscribed
Series: Limited – Modern Design
O.I.P.: U.K. £150.00
U.S. $625.00

U.K.: £125.00
U.S.: $250.00
Can.: $325.00

CT-671
RED ARROWS
Style One

Designer: Alastair MacIntosh
Type: Weight – Teardrop
Issued: 1989 in a limited edition of 750
Status: Fully subscribed
Series: Limited – Modern Design
O.I.P.: U.K. £45.00
U.S. $175.00

U.K.: £ 45.00
U.S.: $ 90.00
Can.: $120.00

CT-672
SCHEHERAZADE

Designer: Margot Thomson
Type: Weight – Teardrop
Issued: 1989 in a limited edition of 250
Status: Fully subscribed
Series: Limited – Modern Design
O.I.P.: U.K. £120.00
U.S. $475.00

U.K.: £125.00
U.S.: $250.00
Can.: $325.00

CT-673
SPACE JOURNEY

Designer: Alastair MacIntosh
Type: Weight – Spherical
Issued: 1989 in a limited edition of 650
Status: Fully subscribed
Series: Limited – Modern Design
O.I.P.: U.K. £65.00
U.S. $275.00

U.K.: £ 65.00
U.S.: $130.00
Can.: $170.00

CT-674
SUMMIT

Designer: Colin Terris
Type: Weight – Spherical
Issued: 1989 in a limited edition of 750
Status: Closed at No. 737
Series: Limited – Modern Design
O.I.P.: U.K. £50.00
U.S. $210.00

U.K.: £ 50.00
U.S.: $100.00
Can.: $130.00

CT-675
TAWNY OWL

Designer: Alastair MacIntosh
Type: Weight – Spherical
Issued: 1989 in a limited
edition of 500
Status: Fully subscribed
O.I.P.: U.K. £80.00
U.S. $325.00

U.K.: £ 80.00
U.S.: $160.00
Can.: $210.00

CT-676
TRINITY

Designer: Colin Terris
Type: Weight – Spherical
Issued: 1989 in a limited
edition of 750
Status: Closed at No. 425
Series: Limited – Modern
Design
O.I.P.: U.K. £60.00
U.S. $250.00

U.K.: £ 60.00
U.S.: $120.00
Can.: $155.00

CT-677
UNISON

Designer: Colin Terris
Type: Weight – Spherical
Issued: 1989 in a limited
edition of 750
Status: Closed at No. 445
Series: Limited – Modern
Design
O.I.P.: U.K. £50.00
U.S. $210.00

U.K.: £ 50.00
U.S.: $100.00
Can.: $130.00

CT-678
VOLCANO

Designer: Alastair MacIntosh
Type: Weight – Domed
Issued: 1989 in a limited
edition of 650
Status: Closed at No. 627
Series: Limited – Modern
Design
O.I.P.: U.K. £65.00
U.S. $250.00

U.K.: £ 65.00
U.S.: $130.00
Can.: $170.00

CT-679
DOLPHIN
Style Three

Designer: William Manson
Type: Weight – Spherical
Issued: 1989 in a limited
edition of 250
Status: Closed at No. 190
Series: Traditional Collection
O.I.P.: U.K. £160.00
U.S. $650.00

U.K.: £175.00
U.S.: $350.00
Can.: $450.00

CT-680
FESTIVE BOUQUET

Designer: William Manson
Type: Weight – Spherical
Issued: 1989 in a limited
edition of 250
Status: Closed at No. 90
Series: Traditional Collection
O.I.P.: U.K. £175.00
U.S. $695.00

U.K.: £200.00
U.S.: $400.00
Can.: $525.00

CT-681
NEWT

Designer: William Manson
Type: Weight – Spherical
Issued: 1989 in a limited
edition of 150
Status: Closed at No. 115
Series: Traditional Collection
O.I.P.: U.K. £200.00
U.S. $775.00

U.K.: £200.00
U.S.: $400.00
Can.: $525.00

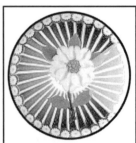

CT-682
ROYAL FLOURISH

Designer: William Manson
Type: Weight – Spherical
Issued: 1989 in a limited
edition of 250
Status: Closed at No. 99
Series: Traditional Collection
O.I.P.: U.K. £130.00
U.S. $750.00

U.K.: £300.00
U.S.: $600.00
Can.: $775.00

CT-683
TIGER FISH
Designer: William Manson
Type: Weight – Spherical
Issued: 1989 in a limited edition of 250
Status: Closed at No. 52
Series: Traditional Collection
O.I.P.: U.K. £185.00
U.S. $750.00

U.K.: £200.00
U.S.: $400.00
Can.: $525.00

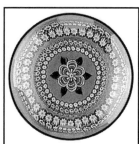

CT-684
FLORIANA
Designer: Harry McKay
Type: Weight – Spherical
Issued: 1989 in a limited edition of 250
Status: Closed at No. 130
Series: Whitefriars Collection
O.I.P.: U.K. £100.00
U.S. $395.00

U.K.; £100.00
U.S.: $200.00
Can.: $260.00

CT-685
PEACOCK
Style One
Designer: Fiona Steele
Type: Weight – Spherical
Issued: 1989 in a limited edition of 250
Status: Closed at No. 205
Series: Whitefriars Collection
O.I.P.: U.K. £125.00
U.S. $495.00

U.K.: £125.00
U.S.: $250.00
Can.: $325.00

CT-686
ROYAL BLUE
Designer: Allan Scott
Type: Weight – Spherical
Issued: 1989 in a limited edition of 250
Status: Closed at No. 68
Series: Whitefriars Collection
O.I.P.: U.K. £100.00
U.S. $395.00

U.K.: £125.00
U.S.: $250.00
Can.: $325.00

CT-687
SCARLET BOUQUET
Designer: Allan Scott
Type: Weight – Spherical
Issued: 1989 in a limited edition of 250
Status: Closed at No. 153
Series: Whitefriars Collection
O.I.P.: U.K. £110.00
U.S. $425.00

U.K.: £110.00
U.S.: $225.00
Can.: $300.00

CT-688
TRIPLE FANCY
Designer: Allan Scott
Type: Weight – Spherical
Issued: 1989 in a limited edition of 250
Status: Closed at No. 81
Series: Whitefriars Collection
O.I.P.: U.K. £100.00
U.S. $375.00

U.K.: £200.00
U.S.: $400.00
Can.: $525.00

CT-689
CINDERELLA
Designer: Alastair MacIntosh
Type: Weight – Domed
Issued: 1989
Status: Closed
Series: Unlimited – Modern Design
O.I.P.: U.K. £22.95
U.S. $87.50

U.K.: £25.00
U.S.: $50.00
Can.: $65.00

CT-690
DAYDREAMS
Designer: Margot Thomson
Type: Weight - Spherical
Issued: 1989
Status: Closed
Series: Unlimited – Modern Design
O.I.P.: U.K. £22.95
U.S. $87.50

U.K.: £25.00
U.S.: $50.00
Can.: $65.00

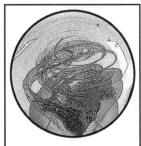

CT-691
DOUBLE MAGNUM AZURE

Designer: Margot Thomson
Type: Weight – Spherical
Size: Double magnum
Issued: 1989
Status: Closed
Series: Unlimited – Modern Design
O.I.P.: U.K. £150.00
U.S. $495.00

U.K.: £150.00
U.S.: $300.00
Can.: $400.00

CT-692
RIBBONS

Designer: Alastair MacIntosh
Type: Weight – Spherical
Colour: See below
Issued: 1989
Status: Closed
Series: Unlimited – Modern Design
O.I.P.: U.K. £19.95
U.S. $72.50

	Blue	Ruby	Topaz
U.K.:	£25.00	25.00	25.00
U.S.:	$50.00	50.00	50.00
Can.:	$65.00	65.00	65.00

CT-693
VIBRANCE

Designer: Alastair MacIntosh
Type: Weight – Spherical
Issued: 1989
Status: Closed
Series: Unlimited – Modern Design
O.I.P. U.K. £26.95
U.S. $99.50

U.K.: £30.00
U.S.: $60.00
Can.: $80.00

CT-694
WINDFALL

Designer: Colin Terris
Type: Weight – Spherical
Colour: See below
Issued: 1989
Status: 1. Emerald (Closed)
2. Ruby (Active)
Series: Unlimited – Modern Design
O.I.P.: U.K. £27.95
U.S. $99.50

	Emerald	Ruby
U.K.:	£ 45.	39.95
U.S.:	$ 90.	110.00
Can.:	$120.	–

CT-695
MINIATURE CORNFLOWER

Designer: Allan Scott
Type: Weight – Spherical
Issued: 1989
Status: Closed
Series: Millefiori Miniatures
O.I.P.: U.K. £27.95
U.S. $79.50

U.K.: £30.00
U.S.: $60.00
Can.: $80.00

CT-696
MINIATURE POSY
First Version

Designer: Allan Scott
Type: Weight – Spherical
Issued: 1989
Status: Closed
Series: Millefiori Miniatures
O.I.P.: U.K. £27.95
U.S. $79.50

U.K.: £30.00
U.S.: $60.00
Can.: $80.00

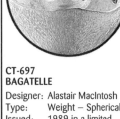

CT-697
BAGATELLE

Designer: Alastair MacIntosh
Type: Weight – Spherical
Issued: 1989 in a limited edition of 750
Status: Closed at No. 481
Series: Limited – Modern Design
O.I.P.: U.K. £45.00
U.S. $150.00

U.K.: £ 45.00
U.S.: $ 90.00
Can.: $120.00

CT-698
BEWITCHED

Designer: Alastair MacIntosh
Type: Weight – Spherical
Issued: 1989 in a limited edition of 750
Status: Fully subscribed
O.I.P.: U.K. £55.00
U.S. $175.00

U.K.: £ 55.00
U.S.: $110.00
Can.: $145.00

CT-699
ELIXIR

Designer: Margot Thomson
Type: Weight – Teardrop
Issued: 1989 in a limited edition of 500
Status: Fully subscribed
Series: Limited – Modern Design
O.I.P.: U.K. £69.00
U.S. $225.00

U.K.: £ 75.00
U.S.: $150.00
Can.: $200.00

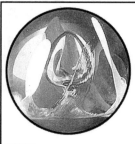

CT-700
FANFARE

Designer: Alastair MacIntosh
Type: Weight – Spherical
Issued: 1989 in a limited edition of 750
Status: Closed at No. 693
O.I.P.: U.K. £43.00
U.S. $135.00

U.K.: £ 45.00
U.S.: $ 90.00
Can.: $120.00

CT-701
GOLDEN HAVEN

Designer: Colin Terris
Type: Weight – Spherical, facets
Issued: 1989 in a limited edition of 500
Status: Closed at No. 414
Series: Limited – Modern Design
O.I.P.: U.K. £90.00
U.S. $285.00

U.K.: £ 90.00
U.S.: $180.00
Can.: $240.00

CT-702
LULLABY

Designer: Colin Terris
Type: Weight – Spherical, facets
Issued: 1989 in a limited edition of 250
Status: Fully subscribed
O.I.P.: U.K. £150.00
U.S. $475.00

U.K.: £175.00
U.S.: $350.00
Can.: $450.00

CT-703
PHOENIX

Designer: Margot Thomson
Type: Weight – Domed
Issued: 1989 in a limited edition of 1,000
Status: Fully subscribed
Series: Collectors' Society
O.I.P.: U.K. £60.00
U.S. $175.00

U.K.: £ 85.00
U.S.: $170.00
Can.: $225.00

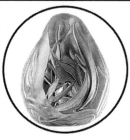

CT-704
SECRET GARDEN

Designer: Colin Terris
Type: Weight – Domed
Issued: 1989 in a limited edition of 200
Status: Fully subscribed
O.I.P.: U.K. £130.00
U.S. $425.00

U.K.: £175.00
U.S.: $350.00
Can.: $450.00

CT-705
SPELLBOUND

Designer: Colin Terris
Type: Weight – Spherical
Issued: 1989 in a limited edition of 750
Status: Fully subscribed
Series: Limited – Modern Design
O.I.P.: U.K. £55.00
U.S. $175.00

U.K.: £ 55.00
U.S.: $110.00
Can.: $145.00

CT-706
TOPSY-TURVY

Designer: Margot Thomson
Type: Weight – Spherical
Issued: 1989 in a limited
edition of 750
Status: Closed at No. 717
O.I.P.: U.K. £48.00
U.S. $150.00

U.K.: £ 50.00
U.S.: $100.00
Can.: $130.00

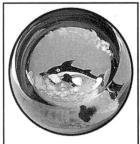

CT-707
OCEAN DUET

Designer: William Manson
Type: Weight – Spherical
Issued: 1989 in a limited
edition of 250
Status: Closed at No. 124
Series: Traditional Collection
O.I.P.: U.K. £185.00
U.S. $595.00

U.K.: £200.00
U.S.: $400.00
Can.: $525.00

CT-708
PENGUINS

Designer: William Manson
Type: Weight – Spherical
Issued: 1989 in a limited
edition of 250
Status: Closed at No. 140
Series: Traditional Collection
O.I.P.: U.K. £185.00
U.S. $595.00

U.K.: £250.00
U.S.: $500.00
Can.: $650.00

CT-709
ARIES
Style Two

Designer: Alastair MacIntosh
Type: Weight – Spherical
Colour: 1. Green
2. Purple
3. Rose
Issued: 1989
Status: Closed
Series: Limited – Modern
Design
O.I.P.: U.K. £25.95
U.S. $90.00

U.K.: £30.00
U.S.: $60.00
Can.: $80.00

CT-710
HIGH SEAS

Designer: Alastair MacIntosh
Type: Weight – Spherical
Issued: 1989
Status: Closed
Series: Unlimited – Modern
Design
O.I.P.: U.K. £22.95
U.S. $79.50

U.K.: £25.00
U.S.: $50.00
Can.: $65.00

CT-711
MOMENTUM

Designer: Margot Thomson
Type: Weight – Spherical
Issued: 1989
Status: Closed
Series: Unlimited – Modern
Design
O.I.P.: U.K. £22.95
U.S. $79.50

U.K.: £25.00
U.S.: $50.00
Can.: $65.00

CT-712
SEA DANCE SABLE

Designer: Colin Terris
Type: Weight – Spherical
Issued: 1989
Status: Closed
O.I.P.: U.K. £29.95
U.S. $99.50

U.K.: £30.00
U.S.: $60.00
Can.: $80.00

CT-713
LUCKENBOOTH

Designer: Colin Terris
Type: Weight – Spherical
Issued: 1989
Status: Active
Series: Romance
O.I.P.: U.K. £35.00
U.S. $135.00

U.K.: £ 49.00
U.S.: $150.00
Can.: –

Note: The Luckenbooth design
is a traditional Scottish
betrothal symbol.

CT-714
CHRISTMAS LANTERN

Designer: Allan Scott
Type: Weight – Spherical
Issued: 1989
Status: Closed
Series: Millefiori Miniatures
O.I.P.:   U.K. £27.95
             U.S. $79.50

U.K.;   £30.00
U.S.: $60.00
Can.: $80.00

ISSUES OF 1990

CT-715
ABSEIL

Designer: Alastair MacIntosh
Type: Weight – Domed
Issued: 1990 in a limited
edition of 1,438
Status: Closed
Series: Collectors' Society
O.I.P.: U.K. £65.00
U.S. $195.00

U.K.: £ 65.00
U.S.: $130.00
Can.: $170.00

CT-716
ALADDIN

Designer: Colin Terris
Type: Weight – Spherical
Issued: 1990 in a limited
edition of 250
Status: Closed at No. 181
Series: Limited – Modern
Design
O.I.P.: U.K. £140.00
U.S. $495.00

U.K.: £150.00
U.S.: $300.00
Can.: $400.00

CT-717
ALCHEMY

Designer: Colin Terris
Type: Weight – Teardrop
Issued: 1990 in a limited
edition of 650
Status: Closed at No. 457
Series: Limited – Modern
Design
O.I.P.: U.K. £75.00
U.S. $295.00

U.K.: £ 75.00
U.S.: $150.00
Can.: $200.00

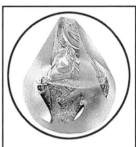

CT-718
AQUARIUS
Style One

Designer: Margot Thomson
Type: Weight – Teardrop
Issued: 1990 in a limited
edition of 500
Status: Closed at No. 455
Series: Limited – Modern
Design
O.I.P.: U.K. £80.00
U.S. $325.00

U.K.: £ 80.00
U.S.: $160.00
Can.: $210.00

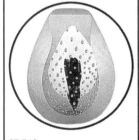

CT-719
BLACK NARCISSUS

Designer: Colin Terris
Type: Weight – Domed
Issued: 1990 in a limited
edition of 500
Status: Fully subscribed
Series: Limited – Modern
Design
O.I.P.: U.K. £85.00
U.S. $325.00

U.K.: £ 85.00
U.S.: $170.00
Can.: $225.00

CT-720
BYZANTIUM

Designer: Margot Thomson
Type: Weight – Spherical
Issued: 1990 in a limited
edition of 750
Status: Closed at No. 651
Series: Limited – Modern
Design
O.I.P.: U.K. £55.00
U.S. $210.00

U.K.: £ 75.00
U.S.: $150.00
Can.: $200.00

CT-721
CASTAWAY

Designer: Margot Thomson
Type: Weight – Spherical
Issued: 1990 in a limited
edition of 750
Status: Closed at No. 716
Series: Limited – Modern
Design
O.I.P.: U.K. £65.00
U.S. $250.00

U.K.: £ 65.00
U.S.: $130.00
Can.: $170.00

CT-722
CAVALCADE

Designer: Alastair MacIntosh
Type: Weight – Spherical
Issued: 1990 in a limited
edition of 250
Status: Closed at No. 150
Series: Limited – Modern
Design
O.I.P.: U.K. £125.00
U.S. $450.00

U.K.: £125.00
U.S.: $250.00
Can.: $325.00

CT-723
CHARISMA

Designer:	Alastair MacIntosh
Type:	Weight – Spherical
Issued:	1990 in a limited edition of 750
Status:	Fully subscribed
Series:	Limited – Modern Design
O.I.P.:	U.K. £50.00
	U.S. $175.00
U.K.:	£ 50.00
U.S.:	$100.00
Can.:	$130.00

CT-724
CLARION CALL

Designer:	Margot Thomson
Type:	Weight – Teardrop
Issued:	1990 in a limited edition of 650
Status:	Closed at No. 401
Series:	Limited – Modern Design
O.I.P.:	U.K. £59.00
	U.S. $210.00
U.K.:	£ 60.00
U.S.:	$120.00
Can.:	$155.00

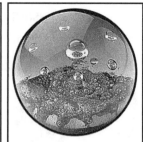

CT-725
CRESCENDO

Designer:	Colin Terris
Type:	Weight – Spherical, magnum size
Issued:	1990 in a limited edition of 350
Status:	Closed at No. 287
Series:	Limited – Modern Design
O.I.P.:	U.K. £110.00
	U.S. $395.00
U.K.:	£110.00
U.S.:	$220.00
Can.:	$300.00

CT-726
DESERT ORCHID

Designer:	Colin Terris
Type:	Weight – Spherical
Issued:	1990 in a limited edition of 750
Status:	Fully subscribed
Series:	Limited – Modern Design
O.I.P.:	U.K. £65.00
	U.S. $250.00
U.K.:	£ 65.00
U.S.:	$130.00
Can.:	$170.00

CT-727
DYNASTY

Designer:	Alastair MacIntosh
Type:	Weight – Pyramid facets
Issued:	1990 in a limited edition of 500
Status:	Closed at No. 317
O.I.P.:	U.K. £65.00
	U.S. $250.00
U.K.:	£ 65.00
U.S.:	$130.00
Can.:	$170.00

CT-728
ELFIN DANCE

Designer:	Alastair MacIntosh
Type:	Weight – Spherical
Issued:	1990 in a limited edition of 750
Status:	Fully subscribed
Series:	Limited – Modern Design
O.I.P.:	U.K. £60.00
	U.S. $225.00
U.K.:	£ 60.00
U.S.:	$120.00
Can.:	$155.00

CT-729
FAR HORIZONS

Designer:	Alastair MacIntosh
Type:	Weight – Spherical
Issued:	1990 in a limited edition of 150
Status:	Fully subscribed
Series:	Limited – Modern Design
O.I.P.:	U.K. £150.00
	U.S. $495.00
U.K.:	£175.00
U.S.:	$350.00
Can.:	$450.00

CT-730
FREEDOM

Designer:	Alastair MacIntosh
Type:	Weight – Spherical
Issued:	1990 in a limited edition of 650
Status:	Closed at No. 475
Series:	Limited – Modern Design
O.I.P.:	U.K. £65.00
	U.S. $225.00
U.K.:	£ 65.00
U.S.:	$130.00
Can.:	$170.00

CT-731
GUARDIAN

Designer:	Colin Terris and Alastair MacIntosh
Type:	Weight – Domed
Issued:	1990 in a limited edition of 500
Status:	Fully subscribed
Series:	Limited – Modern Design
O.I.P.:	U.K. £85.00 U.S. $310.00
U.K.:	£ 85.00
U.S.:	$170.00
Can.:	$225.00

CT-732
HELIUM

Designer:	Alastair MacIntosh
Type:	Weight – Spherical
Issued:	1990 in a limited edition of 750
Status:	Closed at No. 429
Series:	Limited – Modern Design
O.I.P.:	U.K. £50.00 U.S. $190.00
U.K.:	£ 50.00
U.S.:	$100.00
Can.:	$130.00

CT-733
INTERLUDE

Designer:	Margot Thomson
Type:	Weight – Spherical
Issued:	1990 in a limited edition of 750
Status:	Closed at No. 266
Series:	Limited – Modern Design
O.I.P.:	U.K. £65.00 U.S. $250.00
U.K.:	£ 65.00
U.S.:	$130.00
Can.:	$170.00

CT-734
INTO FOCUS

Designer:	Margot Thomson
Type:	Weight – Spherical
Issued:	1990 in a limited edition of 750
Status:	Closed at No. 719
Series:	Limited – Modern Design
O.I.P.:	U.K. £55.00 U.S. $210.00
U.K.:	£ 55.00
U.S.:	$110.00
Can.:	$145.00

CT-735
LAGOON

Designer:	Margot Thomson
Type:	Weight – Spherical
Issued:	1990 in a limited edition of 150
Status:	Fully subscribed
Series:	Limited – Modern Design
O.I.P.:	U.K. £175.00 U.S. $650.00
U.K.:	£200.00
U.S.:	$400.00
Can.:	$525.00

CT-736
MERLIN

Designer:	Margot Thomson
Type:	Weight – Teardrop
Issued:	1990 in a limited edition of 500
Status:	Fully subscribed
Series:	Limited – Modern Design
O.I.P.:	U.K. £80.00 U.S. $325.00
U.K.:	£ 85.00
U.S.:	$170.00
Can.:	$225.00

CT-737
MESSENGER

Designer:	Colin Terris
Type:	Weight – Spherical
Issued:	1990 in a limited edition of 750
Status:	Closed at No. 391
O.I.P.:	U.K. £43.00 U.S. $150.00
U.K.:	£ 50.00
U.S.:	$100.00
Can.:	$130.00

CT-738
MIDSUMMER

Designer:	Colin Terris and Helen MacDonald
Type:	Weight – Domed
Issued:	1990 in a limited edition of 250
Status:	Closed at No. 155
Series:	Limited – Modern Design
O.I.P.:	U.K. £175.00 U.S. $575.00
U.K.:	£200.00
U.S.:	$400.00
Can.:	$525.00

CT-739
MIRAGE

Designer: Colin Terris
Type: Weight – Teardrop
Issued: 1990 in a limited
edition of 500
Status: Closed at No. 479
Series: Limited – Modern
Design
O.I.P.: U.K. £75.00
U.S. $275.00

U.K.: £ 75.00
U.S.: $150.00
Can.: $200.00

CT-740
NEW WORLD

Designer: Stuart Cumming
Type: Weight – Spherical
Issued: 1990 in a limited
edition of 750
Status: Fully subscribed
Series: Limited – Modern
Design
O.I.P.: U.K. £50.00
U.S. $190.00

U.K.: £ 50.00
U.S.: $100.00
Can.: $130.00

CT-741
NIRVANA

Designer: Alastair MacIntosh
Type: Weight – Domed
Issued: 1990 in a limited
edition of 500
Status: Fully subscribed
Series: Limited – Modern
Design
O.I.P.: U.K. £65.00
U.S. $250.00

U.K.: £ 65.00
U.S.: $130.00
Can.: $170.00

CT-742
PANACHE

Designer: Alastair MacIntosh
Type: Weight – Domed
Issued: 1990 in a limited
edition of 750
Status: Closed at No. 449
Series: Limited – Modern
Design
O.I.P.: U.K. £50.00
U.S. $190.00

U.K.: £ 50.00
U.S.: $100.00
Can.: $130.00

CT-743
PATHFINDER

Designer: Alastair MacIntosh
Type: Weight – Spherical
Issued: 1990 in a limited
edition of 750
Status: Closed at No. 309
Series: Limited – Modern
Design
O.I.P.: U.K. £60.00
U.S. $250.00

U.K.: £ 60.00
U.S.: $120.00
Can.: $160.00

CT-744
POT POURRI

Designer: Margot Thomson
Type: Weight – Spherical
Issued: 1990 in a limited
edition of 750
Status: Closed at No. 726
Series: Limited – Modern
Design
O.I.P.: U.K. £65.00
U.S. $250.00

U.K.: £ 65.00
U.S.: $130.00
Can.: $170.00

CT-745
PRELUDE

Designer: Colin Terris
Type: Weight – Spherical
Issued: 1990 in a limited
edition of 750
Status: Closed at No. 410
Series: Limited – Modern
Design
O.I.P.: U.K. £65.00
U.S. $250.00

U.K.: £ 65.00
U.S.: $130.00
Can.: $170.00

CT-746
QUEST

Designer: Margot Thomson
Type: Weight – Teardrop
Edition: 1990 in a limited
edition of 650
Status: Closed at No. 628
O.I.P.: U.K. £69.00
U.S. $250.00

U.K.: £ 70.00
U.S.: $140.00
Can.: $180.00

CT-747
QUORUM

Designer:	Margot Thomson
Type:	Weight – Teardrop
Issued:	1990 in a limited edition of 750
Status:	Closed at No. 693
Series:	Limited – Modern Design
O.I.P.:	U.K. £45.00
	U.S. $175.00
U.K.:	£ 70.00
U.S.:	$140.00
Can.:	$180.00

CT-748
RADIANCE

Designer:	Alastair MacIntosh
Type:	Weight – Domed
Issued:	1990 in a limited edition of 650
Status:	Closed at No. 526
Series:	Limited – Modern Design
O.I.P.:	U.K. £75.00
	U.S. $295.00
U.K.:	£ 80.00
U.S.:	$160.00
Can.:	$210.00

CT-749
SAND DEVIL

Designer:	Margot Thomson
Type:	Weight – Spherical
Issued:	1990 in a limited edition of 750
Status:	Closed at No. 725
Series:	Limited – Modern Design
O.I.P.:	U.K. £69.00
	U.S. $250.00
U.K.:	£ 75.00
U.S.:	$150.00
Can.:	$200.00

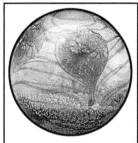

CT-750
SUMMER BREEZE

Designer:	Colin Terris
Type:	Weight – Spherical
Issued:	1990 in a limited edition of 750
Status:	Closed at No. 522
Series:	Limited – Modern Design
O.I.P.:	U.K. £43.00
	U.S. $165.00
U.K.:	£ 70.00
U.S.:	$140.00
Can.:	$180.00

CT-751
TRAILBLAZER

Designer:	Alastair MacIntosh
Type:	Weight – Spherical
Issued:	1990 in a limited edition of 750
Status:	Closed at No. 698
Series:	Limited – Modern Design
O.I.P.:	U.K. £45.00
	U.S. $175.00
U.K.:	£ 70.00
U.S.:	$140.00
Can.:	$180.00

CT-752
VISION

Designer:	Colin Terris
Type:	Weight – Spherical
Issued:	1990 in a limited edition of 750
Status:	Closed at No. 478
Series:	Limited – Modern Design
O.I.P.:	U.K. £65.00
	U.S. $250.00
U.K.:	£ 70.00
U.S.:	$140.00
Can.:	$180.00

CT-753
ZOOM

Designer:	Alastair MacIntosh
Type:	Weight – Spherical
Issued:	1990 in a limited edition of 750
Status:	Closed at No. 740
Series:	Limited – Modern Design
O.I.P.:	U.K. £60.00
	U.S. $225.00
U.K.:	£ 60.00
U.S.:	$120.00
Can.:	$160.00

CT-754A
BEZIQUE

Designer:	Colin Terris
Type:	Weight – Spherical
Issued:	1990 in a limited edition of 150
Status:	Closed at No. 61
Series:	Limited – Modern Design
O.I.P.:	U.K. £350.00/set
	U.S. $1,250.00/set
U.K.:	£300.00
U.S.:	$600.00
Can.:	$775.00

Note: CT-754A and B were issued and sold as a set.

CT-754B
BEZIQUE PERFUME BOTTLE
Designer: Colin Terris
Type: Perfume bottle
Issued: 1990 in a limited
edition of 150
Status: Closed at No. 61
Series: Limited – Modern
Design
O.I.P.: U.K. £350.00/set
U.S. $1,250.00/set

	Perfume	Set
U.K.:	£ 475.	775.
U.S.:	$ 950.	1,550.
Can.:	$1,250.	2,000.

CT-755
SUMMER BREEZE PERFUME BOTTLE
Designer: Colin Terris
Type: Perfume bottle
Issued: 1990 in a limited
edition of 250
Status: Closed at No. 107
Series: Limited – Modern
Design
O.I.P.: U.K. £85.00
U.S. $350.00

U.K.:	£ 85.00
U.S.:	$170.00
Can.:	$225.00

CT-756
BLACKBERRIES and LADYBIRD
Designer: William Manson
Type: Weight – Spherical
Issued: 1990 in a limited
edition of 250
Status: Closed at No. 116
Series: Traditional Collection
O.I.P.: U.K. £175.00
U.S. $595.00

U.K.	£175.00
U.S.:	$350.00
Can.:	$450.00

CT-757
CARNATION
Style One
Designer: William Manson
Type: Weight – Spherical
Issued: 1990 in a limited
edition of 250
Status: Closed at No. 100
Series: Traditional Collection
O.I.P.: U.K. £175.00
U.S. $595.00

U.K.:	£175.00
U.S.:	$350.00
Can.:	$450.00

CT-758
DAISY and LADYBIRD
Designer: William Manson
Type: Weight – Spherical
Issued: 1990 in a limited
edition of 250
Status: Closed at No. 89
Series: Traditional Collection
O.I.P.: U.K. £185.00
U.S. $595.00

U.K.:	£185.00
U.S.:	$375.00
Can.:	$475.00

CT-759
DAWN CHORUS
Designer: William Manson
Type: Weight – Spherical
Issued: 1990 in a limited
edition of 250
Status: Closed at No. 128
Series: Traditional Collection
O.I.P.: U.K. £175.00
U.S. $595.00

U.K.:	£175.00
U.S.:	$350.00
Can.:	$450.00

CT-760
DRAGONFLY GARLAND
Designer: William Manson
Type: Weight – Spherical
Issued: 1990 in a limited
edition of 250
Status: Closed at No. 109
Series: Traditional Collection
O.I.P.: U.K. £185.00
U.S. $595.00

U.K.:	£185.00
U.S.:	$375.00
Can.:	$475.00

CT-761
FLAMINGOES
Designer: William Manson
Type: Weight – Spherical
Issued: 1990 in a limited
edition of 150
Status: Closed at No. 141
Series: Traditional Collection
O.I.P.: U.K. £200.00
U.S. $695.00

U.K.:	£200.00
U.S.:	$400.00
Can.:	$525.00

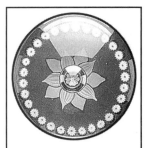

CT-762
FLORAL REFLECTIONS
Designer: William Manson
Type: Weight – Spherical
Issued: 1990 in a limited edition of 500
Status: Closed at No. 213
Series: Traditional Collection
O.I.P.: U.K. £70.00
U.S. $250.00

U.K.: £ 70.00
U.S.: $140.00
Can.: $180.00

CT-763
SEALS
Designer: William Manson
Type: Weight – Spherical
Issued: 1990 in a limited edition of 150
Status: Closed at No. 105
Series: Traditional Collection
O.I.P.: U.K. £220.00
U.S. $775.00

U.K.: £225.00
U.S.: $450.00
Can.: $575.00

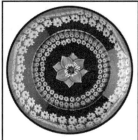

CT-764
ANEMONE
Style Two
Designer: Margot Thomson
Type: Weight – Spherical
Issued: 1990 in a limited edition of 250
Status: Closed at No. 137
Series: Whitefriars Collection
O.I.P.: U.K. £100.00
U.S. $375.00

U.K.: £100.00
U.S.: $200.00
Can.: $260.00

CT-765
AQUILEGIA
Designer: Margot Thomson
Type: Weight – Spherical
Issued: 1990 in a limited edition of 150
Status: Closed at No. 133
Series: Whitefriars Collection
O.I.P.: U.K. £165.00
U.S. $575.00

U.K.: £175.00
U.S.: $350.00
Can.: $450.00

CT-766
BUTTERFLIES
Style Two
Designer: Margot Thomson
Type: Weight – Spherical
Issued: 1990 in a limited edition of 250
Status: Closed at No. 115
Series: Whitefriars Collection
O.I.P.: U.K. £100.00
U.S. $375.00

U.K.: £100.00
U.S.: $200.00
Can.: $260.00

CT-767
DAISY CHAIN
Designer: Margot Thomson
Type: Weight – Spherical
Issued: 1990 in a limited edition of 250
Status: Closed at No. 117
Series: Whitefriars Collection
O.I.P.: U.K. £125.00
U.S. $425.00

U.K.: £125.00
U.S.: $250.00
Can.: $325.00

CT-768
DELPHINIUM
Designer: Margot Thomson
Type: Weight – Spherical
Issued: 1990 in a limited edition of 250
Status: Closed at No. 77
Series: Whitefriars Collection
O.I.P.: U.K. £125.00
U.S. $425.00

U.K.: £125.00
U.S.: $250.00
Can.: $325.00

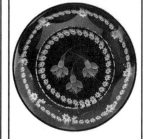

CT-769
FUCHSIAS
Style One
Designer: Margot Thomson
Type: Weight – Spherical
Issued: 1990 in a limited edition of 250
Status: Fully subscribed
Series: Whitefriars Collection
O.I.P.: U.K. £100.00
U.S. $375.00

U.K.: £100.00
U.S.: $200.00
Can.: $260.00

CT-770
ORCHIDS
Style Two

Designer: Allan Scott
Type: Weight – Spherical
Issued: 1990 in a limited
          edition of 250
Status: Closed at No. 224
Series: Whitefriars Collection
O.I.P.:   U.K. £90.00
          U.S. $325.00

U.K.:   £ 90.00
U.S.: $180.00
Can.: $235.00

CT-771
POPPIES
Style Two

Designer: Margot Thomson
Type: Weight – Spherical
Issued: 1990 in a limited
          edition of 250
Status: Closed at No. 93
Series: Whitefriars Collection
O.I.P.:   U.K. £90.00
          U.S. $325.00

U.K.:   £ 90.00
U.S.: $180.00
Can.: $235.00

CT-772
PRIMULA

Designer: Margot Thomson
Type: Weight – Spherical
Issued: 1990 in a limited
          edition of 250
Status: Closed at No. 143
Series: Whitefriars Collection
O.I.P.:   U.K. £100.00
          U.S. $325.00

U.K.:   £100.00
U.S.: $200.00
Can.: $260.00

CT-773
SCOTS THISTLE
Style One

Designer: Allan Scott
Type: Weight – Spherical
Issued: 1990 in a limited
          edition of 250
Status: Closed at No. 136
Series: Whitefriars Collection
O.I.P.:   U.K. £90.00
          U.S. $325.00

U.K.:   £ 90.00
U.S.: $180.00
Can.: $235.00

CT-774
SPRING FLOWERS

Designer: Margot Thomson
Type: Weight – Spherical
Issued: 1990 in a limited
          edition of 250
Status: Closed at No. 127
Series: Whitefriars Collection
O.I.P.:   U.K. £125.00
          U.S. $425.00

U.K.:   £125.00
U.S.: $250.00
Can.: $325.00

CT-775
SWEET PEA

Designer: Margot Thomson
Type: Weight – Spherical
Issued: 1990 in a limited
          edition of 250
Status: Closed at No. 244
Series: Whitefriars Collection
O.I.P.:   U.K. £125.00
          U.S. $425.00

U.K.:   £125.00
U.S.: $250.00
Can.: $325.00

CT-776
ROYAL BIRTHDAY BOUQUET

Designer: Allan Scott
Type: Weight – Spherical
Issued: 1990 in a limited edition of 90
Status: Fully subscribed
O.I.P.:   £250.00

U.K.:   £250.00
U.S.: $500.00
Can.: $650.00

Note: CT-776, 777 and 778 were issued to commemorate HM The Queen Mother's 90th birthday. This paperweight was not issued in the U.S.

CT-777
ROYAL BIRTHDAY PERFUME
BOTTLE

Designer: Colin Terris
Type: Perfume bottle
Issued: 1990 in a limited
edition of 90
Status: Fully subscribed
O.I.P.: £250.00

U.K.: £250.00
U.S.: $500.00
Can.: $650.00

Note: This perfume bottle was
not issued in the U.S.

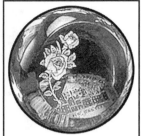

CT-778
ROYAL BIRTHDAY GLAMIS
ROSE

Designer: Colin Terris
Type: Weight – Spherical,
engraved
Issued: 1990 in a limited
edition of 500
Status: Fully subscribed
O.I.P.: £65.00

U.K.: £ 65.00
U.S.: $130.00
Can.: $170.00

CT-779
COSMOS
Style One

Designer: Margot Thomson
Type: Weight – Spherical
Issued: 1990
Status: Closed
Series: Unlimited – Modern
Design
O.I.P.: U.K. £26.95
U.S. $99.50

U.K.: £30.00
U.S.: $60.00
Can.: $80.00

CT-780
DOUBLE MAGNUM JADE

Designer: Margot Thomson
Type: Weight – Spherical
Size: Double magnum
Issued: 1990
Status: Closed
Series: Unlimited – Modern
Design
O.I.P.: U.K. £150.00
U.S. $495.00

U.K.: £150.00
U.S.: $300.00
Can.: $400.00

CT-781
FREEFORM

Designer: Alastair MacIntosh
Type: Weight – Spherical
Colour: 1. Gold
2. Green
Issued: 1990
Status: Closed
Series: Unlimited – Modern
Design
O.I.P.: U.K. £24.95
U.S. $87.50

	Gold	Green
U.K.:	£25.00	25.00
U.S.:	$50.00	50.00
Can.:	$65.00	65.00

CT-782
LIMELIGHT

Designer: Margot Thomson
Type: Weight – Spherical
Issued: 1990
Status: Closed
Series: Unlimited – Modern
Design
O.I.P.: U.K. £21.95
U.S. $87.50

U.K.: £25.00
U.S.: $50.00
Can.: $65.00

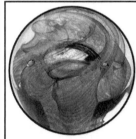

CT-783
MISCHIEF

Designer: Margot Thomson
Type: Weight – Spherical
Issued: 1990
Status: Closed
Series: Unlimited – Modern
Design
O.I.P.: U.K. £24.95
U.S. $87.50

U.K.: £25.00
U.S.: $50.00
Can.: $65.00

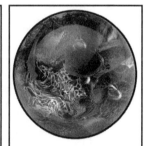

CT-784
BRIMSTONE

Designer: Alastair MacIntosh
Type: Weight – Spherical
Colour: 1. Blue
2. Red
Issued: 1990
Status: Closed
Series: Medium and
Miniature Size
O.I.P.: U.K. £16.95
U.S. $62.50

U.K.: £20.00
U.S.: $40.00
Can.: $50.00

CT-785
FANDANGO
Style One

Designer:	Margot Thomson
Type:	Weight – Spherical
Issued:	1990
Status:	Closed
Series:	Unlimited – Modern Design
O.I.P.:	U.K. £19.95
	U.S. $62.50
U.K.:	£20.00
U.S.:	$40.00
Can.:	$50.00

CT-786
STREAMERS

Designer:	Margot Thomson
Type:	Weight – Spherical
Colour:	1. Aqua
	2. Rose
	3. Sable
Issued:	1990
Status:	Closed
Series:	Medium and Miniature Size
O.I.P.:	U.K. £16.95
	U.S. $62.50
U.K.:	£20.00
U.S.:	$40.00
Can.:	$50.00

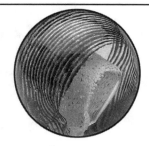

CT-787
TRAPEZE

Designer:	Margot Thomson
Type:	Weight – Spherical
Colour:	See below
Issued:	1990
Status:	Closed
Series:	Unlimited – Modern Design
O.I.P.:	U.K. £15.95
	U.S. $62.50

	Coral	Emerald	Jet	Sapphire
U.K.:	£20.00	20.00	20.00	20.00
U.S.:	$40.00	40.00	40.00	40.00
Can.:	$50.00	50.00	50.00	50.00

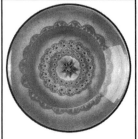

CT-788
MINIATURE CORNFLOWER

Designer:	Allan Scott
Type:	Weight – Spherical
Issued:	1990
Status:	Closed
Series:	Millefiori Miniatures
O.I.P.:	U.K. £24.95
	U.S. $89.50
U.K.:	£25.00
U.S.:	$50.00
Can.:	$65.00

Note: This paperweight has a top facet only.

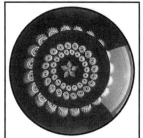

CT-789
MINIATURE FORGET-ME-NOT
Style Two

Designer:	Allan Scott
Type:	Weight – Spherical
Issued:	1990
Status:	Closed
Series:	Millefiori Miniatures
O.I.P.:	U.K. £24.95
	U.S. $89.50
U.K.:	£25.00
U.S.:	$50.00
Can.:	$65.00

Note: This paperweight has a top facet only.

CT-790
MINIATURE HEART
Style One, Third Version

Designer:	Allan Scott
Type:	Weight – Spherical
Issued:	1990
Status:	Closed
Series:	Romance
O.I.P.:	U.K. £24.95
	U.S. $89.50
U.K.:	£25.00
U.S.:	$50.00
Can.:	$65.00

Note: This paperweight has a top facet only.

CT-791
MINIATURE LADYBIRD
Second Version

Designer:	Allan Scott
Type:	Weight – Spherical
Issued:	1990
Status:	Closed
Series:	Millefiori Miniatures
O.I.P.:	U.K. £24.95
	U.S. $89.50
U.K.:	£25.00
U.S.:	$50.00
Can.:	$65.00

Note: This paperweight has a top facet only.

Photograph not
available
at press time

CT-792
MINIATURE POSY
Second Version

Designer:	Allan Scott
Type:	Weight – Spherical
Issued:	1990
Status:	Closed
Series:	Millefiori Miniatures
O.I.P.:	U.K. £24.95
	U.S. $89.50
U.K.:	£25.00
U.S.:	$50.00
Can.:	$65.00

Note: This paperweight has a
top facet only.

CT-793
MINIATURE ROSE
Style One, Second Version

Designer:	Allan Scott
Type:	Weight – Spherical
Issued:	1990
Status:	Closed
Series:	Millefiori Miniatures
O.I.P.:	U.K. £24.95
	U.S. $89.50
U.K.:	£25.00
U.S.:	$50.00
Can.:	$65.00

Note: This paperweight has a
top facet only.

CT-794
MINIATURE THISTLE
Second Version

Designer:	Allan Scott
Type:	Weight – Spherical
Issued:	1990
Status:	Closed
Series:	Millefiori Miniatures
O.I.P.:	U.K. £24.95
	U.S. $89.50
U.K.:	£25.00
U.S.:	$50.00
Can.:	$65.00

Note: This paperweight has a
top facet only.

BATTLE OF BRITAIN
Style One

Designer:	Unknown
Type:	Unknown
Issued:	1990 in a limited edition of 750
Status:	Closed
Series:	Unknown
O.I.P.:	£39.95
U.K.:	£ 40.00
U.S.:	$ 80.00
Can.:	$100.00

ISSUES OF 1991

CT-795
ARABESQUE

Designer: Margot Thomson
Type: Weight – Teardrop
Issued: 1991 in a limited edition of 750
Status: Closed at No. 504
Series: Limited – Modern Design
O.I.P.: U.K. £65.00
U.S. $230.00

U.K.: £ 65.00
U.S.: $130.00
Can.: $170.00

CT-796
ARCTIC ORCHID

Designer: Colin Terris
Type: Weight – Spherical
Issued: 1991 in a limited edition of 750
Status: Closed at No. 736
Series: Limited – Modern Design
O.I.P.: U.K. £75.00
U.S. $275.00

U.K.: £ 75.00
U.S.: $150.00
Can.: $200.00

CT-797
ARGON

Designer: Colin Terris
Type: Weight – Spherical
Issued: 1991 in a limited edition of 750
Status: Closed at No. 472
Series: Limited – Modern Design
O.I.P.: U.K. £70.00
U.S. $250.00

U.K.: £ 70.00
U.S.: $140.00
Can.: $180.00

CT-798
ASPIRATION

Designer: Colin Terris
Type: Weight – Spherical
Issued: 1991 in a limited edition of 750
Status: Fully subscribed
Series: Limited – Modern Design
O.I.P.: U.K. £55.00
U.S. $195.00

U.K.: £ 55.00
U.S.: $110.00
Can.: $145.00

CT-799
BECALMED

Designer: Margot Thomson
Type: Weight – Spherical
Issued: 1991 in a limited edition of 750
Status: Closed at No. 263
Series: Limited – Modern Design
O.I.P.: U.K. £55.00
U.S. $200.00

U.K.: £ 55.00
U.S.: $110.00
Can.: $145.00

CT-800
CHRYSALIS

Designer: Margot Thomson
Type: Weight – Spherical
Issued: 1991 in a limited edition of 750
Status: Closed at No. 718
Series: Limited – Modern Design
O.I.P.: U.K. £60.00
U.S. $225.00

U.K.: £ 60.00
U.S.: $120.00
Can.: $160.00

CT-801
CLAIRVOYANT

Designer: Alastair MacIntosh
Type: Weight – Spherical
Issued: 1991 in a limited edition of 750
Status: Closed at No. 371
Series: Limited – Modern Design
O.I.P.: U.K. £60.00
U.S. $225.00

U.K.: £ 60.00
U.S.: $120.00
Can.: $160.00

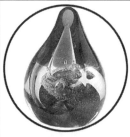

CT-802
CORAL VOYAGER

Designer: Margot Thomson
Type: Weight – Teardrop
Issued: 1991 in a limited edition of 500
Status: Closed at No. 268
Series: Limited – Modern Design
O.I.P.: U.K. £95.00
U.S. $350.00

U.K.: £100.00
U.S.: $200.00
Can.: $260.00

CT-803
DISCOVERY

Designer: Colin Terris
Type: Weight – Spherical
Issued: 1991 in a limited
edition of 750
Status: Fully subscribed
Series: Limited – Modern
Design
O.I.P.: U.K. £69.00
U.S. $250.00

U.K.: £ 70.00
U.S.: $140.00
Can.: $180.00

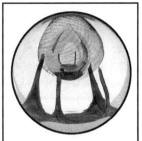

CT-804
EXPLORER

Designer: Colin Terris
Type: Weight – Spherical
Issued: 1991 in a limited
edition of 750
Status: Closed at No. 630
Series: Limited – Modern
Design
O.I.P.: U.K. £70.00
U.S. $250.00

U.K.: £ 70.00
U.S.: $140.00
Can.: $180.00

CT-805
FLORAL ILLUSION

Designer: Colin Terris
Type: Weight – Spherical
Issued: 1991 in a limited
edition of 1,773
Status: Closed
Series: Collectors' Society
O.I.P.: U.K. £75.00
U.S. $215.00

U.K.: £ 75.00
U.S.: $150.00
Can.: $200.00

CT-806
FREE FALL

Designer: Colin Terris
Type: Weight – Spherical
Issued: 1991 in a limited
edition of 750
Status: Fully subscribed
Series: Limited – Modern
Design
O.I.P.: U.K. £45.00
U.S. $150.00

U.K.: £ 45.00
U.S.: $ 90.00
Can.: $120.00

CT-807
HIGH FLYER

Designer: Margot Thomson
Type: Weight – Domed
Issued: 1991 in a limited
edition of 650
Status: Closed at No. 641
Series: Limited – Modern
Design
O.I.P.: U.K. £85.00
U.S. $310.00

U.K.: £ 85.00
U.S.: $170.00
Can.: $225.00

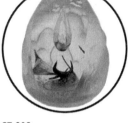

CT-808
INDIAN SUMMER

Designer: Helen MacDonald/
Alastair MacIntosh
Type: Weight – Domed
Issued: 1991 in a limited
edition of 250
Status: Closed at No. 194
Series: Limited – Modern
Design
O.I.P.: U.K. £200.00
U.S. $735.00

U.K.: £200.00
U.S.: $400.00
Can.: $525.00

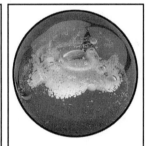

CT-809
MILKY WAY

Designer: Colin Terris
Type: Weight – Spherical
Issued: 1991 in a limited
edition of 750
Status: Fully subscribed
Series: Limited – Modern
Design
O.I.P.: U.K. £55.00
U.S. $200.00

U.K.: £ 55.00
U.S.: $110.00
Can.: $145.00

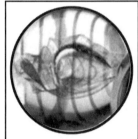

CT-810
MISSION

Designer: Colin Terris
Type: Weight – Spherical
Issued: 1991 in a limited
edition of 750
Status: Closed at No. 233
Series: Limited – Modern
Design
O.I.P.: U.K. £72.00
U.S. $265.00

U.K.: £ 75.00
U.S.: $150.00
Can.: $200.00

CT-811
OPTIMA

Designer:	Colin Terris
Type:	Weight – Teardrop
Issued:	1991 in a limited edition of 500
Status:	Fully subscribed
Series:	Limited – Modern Design
O.I.P.:	U.K. £85.00
	U.S. $310.00
U.K.:	£ 85.00
U.S.:	$170.00
Can.:	$225.00

CT-812
PAINTBOX

Designer:	Alastair MacIntosh
Type:	Weight – Spherical
Issued:	1991 in a limited edition of 750
Status:	Closed at No. 714
Series:	Limited – Modern Design
O.I.P.:	U.K. £45.00
	U.S. $150.00
U.K.:	£ 45.00
U.S.:	$ 90.00
Can.:	$120.00

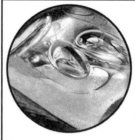

CT-813
PARADE

Designer:	Margot Thomson
Type:	Weight – Spherical
Issued:	1991 in a limited edition of 750
Status:	Fully subscribed
Series:	Limited – Modern Design
O.I.P.:	U.K. £43.00
	U.S. $150.00
U.K.:	£ 45.00
U.S.:	$ 90.00
Can.:	$120.00

CT-814
PURSUIT

Designer:	Margot Thomson
Type:	Weight – Spherical
Issued:	1991 in a limited edition of 750
Status:	Closed at No. 385
Series:	Limited – Modern Design
O.I.P.:	U.K. £55.00
	U.S. $200.00
U.K.:	£ 55.00
U.S.:	$110.00
Can.:	$145.00

CT-815
PYROTECHNICS

Designer:	Alastair MacIntosh
Type:	Weight – Spherical
Issued:	1991 in a limited edition of 750
Status:	Fully subscribed
Series:	Limited – Modern Design
O.I.P.:	U.K. £49.00
	U.S. $175.00
U.K.:	£ 50.00
U.S.:	$100.00
Can.:	$130.00

CT-816
REVELATION

Designer:	Colin Terris
Type:	Weight – Spherical
Issued:	1991 in a limited edition of 250
Status:	Closed at No. 235
O.I.P.:	U.K. £110.00
	U.S. $385.00
U.K.:	£110.00
U.S.:	$220.00
Can.:	$290.00

CT-817
SKYHIGH

Designer:	Margot Thomson
Type:	Weight - Domed
Issued:	1991 in a limited edition of 750
Status:	Fully subscribed
Series:	Limited – Modern Design
O.I.P.:	U.K. £53.00
	U.S. $175.00
U.K.:	£ 55.00
U.S.:	$110.00
Can.:	$145.00

CT-818
SNOWFLAKE ORCHID

Designer:	Colin Terris
Type:	Weight – Spherical, facets
Issued:	1991 in a limited edition of 150
Status:	Fully subscribed
Series:	Limited – Modern Design
O.I.P.:	U.K. £175.00
	U.S. $635.00
U.K.:	£175.00
U.S.:	$350.00
Can.:	$450.00

CT-819
SPLASH

Designer: Margot Thomson
Type: Weight – Teardrop
Issued: 1991 in a limited
edition of 750
Status: Closed at No. 306
O.I.P.: U.K. £85.00
U.S. $310.00

U.K.: £ 85.00
U.S.: $170.00
Can.: $220.00

CT-820
SPRING MELODY
Style One

Designer: Colin Terris
Type: Weight – Spherical
Issued: 1991 in a limited
edition of 150
Status: Fully subscribed
Series: Limited – Modern
Design
O.I.P.: U.K. £175.00
U.S. $635.00

U.K.: £175.00
U.S.: $350.00
Can.: $450.00

CT-821
STARGAZER

Designer: Alastair MacIntosh
Type: Weight – Spherical
Issued: 1991 in a limited
edition of 750
Status: Closed at No. 733
Series: Limited – Modern
Design
O.I.P.: U.K. £49.00
U.S. $175.00

U.K.: £ 50.00
U.S.: $100.00
Can.: $130.00

CT-822
SUN SEEKERS

Designer: Colin Terris
Type: Weight – Spherical,
Size: Magnum
Issued: 1991 in a limited
edition of 350
Status: Closed at No. 323
Series: Limited – Modern
Design
O.I.P.: U.K. £110.00
U.S. $385.00

U.K.: £110.00
U.S.: $220.00
Can.: $290.00

CT-823
SUPER NOVA

Designer: Colin Terris
Type: Weight – Spherical
Issued: 1991 in a limited
edition of 750
Status: Closed at No. 622
Series: Limited – Modern
Design
O.I.P.: U.K. £65.00
U.S. $230.00

U.K.: £ 65.00
U.S.: $130.00
Can.: $170.00

CT-824
SWORD DANCE

Designer: Alastair MacIntosh
Type: Weight – Spherical
Issued: 1991 in a limited
edition of 750
Status: Closed at No. 714
Series: Limited – Modern
Design
O.I.P.: U.K. £65.00
U.S. $230.00

U.K.: £ 65.00
U.S.: $130.00
Can.: $170.00

CT-825
TAILSPIN

Designer: Alastair MacIntosh
Type: Weight – Spherical
Issued: 1991 in a limited
edition of 750
Status: Closed at No. 409
Series: Limited – Modern
Design
O.I.P.: U.K. £65.00
U.S. $230.00

U.K.: £ 65.00
U.S.: $130.00
Can.: $170.00

CT-826
TAPESTRY

Designer: Margot Thomson
Type: Weight – Domed
Issued: 1991 in a limited
edition of 500
Status: Closed at No. 496
Series: Limited – Modern
Design
O.I.P.: U.K. £100.00
U.S. $365.00

U.K.: £100.00
U.S.: $200.00
Can.: $260.00

CT-827
TRAMPOLINE

Designer:	Alastair MacIntosh
Type:	Weight – Domed
Issued:	1991 in a limited edition of 650
Status:	Closed at No. 635
O.I.P.:	U.K. £75.00
	U.S. $275.00
U.K.:	£ 75.00
U.S.:	$150.00
Can.:	$200.00

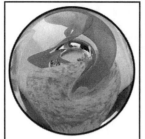

CT-828
TRIUMPH

Designer:	Alastair MacIntosh
Type:	Weight – Spherical
Issued:	1991 in a limited edition of 750
Status:	Closed at No. 394
Series:	Limited – Modern Design
O.I.P.:	U.K. £55.00
	U.S. $200.00
U.K.:	£ 55.00
U.S.:	$110.00
Can.:	$145.00

CT-829
UTOPIA

Designer:	Margot Thomson
Type:	Weight – Spherical
Issued:	1991 in a limited edition of 650
Status:	Closed at No. 438
Series:	Limited – Modern Design
O.I.P.:	U.K. £85.00
	U.S. $310.00
U.K.:	£ 85.00
U.S.:	$170.00
Can.:	$225.00

CT-830
VIRTUOSO

Designer:	Alastair MacIntosh
Type:	Weight – Spherical
Issued:	1991 in a limited edition of 750
Status:	Closed at No. 631
Series:	Limited – Modern Design
O.I.P.:	U.K. £60.00
	U.S. $225.00
U.K.:	£ 60.00
U.S.:	$120.00
Can.:	$160.00

CT-831
WANDERLUST

Designer:	Margot Thomson
Type:	Weight – Spherical
Issued:	1991 in a limited edition of 350
Status:	Closed at No. 298
Series:	Limited – Modern Design
O.I.P.:	U.K. £95.00
	U.S. $350.00
U.K.:	£ 95.00
U.S.:	$190.00
Can.:	$250.00

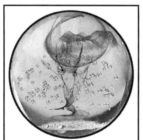

CT-832
WINDCHIMES

Designer:	Colin Terris
Type:	Weight – Spherical
Issued:	1991 in a limited edition of 750
Status:	Closed at No. 302
Series:	Limited – Modern Design
O.I.P.:	U.K. £65.00
	U.S. $230.00
U.K.:	£ 65.00
U.S.:	$130.00
Can.:	$170.00

CT-833
ALPINE PINK

Designer:	Margot Thomson
Type:	Weight – Spherical
Issued:	1991 in a limited edition of 250
Status:	Closed at No. 145
Series:	Whitefriars Collection
O.I.P.:	U.K. £150.00
	U.S. $540.00
U.K.:	£150.00
U.S.:	$300.00
Can.:	$400.00

CT-834
CLEMATIS
Style One

Designer:	Margot Thomson
Type:	Weight – Spherical
Issued:	1991 in a limited edition of 150
Status:	Closed at No. 112
Series:	Whitefriars Collection
O.I.P.:	U.K. £185.00
	U.S. $675.00
U.K.:	£185.00
U.S.:	$375.00
Can.:	$475.00

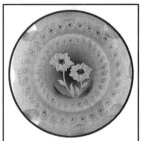

CT-835
EDELWEISS

Designer: Margot Thomson
Type: Weight – Spherical
Issued: 1991 in a limited
edition of 250
Status: Closed at No. 209
Series: Whitefriars Collection
O.I.P.: U.K. £135.00
U.S. $495.00

U.K.: £135.00
U.S.: $270.00
Can.: $350.00

CT-836
FLAG IRIS

Designer: Margot Thomson
Type: Weight – Spherical
Issued: 1991 in a limited
edition of 250
Status: Closed at No. 165
Series: Whitefriars Collection
O.I.P.: U.K. £135.00
U.S. $495.00

U.K.: £135.00
U.S.: $270.00
Can.: $350.00

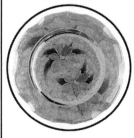

CT-837
PERUVIAN LILIES

Designer: Margot Thomson
Type: Weight – Spherical
Issued: 1991 in a limited
edition of 250
Status: Closed at No. 145
Series: Whitefriars Collection
O.I.P.: U.K. £125.00
U.S. $450.00

U.K.: £125.00
U.S.: $250.00
Can.: $325.00

CT-838
BARRIER REEF

Designer: William Manson
Type: Weight – Spherical
Issued: 1991 in a limited
edition of 250
Status: Closed at No. 183
Series: Traditional Collection
O.I.P.: U.K. £175.00
U.S. $635.00

U.K.: £175.00
U.S.: $350.00
Can.: $450.00

CT-839
CAVERN

Designer: William Manson
Type: Weight – Spherical
Issued: 1991 in a limited
edition of 250
Status: Closed at No. 145
Series: Traditional Collection
O.I.P.: U.K. £160.00
U.S. $575.00

U.K.: £160.00
U.S.: $320.00
Can.: $415.00

CT-840
DRAGONFLY and WATERLILIES

Designer: William Manson
Type: Weight – Spherical
Issued: 1991 in a limited
edition of 250
Status: Closed at No. 192
Series: Traditional Collection
O.I.P.: U.K. £175.00
U.S. $635.00

U.K.: £175.00
U.S.: $350.00
Can.: $450.00

CT-841
LILIES and LADYBIRD

Designer: William Manson
Type: Weight – Spherical
Issued: 1991 in a limited
edition of 250
Status: Closed at No. 86
Series: Traditional Collection
O.I.P.: U.K. £175.00
U.S. $635.00

U.K.: £175.00
U.S.: $350.00
Can.: $450.00

CT-842
SCORPION

Designer: William Manson
Type: Weight – Spherical
Issued: 1991 in a limited
edition of 250
Status: Closed at No. 76
Series: Traditional Collection
O.I.P.: U.K. £185.00
U.S. $675.00

U.K.: £185.00
U.S.: $375.00
Can.: $475.00

CT-843
SEA BED

Designer:	William Manson
Type:	Weight – Spherical
Issued:	1991 in a limited edition of 250
Status:	Closed at No. 154
Series:	Traditional Collection
O.I.P.:	U.K. £175.00
	U.S. $635.00
U.K.:	£175.00
U.S.:	$350.00
Can.:	$450.00

CT-844
WILD ROSE BOUQUET

Designer:	William Manson
Type:	Weight – Spherical
Issued:	1991 in a limited edition of 250
Status:	Closed at No. 113
O.I.P.:	U.K. £200.00
	U.S. $735.00
U.K.:	£200.00
U.S.:	$400.00
Can.:	$525.00

CT-845
CRUCIBLE

Designer:	Alastair MacIntosh
Type:	Weight – Spherical
Issued:	1991
Status:	Closed
Series:	Unlimited – Modern Design
O.I.P.:	U.K. £29.95
	U.S. $99.50
U.K.:	£30.00
U.S.:	$60.00
Can.:	$80.00

CT-846
DOUBLE MAGNUM MAGENTA

Designer:	Margot Thomson
Type:	Weight – Spherical
Size:	Double magnum
Issued:	1991
Status:	Closed
Series:	Unlimited – Modern Design
O.I.P.:	U.K. £165.00
	U.S. $575.00
U.K.:	£165.00
U.S.:	$325.00
Can.:	$425.00

CT-847
ECHO

Designer:	Alastair MacIntosh
Type:	Weight – Spherical
Issued:	1991
Status:	Closed
Series:	Unlimited – Modern Design
O.I.P.:	U.K. £29.95
	U.S. $99.50
U.K.:	£30.00
U.S.:	$60.00
Can.:	$80.00

CT-848
ESCAPE

Designer:	Alastair MacIntosh
Type:	Weight – Spherical
Issued:	1991
Status:	Closed
Series:	Unlimited – Modern Design
O.I.P.:	U.K. £32.50
	U.S. $115.00
U.K.:	£35.00
U.S.:	$70.00
Can.:	$90.00

CT-849
GOLF DOME
Style Two

Designer:	Caithness Studios
Type:	Weight – Domed
Issued:	1991
Status:	Closed
Series:	Unlimited – Modern Design
O.I.P.:	U.K. £29.95
	U.S. $115.00
U.K.:	£30.00
U.S.:	$60.00
Can.:	$80.00

CT-850
GOLFER

Designer:	Caithness Studios
Type:	Weight – Spherical
Issued:	1991
Status:	Closed
Series:	Unlimited – Modern Design
O.I.P.:	U.K. £37.50
	U.S. $135.00
U.K.:	£ 40.00
U.S.:	$ 80.00
Can.:	$100.00

CT-851
JACOB'S LADDER

Designer: Alastair MacIntosh
Type: Weight – Spherical
Issued: 1991
Status: Closed
Series: Unlimited – Modern Design
O.I.P.: U.K. £29.95
U.S. $110.00

U.K.: £30.00
U.S.: $60.00
Can.: $80.00

CT-852
LIBERTY

Designer: Alastair MacIntosh
Type: Weight – Spherical
Issued: 1991
Status: Closed
Series: Unlimited – Modern Design
O.I.P.: U.K. £29.95
U.S. $110.00

U.K.: £30.00
U.S.: $60.00
Can.: $80.00

CT-853
SIROCCO

Designer: Margot Thomson
Type: Weight – Spherical
Colour: 1. Aqua
2. Magenta
Issued: 1991
Status: Closed
Series: Unlimited – Modern Design
O.I.P.: U.K. £19.95
U.S. $75.00

	Aqua	Magenta
U.K.:	£25.	25.
U.S.:	$50.	50.
Can.:	$65.	65.

CT-854
SNOW TRAIL BLUE

Designer: Margot Thomson
Type: Weight – Spherical
Issued: 1991
Status: Closed
Series: Unlimited – Modern Design
O.I.P.: U.K. £29.95
U.S. $99.50

U.K.: £30.00
U.S.: $60.00
Can.: $80.00

CT-855
SPIN OFF

Designer: Alastair MacIntosh
Type: Weight – Spherical
Issued: 1991
Status: Closed
Series: Unlimited – Modern Design
O.I.P.: U.K. £29.95
U.S. $110.00

U.K.: £30.00
U.S.: $60.00
Can.: $80.00

CT-856
STARLIGHT

Designer: Colin Terris
Type: Weight – Spherical
Colour: See below
Issued: 1991
Status: Closed
Series: Unlimited – Modern Design
O.I.P.: U.K. £19.95
U.S. $79.50

	Blue	Sable
U.K.:	£25.	25.
U.S.:	$50.	50.
Can.:	$65.	65.

CT-857
STEEL BLUE

Designer: Alastair MacIntosh
Type: Weight – Spherical
Issued: 1991
Status: Closed
Series: Unlimited – Modern Design
O.I.P.: U.K. £23.95
U.S. $95.00

U.K.: £30.00
U.S.: $60.00
Can.: $80.00

CT-858
WHITE HORSES

Designer: Margot Thomson
Type: Weight – Spherical
Issued: 1991
Status: Closed
Series: Unlimited – Modern Design
O.I.P.: U.K. £29.95
U.S. $110.00

U.K.: £30.00
U.S.: $60.00
Can.: $80.00

CT-859
DIZZY
Designer: Margot Thomson
Type: Weight – Spherical
Colour: See below
Issued: 1991
Status: Closed
Scries: Unlimited – Modern
Design
O.I.P.: U.K. £19.95
U.S. $69.50

	Green	Pink
U.K.:	£20.	20.
U.S.:	$40.	40.
Can.:	$50.	50.

CT-860
PIXIE
Designer: Alastair MacIntosh
Type: Weight – Low Dome
Size: Miniature
Colour: 1. Blue
2. Pink
3. White
Issued: 1991
Status: Closed
Series: Medium and
Miniature Size
O.I.P.: U.K. £13.95
U.S. $49.50

U.K.: £20.00
U.S.: $40.00
Can.: $50.00

CT-861
MINIATURE BUTTERFLY
Designer: Allan Scott
Type: Weight – Spherical
Issued: 1991
Status: Closed
Series: Millefiori Miniatures
O.I.P.: U.K. £29.95
U.S. $99.50

U.K.: £30.00
U.S.: $60.00
Can.: $80.00

CT-862
MINIATURE HEART
Style Three
Designer: Allan Scott
Type: Weight – Spherical
Issued: 1991
Status: Closed
Series: Millefiori Miniatures
O.I.P.: U.K. £29.95
U.S. $99.50

U.K.: £30.00
U.S.: $60.00
Can.: $80.00

CT-863
MINIATURE ORCHID
Designer: Allan Scott
Type: Weight – Spherical
Issued: 1991
Status: Closed
Series: Millefiori Miniatures
O.I.P.: U.K. £29.95
U.S. $99.50

U.K.: £30.00
U.S.: $60.00
Can.: $80.00

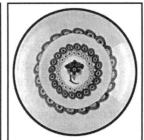

CT-864
MINIATURE PANSY
Designer: Allan Scott
Type: Weight – Spherical
Issued: 1991
Status: Closed
Series: Millefiori Miniatures
O.I.P.: U.K. £29.95
U.S. $99.50

U.K.: £30.00
U.S.: $60.00
Can.: $80.00

CT-865
MINIATURE ROSE
Style Two
Designer: Allan Scott
Type: Weight – Spherical
Issued: 1991
Status: Closed
Series: Millefiori Miniatures
O.I.P.: U.K. £29.95
U.S. $99.50

U.K.: £30.00
U.S.: $60.00
Can.: $80.00

SS POLITICIAN
Designer: Colin Terris
Type: Spherical
Issued: 1991 in a limited
edition of 750
Status: Closed
Series: Unknown
O.I.P.: Unknown

U.K.: £30.00
U.S.: $60.00
Can.: $80.00

ISSUES OF 1992

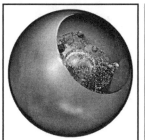

CT-866A
ALPHA
Style Two
Designer: Colin Terris
Type: Weight – Spherical
Issued: 1992 in a limited
          edition of 150
Status: Fully subscribed
Series: Limited – Modern
          Design
O.I.P.:   U.K. £215.00/set
          U.S. $695.00/set

	Alpha	Set
U.K.:	£150.	300.
U.S.:	$300.	600.
Can.:	$400.	775.

CT-866B
OMEGA
Designer: Colin Terris
Type: Weight – Spherical
Issued: 1992 in a limited
          edition of 150
Status: Fully subscribed
Series: Limited – Modern
          Design
O.I.P.:   U.K. £215.00/set
          U.S. $695.00/set

U.K.:	£150.00
U.S.:	$300.00
Can.:	$400.00

Note: CT-866A and B were
issued and sold as a set.

CT-867
ARGO
Designer: Alastair MacIntosh
Type: Weight – Low Dome
Issued: 1992 in a limited
          edition of 650
Status: Closed at No. 420
Series: Limited – Modern
          Design
O.I.P.:   U.K. £75.00
          U.S. $250.00

U.K.:	£ 75.00
U.S.:	$150.00
Can.:	$200.00

CT-868
CASTILLION
Designer: Alastair MacIntosh
Type: Weight – Low Dome
Issued: 1992 in a limited
          edition of 650
Status: Closed at No. 391
Series: Limited – Modern
          Design
O.I.P.:   U.K. £85.00
          U.S. $290.00

U.K.:	£ 85.00
U.S.:	$170.00
Can.:	$225.00

CT-869
CONTOURS
Designer: Alastair MacIntosh
Type: Weight – Low Dome
Issued: 1992 in a limited
          edition of 750
Status: Closed at No. 371
Series: Limited – Modern
          Design
O.I.P.:   U.K. £50.00
          U.S. $175.00

U.K.:	£ 50.00
U.S.:	$100.00
Can.:	$130.00

CT-870
DARK SECRET
Designer: Alastair MacIntosh
Type: Weight – Low Dome
Issued: 1992 in a limited
          edition of 750
Status: Fully subscribed
Series: Limited – Modern
          Design
O.I.P.:   U.K. £45.00
          U.S. $150.00

U.K.:	£ 45.00
U.S.:	$ 90.00
Can.:	$120.00

CT-871
HARVEST TIME
Designer: Helen MacDonald
Type: Weight – Domed
Issued: 1992 in a limited
          edition of 100
Status: Fully subscribed
O.I.P.:   U.K. £100.00
          U.S. $675.00

U.K.:	£200.00
U.S.:	$400.00
Can.:	$525.00

CT-872
HYDROPONIC
Designer: Colin Terris
Type: Weight – Low Dome
Issued: 1992 in a limited
          edition of 750
Status: Fully subscribed
Series: Limited – Modern
          Design
O.I.P.:   U.K. £55.00
          U.S. $190.00

U.K.:	£ 55.00
U.S.:	$110.00
Can.:	$145.00

CT-873
IMPRESSIONS

Designer:	Alastair MacIntosh
Type:	Weight – Low Dome
Issued:	1992 in a limited edition of 750
Status:	Closed at No. 371
Series:	Limited – Modern Design
O.I.P.:	U.K. £65.00
	U.S. $225.00
U.K.:	£ 65.00
U.S.:	$130.00
Can.:	$170.00

CT-874
ISTANBUL

Designer:	Shona Spittal
Type:	Weight – Low Dome
Issued:	1992 in a limited edition of 650
Status:	Closed at No. 279
Series:	Limited – Modern Design
O.I.P.:	U.K. £99.00
	U.S. $350.00
U.K.:	£100.00
U.S.:	$200.00
Can.:	$260.00

CT-875
LILAC POOL

Designer:	Stuart Cumming
Type:	Weight – Spherical
Issued:	1992 in a limited edition of 750
Status:	Closed at No. 740
Series:	Limited – Modern Design
O.I.P.:	U.K. £69.00
	U.S. $230.00
U.K.:	£ 70.00
U.S.:	$140.00
Can.:	$180.00

CT-876
MEDITATION

Designer:	Margot Thomson
Type:	Weight – Domed
Issued:	1992 in a limited edition of 350
Status:	Fully subscribed
Series:	Limited – Modern Design
O.I.P.:	U.K. £99.00
	U.S. $350.00
U.K.:	£100.00
U.S.:	$200.00
Can.:	$260.00

CT-877
MYSTIC ISLAND

Designer:	Colin Terris
Type:	Weight – Spherical
Issued:	1992 in a limited edition of 350
Status:	Fully subscribed
Series:	Limited – Modern Design
O.I.P.:	U.K. £110.00
	U.S. $350.00
U.K.:	£110.00
U.S.:	$220.00
Can.:	$290.00

CT-878
NAVIGATOR

Designer:	Margot Thomson
Type:	Weight – Low Dome faceted
Issued:	1992 in a limited edition of 100
Status:	Fully subscribed
Series:	Limited – Modern Design
O.I.P.:	U.K. £135.00
	U.S. $450.00
U.K.:	£175.00
U.S.:	$350.00
Can.:	$450.00

CT-879
ORIGIN

Designer:	Margot Thomson
Type:	Weight – Domed
Issued:	1992 in a limited edition of 750
Status:	Fully subscribed
Series:	Limited – Modern Design
O.I.P.:	U.K. £50.00
	U.S. $175.00
U.K.:	£ 50.00
U.S.:	$100.00
Can.:	$130.00

CT-880
PAINTED DESERT

Designer:	Margot Thomson
Type:	Weight – Low Dome
Issued:	1992 in a limited edition of 750
Status:	Closed at No. 558
Series:	Limited – Modern Design
O.I.P.:	U.K. £65.00
	U.S. $225.00
U.K.:	£ 65.00
U.S.:	$130.00
Can.:	$170.00

CT-881
PROPHECY

Designer: Margot Thomson
Type: Weight – Spherical
Issued: 1992 in a limited
edition of 750
Status: Fully subscribed
Series: Limited – Modern
Design
O.I.P.: U.K. £55.00
U.S. $190.00

U.K.: £ 55.00
U.S.: $110.00
Can.: $145.00

CT-882
SCARAB

Designer: Colin Terris
Type: Weight – Spherical
Issued: 1992 in a limited
edition of 750
Status: Closed at No. 650
Series: Limited – Modern
Design
O.I.P.: U.K. £70.00
U.S. $250.00

U.K.: £ 70.00
U.S.: $140.00
Can.: $180.00

CT-883
SERGEANT MAJOR

Designer: Sarah Peterson
Type: Weight – Domed
Issued: 1992 in a limited
edition of 650
Status: Closed at No. 240
Series: Limited – Modern
Design
O.I.P.: U.K. £75.00
U.S. $250.00

U.K.: £ 75.00
U.S.: $150.00
Can.: $200.00

CT-884
SPACE CRYSTAL

Designer: Colin Terris
Type: Weight – Low Dome,
facets
Issued: 1992 in a limited
edition of 50
Status: Fully subscribed
Series: Limited – Modern
Design
O.I.P.: U.K. £175.00
U.S. $595.00

U.K.: £200.00
U.S.: $400.00
Can.: $525.00

CT-885
SPACE LANDING

Designer: Alastair MacIntosh
Type: Weight – Spherical
Issued: 1992 in a limited
edition of 750
Status: Closed at No. 483
Series: Limited – Modern
Design
O.I.P.: U.K. £69.00
U.S. $250.00

U.K.: £ 70.00
U.S.: $140.00
Can.: $180.00

CT-886
STAR ORCHID

Designer: Colin Terris
Type: Weight – Spherical
Issued: 1992 in a limited
edition of 150
Status: Fully subscribed
Series: Limited – Modern
Design
O.I.P.: U.K. £125.00
U.S. $425.00

U.K.: £150.00
U.S.: $300.00
Can.: $400.00

CT-887
SURVEILLANCE

Designer: Alastair MacIntosh
Type: Weight – Spherical
Issued: 1992 in a limited
edition of 650
Status: Closed at No. 645
Series: Limited – Modern
Design
O.I.P.: U.K. £79.00
U.S. $275.00

U.K.: £ 80.00
U.S.: $160.00
Can.: $210.00

CT-888
TROPICAL POOL

Designer: Helen MacDonald
Type: Weight – Domed
Issued: 1992 in a limited
edition of 100
Status: Fully subscribed
Series: Limited – Modern
Design
O.I.P.: U.K. £200.00
U.S. $275.00

U.K.: £200.00
U.S.: $400.00
Can.: $525.00

CT-889
DOG ROSE
Designer: Margot Thomson
Type: Weight – Spherical
Issued: 1992 in a limited edition of 100
Status: Closed at No. 69
Series: Whitefriars Collection
O.I.P.: U.K. £155.00
U.S. $525.00

U.K.: £155.00
U.S.: $310.00
Can.: $400.00

CT-890
FUCHSIA PERFUME BOTTLE
Style One
Designer: Margot Thomson
Type: Perfume bottle
Issued: 1992 in a limited edition of 100
Status: Closed at No. 97
Series: Whitefriars Collection
O.I.P.: U.K. £195.00
U.S. $675.00

U.K.: £200.00
U.S.: $400.00
Can.: $525.00

CT-891
HONEYSUCKLE
Designer: Allan Scott
Type: Weight – Spherical, facets
Issued: 1992 in a limited edition of 100
Status: Closed at No. 94
Series: Whitefriars Collection
O.I.P.: U.K. £145.00
U.S. $495.00

U.K.: £150.00
U.S.: $300.00
Can.: $400.00

CT-892
JASMINE
Designer: Margot Thomson
Type: Weight – Spherical
Issued: 1992 in a limited edition of 100
Status: Closed at No. 92
Series: Whitefriars Collection
O.I.P.: U.K. £145.00
U.S. $495.00

U.K.: £150.00
U.S.: $300.00
Can.: $400.00

CT-893
NARCISSUS
Designer: Margot Thomson
Type: Weight – Spherical
Issued: 1992 in a limited edition of 100
Status: Closed at No. 95
Series: Whitefriars Collection
O.I.P.: U.K. £155.00
U.S. $595.00

U.K.: £150.00
U.S.: $300.00
Can.: $400.00

CT-894
NASTURTIUM
Designer: Margot Thomson
Type: Weight – Spherical
Issued: 1992 in a limited edition of 100
Status: Closed at No. 73
Series: Whitefriars Collection
O.I.P.: U.K. £145.00
U.S. $495.00

U.K.: £150.00
U.S.: $300.00
Can.: $400.00

CT-895
BUTTERFLY
Style Three
Designer: William Manson
Type: Weight – Spherical
Cane: WM (William Manson)
Issued: 1992 in a limited edition of 50
Status: Fully subscribed
Series: Traditional Collection
O.I.P.: U.K. £225.00
U.S. $775.00

U.K.: £225.00
U.S.: $450.00
Can.: $575.00

CT-896
LIZARD
Designer: William Manson
Type: Weight – Low Dome
Cane: WM (William Manson)
Issued: 1992 in a limited edition of 50
Status: Fully subscribed
Series: Traditional Collection
O.I.P.: U.K. £225.00
U.S. $775.00

U.K.: £225.00
U.S.: $450.00
Can.: $575.00

CT-897
PRIMROSES
Style Two

Designer: William Manson
Type: Weight – Spherical
Cane: WM (William Manson)
Issued: 1992 in a limited
edition of 250
Status: Closed at No. 150
Series: Traditional Collection
O.I.P.: U.K. £95.00
U.S. $325.00

U.K.: £ 95.00
U.S.: $190.00
Can.: $250.00

CT-898
PUFFIN
Style Three

Designer: William Manson
Type: Weight – Spherical
Cane: WM (William Manson)
Issued: 1992 in a limited
edition of 100
Status: Fully subscribed
Series: Traditional Collection
O.I.P.: U.K. £175.00
U.S. $595.00

U.K.: £175.00
U.S.: $350.00
Can.: $450.00

CT-899
ROSE GARLAND

Designer: William Manson
Type: Weight – Spherical
Cane: WM (William Manson)
Issued: 1992 in a limited
edition of 100
Status: Closed at No. 95
Series: Traditional Collection
O.I.P.: U.K. £175.00
U.S. $595.00

U.K.: £175.00
U.S.: $350.00
Can.: $450.00

CT-900
SERPENT

Designer: William Manson
Type: Weight – Spherical
Cane: WM (William Manson)
Issued: 1992 in a limited
edition of 50
Status: Fully subscribed
Series: Traditional Collection
O.I.P.: U.K. £195.00
U.S. $675.00

U.K.: £200.00
U.S.: $400.00
Can.: $525.00

CT-901
STRAWBERRY
Style One

Designer: William Manson
Type: Weight – Spherical
Cane: WM (William Manson)
Issued: 1992 in a limited
edition of 50
Status: Fully subscribed
Series: Traditional Collection
O.I.P.: U.K. £195.00
U.S. $675.00

U.K.: £200.00
U.S.: $400.00
Can.: $525.00

CT-902
THISTLE
Style Two

Designer: William Manson
Type: Weight – Spherical
Cane: WM (William Manson)
Issued: 1992 in a limited
edition of 100
Status: Closed at No. 76
Series: Traditional Collection
O.I.P.: U.K. £175.00
U.S. $595.00

U.K.: £175.00
U.S.: $350.00
Can.: $450.00

CT-903
WEATHERVANE

Designer: Colin Terris
Type: Weight – Spherical
Issued: 1992 in a limited
edition of 1,617
Status: Closed
Series: Collectors' Society
O.I.P.: U.K. £75.00
U.S. $215.00

U.K.: £ 75.00
U.S.: $150.00
Can.: $200.00

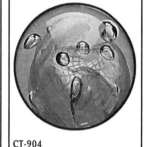

CT-904
CHECKPOINTS

Designer: Alastair MacIntosh
Type: Weight – Spherical
Issued: 1992
Status: Closed
Series: Unlimited
O.I.P.: U.K. £29.95
U.S. $99.50

U.K.: £30.00
U.S.: $60.00
Can.: $80.00

CT-905
DOUBLE MAGNUM 92

Designer:	Margot Thomson
Type:	Weight – Spherical
Size:	Double magnum
Issued:	1992
Status:	Closed
Series:	Unlimited – Modern Design
O.I.P.:	U.K. £175.00
	U.S. $595.00
U.K.:	£175.00
U.S.:	$350.00
Can.:	$450.00

CT-906
MOONFLOWER MAGENTA

Designer:	Colin Terris
Type:	Weight – Spherical
Issued:	1992
Status:	Closed
Series:	Unlimited – Modern Design
O.I.P.:	U.K. £29.95
	U.S. $110.00
U.K.:	£30.00
U.S.:	$60.00
Can.:	$80.00

CT-907
RAZZAMATAZZ

Designer:	Alastair MacIntosh
Type:	Weight – Low Dome
Colour:	See below
Issued:	1992
Status:	Closed
Series:	Unlimited – Modern Design
O.I.P.:	U.K. £24.95
	U.S. $87.50

	Ruby	Sable
U.K.:	£25.	25.
U.S.:	$50.	50.
Can.:	$65.	65.

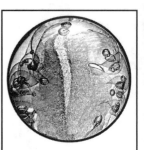

CT-908
RUFFLES

Designer:	Alastair MacIntosh
Type:	Weight – Spherical
Issued:	1992
Status:	Closed
Series:	Unlimited – Modern Design
O.I.P.:	U.K. £24.95
	U.S. $87.50
U.K.:	£30.00
U.S.:	$60.00
Can.:	$80.00

CT-909
SILVER RAIN

Designer:	Alastair MacIntosh
Type:	Weight – Low Dome
Issued:	1992
Status:	Closed
Series:	Unlimited – Modern Design
O.I.P.:	U.K. £24.95
	U.S. $87.50
U.K.:	£25.00
U.S.:	$50.00
Can.:	$65.00

CT-910
MINIATURE BUTTERFLY PERFUME BOTTLE

Designer:	Allan Scott
Type:	Perfume bottle
Issued:	1992
Status:	Closed
Series:	Millefiori Miniatures
O.I.P.:	U.K. £49.95
	U.S. $175.00
U.K.:	£ 50.00
U.S.:	$100.00
Can.:	$130.00

CT-911
MINIATURE HEART PERFUME BOTTLE

Designer:	Allan Scott
Type:	Perfume bottle
Issued:	1992
Status:	Closed
Series:	Romance
O.I.P.:	U.K. £49.95
	U.S. $175.00
U.K.:	£ 50.00
U.S.:	$100.00
Can.:	$130.00

CT-912
MINIATURE ROSE PERFUME BOTTLE

Designer:	Allan Scott
Type:	Perfume bottle
Issued:	1992
Status:	Closed
Series:	Millefiori Miniatures
O.I.P.:	U.K. £49.95
	U.S. $175.00
U.K.:	£ 50.00
U.S.:	$100.00
Can.:	$130.00

CT-913
MINIATURE THISTLE PERFUME BOTTLE

Designer:	Allan Scott
Type:	Perfume bottle
Issued:	1992
Status:	Closed
Series:	Millefiori Miniatures
O.I.P.:	U.K. £49.95
	U.S. $175.00
U.K.:	£ 50.00
U.S.:	$100.00
Can.:	$130.00

CT-914A
WINTER CELEBRATION – ACONITES

Designer:	Margot Thomson
Type:	Weight – Spherical, facets
Issued:	1992 in a limited edition of 50
Status:	Fully subscribed
Series:	Limited – Modern Design
O.I.P.:	U.K. £295.00/set
	U.S. $995.00/set

	Weight	Set
U.K.:	£200.	400.
U.S.:	$400.	800.
Can.:	$525.	1,000.

Note: CT-914A and B were issued and sold as a set.

CT-914B
WINTER CELEBRATION – SNOWDROPS

Designer:	Margot Thomson
Type:	Weight – Spherical, facets
Issued:	1992 in a limited edition of 50
Status:	Fully subscribed
Series:	Limited – Modern Design
O.I.P.:	U.K. £295.00/set
	U.S. $995.00/set
U.K.:	£200.00
U.S.:	$400.00
Can.:	$525.00

CT-915
TREE LIZARD

Designer:	William Manson
Type:	Weight – Spherical
Issued:	1992 in a limited edition of 50
Status:	Fully subscribed
Series:	Traditional Collection
O.I.P.:	U.K. £225.00
	U.S. $775.00
U.K.:	£225.00
U.S.:	$450.00
Can.:	$600.00

CT-916
DRAGONFLY and SNAIL

Designer:	William Manson
Type:	Weight – Spherical
Issued:	1992 in a limited edition of 50
Status:	Fully subscribed
Series:	Traditional Collection
O.I.P.:	U.K. £195.00
	U.S. $675.00
U.K.:	£200.00
U.S.:	$400.00
Can.:	$525.00

CT-917
RASPBERRIES

Designer:	William Manson
Type:	Weight – Spherical, facets
Issued:	1992 in a limited edition of 50
Status:	Fully subscribed
Series:	Traditional Collection
O.I.P.:	U.K. £195.00
	U.S. $675.00
U.K.:	£200.00
U.S.:	$400.00
Can.:	$525.00

CT-918
DESERT SPRING

Designer:	Alastair MacIntosh
Type:	Weight – Spherical
Issued:	1992
Status:	Closed
Series:	Unlimited – Modern Design
O.I.P.:	U.K. £19.95
	U.S. $72.50
U.K.:	£25.00
U.S.:	$50.00
Can.:	$65.00

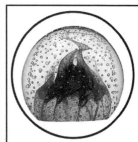

CT-919
FASCINATION

Designer:	Alastair MacIntosh
Type:	Weight – Low Dome
Issued:	1992
Status:	Closed
Series:	Unlimited – Modern Design
O.I.P.:	U.K. £24.95
	U.S. $87.50
U.K.:	£25.00
U.S.:	$50.00
Can.:	$65.00

CT-920
MOSAIC

Designer: Alastair MacIntosh
Type: Weight – Spherical
Issued: 1992
Status: Closed
Series: Unlimited – Modern Design
O.I.P.: U.K. £24.95
U.S. $87.50

U.K.: £25.00
U.S.: $50.00
Can.: $65.00

CT-921
OBSESSION

Designer: Alastair MacIntosh
Type: Weight – Low Dome
Issued: 1992
Status: Closed
Series: Unlimited – Modern Design
O.I.P.: U.K. £19.95
U.S. $72.50

U.K.: £25.00
U.S.: $50.00
Can.: $65.00

CT-922
SUNSET ORCHID

Designer: Colin Terris
Type: Weight – Domed
Issued: 1992 in a limited edition of 100
Status: Fully subscribed
Series: Limited – Modern Design
O.I.P.: U.K. £200.00
U.S. $675.00

U.K.: £200.00
U.S.: $400.00
Can.: $525.00

CT-923
ENCHANTED CASTLE

Designer: Helen MacDonald/ Alastair MacIntosh
Type: Weight – Domed
Issued: 1992 in a limited edition of 100
Status: Fully subscribed
Series: Limited – Modern Design
O.I.P.: U.K. £200.00
U.S. $675.00

U.K.: £200.00
U.S.: $400.00
Can.: $525.00

CT-924
TIME TRAVELLER

Designer: Colin Terris
Type: Weight – Spherical
Issued: 1992 in a limited edition of 750
Status: Closed at No. 741
Series: Limited – Modern Design
O.I.P.: U.K. £49.00
U.S. $175.00

U.K.: £ 50.00
U.S.: $100.00
Can.: $130.00

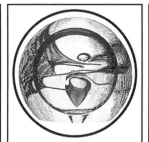

CT-925
CORAL ENCOUNTER

Designer: Alastair MacIntosh
Type: Weight – Spherical
Issued: 1992 in a limited edition of 750
Status: Closed at No. 517
Series: Limited – Modern Design
O.I.P.: U.K. £55.00
U.S. $190.00

U.K.: £ 55.00
U.S.: $110.00
Can.: $145.00

CT-926
DOUBLE EXPOSURE

Designer: Colin Terris
Type: Weight – Spherical
Issued: 1992 in a limited edition of 50
Status: Fully subscribed
Series: Limited – Modern Design
O.I.P.: U.K. £175.00
U.S. $595.00

U.K.: £325.00
U.S.: $650.00
Can.: $850.00

CT-927
SANDFLOWER

Designer: Colin Terris
Type: Weight – Spherical
Issued: 1992 in a limited edition of 350
Status: Closed at No. 284
Series: Limited – Modern Design
O.I.P.: U.K. £99.00
U.S. $350.00

U.K.: £100.00
U.S.: $200.00
Can.: $260.00

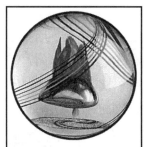

CT-928	
GOLDEN RAINBOW	
Designer:	Margot Thomson
Type:	Weight – Spherical
Issued:	1992 in a limited edition of 750
Status:	Closed at No. 595
Series:	Limited – Modern Design
O.I.P.:	U.K. £55.00
	U.S. $190.00
U.K.:	£ 55.00
U.S.:	$110.00
Can.:	$145.00

CT-929	
INNOVATION	
Designer:	Alastair MacIntosh
Type:	Weight – Domed
Issued:	1992 in a limited edition of 750
Status:	Closed at No. 486
Series:	Limited – Modern Design
O.I.P.:	U.K. £45.00
	U.S. $150.00
U.K.:	£ 45.00
U.S.:	$ 90.00
Can.:	$120.00

HEART PERFUME BOTTLE	
Designer:	Allan Scott
Type:	Perfume Bottle
Issued:	1992
Status:	Closed
Series:	Unknown - Unlimited
O.I.P.:	Unknown
U.K.:	£ 85.00
U.S.:	$170.00
Can.:	$225.00

ISSUES OF 1993

CT-930
ARCTIC CARNATION

Designer: Alastair MacIntosh
Type: Weight – Domed
Issued: 1993 in a limited
           edition of 650
Status: Fully subscribed
Series: Limited – Modern
           Design
O.I.P.:   U.K. £80.00
           U.S. $275.00

U.K.:   £ 80.00
U.S.: $160.00
Can.: $210.00

CT-931
BALLERINA

Designer: Colin Terris
Type: Weight – Spherical,
           facets
Issued: 1993 in a limited
           edition of 50
Status: Fully subscribed
Series: Limited – Modern
           Design
O.I.P.:   U.K. £175.00
           U.S. $595.00

U.K.:   £175.00
U.S.: $350.00
Can.: $450.00

CT-932
BLUE ICE

Designer: Colin Terris
Type: Weight – Spherical
Issued: 1993 in a limited
           edition of 75
Status: Fully subscribed
Series: Limited – Modern
           Design
O.I.P.:   U.K. £150.00
           U.S. $525.00

U.K.:   £175.00
U.S.: $350.00
Can.: $450.00

CT-933
CLOCKWORK

Designer: Alastair MacIntosh
Type: Weight – Spherical
Issued: 1993 in a limited
           edition of 750
Status: Closed at No. 153
Series: Limited – Modern
           Design
O.I.P.:   U.K. £45.00
           U.S. $150.00

U.K.:   £ 50.00
U.S.: $100.00
Can.: $130.00

CT-934
CORONA

Designer: Alastair MacIntosh
Type: Weight – Spherical
Issued: 1993 in a limited
           edition of 750
Status: Closed at No. 161
Series: Limited – Modern
           Design
O.I.P.:   U.K. £55.00
           U.S. $195.00

U.K.:   £ 55.00
U.S.: $110.00
Can.: $145.00

CT-935
CRESCENT MOON

Designer: Colin Terris
Type: Weight – Spherical
Issued: 1993 in a limited
           edition of 750
Status: Fully subscribed
Series: Limited – Modern
           Design
O.I.P.:   U.K. £50.00
           U.S. $175.00

U.K.:   £ 50.00
U.S.: $100.00
Can.: $130.00

CT-936
CYCLOID

Designer: Margot Thomson
Type: Weight – Spherical
Issued: 1993 in a limited
           edition of 750
Status: Closed at No. 470
Series: Limited – Modern
           Design
O.I.P.:   U.K. £50.00
           U.S. $175.00

U.K.:   £ 50.00
U.S.: $100.00
Can.: $130.00

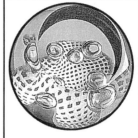

CT-937
DINNER PARTY

Designer: Alastair MacIntosh
Type: Weight – Spherical
Issued: 1993 in a limited
           edition of 750
Status: Closed at No. 197
Series: Limited – Modern
           Design
O.I.P.:   U.K. £60.00
           U.S. $225.00

U.K.:   £ 60.00
U.S.: $120.00
Can.: $160.00

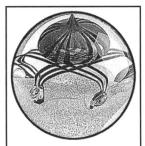

CT-938
DOUBLE CROSS

Designer:	Margot Thomson
Type:	Weight – Spherical
Issued:	1993 in a limited edition of 750
Status:	Closed at No. 326
Series:	Limited – Modern Design
O.I.P.:	U.K. £55.00
	U.S. $210.00
U.K.:	£ 55.00
U.S.:	$110.00
Can.:	$145.00

CT-939
DOUBLE MAGNUM 93

Designer:	Margot Thomson
Type:	Weight – Spherical
Size:	Double magnum
Issued:	1993 in a limited edition of 150
Status:	Closed at No. 101
Series:	Limited – Modern Design
O.I.P.:	U.K. £175.00
	U.S. $595.00
U.K.:	£175.00
U.S.:	$350.00
Can.:	$450.00

CT-940
EXUBERANCE

Designer:	Alastair MacIntosh
Type:	Weight – Spherical
Issued:	1993 in a limited edition of 750
Status:	Closed at No. 436
Series:	Limited – Modern Design
O.I.P.:	U.K. £55.00
	US 195.00
U.K.:	£ 55.00
U.S.:	$110.00
Can.:	$145.00

CT-941
FANTASY ORCHID

Designer:	Alastair MacIntosh
Type:	Weight – Domed
Issued:	1993 in a limited edition of 1,653
Status:	Closed
Series:	Collectors' Society
O.I.P.:	U.K. £75.00
	U.S. $215.00
U.K.:	£ 75.00
U.S.:	$150.00
Can.:	$200.00

CT-942
GLACIER

Designer:	Helen MacDonald and Alastair MacIntosh
Type:	Weight – Domed
Issued:	1993 in a limited edition of 100
Status:	Closed at No. 95
Series:	Limited – Modern Design
O.I.P.:	U.K. £200.00
	U.S. $695.00
U.K.:	£225.00
U.S.:	$450.00
Can.:	$600.00

CT-943
GO-BETWEEN

Designer:	Margot Thomson
Type:	Weight – Spherical
Issued:	1993 in a limited edition of 750
Status:	Closed at No. 317
Series:	Limited – Modern Design
O.I.P.:	U.K. £60.00
	U.S. $225.00
U.K.:	£ 60.00
U.S.:	$120.00
Can.:	$160.00

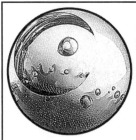

CT-944
HIGH DIVE

Designer:	Alastair MacIntosh
Type:	Weight – Spherical
Issued:	1993 in a limited edition of 750
Status:	Closed at No. 327
Series:	Limited – Modern Design
O.I.P.:	U.K. £55.00
	U.S. $195.00
U.K.:	£ 55.00
U.S.:	$110.00
Can.:	$145.00

CT-945
HUMBUG

Designer:	Margot Thomson
Type:	Weight – Spherical
Issued:	1993 in a limited edition of 750
Status:	Closed at No. 490
Series:	Limited – Modern Design
O.I.P.:	U.K. £60.00
	U.S. $210.00
U.K.:	£ 60.00
U.S.:	$120.00
Can.:	$160.00

CT-946
INTERCEPTOR

Designer: Colin Terris
Type: Weight – Spherical
Issued: 1993 in a limited
         edition of 75
Status: Fully subscribed
Series: Limited – Modern
         Design
O.I.P.:   U.K. £150.00
         U.S. $525.00

U.K.:   £300.00
U.S.: $600.00
Can.: $775.00

CT-947
INTERMEZZO

Designer: Colin Terris
Type: Weight – Spherical
Issued: 1993 in a limited
         edition of 750
Status: Closed at No. 411
Series: Limited – Modern
         Design
O.I.P.:   U.K. £50.00
         U.S. $175.00

U.K.:   £ 50.00
U.S.: $100.00
Can.: $130.00

CT-948
ISLAND FANTASY

Designer: Colin Terris
Type: Weight – Domed,
         pyramid facets
Issued: 1993 in a limited
         edition of 350
Status: Fully subscribed
O.I.P.:   U.K. £99.00
         U.S. $350.00

U.K.:   £100.00
U.S.: $200.00
Can.: $260.00

CT-949
LUNAR ORCHID

Designer: Alastair MacIntosh
Type: Weight – Spherical
Issued: 1993 in a limited
         edition of 750
Status: Fully subscribed
Series: Limited – Modern
         Design
O.I.P.:   U.K. £50.00
         U.S. $175.00

U.K.:   £ 50.00
U.S.: $100.00
Can.: $130.00

CT-950
MATADOR

Designer: Colin Terris
Type: Weight – Spherical
Issued: 1993 in a limited
         edition of 750
Status: Closed at No. 504
Series: Limited – Modern
         Design
O.I.P.:   U.K. £60.00
         U.S. $225.00

U.K.:   £ 60.00
U.S.: $120.00
Can.: $160.00

CT-951
MAZE

Designer: Alastair MacIntosh
Type: Weight – Spherical
Issued: 1993 in a limited
         edition of 750
Status: Closed at No. 535
Series: Limited – Modern
         Design
O.I.P.:   U.K. £45.00
         U.S. $150.00

U.K.:   £ 45.00
U.S.: $ 90.00
Can.: $120.00

CT-952
MOON MOUNTAINS

Designer: Colin Terris
Type: Weight – Spherical
Issued: 1993 in a limited
         edition of 750
Status: Closed at No. 284
Series: Limited – Modern
         Design
O.I.P.:   U.K. £65.00
         U.S. $230.00

U.K.:   £ 65.00
U.S.: $130.00
Can.: $170.00

CT-953
NIMBUS

Designer: Margot Thomson
Type: Weight – Spherical
Issued: 1993 in a limited
         edition of 750
Status: Fully subscribed
Series: Limited – Modern
         Design
O.I.P.:   U.K. £39.95
         U.S. $140.00

U.K.:   £ 40.00
U.S.: $ 80.00
Can.: $100.00

CT-954
NORDIC GLADE
Designer: Helen MacDonald/
Alastair MacIntosh
Type: Weight – Domed
Issued: 1993 in a limited
edition of 100
Status: Fully subscribed
Series: Limited – Modern
Design
O.I.P.: U.K. £200.00
U.S. $695.00

U.K.: £225.00
U.S.: $450.00
Can.: $600.00

CT-955
OCEAN WAVE
Designer: Helen MacDonald/
Alastair MacIntosh
Type: Weight – Domed
Issued: 1993 in a limited
edition of 100
Status: Fully subscribed
Series: Limited – Modern
Design
O.I.P.: U.K. £200.00
U.S. $695.00

U.K.: £225.00
U.S.: $450.00
Can.: $600.00

CT-956
PILGRIMAGE
Designer: Colin Terris
Type: Weight – Spherical
Issued: 1993 in a limited
edition of 750
Status: Closed at No. 202
Series: Limited – Modern
Design
O.I.P.: U.K. £65.00
U.S. $230.00

U.K.: £ 65.00
U.S.: $130.00
Can.: $170.00

CT-957
PULSAR
Designer: Colin Terris
Type: Weight – Spherical
Issued: 1993 in a limited
edition of 750
Status: Closed at No. 612
Series: Limited – Modern
Design
O.I.P.: U.K. £55.00
U.S. $195.00

U.K.: £ 55.00
U.S.: $110.00
Can.: $145.00

CT-958
SEA CRYSTAL
Designer: Alastair MacIntosh
Type: Weight – Spherical
Issued: 1993 in a limited
edition of 75
Status: Fully subscribed
Series: Limited – Modern
Design
O.I.P.: U.K. £150.00
U.S. $525.00

U.K.: £175.00
U.S.: $350.00
Can.: $450.00

CT-959
SMOKE SIGNAL
Designer: Colin Terris
Type: Weight – Spherical
Issued: 1993 in a limited
edition of 750
Status: Fully subscribed
Series: Limited – Modern
Design
O.I.P.: U.K. £65.00
U.S. $230.00

U.K.: £ 65.00
U.S.: $130.00
Can.: $170.00

CT-960
SOLSTICE
Designer: Margot Thomson
Type: Weight – Domed
Issued: 1993 in a limited
edition of 350
Status: Fully subscribed
Series: Limited – Modern
Design
O.I.P.: U.K. £99.00
U.S. $350.00

U.K.: £100.00
U.S: $200.00
Can.: $260.00

CT-961
SPINNING JENNY
Designer: Margot Thomson
Type: Weight – Spherical
Issued: 1993 in a limited
edition of 350
Status: Closed at No. 120
Series: Limited – Modern
Design
O.I.P.: U.K. £110.00
U.S. $395.00

U.K.: £150.00
U.S.: $300.00
Can.: $400.00

CT-962
THE DEEP

Designer: Colin Terris
Type: Weight – Spherical
Issued: 1993 in a limited edition of 100
Status: Closed at No. 74
O.I.P.: U.K. £200.00
U.S. $695.00

U.K.: £200.00
U.S.: $400.00
Can.: $525.00

CT-963
THISTLEDOWN

Designer: Colin Terris
Type: Weight – Spherical
Issued: 1993 in a limited edition of 750
Status: Closed at No. 343
Series: Limited – Modern Design
O.I.P.: U.K. £55.00
U.S. $195.00

U.K.: £ 55.00
U.S.: $110.00
Can.: $145.00

CT-964
5-4-3-2-1

Designer: Margot Thomson
Type: Weight – Domed
Issued: 1993 in a limited edition of 650
Status: Closed at No. 431
Series: Limited – Modern Design
O.I.P.: U.K. £75.00
U.S. $275.00

U.K.: £ 75.00
U.S.: $150.00
Can.: $200.00

CT-965
FIRENZE FLASK

Designer: Alastair MacIntosh
Type: Flask
Issued: 1993 in a limited edition of 50
Status: Closed at No. 42
Series: Limited – Modern Design
O.I.P.: U.K. £195.00
U.S. $695.00

U.K.: £200.00
U.S.: $400.00
Can.: $525.00

CT-966
MILANO FLASK

Designer: Alastair MacIntosh
Type: Flask
Issued: 1993 in a limited edition of 50
Status: Fully subscribed
Series: Limited – Modern Design
O.I.P.: U.K. £195.00
U.S. $695.00

U.K.: £200.00
U.S.: $400.00
Can.: $525.00

CT-967
VERONA FLASK

Designer: Alastair MacIntosh
Type: Flask
Issued: 1993 in a limited edition of 50
Status: Closed at No. 46
Series: Limited – Modern Design
O.I.P.: U.K. £175.00
U.S. $695.00

U.K.: £200.00
U.S.: $400.00
Can.: $525.00

CT-968A
MOONLIGHT

Designer: Colin Terris
Type: Weight – Spherical
Issued: 1993 in a limited edition of 75
Status: Closed at No. 72
Series: Limited – Modern Design
O.I.P.: U.K. 195.00/set
U.S. $695.00/set

U.K.: £200.00
U.S.: $400.00
Can.: $525.00

Note: CT-968A and B were issued and sold as a set.

CT-968B
MOONLIGHT PERFUME BOTTLE

Designer: Colin Terris
Type: Perfume bottle
Issued: 1993 in a limited edition of 75
Status: Closed at No. 72
Series: Limited – Modern Design
O.I.P.: U.K. £195.00/set
U.S. $695.00/set

	Perfume	Set
U.K.:	£300.	500.
U.S.:	$600.	1,000.
Can.:	$775.	1,250.

CT-969
BUTTERCUPS and DAISIES

Designer:	Margot Thomson
Type:	Weight – Spherical
Cane:	Whitefriar
Issued:	1993 in a limited edition of 100
Status:	Closed at No. 70
Series:	Whitefriars Collection
O.I.P.:	U.K. £155.00
	U.S. $550.00
U.K.:	£155.00
U.S.:	$300.00
Can.:	$400.00

CT-970
CYCLAMEN

Designer:	Margot Thomson
Type:	Weight – Spherical
Cane:	Whitefriar
Issued:	1993 in a limited edition of 100
Status:	Fully subscribed
Series:	Whitefriars Collection
O.I.P.:	U.K. £135.00
	U.S. $525.00
U.K.:	£135.00
U.S.:	$270.00
Can.:	$350.00

CT-971
HAREBELLS

Designer:	Margot Thomson
Type:	Weight – Spherical
Cane:	Whitefriar
Issued:	1993 in a limited edition of 100
Status:	Closed at No. 53
Series:	Whitefriars Collection
O.I.P.:	U.K. £145.00
	U.S. $575.00
U.K.:	£150.00
U.S.:	$300.00
Can.:	$400.00

CT-972
POPPIES PERFUME BOTTLE

Designer:	Margot Thomson
Type:	Perfume bottle
Cane:	Whitefriar
Issued:	1993 in a limited edition of 100
Status:	Closed at No. 54
Series:	Whitefriars Collection
O.I.P.:	U.K. £195.00
	U.S. $695.00
U.K.:	£200.00
U.S.:	$400.00
Can.:	$525.00

CT-973
REGAL LILY

Designer:	Margot Thomson
Type:	Weight – Spherical
Cane:	Whitefriar
Issued:	1993 in a limited edition of 100
Status:	Closed at No. 70
Series:	Whitefriars Collection
O.I.P.:	U.K. £135.00
	U.S. $525.00
U.K.:	£135.00
U.S.:	$270.00
Can.:	$350.00

CT-974A
SPRING CELEBRATION - ONE

Designer:	Margot Thomson
Type:	Weight – Spherical
Cane:	Whitefriar
Issued:	1993 in a limited edition of 50
Status:	Fully subscribed
Series:	Whitefriars Collection
O.I.P.:	U.K. £295.00/set
	U.S. $1,150.00/set

	Spring	Set
U.K.:	£200.	400.
U.S.:	$400.	800.
Can.:	$525.	1,050.

Note: CT-974A and B were issued and sold as a set.

CT-974B
SPRING CELEBRATION TWO

Designer:	Margot Thomson
Type:	Weight – Spherical
Cane:	Whitefriar
Issued:	1993 in a limited edition of 50
Status:	Fully subscribed
Series:	Whitefriars Collection
O.I.P.:	U.K. £295.00/set
	U.S. $1,150.00/set
U.K.:	£200.00
U.S.:	$400.00
Can.:	$525.00

CT-975
SUMMER FLOWERS

Designer:	Margot Thomson
Type:	Weight – Spherical
Cane:	Whitefriar
Issued:	1993 in a limited edition of 100
Status:	Closed at No. 73
Series:	Whitefriars Collection
O.I.P.:	U.K. £195.00
	U.S. $695.00
U.K.:	£200.00
U.S.:	$400.00
Can.:	$525.00

CT-976
WILD PANSY and STORKSBILL
Designer: Margot Thomson
Type: Weight – Spherical
Cane: Whitefriar
Issued: 1993 in a limited
edition of 100
Status: Closed at No. 97
Series: Whitefriars Collection
O.I.P.: U.K. £135.00
U.S. $475.00

U.K.: £135.00
U.S.: $275.00
Can.: $360.00

CT-977
CATERPILLAR
Designer: William Manson
Type: Weight – Spherical
Cane: WM (William Manson)
Issued: 1993 in a limited
edition of 50
Status: Fully subscribed
Series: Traditional Collection
O.I.P.: U.K. £195.00
U.S. $695.00

U.K.: £200.00
U.S.: $400.00
Can.: $525.00

CT-978
CHERRIES
Style Two
Designer: William Manson
Type: Weight – Spherical
Cane: WM (William Manson)
Issued: 1993 in a limited
edition of 50
Status: Fully subscribed
Series: Traditional Collection
O.I.P.: U.K. £215.00
U.S. $750.00

U.K.: £225.00
U.S.: $450.00
Can.: $600.00

CT-979
COCKATOO
Designer: William Manson
Type: Weight – Spherical
Cane: WM (William Manson)
Issued: 1993 in a limited
edition of 50
Status: Fully subscribed
Series: Traditional Collection
O.I.P.: U.K. £195.00
U.S. $695.00

U.K.: £200.00
U.S.: $400.00
Can.: $525.00

CT-980
DOVES
Designer: William Manson
Type: Weight – Spherical
Cane: WM (William Manson)
Issued: 1993 in a limited
edition of 50
Status: Fully subscribed
Series: Traditional Collection
O.I.P.: U.K. £195.00
U.S. $695.00

U.K.: £200.00
U.S.: $400.00
Can.: $525.00

CT-981
GRAPES
Style One
Designer: William Manson
Type: Weight – Spherical
Cane: WM (William Manson)
Issued: 1993 in a limited
edition of 50
Status: Closed at No. 43
Series: Traditional Collection
O.I.P.: U.K. £215.00
U.S. $750.00

U.K.: £225.00
U.S.: $450.00
Can.: $600.00

CT-982
SUMMER TRILOGY
Designer: William Manson
Type: Weight – Spherical
Cane: WM (William Manson)
Issued: 1993 in a limited
edition of 50
Status: Fully subscribed
Series: Traditional Collection
O.I.P.: U.K. £195.00
U.S. $695.00

U.K.: £200.00
U.S.: $400.00
Can.: $525.00

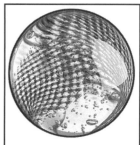

CT-983
TUNA FISH
Designer: William Manson
Type: Weight – Spherical
Cane: WM (William Manson)
Issued: 1993 in a limited
edition of 50
Status: Fully subscribed
Series: Traditional Collection
O.I.P.: U.K. £195.00
U.S. $695.00

U.K.: £200.00
U.S.: $400.00
Can.: $525.00

CT-984
BLUE SPLASH
Designer: Alastair MacIntosh
Type: Weight – Spherical
Issued: 1993
Status: Closed
Series: Unlimited – Modern Design
O.I.P.: U.K. £24.95
U.S. $87.50

U.K.: £25.00
U.S.: $50.00
Can.: $65.00

CT-985
CONGRATULATIONS
Style Two
Designer: Margot Thomson
Type: Weight – Spherical
Colour: 1. Gold
2. Ruby
3. Silver
Issued: 1993
Status: Active
Series: Unlimited – Modern Design
O.I.P.: U.K. £24.95
U.S. $87.50

U.K.: £34.95
U.S.: $95.00
Can.: –

CT-986
DIABOLO
Designer: Alastair MacIntosh
Type: Weight – Spherical
Issued: 1993
Status: Closed
Series: Unlimited – Modern Design
O.I.P.: U.K. £23.95
U.S. $79.50

U.K.: £25.00
U.S.: $50.00
Can.: $65.00

CT-987
FOUNTAIN
Designer: Colin Terris
Type: Weight – Spherical
Issued: 1993
Status: Closed
Series: Unlimited – Modern Design
O.I.P.: U.K. £29.95
U.S. $99.50

U.K.: £30.00
U.S.: $60.00
Can.: $80.00

CT-988
ORIENTAL SILK
Designer: Margot Thomson
Type: Weight – Spherical
Issued: 1993
Status: Closed
Series: Unlimited – Modern Design
O.I.P.: U.K. £23.95
U.S. $79.50

U.K.: £25.00
U.S.: $50.00
Can.: $65.00

CT-989
TARTAN TWIST
Designer: Alastair MacIntosh
Type: Weight – Spherical
Issued: 1993
Status: Closed
Series: Unlimited – Modern Design
O.I.P.: U.K. £21.95
U.S. $79.50

U.K.: £25.00
U.S.: $50.00
Can.: $65.00

CT-990
TWIRL
Designer: Margot Thomson
Type: Weight – Spherical
Size: Medium
Colour: 1. Blue
2. Gold
3. Pink
Issued: 1993
Status: Closed
Series: Medium and Miniature Size
O.I.P.: U.K. £12.95
U.S. $45.00

U.K.: £20.00
U.S.: $40.00
Can.: $50.00

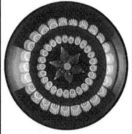

CT-991
CLEMATIS
Style Two
Designer: Allan Scott
Type: Weight – Spherical
Issued: 1993
Status: Closed
Series: Millefiori Miniatures
O.I.P.: U.K. £29.95
U.S. $115.00

U.K.: £30.00
U.S.: $60.00
Can.: $80.00

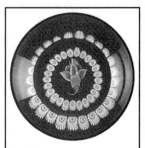

CT-992
FUCHSIA
Style Two
Designer: Allan Scott
Type: Weight – Spherical
Issued: 1993
Status: Closed
Series: Millefiori Miniatures
O.I.P.: U.K. £29.95
U.S. $115.00

U.K.: £30.00
U.S.: $60.00
Can.: $80.00

CT-993
IRIS
Style Two
Designer: Allan Scott
Type: Weight – Spherical
Issued: 1993
Status: Closed
Series: Millefiori Miniatures
O.I.P.: U.K. £29.95
U.S. $115.00

U.K.: £30.00
U.S.: $60.00
Can.: $80.00

CT-994
CLEMATIS PERFUME BOTTLE
Designer: Allan Scott
Type: Perfume bottle
Issued: 1993
Status: Closed
Series: Millefiori Miniatures
O.I.P.: U.K. £49.95
U.S. $175.00

U.K.: £ 50.00
U.S.: $100.00
Can.: $130.00

CT-995
FUCHSIA PERFUME BOTTLE
Style Two
Designer: Allan Scott
Type: Perfume bottle
Issued: 1993
Status: Closed
Series: Millefiori Miniatures
O.I.P.: U.K. £49.95
U.S. $175.00

U.K.: £ 50.00
U.S.: $100.00
Can.: $130.00

CT-996
IRIS PERFUME BOTTLE
Designer: Allan Scott
Type: Perfume bottle
Issued: 1993
Status: Closed
Series: Millefiori Miniatures
O.I.P.: U.K. £49.95
U.S. $175.00

U.K.: £ 50.00
U.S.: $100.00
Can.: $130.00

CT-997
BALMORAL INKWELL
Designer: Colin Terris
Type: Inkwell
Issued: 1993 in a limited
edition of 50
Status: Closed at No. 30
Series: Limited – Modern
Design
O.I.P.: U.K. £295.00
U.S. $995.00

U.K.: £300.00
U.S.: $600.00
Can.: $775.00

CT-998
DUNVEGAN INKWELL
Designer: Colin Terris
Type: Inkwell
Issued: 1993 in a limited
edition of 50
Status: Closed at No. 29
Series: Limited – Modern
Design
O.I.P.: U.K. £295.00
U.S. $995.00

U.K.: £300.00
U.S.: $600.00
Can.: $775.00

CT-999
OCEAN PEARL
Designer: Alastair MacIntosh
Type: Weight – Spherical
Issued: 1993 in a limited
edition of 50
Status: Fully subscribed
Series: Limited – Modern
Design
O.I.P.: U.K. £225.00
U.S. $695.00

U.K.: £250.00
U.S.: $500.00
Can.: $650.00

CT-1000
POLE STAR
Designer: Colin Terris
Type: Weight – Spherical, facets
Issued: 1993 in a limited edition of 75
Status: Fully subscribed
Series: Limited – Modern Design
O.I.P.: U.K. £185.00
U.S. $595.00

U.K.: £225.00
U.S.: $450.00
Can.: $575.00

CT-1001
CELESTIAL CRYSTAL
Designer: Colin Terris
Type: Weight – Spherical, facets
Issued: 1993 in a limited edition of 50
Status: Fully subscribed
Series: Limited – Modern Design
O.I.P.: U.K. £225.00
U.S. $695.00

U.K.: £250.00
U.S.: $500.00
Can.: $650.00

CT-1002
EURYTHMIC
Designer: Margot Thomson
Type: Weight – Spherical
Issued: 1993 in a limited edition of 750
Status: Closed at No. 488
Series: Limited – Modern Design
O.I.P.: U.K. £65.00
U.S. $225.00

U.K.: £ 65.00
U.S.: $130.00
Can.: $170.00

CT-1003
STRATOSPHERE
Designer: Colin Terris
Type: Weight – Spherical, facets
Issued: 1993 in a limited edition of 75
Status: Fully subscribed
Series: Limited – Modern Design
O.I.P.: U.K. £185.00
U.S. $595.00

U.K.: £225.00
U.S.: $450.00
Can.: $575.00

CT-1004
TRICOLOUR
Designer: Margot Thomson
Type: Weight – Spherical
Issued: 1993 in a limited edition of 750
Status: Closed at No. 318
Series: Limited – Modern Design
O.I.P.: U.K. £60.00
U.S. $235.00

U.K.: £ 60.00
U.S.: $120.00
Can.: $160.00

CT-1005
JACUZZI
Designer: Margot Thomson
Type: Weight – Spherical
Issued: 1993 in a limited edition of 650
Status: Closed at No. 287
Series: Limited – Modern Design
O.I.P.: U.K. £65.00
U.S. $225.00

U.K.: £ 65.00
U.S.: $130.00
Can.: $170.00

CT-1006
HYDROFOIL
Designer: Margot Thomson
Type: Weight – Spherical
Issued: 1993 in a limited edition of 750
Status: Closed at No. 493
Series: Limited – Modern Design
O.I.P.: U.K. £55.00
U.S. $190.00

U.K.: £ 55.00
U.S.: $110.00
Can.: $145.00

CT-1007
EVEREST
Designer: Alastair MacIntosh
Type: Weight – Domed
Issued: 1993 in a limited edition of 750
Status: Fully subscribed
Series: Limited – Modern Design
O.I.P.: U.K. £60.00
U.S. $210.00

U.K.: £ 60.00
U.S.: $120.00
Can.: $160.00

CT-1008
OCEAN ODYSSEY

Designer: Margot Thomson
Type: Weight – Teardrop, facets
Issued: 1993 in a limited edition of 350
Status: Closed at No. 285
Series: Limited – Modern Design
O.I.P.: U.K. £99.00
U.S. $350.00

U.K.: £100.00
U.S.: $200.00
Can.: $260.00

CT-1009
NIGHT VISION

Designer: Margot Thomson
Type: Weight – Spherical
Issued: 1993 in a limited edition of 150
Status: Closed at No. 121
Series: Limited – Modern Design
O.I.P.: U.K. £135.00
U.S. $525.00

U.K.: £150.00
U.S.: $300.00
Can.: $350.00

CT-1010
SUNBURST

Designer: Margot Thomson
Type: Weight – Spherical
Issued: 1993 in a limited edition of 750
Status: Closed at No. 395
Series: Limited – Modern Design
O.I.P.: U.K. £50.00
U.S. $175.00

U.K.: £ 50.00
U.S.: $100.00
Can.: $130.00

CT-1011
BLUETITS

Designer: William Manson
Type: Weight – Spherical
Issued: 1993 in a limited edition of 50
Status: Fully subscribed
Series: Traditional Collection
O.I.P.: U.K. £199.00
U.S. $695.00

U.K.: £200.00
U.S.: $400.00
Can.: $525.00

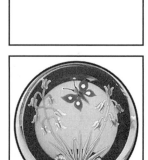

CT-1012
BUTTERFLY and BLUEBELLS

Designer: William Manson
Type: Weight – Spherical
Issued: 1993 in a limited edition of 50
Status: Closed at No. 38
Series: Traditional Collection
O.I.P.: U.K. £199.00
U.S. $695.00

U.K.: £200.00
U.S.: $400.00
Can.: $525.00

CT-1013
DOUBLE SALAMANDER

Designer: William Manson
Type: Weight – Spherical
Issued: 1993 in a limited edition of 25
Status: Fully subscribed
Series: Traditional Collection
O.I.P.: U.K. £395.00
U.S. $1,375.00

U.K.: £ 450.00
U.S.: $ 900.00
Can.: $1,175.00

CT-1014
WATERLILIES and DRAGONFLY

Designer: William Manson
Type: Weight – Spherical
Issued: 1993 in a limited edition of 50
Status: Closed at No. 42
Series: Traditional Collection
O.I.P.: U.K. £215.00
U.S. $750.00

U.K.: £225.00
U.S.: $450.00
Can.: $600.00

CT-1015
HUMMING BIRD
Style Two

Designer: William Manson
Type: Weight – Spherical
Issued: 1993 in a limited edition of 50
Status: Fully subscribed
Series: Traditional Collection
O.I.P.: U.K. £199.00
U.S. $695.00

U.K.: £200.00
U.S.: $400.00
Can.: $525.00

WHITEFRIARS

Blue Rhapsody

Triple Fancy

Village Pond

The historic name of Whitefriars was saved from dying out in 1981 when Caithness purchased the name. Ever since Caithness has created paperweights inspired by the traditional styles for which Whitefriars is known. Each paperweight still contains the hallmark Whitefriar cane, which was the company's emblem for many years based on its original location on the site of a Carmelite Monastery.

Golden Glory

Summer Bouquet

Bluebell Ballet

Summer Meadow Butterfly

WHITEFRIARS

Orchids
(Style Two)

Victorian Bouquet

Floral Diamond

Latticino Posy

Amethyst Bouquet

Floriana

Golden Awakening

Royal Blue

Fuchsias, Style One

WHITEFRIARS

Poppies, Style Two

Garden Fuchsias

Sweet Pea

Cliff Top

Sand Dunes

Swans by the Riverbank

JAPANESE INSPIRED

Japanese Ikebana

Japanese Tea Ceremony

Japanese White Crane

TRADITIONAL

Bluetits

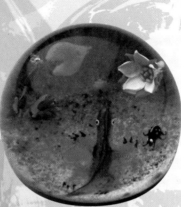

Newt

Duck Pond

Royal Flourish

Butterfly and Flower
(Second Version)

Flora

Harvest Mouse

Swan Lake

Kingfisher, Style One

TRADITIONAL

Daisy and Ladybird

Damsel Fly

National Flowers

Rock Pool

Pond Life

Dawn Chorus

Wild Rose Bouquet

Mayfly and Flowers

Nature Study

PERFUME BOTTLES AND FLASKS

Caithness continues to deliver a stunning range of hand crafted perfume bottles. Each bottle makes use of the paperweight making techniques for which the company is famous.

Milano Flask

Burning Passion Perfume Bottle

HM Queen Elizabeth II 70th Birthday Rose Perfume Bottle

Valentine Perfume Bottle

Honeysuckle Perfume Bottle

Summer Breeze Perfume Bottle

Bouquet Perfume Bottle

PERFUME BOTTLE AND WEIGHT SETS

DAWN TO DUSK

Morning Sunshine
Perfume Bottle
and Weight Set

Lazy Afternoon
Perfume Bottle
and Weight Set

Sultry Evening
Perfume Bottle
and Weight Set
(To be Issued 2005)

Lilac Time
Perfume Bottle
and Weight Set

Cantata Perfume Bottle
and Weight Set

Camilla Perfume Bottle
and Weight Set

NATURE STUDY

**Butterfly
Purple Flower**

Sunflower

**Dragonfly
White Flower**

Fruit

**Fruit and
Vegetable Set**

Veg.

COLLECTABLE EGGS

Confetti Cascade

From the Flames

Turquoise Delight

CT-1016
TADPOLES

Designer:	William Manson
Type:	Weight – Spherical
Issued:	1993 in a limited edition of 50
Status:	Fully subscribed
Series:	Traditional Collection
O.I.P.:	U.K. £215.00
	U.S. $750.00
U.K.:	£225.00
U.S.:	$450.00
Can.:	$600.00

CT-1017
RED ROSES

Designer:	William Manson
Type:	Weight – Spherical
Issued:	1993 in a limited edition of 50
Status:	Fully subscribed
Series:	Traditional Collection
O.I.P.:	U.K. £215.00
	U.S. $750.00
U.K.:	£225.00
U.S.:	$450.00
Can.:	$600.00

CT-1018
BUTTERFLY
Style Four

Designer:	William Manson
Type:	Weight – Spherical
Issued:	1993 in a limited edition of 150
Status:	Closed at No. 141
Series:	Traditional Collection
O.I.P.:	U.K. £60.00
	U.S. $210.00
U.K.:	£ 60.00
U.S.:	$120.00
Can.:	$160.00

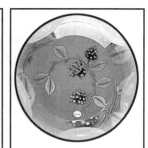

CT-1019
LADYBIRD
Style Three

Designer:	William Manson
Type:	Weight – Spherical
Issued:	1993 in a limited edition of 150
Status:	Fully subscribed
Series:	Traditional Collection
O.I.P.:	U.K. £60.00
	U.S. $210.00
U.K.:	£ 60.00
U.S.:	$120.00
Can.:	$160.00

CT-1020
WATERLILY

Designer:	William Manson
Type:	Weight – Spherical
Issued:	1993 in a limited edition of 150
Status:	Closed at No. 138
Series:	Traditional Collection
O.I.P.:	U.K. £60.00
	U.S. $210.00
U.K.:	£ 60.00
U.S.:	$120.00
Can.:	$160.00

CT-1021
WOODLAND FLOWERS

Designer:	William Manson
Type:	Weight – Spherical
Issued:	1993 in a limited edition of 150
Status:	Fully subscribed
Series:	Traditional Collection
O.I.P.:	U.K. £60.00
	U.S. $210.00
U.K.:	£ 60.00
U.S.:	$120.00
Can.:	$160.00

CT-1022
MIDNIGHT ORCHIDS

Designer:	Colin Terris and Allan Scott
Type:	Weight – Spherical, quadruple overlay
Issued:	1993 in a limited edition of 25
Status:	Fully subscribed
Series:	Whitefriars Collection
O.I.P.:	U.K. £495.00
	U.S. $1,725.00
U.K.:	£ 650.00
U.S.:	$1,300.00
Can.:	$1,700.00

CT-1023A
SUMMER CELEBRATION –
ONE

Designer:	Margot Thomson
Type:	Weight – Spherical
Issued:	1993 in a limited edition of 50
Status:	Fully subscribed
Series:	Whitefriars Collection
O.I.P.:	U.K. £299.00/set
	U.S. $1,150.00/set

	Weight	Set
U.K.:	£200.	400.
U.S.:	$400.	800.
Can.:	$525.	1,000.

Note: CT-1023A and B were issued and sold as a set.

CT-1023B
SUMMER CELEBRATION –
TWO
Designer: Margot Thomson
Type: Weight – Spherical
Issued: 1993 in a limited
edition of 50
Status: Fully subscribed
Series: Whitefriars Collection
O.I.P.: U.K. £299.00/set
U.S. $1,150.00/set

U.K.: £200.00
U.S.: $400.00
Can.: $525.00

CT-1024
MYRIAD RED
Designer: Caithness Studios
Type: Weight – Spherical
Issued: 1993
Status: Closed
O.I.P.: U.K. £29.95
U.S. $110.00

U.K.: £30.00
U.S.: $60.00
Can.: $80.00

CT-1025
MOONFLOWER RED
Designer: Colin Terris
Type: Weight – Spherical
Issued: 1993
Status: Closed
Series: Unlimited – Modern
Design
O.I.P.: U.K. £31.95
U.S. $99.50

U.K.: £35.00
U.S.: $70.00
Can.: $90.00

CT-1026
PARALLEL LINES
Designer: Margot Thomson
Type: Weight – Spherical
Issued: 1993
Status: Closed
Series: Unlimited – Modern
Design
O.I.P.: U.K. £29.95
U.S. $99.50

U.K.: £30.00
U.S.: $60.00
Can.: $80.00

CT-1027
FESTIVAL
Designer: Margot Thomson
Type: Weight – Spherical
Issued: 1993
Status: Closed
Series: Unlimited – Modern
Design
O.I.P.: U.K. £16.95
U.S. $58.50

U.K.: £20.00
U.S.: $40.00
Can.: $50.00

ISSUES OF 1994

CT-1028
LEVITATION

Designer: Alastair MacIntosh
Type: Weight – Spherical
Issued: 1994 in a limited
edition of 750
Status: Closed at No. 251
Series: Limited – Modern
Design
O.I.P.: U.K. £70.00
U.S. $225.00

U.K.: £ 70.00
U.S.: $140.00
Can.: $180.00

CT-1029
AUTUMN DREAM

Designer: Colin Terris
Type: Weight – Domed
Issued: 1994 in a limited
edition of 650
Status: Closed at No. 420
Series: Limited – Modern
Design
O.I.P.: U.K. £85.00
U.S. $275.00

U.K.: £ 85.00
U.S.: $170.00
Can.: $225.00

CT-1030
GAUCHO

Designer: Margot Thomson
Type: Weight – Teardrop
Issued: 1994 in a limited
edition of 650
Status: Closed at No. 437
Series: Limited – Modern
Design
O.I.P.: U.K. £75.00
U.S. $250.00

U.K.: £ 75.00
U.S.: $150.00
Can.: $200.00

CT-1031
DOUBLE MAGNUM 94

Designer: Margot Thomson
Type: Weight – Spherical
Size: Double magnum
Issued: 1994 in a limited
edition of 150
Status: Closed at No. 86
Series: Limited – Modern
Design
O.I.P.: U.K. £195.00
U.S. $595.00

U.K.: £200.00
U.S.: $400.00
Can.: $525.00

CT-1032
IMAGES

Designer: Colin Terris
Type: Weight – Spherical,
facets
Issued: 1994 in a limited
edition of 50
Status: Fully subscribed
Series: Limited – Modern
Design
O.I.P.: U.K. £235.00
U.S. $750.00

U.K.: £275.00
U.S.: $550.00
Can.: $725.00

CT-1033
SERENADE

Designer: Colin Terris
Type: Weight – Spherical,
facets
Issued: 1994 in a limited
edition of 50
Status: Fully subscribed
Series: Limited – Modern
Design
O.I.P.: U.K. £235.00
U.S. $750.00

U.K.: £250.00
U.S.: $500.00
Can.: $650.00

CT-1034
SEVENTH HEAVEN

Designer: Alastair MacIntosh
Type: Weight – Domed,
facets
Issued: 1994 in a limited
edition of 150
Status: Fully subscribed
Series: Limited – Modern
Design
O.I.P.: U.K. £150.00
U.S. $495.00

U.K.: £175.00
U.S.: $350.00
Can.: $450.00

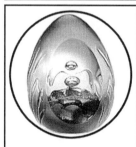

CT-1035
SWAN FLIGHT

Designer: Margot Thomson
Type: Weight – Domed
Issued: 1994 in a limited
edition of 75
Status: Fully subscribed
O.I.P.: U.K. £195.00
U.S. $650.00

U.K.: £200.00
U.S.: $400.00
Can.: $525.00

CT-1036
PINK CHIFFON

Designer: Alastair MacIntosh
Type: Weight – Spherical
Size: Magnum
Issued: 1994 in a limited
edition of 250
Status: Closed at No. 87
Series: Limited – Modern
Design
O.I.P.: U.K. £125.00
U.S. $395.00

U.K.: £125.00
U.S.: $250.00
Can.: $325.00

CT-1037
PASSION

Designer: Colin Terris
Type: Weight – Spherical
Issued: 1994 in a limited
edition of 50
Status: Fully subscribed
Series: Limited – Modern
Design
O.I.P.: U.K. £250.00
U.S. $750.00

U.K.: £250.00
U.S.: $500.00
Can.: $650.00

CT-1038
STAR CONQUEST

Designer: Alastair MacIntosh
Type: Weight – Spherical
Issued: 1994 in a limited
edition of 750
Status: Closed at No. 428
O.I.P.: U.K. £70.00
U.S. $230.00

U.K.: £ 70.00
U.S.: $140.00
Can.: $185.00

CT-1039
STORM WATCH

Designer: Helen MacDonald
Alastair MacIntosh
Type: Weight – Domed
Issued: 1994 in a limited
edition of 100
Status: Fully subscribed
O.I.P.: U.K. £235.00
U.S. $750.00

U.K.: £250.00
U.S.: $500.00
Can.: $650.00

CT-1040
DRUID

Designer: Alastair MacIntosh
Type: Weight – Domed
Issued: 1994 in a limited
edition of 650
Status: Closed at No. 568
Series: Limited – Modern
Design
O.I.P.: U.K. £85.00
U.S. $295.00

U.K.: £ 85.00
U.S.: $170.00
Can.: $225.00

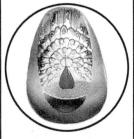

CT-1041
PEACOCK
Style Two

Designer: Helen MacDonald
Type: Weight – Domed
Issued: 1994 in a limited
edition of 100
Status: Fully subscribed
O.I.P.: U.K. £235.00
U.S. $750.00

U.K.: £235.00
U.S.: $475.00
Can.: $625.00

CT-1042
BIRDS OF PARADISE

Designer: Helen MacDonald
Type: Weight – Domed
Issued: 1994 in a limited
edition of 100
Status: Fully subscribed
Series: Limited – Modern
Design
O.I.P.: U.K. £235.00
U.S. $750.00

U.K.: £235.00
U.S.: $475.00
Can.: $625.00

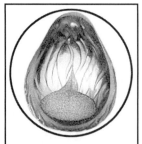

CT-1043
FIREFLAME

Designer: Helen MacDonald
Alastair MacIntosh
Type: Weight – Domed
Issued: 1994 in a limited
edition of 100
Status: Fully subscribed
Series: Limited – Modern
Design
O.I.P.: U.K. £235.00
U.S. $750.00

U.K.: £235.00
U.S.: $475.00
Can.: $625.00

CT-1044
DIVINE LIGHT

Designer:	Margot Thomson
Type:	Weight – Spherical
Issued:	1994 in a limited edition of 750
Status:	Closed at No. 429
Series:	Limited – Modern Design
O.I.P.:	U.K. £70.00 U.S. $225.00
U.K.:	£ 70.00
U.S.:	$140.00
Can.:	$185.00

CT-1045
OVERSEER

Designer:	Margot Thomson
Type:	Weight – Spherical
Issued:	1994 in a limited edition of 750
Status:	Closed at No. 527
Series:	Limited – Modern Design
O.I.P.:	U.K. £40.00 U.S. $140.00
U.K.:	£ 40.00
U.S.:	$ 80.00
Can.:	$100.00

CT-1046
BLUE SAIL

Designer:	Alastair MacIntosh
Type:	Weight – Spherical
Issued:	1994 in a limited edition of 750
Status:	Fully subscribed
Series:	Limited – Modern Design
O.I.P.:	U.K. £50.00 U.S. $150.00
U.K.:	£ 50.00
U.S.:	$100.00
Can.:	$130.00

CT-1047
ACCORD

Designer:	Margot Thomson
Type:	Weight – Spherical
Issued:	1994 in a limited edition of 750
Status:	Closed at No. 564
Series:	Limited – Modern Design
O.I.P.:	U.K. £70.00 U.S. $225.00
U.K.:	£ 70.00
U.S.:	$140.00
Can.:	$185.00

CT-1048
MAYPOLE

Designer:	Margot Thomson
Type:	Weight – Domed
Issued:	1994 in a limited edition of 750
Status:	Closed at No. 472
Series:	Limited – Modern Design
O.I.P.:	U.K. £55.00 U.S. $175.00
U.K.:	£ 55.00
U.S.:	$110.00
Can.:	$145.00

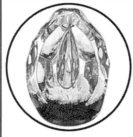

CT-1049
TRANSATLANTIC

Designer:	Margot Thomson
Type:	Weight – Domed, facets
Issued:	1994 in a limited edition of 150
Status:	Closed at No. 124
Series:	Limited – Modern Design
O.I.P.:	U.K. £150.00 U.S. $550.00
U.K.:	£150.00
U.S.:	$300.00
Can.:	$400.00

CT-1050
MOONRISE

Designer:	Margot Thomson
Type:	Weight – Domed
Issued:	1994 in a limited edition of 750
Status:	Closed at No. 404
Series:	Limited – Modern Design
O.I.P.:	U.K. £65.00 U.S. $225.00
U.K.:	£ 65.00
U.S.:	$130.00
Can.:	$170.00

CT-1051
THE HEALER

Designer:	Colin Terris
Type:	Weight – Spherical
Issued:	1994 in a limited edition of 750
Status:	Closed at No. 486
Series:	Limited – Modern Design
O.I.P.:	U.K. £70.00 U.S. $225.00
U.K.:	£ 70.00
U.S.:	$140.00
Can.:	$185.00

CT-1052
SUBMARINER

Designer: Colin Terris
Type: Weight – Spherical
Issued: 1994 in a limited
          edition of 750
Status: Closed at No. 678
Series: Limited – Modern
          Design
O.I.P.:   U.K. £65.00
          U.S. $225.00

U.K.:   £ 65.00
U.S.: $130.00
Can.: $170.00

CT-1053
MELODY

Designer: Margot Thomson
Type: Weight – Spherical
Issued: 1994 in a limited
          edition of 650
Status: Closed at No. 558
Series: Limited – Modern
          Design
O.I.P.:   U.K. £75.00
          U.S. $250.00

U.K.:   £ 75.00
U.S.: $150.00
Can.: $200.00

CT-1054
RING O' ROSES

Designer: Margot Thomson
Type: Weight – Spherical
Issued: 1994 in a limited
          edition of 750
Status: Closed at No. 530
Series: Limited – Modern
          Design
O.I.P.:   U.K. £65.00
          U.S. $225.00

U.K.:   £ 65.00
U.S.: $130.00
Can.: $170.00

CT-1055
ENDEARMENT

Designer: Colin Terris
Type: Weight – Spherical
Issued: 1994 in a limited
          edition of 75
Status: Fully subscribed
Series: Limited – Modern
          Design
O.I.P.:   U.K. £175.00
          U.S. $575.00

U.K.:   £175.00
U.S.: $350.00
Can.: $450.00

CT-1056
REVERENCE

Designer: Colin Terris
Type: Weight – Spherical
Issued: 1994 in a limited
          edition of 75
Status: Fully subscribed
Series: Limited – Modern
          Design
O.I.P.:   U.K. £175.00
          U.S. $550.00

U.K.:   £175.00
U.S.: $350.00
Can.: $450.00

CT-1057
HARLEQUIN DOUBLE
Style Two

Designer: Paul Ysart derivative
Type: Weight – Domed
Cane: 94
Issued: 1994 in a limited edition of 500
Status: Closed at No. 437
Series: Classic Collection
O.I.P.:   U.K. £55.00
           U.S. $175.00

U.K.:   £ 55.00
U.S.: $110.00
Can.: $145.00

Note: Weights CT-1057 through 1061 were issued to commemorate the 25th anniversary of the Caithness Glass paperweight collection.

CT-1058
HARLEQUIN SINGLE
Style Two

Designer: Paul Ysart
          derivative
Type: Weight – Spherical
Cane: 94
Issued: 1994 in a limited
          edition of 500
Status: Closed at No. 403
Series: Classic Collection
O.I.P.:   U.K. £45.00
          U.S. $150.00

U.K.:   £ 45.00
U.S.: $ 90.00
Can.: $120.00

CT-1059
FLOWER IN THE RAIN
Style Two

Designer: Colin Terris
Type: Weight – Spherical
Cane: 94
Issued: 1994 in a limited
edition of 500
Status: Closed at No. 409
Series: Classic Collection
O.I.P.: U.K. £60.00
U.S. $185.00

U.K.: £ 60.00
U.S.: $120.00
Can.: $160.00

CT-1060
SILVER CORAL

Designer: Colin Terris
Type: Weight – Spherical
Cane: 94
Issued: 1994 in a limited
edition of 500
Status: Closed at No. 282
Series: Classic Collection
O.I.P.: U.K. £65.00
U.S. $210.00

U.K.: £ 65.00
U.S.: $130.00
Can.: $170.00

CT-1061
SILVER MOONFLOWER

Designer: Colin Terris
Type: Weight – Spherical,
magnum size
Cane: 94
Issued: 1994 in a limited
edition of 350
Status: Fully subscribed
Series: Classic Collection
O.I.P.: U.K. £65.00
U.S. $225.00

U.K.: £ 65.00
U.S.: $130.00
Can.: $170.00

CT-1062
JUBILEE ORCHID

Designer: Colin Terris
Type: Weight – Spherical
Issued: 1994 in a limited
edition of 1,883
Status: Fully subscribed
O.I.P.: U.K. £99.00
U.S. $275.00

U.K.: £100.00
U.S.: $200.00
Can.: $260.00

Note: This is the 1994
Collectors' Paperweight

CT-1063
WOOD ANEMONES

Designer: Margot Thomson
Type: Weight – Spherical
Issued: 1994 in a limited
edition of 50
Status: Closed at No. 39
Series: Whitefriars Collection
O.I.P.: U.K. £165.00
U.S. $595.00

U.K.: £165.00
U.S.: $330.00
Can.: $425.00

CT-1064
LILY OF THE VALLEY

Designer: Margot Thomson
Type: Weight – Spherical
Issued: 1994 in a limited
edition of 50
Status: Fully subscribed
Series: Whitefriars Collection
O.I.P.: U.K. £175.00
U.S. $650.00

U.K.: £175.00
U.S.: $350.00
Can.: $450.00

CT-1065
CHRISTMAS ROSE
Style Three

Designer: Margot Thomson
Type: Weight – Spherical
Issued: 1994 in a limited
edition of 50
Status: Closed at No. 45
Series: Whitefriars Collection
O.I.P.: U.K. £165.00
U.S. $595.00

U.K.: £165.00
U.S.: $330.00
Can.: $425.00

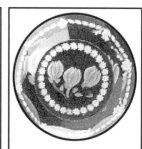

CT-1066
MAGNOLIA

Designer: Margot Thomson
Type: Weight – Spherical
Issued: 1994 in a limited
edition of 50
Status: Fully subscribed
Series: Whitefriars Collection
O.I.P.: U.K. £150.00
U.S. $575.00

U.K.: £150.00
U.S.: $300.00
Can.: $400.00

CT-1067A
AUTUMN CELEBRATION ONE

Designer: Margot Thomson
Type: Weight – Spherical
Issued: 1994 in a limited
edition of 50
Status: Fully subscribed
Series: Whitefriars Collection
O.I.P.: U.K. £325.00/set,
U.S. $1,150.00/set

	Weight	Set
U.K.:	£200.	400.
U.S.:	$400.	800.
Can.:	$525.	1,050.

Note: CT-1067A and B were
issued and sold as a set.

CT-1067B
AUTUMN CELEBRATION TWO

Designer: Margot Thomson
Type: Weight – Spherical
Issued: 1994 in a limited
edition of 50
Status: Fully subscribed
Series: Whitefriars Collection
O.I.P.: U.K. £325.00/set
U.S. $1,150.00/set

U.K.: £200.00
U.S.: $400.00
Can.: $525.00

CT-1068
PANSIES

Designer: Margot Thomson
Type: Weight – Spherical
Issued: 1994 in a limited
edition of 50
Status: Fully subscribed
Series: Whitefriars Collection
O.I.P.: U.K. £215.00
U.S. $750.00

U.K.: £225.00
U.S.: $450.00
Can.: $600.00

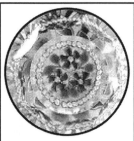

CT-1069
PERIWINKLES
Style One

Designer: Margot Thomson
Type: Weight – Spherical
Issued: 1994 in a limited
edition of 50
Status: Closed at No. 46
Series: Whitefriars Collection
O.I.P.: U.K. £175.00
U.S. $650.00

U.K.: £175.00
U.S.: $350.00
Can.: $450.00

CT-1070
WINTER FLOWERS

Designer: Margot Thomson
Type: Weight – Spherical
Issued: 1994 in a limited
edition of 50
Status: Closed at No. 44
Series: Whitefriars Collection
O.I.P.: U.K. £215.00
U.S. $750.00

U.K.: £225.00
U.S.: $450.00
Can.: $600.00

CT-1071
**CHERRY BLOSSOM PERFUME
BOTTLE**

Designer: Margot Thomson
Type: Perfume bottle
Issued: 1994 in a limited
edition of 50
Status: Closed at No. 30
Series: Whitefriars Collection
O.I.P.: U.K. £215.00
U.S. $775.00

U.K.: £225.00
U.S.: $450.00
Can.: $600.00

CT-1072A
CARNATION PERFUME BOTTLE

Designer: Margot Thomson
Type: Perfume bottle
Issued: 1994 in a limited
edition of 50
Status: Closed at No. 38
Series: Whitefriars Collection
O.I.P.: U.K. £395.00/set
U.S. $1,375.00/set

	Perfume	Set
U.K.:	£325.	575.
U.S.:	$650.	1,150.
Can.:	$850.	1,500.

Note: CT-1072A and B were
issued and sold as a set.

CT-1072B
CARNATION
Style Two

Designer: Margot Thomson
Type: Weight – Spherical
Issued: 1994 in a limited
edition of 50
Status: Closed at No. 38
Series: Whitefriars Collection
O.I.P.: U.K. £395.00/set
U.S. $1,375.00/set

U.K.: £250.00
U.S.: $500.00
Can.: $650.00

CT-1073
WOODLAND GLADE

Designer: Colin Terris and
Allan Scott
Type: Weight – Spherical,
quadruple overlay
Issued: 1994 in a limited
edition of 25
Status: Fully subscribed
Series: Whitefriars Collection
O.I.P.: U.K. £595.00
U.S. $2,100.00

U.K.: £ 600.00
U.S.: $1,200.00
Can.: $1,550.00

CT-1074
ZEBRA FISH

Designer: William Manson
Type: Weight – Spherical
Issued: 1994 in a limited
edition of 50
Status: Closed at No. 39
Series: Traditional Collection
O.I.P.: U.K. £215.00
U.S. $775.00

U.K.: £225.00
U.S.: $450.00
Can.: $600.00

CT-1075
BUTTERFLY GARLAND

Designer: William Manson
Type: Weight – Spherical
Issued: 1994 in a limited
edition of 50
Status: Closed at No. 41
Series: Traditional Collection
O.I.P.: U.K. £215.00
U.S. $695.00

U.K.: £225.00
U.S.: $450.00
Can.: $600.00

CT-1076
LADYBIRD and BUTTERFLY

Designer: William Manson
Type: Weight – Spherical
Issued: 1994 in a limited
edition of 50
Status: Closed at No. 44
Series: Traditional Collection
O.I.P.: U.K. £215.00
U.S. $750.00

U.K.: £225.00
U.S.: $450.00
Can.: $600.00

CT-1077
WATERHEN

Designer: William Manson
Type: Weight – Spherical
Issued: 1994 in a limited
edition of 50
Status: Closed at No. 34
Series: Traditional Collection
O.I.P.: U.K. £215.00
U.S. $775.00

U.K.: £225.00
U.S.: $450.00
Can.: $600.00

CT-1078
SPINOSAURUS

Designer: William Manson
Type: Weight – Spherical
Issued: 1994 in a limited
edition of 50
Status: Closed at No. 45
Series: Traditional Collection
O.I.P.: U.K. £275.00
U.S. $995.00

U.K.: £275.00
U.S.: $550.00
Can.: $725.00

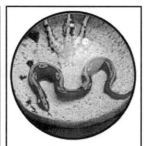

CT-1079
SIDEWINDER

Designer: William Manson
Type: Weight – Spherical
Issued: 1994 in a limited
edition of 50
Status: Closed at No. 38
Series: Traditional Collection
O.I.P.: U.K. £275.00
U.S. $995.00

U.K.: £275.00
U.S.: $550.00
Can.: $725.00

CT-1080
PILOT FISH

Designer: William Manson
Type: Weight – Spherical
Issued: 1994 in a limited
edition of 50
Status: Closed at No. 42
Series: Traditional Collection
O.I.P.: U.K. £235.00
U.S. $850.00

U.K.: £235.00
U.S.: $475.00
Can.: $625.00

CT-1081
MORNING GLORY
Designer: William Manson
Type: Weight – Spherical
Issued: 1994 in a limited
edition of 50
Status: Fully subscribed
Series: Traditional Collection
O.I.P.: U.K. £225.00
U.S. $750.00

U.K.: £225.00
U.S.: $450.00
Can.: $600.00

CT-1082
FOSSIL
Designer: William Manson
Type: Weight – Spherical
Issued: 1994 in a limited
edition of 50
Status: Closed at No. 33
Series: Traditional Collection
O.I.P.: U.K. £225.00
U.S. $775.00

U.K.: £225.00
U.S.: $450.00
Can.: $600.00

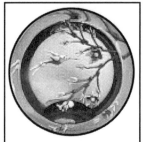

CT-1083
HUMMING BIRD
Style Three
Designer: William Manson
Type: Weight – Spherical
Issued: 1994 in a limited
edition of 50
Status: Fully subscribed
Series: Traditional Collection
O.I.P.: U.K. £215.00
U.S. $775.00

U.K.: £225.00
U.S.: $450.00
Can.: $600.00

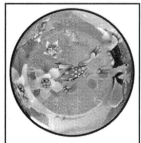

CT-1084
FROG
Designer: William Manson
Type: Weight – Spherical
Issued: 1994 in a limited
edition of 50
Status: Closed at No. 47
Series: Traditional Collection
O.I.P.: U.K. £225.00
U.S. $825.00

U.K.: £225.00
U.S.: $450.00
Can.: $600.00

CT-1085
BUTTERCUPS
Designer: William Manson
Type: Weight – Spherical
Size: Medium
Issued: 1994 in a limited
edition of 150
Status: Closed at No. 138
Series: Traditional Collection
O.I.P.: U.K. £65.00
U.S. $210.00

U.K.: £ 65.00
U.S.: $130.00
Can.: $170.00

CT-1086
RED ROSE
Style Two
Designer: William Manson
Type: Weight – Spherical
Size: Medium
Issued: 1994 in a limited
edition of 150
Status: Fully subscribed
Series: Traditional Collection
O.I.P.: U.K. £65.00
U.S. $210.00

U.K.: £ 65.00
U.S.: $130.00
Can.: $170.00

CT-1087
YELLOW ROSE
Style One
Designer: William Manson
Type: Weight – Spherical
Size: Medium
Issued: 1994 in a limited
edition of 150
Status: Fully subscribed
Series: Traditional Collection
O.I.P.: U.K. £65.00
U.S. $210.00

U.K.: £ 65.00
U.S.: $130.00
Can.: $170.00

CT-1088
PANSY
Style Two
Designer: William Manson
Type: Weight – Spherical
Size: Medium
Issued: 1994 in a limited
edition of 150
Status: Closed at No. 142
Series: Traditional Collection
O.I.P.: U.K. £65.00
U.S. $210.00

U.K.: £ 65.00
U.S.: $130.00
Can.: $170.00

CT-1089
FEATHERS

Designer: Alastair MacIntosh
Type: Weight – Spherical
Issued: 1994
Status: Closed
Series: Unlimited – Modern Design
O.I.P.: U.K. £26.95
U.S. $87.50

U.K.: £30.00
U.S.: $60.00
Can.: $80.00

CT-1090
GULF STREAM

Designer: Alastair MacIntosh
Type: Weight – Spherical
Issued: 1994
Status: Closed
Series: Unlimited – Modern Design
O.I.P.: U.K. £28.95
U.S. $99.50

U.K.: £30.00
U.S.: $60.00
Can.: $80.00

CT-1091
INNER CIRCLE

Designer: Alastair MacIntosh
Type: Weight – Spherical
Issued: 1994
Status: Closed
Series: Unlimited – Modern Design
O.I.P.: U.K. £32.95
U.S. $115.00

U.K.: £35.00
U.S.: $70.00
Can.: $90.00

CT-1092
MOONFLOWER RAINBOW

Designer: Colin Terris
Type: Weight – Spherical
Colour: Blue, green, white and fuchsia
Issued: 1994
Status: Closed
Series: Unlimited – Modern Design
O.I.P.: U.K. £32.95
U.S. $99.50

U.K.: £35.00
U.S.: $70.00
Can.: $90.00

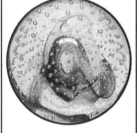

CT-1093
SPARKLE

Designer: Colin Terris
Type: Weight – Spherical
Colour: 1. Blue
2. Purple
Issued: 1994
Status: Closed
Series: Unlimited – Modern Design
O.I.P.: U.K. £26.95
U.S. $87.50

	Blue	Purple
U.K.:	£30.	30.
U.S.:	$60.	60.
Can.:	$80.	80.

Note: Weight illustrated is blue.

CT-1094
JUBILEE 94 DOUBLE MAGNUM

Designer: Colin Terris
Type: Weight – Spherical
Size: Double magnum
Issued: 1994 in a limited edition of 25
Status: Fully subscribed
Series: Limited – Modern Design
O.I.P.: U.K. £850.00
U.S. $2,750.00

U.K.: £1,200.00
U.S.: $2,400.00
Can.: $3,150.00

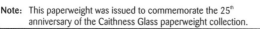

Note: This paperweight was issued to commemorate the 25th anniversary of the Caithness Glass paperweight collection.

CT-1095
FAIRY TALE

Designer: Alastair MacIntosh
Type: Weight – Domed
Issued: 1994 in a limited edition of 650
Status: Fully subscribed
Series: Limited – Modern Design
O.I.P.: U.K. £75.00
U.S. $225.00

U.K.: £ 75.00
U.S.: $150.00
Can.: $200.00

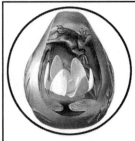

CT-1096
LILY POND

Designer: Helen MacDonald
Type: Weight – Domed
Issued: 1994 in a limited
edition of 100
Status: Closed at No. 93
Series: Limited – Modern
Design
O.I.P.: U.K. £235.00
U.S. $695.00

U.K.: £250.00
U.S.: $500.00
Can.: $650.00

CT-1097
AZTEC

Designer: Alastair MacIntosh
Type: Weight – Spherical
Issued: 1994 in a limited
edition of 500
Status: Closed at No. 135
Series: Limited – Modern
Design
O.I.P.: U.K. £85.00
U.S. $250.00

U.K.: £ 85.00
U.S.: $170.00
Can.: $225.00

CT-1098
BLOSSOM

Designer: Colin Terris
Type: Weight – Spherical,
facets
Issued: 1994 in a limited
edition of 75
Status: Fully subscribed
Series: Limited – Modern
Design
O.I.P.: U.K. £175.00
U.S. $495.00

U.K.: £175.00
U.S.: $350.00
Can.: $450.00

CT-1099
GOLDEN SUNRISE

Designer: Alan Scrimgeour
Type: Weight – Spherical
Issued: 1994 in a limited
edition of 750
Status: Closed at No. 465
Series: Limited – Modern
Design
O.I.P.: U.K. £65.00
U.S. $195.00

U.K.: £ 65.00
U.S.: $130.00
Can.: $170.00

CT-1100
BLACK MAGIC

Designer: Alastair MacIntosh
Type: Weight – Spherical
Issued: 1994 in a limited
edition of 750
Status: Closed at No. 541
Series: Limited – Modern
Design
O.I.P.: U.K. £50.00
U.S. $165.00

U.K.: £ 50.00
U.S.: $100.00
Can.: $130.00

CT-1101
L'AMOUR

Designer: Colin Terris
Type: Weight – Spherical
Issued: 1994 in a limited
edition of 50
Status: Fully subscribed
Series: Limited – Modern
Design
O.I.P.: U.K. £250.00
U.S. $750.00

U.K.: £275.00
U.S.: $550.00
Can.: $725.00

CT-1102
MONET TRIBUTE

Designer: Colin Terris
Type: Weight – Spherical,
double overlay
Issued: 1994 in a limited
edition of 50
Status: Fully subscribed
Series: Limited – Modern
Design
O.I.P.: U.K. £350.00
U.S. $1,000.00

U.K.: £350.00
U.S.: $700.00
Can.: $900.00

CT-1103
FROSTY MORNING

Designer: John Spittal
Type: Weight – Domed
Issued: 1994 in a limited
edition of 350
Status: Fully subscribed
Series: Limited – Modern
Design
O.I.P.: U.K. £99.00
U.S. $295.00

U.K.: £100.00
U.S.: $200.00
Can.: $260.00

CT-1104
GUARDIAN ANGEL

Designer: Helen MacDonald
Type: Weight – Domed
Issued: 1994 in a limited
edition of 500
Status: Closed at No. 465
Series: Limited – Modern
Design
O.I.P.: U.K. £90.00
U.S. $250.00

U.K.: £ 90.00
U.S.: $180.00
Can.: $235.00

CT-1105
SHIFTING SANDS

Designer: Helen MacDonald
Type: Weight – Domed
Issued: 1994 in a limited
edition of 650
Status: Fully subscribed
Series: Limited – Modern
Design
O.I.P.: U.K. £70.00
U.S. $210.00

U.K.: £ 70.00
U.S.: $140.00
Can.: $180.00

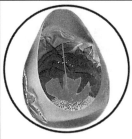

CT-1106
SCARLET HIBISCUS

Designer: Helen MacDonald
Type: Weight – Domed
Issued: 1994 in a limited
edition of 100
Status: Closed at No. 93
Series: Limited – Modern
Design
O.I.P.: U.K. £245.00
U.S. $695.00

U.K.: £250.00
U.S.: $500.00
Can.: $650.00

CT-1107
ARCTIC AWAKENING

Designer: Colin Terris
Type: Weight – Domed,
quadruple overlay
Issued: 1994 in a limited
edition of 25
Status: Fully subscribed
Series: Limited – Modern
Design
O.I.P.: U.K. £495.00
U.S. $1,500.00

U.K.: £ 800.00
U.S.: $1,600.00
Can.: $2,000.00

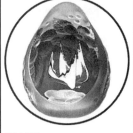

CT-1108
SUMMER GLADE

Designer: Helen MacDonald
Type: Weight – Domed
Issued: 1994 in a limited
edition of 100
Status: Closed at No. 77
Series: Limited – Modern
Design
O.I.P.: U.K. £245.00
U.S. $695.00

U.K.: £250.00
U.S.: $500.00
Can.: $650.00

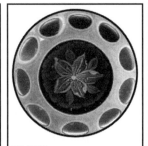

CT-1109
AZALEA

Designer: Colin Terris
Allan Scott
Type: Weight – Spherical,
triple overlay
Issued: 1994 in a limited
edition of 25
Status: Fully subscribed
Series: Whitefriars Collection
O.I.P.: U.K. £595.00
U.S. $1,750.00

U.K.: £ 650.00
U.S.: $1,300.00
Can.: $1,700.00

CT-1110
AZURE BOUQUET

Designer: Allan Scott
Type: Weight – Spherical
Issued: 1994 in a limited
edition of 50
Status: Closed at No. 35
Series: Whitefriars Collection
O.I.P.: U.K. £175.00
U.S. $595.00

U.K.: £175.00
U.S.: $350.00
Can.: $450.00

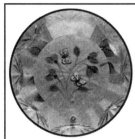

CT-1111
BUTTERFLY BOUQUET

Designer: Allan Scott
Type: Weight – Spherical
Issued: 1994 in a limited
edition of 50
Status: Fully subscribed
Series: Whitefriars Collection
O.I.P.: U.K. £165.00
U.S. $495.00

U.K.: £165.00
U.S.: $330.00
Can.: $430.00

CT-1112
CINQUEFOIL
Designer: Allan Scott
Type: Weight – Spherical
Issued: 1994 in a limited
edition of 50
Status: Closed at No. 41
Series: Whitefriars Collection
O.I.P.: U.K. £175.00
U.S. $595.00

U.K.: £175.00
U.S.: $350.00
Can.: $450.00

CT-1113
HIBISCUS
Designer: Allan Scott
Type: Weight – Spherical
Issued: 1994 in a limited
edition of 50
Status: Closed at No. 45
Series: Whitefriars Collection
O.I.P.: U.K. £215.00
U.S. $750.00

U.K.: £225.00
U.S.: $450.00
Can.: $600.00

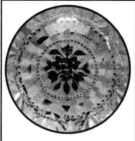

CT-1114
SUMMER POSY
Style One
Designer: Allan Scott
Type: Weight – Spherical
Issued: 1994 in a limited
edition of 50
Status: Fully subscribed
Series: Whitefriars Collection
O.I.P.: U.K. £185.00
U.S. $650.00

U.K.: £185.00
U.S.: $375.00
Can.: $475.00

CT-1115
FLORAL GARDEN
Designer: William Manson
Type: Weight – Spherical
Issued: 1994 in a limited
edition of 50
Status: Closed at No. 34
Series: Traditional Collection
O.I.P.: U.K. £250.00
U.S. $695.00

U.K.: £250.00
U.S.: $500.00
Can.: $650.00

CT-1116
LILIUM
Style One
Designer: William Manson
Type: Weight – Spherical
Issued: 1994 in a limited
edition of 50
Status: Closed at No. 30
Series: Traditional Collection
O.I.P.: U.K. £235.00
U.S. $795.00

U.K.: £235.00
U.S.: $470.00
Can.: $600.00

CT-1117
LORIKEET
Designer: William Manson
Type: Weight – Spherical
Issued: 1994 in a limited
edition of 50
Status: Closed at No. 31
Series: Traditional Collection
O.I.P.: U.K. £225.00
U.S. $750.00

U.K.: £225.00
U.S.: $450.00
Can.: $600.00

CT-1118
SEASCAPE
Designer: William Manson
Type: Weight – Spherical
Issued: 1994 in a limited
edition of 50
Status: Fully subscribed
Series: Traditional Collection
O.I.P.: U.K. £275.00
U.S. $825.00

U.K.: £275.00
U.S.: $550.00
Can.: $725.00

CT-1119
SNOWMAN
Designer: William Manson
Type: Weight – Spherical
Issued: 1994 in a limited
edition of 50
Status: Fully subscribed
Series: Traditional Collection
O.I.P.: U.K. £250.00
U.S. $750.00

U.K.: £250.00
U.S.: $500.00
Can.: $650.00

CT-1120
STINGRAY
Designer: William Manson
Type: Weight – Spherical
Issued: 1994 in a limited
edition of 50
Status: Fully subscribed
Series: Traditional Collection
O.I.P.: U.K. £275.00
U.S. $895.00
U.K.: £275.00
U.S.: $550.00
Can.: $725.00

CT-1121
SUNFLOWER
Style Two
Designer: William Manson
Type: Weight – Spherical
Issued: 1994 in a limited
edition of 50
Status: Closed at No. 33
Series: Traditional Collection
O.I.P.: U.K. £215.00
U.S. $750.00
U.K.: £225.00
U.S.: $450.00
Can.: $600.00

CT-1122
MINI BUTTERFLY and ORANGE
FLOWER
Designer: Allan Scott
Type: Weight – Spherical
Issued: 1994 in a limited
edition of 150
Status: Closed at No. 102
Series: Traditional Collection
Nature Study
O.I.P.: U.K. £70.00
U.S. $210.00
U.K.: £ 70.00
U.S.: $140.00
Can.: $185.00

CT-1123
MINI BUTTERFLY and YELLOW
FLOWER
Designer: Allan Scott
Type: Weight – Spherical
Issued: 1994 in a limited
edition of 150
Status: Closed at No. 95
Series: Traditional Collection
Nature Study
O.I.P.: U.K. £70.00
U.S. $210.00
U.K.: £ 70.00
U.S.: $140.00
Can.: $185.00

CT-1124
ORANGE BUTTERFLY
Designer: Allan Scott
Type: Weight – Spherical
Issued: 1994 in a limited
edition of 50
Status: Fully subscribed
Series: Traditional Collection
Nature Study
O.I.P.: U.K. £125.00
U.S. $375.00
U.K.: £125.00
U.S.: $250.00
Can.: $325.00

CT-1125
YELLOW BUTTERFLY
Designer: Allan Scott
Type: Weight – Spherical
Issued: 1994 in a limited
edition of 50
Status: Fully subscribed
Series: Traditional Collection
Nature Study
O.I.P.: U.K. £125.00
U.S. $375.00
U.K.: £125.00
U.S.: $250.00
Can.: $325.00

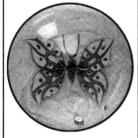

CT-1126
YELLOW BUTTERFLY –
LATTICINO BASE
Designer: Allan Scott
Type: Weight – Spherical
Issued: 1994 in a limited
edition of 50
Status: Fully subscribed
Series: Traditional Collection
Nature Study
O.I.P.: U.K. £99.00
U.S. $295.00
U.K.: £100.00
U.S.: $200.00
Can.: $260.00

CT-1127
CHERRY BLOSSOM
Designer: William Manson
Type: Weight – Spherical
Issued: 1994 in a limited
edition of 150
Status: Closed at No. 123
Series: Traditional Collection
O.I.P.: U.K. £70.00
U.S. $210.00
U.K.: £ 70.00
U.S.: $140.00
Can.: $185.00

CT-1128
GRAPES
Style Two

Designer: William Manson
Type: Weight – Spherical
Issued: 1994 in a limited
edition of 150
Status· Closed at No. 87
Series: Traditional Collection
O.I.P.: U.K. £70.00
U.S. $210.00

U.K.: £ 70.00
U.S.: $140.00
Can.: $185.00

CT-1129
SONGBIRD

Designer: William Manson
Type: Weight – Spherical
Issued: 1994 in a limited
edition of 150
Status: Closed at No. 110
Series: Traditional Collection
O.I.P.: U.K. £70.00
U.S. $210.00

U.K.: £ 70.00
U.S.: $140.00
Can.: $185.00

CT-1130
STRAWBERRY
Style Two

Designer: William Manson
Type: Weight – Spherical
Issued: 1994 in a limited
edition of 150
Status. Closed at No. 125
Series: Traditional Collection
O.I.P.: U.K. £70.00
U.S. $210.00

U.K.: £ 70.00
U.S.: $140.00
Can.: $185.00

CT-1131
ASCENSION

Designer: Alastair MacIntosh
Type: Weight – Domed
Issued: 1994
Status: Closed
Series: Unlimited – Modern
Design
O.I.P.: U.K. £28.50
U.S. $87.50

U.K.: £30.00
U.S.: $60.00
Can.: $80.00

CT-1132
ESCAPADE

Designer: David Nicoll
Type: Weight – Spherical
Issued: 1994
Status: Closed
Series: Unlimited – Modern
Design
O.I.P.: U.K. £29.50
U.S. $95.00

U.K.: £30.00
U.S.: $60.00
Can.: $80.00

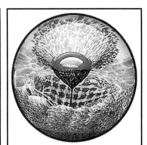

CT-1133
FLOWER OF SCOTLAND

Designer: Alastair MacIntosh
Type: Weight – Spherical
Issued: 1994
Status: Active
Series: Unlimited – Modern
Design
O.I.P.: U.K. £33.50
U.S. $95.00

U.K.: £ 39.95
U.S.: $110.00
Can.: –

CT-1134
OCEAN BREEZE

Designer: Alastair MacIntosh
Type: Weight – Spherical
Issued: 1994
Status: Closed
Series: Unlimited – Modern
Design
O.I.P.: U.K. £30.00
U.S. $87.50

U.K.: £30.00
U.S.: $60.00
Can.: $80.00

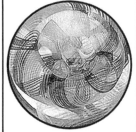

CT-1135
SORCERER

Designer: Alastair MacIntosh
Type: Weight – Spherical
Issued: 1994
Status: Closed
Series: Unlimited – Modern
Design
O.I.P.: U.K. £26.50
U.S. $75.00

U.K.: £30.00
U.S.: $60.00
Can.: $80.00

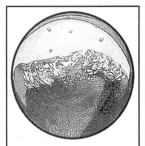

CT-1136
WAVECREST

Designer:	Alastair MacIntosh
Type:	Weight – Spherical
Issued:	1994
Status:	Closed
Series:	Unlimited – Modern Design
O.I.P.:	U.K. £29.50
	U.S. $87.50
U.K.:	£30.00
U.S.:	$60.00
Can.:	$80.00

CT-1137
THISTLE INKWELL

Designer:	Allan Scott
Type:	Inkwell
Issued:	1994
Status:	Closed
Series:	Millefiori Miniatures
O.I.P.:	U.K. £55.00
	U.S. $175.00
U.K.:	£ 55.00
U.S.:	$110.00
Can.:	$145.00

CT-1138
ROSE INKWELL

Designer:	Allan Scott
Type:	Inkwell
Issued:	1994
Status:	Closed
Series:	Millefiori Miniatures
O.I.P.:	U.K. £55.00
	U.S. $175.00
U.K.:	£ 55.00
U.S.:	$110.00
Can.:	$145.00

CT-1139
FUCHSIA INKWELL

Designer:	Allan Scott
Type:	Inkwell
Issued:	1994
Status:	Closed
Series:	Millefiori Miniatures
O.I.P.:	U.K. £55.00
	U.S. $175.00
U.K.:	£ 55.00
U.S.:	$110.00
Can.:	$145.00

CT-1140
HEART INKWELL

Designer:	Allan Scott
Type:	Inkwell
Issued:	1994
Status:	Closed
Series:	Millefiori Miniatures
O.I.P.:	U.K. £55.00
	U.S. $175.00
U.K.:	£ 55.00
U.S.:	$110.00
Can.:	$145.00

CT-1141
LUNAR TOUCHDOWN

Designer:	Colin Terris
Type:	Weight – Domed
Issued:	1994 in a limited edition of 50
Status:	Fully subscribed
Series:	Limited – Modern Design
O.I.P.:	U.K. £250.00
	U.S. $675.00
U.K.:	£300.00
U.S.:	$600.00
Can.:	$800.00

Note: CT-1141, 1142 and 1143 were issued to commemorate the 25th anniversary of the 1969 lunar landing.

CT-1142
THE EAGLE HAS LANDED

Designer:	Colin Terris
Type:	Weight – Spherical
Issued:	1994 in a limited edition of 500
Status:	Closed at No. 336
Series:	Limited – Modern Design
O.I.P.:	U.K. £65.00
	U.S. $190.00
U.K.:	£ 65.00
U.S.:	$130.00
Can.:	$170.00

CT-1143
MISSION APOLLO XI

Designer:	Colin Terris
Type:	Weight – Domed
Issued:	1994 in a limited edition of 750
Status:	Closed at No. 242
O.I.P.:	U.K. £39.95
	U.S. $99.50
U.K.:	£ 40.00
U.S.:	$ 80.00
Can.:	$100.00

ISSUES OF 1995

CT-1144
PAPER CHASE

Designer: Alastair MacIntosh
Type: Weight – Spherical
Issued: 1995 in a limited
          edition of 750
Status: Closed at No. 692
Series: Limited – Modern
          Design
O.I.P.:   U.K. £40.00
          U.S. $140.00

U.K.:   £ 40.00
U.S.: $ 80.00
Can.: $100.00

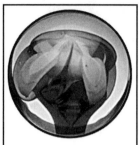

CT-1145
ORGANZA

Designer: Colin Terris
Type: Weight – Spherical
Issued: 1995 in a limited
          edition of 650
Status: Closed at No. 411
Series: Limited – Modern
          Design
O.I.P.:   U.K. £65.00
          U.S. $225.00

U.K.:   £ 65.00
U.S.: $130.00
Can.: $170.00

CT-1146
EMERALD VISION

Designer: Philip Chaplain
Type: Weight – Spherical
Issued: 1995 in a limited
          edition of 750
Status: Fully subscribed
Series: Limited – Modern
          Design
O.I.P.:   U.K. £45.00
          U.S. $150.00

U.K.:   £ 65.00
U.S.: $130.00
Can.: $170.00

CT-1147
SUPERSONIC

Designer: Alastair MacIntosh
Type: Weight – Spherical
Issued: 1995 in a limited
          edition of 750
Status: Closed at No. 739
Series: Limited – Modern
          Design
O.I.P.:   U.K. £40.00
          U.S. $140.00

U.K.:   £ 40.00
U.S.: $ 80.00
Can.: $100.00

CT-1148
AMORE

Designer: Colin Terris
Type: Weight – Spherical
Issued: 1995 in a limited
          edition of 50
Status: Fully subscribed
Series: Limited – Modern
          Design
O.I.P.:   U.K. £275.00
          U.S. $775.00

U.K.:   £275.00
U.S.: $550.00
Can.: $725.00

CT-1149
DEBUT

Designer: Helen MacDonald
Type: Weight – Domed,
          faceted
Issued: 1995 in a limited
          edition of 50
Status: Fully subscribed
Series: Limited – Modern
          Design
O.I.P.:   U.K. £275.00
          U.S. $850.00

U.K.:   £275.00
U.S.: $550.00
Can.: $725.00

CT-1150
COMMUNICATION

Designer: Philip Chaplain
Type: Weight – Spherical
Issued: 1995 in a limited
          edition of 750
Status: Fully subscribed
Series: Limited – Modern
          Design
O.I.P.:   U.K. £45.00
          U.S. $150.00

U.K.:   £ 45.00
U.S.: $ 90.00
Can.: $120.00

CT-1151
VOGUE

Designer: Colin Terris
Type: Weight – Spherical
Issued: 1995 in a limited
          edition of 650
Status: Fully subscribed
Series: Limited – Modern
          Design
O.I.P.:   U.K. £65.00
          U.S. $225.00

U.K.:   £ 65.00
U.S.: $130.00
Can.: $170.00

CT-1152
INDIGO

Designer: Alastair MacIntosh
Type: Weight – Spherical
Issued: 1995 in a limited
 edition of 650
Status: Fully subscribed
Series: Limited – Modern
 Design
O.I.P.: U.K. £65.00
 U.S. $225.00

U.K.: £ 65.00
U.S.: $130.00
Can.: $170.00

CT-1153
WATCHTOWER

Designer: Philip Chaplain
Type: Weight – Spherical
Issued: 1995 in a limited
 edition of 750
Status: Closed at No. 730
Series: Limited – Modern
 Design
O.I.P.: U.K. £50.00
 U.S. $165.00

U.K.: £ 50.00
U.S.: $100.00
Can.: $130.00

CT-1154
DREAM MAKER

Designer: Philip Chaplain
Type: Weight – Domed
Issued: 1995 in a limited
 edition of 750
Status: Fully subscribed
Series: Limited – Modern
 Design
O.I.P.: U.K. £50.00
 U.S. $165.00

U.K.: £ 50.00
U.S.: $100.00
Can.: $130.00

CT-1155
SIENA PERFUME BOTTLE

Designer: Alastair MacIntosh
Type: Perfume Bottle
Issued: 1995 in a limited
 edition of 50
Status: Closed at No. 41
Series: Limited – Modern
 Design
O.I.P.: U.K. £195.00
 U.S. $595.00

U.K.: £200.00
U.S.: $400.00
Can.: $525.00

CT-1156
TORINO PERFUME BOTTLE

Designer: Alastair MacIntosh
Type: Perfume Bottle
Issued: 1995 in a limited
 edition of 50
Status: Closed at No. 34
Series: Limited – Modern
 Design
O.I.P.: U.K. £175.00
 U.S. $550.00

U.K.: £200.00
U.S.: $400.00
Can.: $525.00

CT-1157
SORRENTO PERFUME BOTTLE

Designer: Alastair MacIntosh
Type: Perfume Bottle
Issued: 1995 in a limited
 edition of 50
Status: Closed at No. 43
Series: Limited – Modern
 Design
O.I.P.: U.K. £195.00
 U.S. $595.00

U.K.: £200.00
U.S.: $400.00
Can.: $525.00

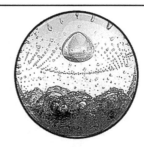

CT-1158A
MERCURY
Style Three

Designer: Colin Terris
Type: Weight – Spherical
Issued: 1995 in a limited edition of 350
Status: Closed at No. 232
Series: Planets, Set Three
O.I.P.: U.K. £395.00/set
 U.S. $1,250.00/set

	Mercury	Set
U.K.:	£100.00	400.00
U.S.:	$200.00	800.00
Can.:	$260.00	1,050.00

Note: CT-1158a, b, c and d were issued and sold as a set and
 are a new design interpretation of the 1969 original.

CT-1158B
VENUS
Style Two
Designer: Colin Terris
Type: Weight – Spherical
Issued: 1995 in a limited
          edition of 350
Status: Closed at No. 232
Series: Planets, Set Three
O.I.P.:   U.K. £395.00/set
          U.S. $1,250.00/set

U.K.:   £100.00
U.S.: $200.00
Can.: $260.00

CT-1158C
SATURN
Style Two
Designer: Colin Terris
Type: Weight – Spherical
Issued: 1995 in a limited
          edition of 350
Status: Closed at No. 232
Series: Planets, Set Three
O.I.P.:   U.K. £395.00/set
          U.S. $1,250.00/set

U.K.:   £100.00
U.S.: $200.00
Can.: $260.00

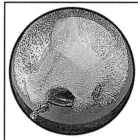

CT-1158D
MARS
Style Two
Designer: Colin Terris
Type: Weight – Spherical
Issued: 1995 in a limited
          edition of 350
Status: Closed at No. 232
Series: Planets, Set Three
O.I.P.:   U.K. £395.00/set
          U.S. $1,250.00/set

U.K.:   £100.00
U.S.: $200.00
Can.: $260.00

CT-1159
FUSION
Designer: Alastair MacIntosh
Type: Weight – Spherical
Issued: 1995 in a limited
          edition of 50
Status: Fully subscribed
Series: Limited – Modern
          Design
O.I.P.:   U.K. £250.00
          U.S. $750.00

U.K.:   £250.00
U.S.: $500.00
Can.: $650.00

CT-1160
FINESSE
Designer: Colin Terris
Type: Weight – Spherical
Issued: 1995 in a limited
          edition of 75
Status: Fully subscribed
Series: Limited – Modern
          Design
O.I.P.:   U.K. £175.00
          U.S. $550.00

U.K.:   £175.00
U.S.: $350.00
Can.: $450.00

CT-1161
FORCEFIELD
Designer: Alastair MacIntosh
Type: Weight – Spherical
Issued: 1995 in a limited
          edition of 50
Status: Fully subscribed
Series: Limited – Modern
          Design
O.I.P.:   U.K. £250.00
          U.S. $750.00

U.K.:   £250.00
U.S.: $500.00
Can.: $650.00

CT-1162
DOUBLE MAGNUM '95
Designer: Colin Terris
Type: Weight – Spherical
Size: Double magnum
Issued: 1995 in a limited
          edition of 150
Status: Closed at No. 48
Series: Limited – Modern
          Design
O.I.P.:   U.K. £195.00
          U.S. $595.00

U.K.:   £200.00
U.S.: $400.00
Can.: $525.00

CT-1163
TYROLEAN SUMMER
Designer: Alastair MacIntosh
Type: Weight – Domed
Issued: 1995 in a limited
          edition of 500
Status: Closed at No. 475
Series: Limited – Modern
          Design
O.I.P.:   U.K. £75.00
          U.S. $250.00

U.K.:   £ 75.00
U.S.: $150.00
Can.: $200.00

CT-1164
PARADISE

Designer: Alastair MacIntosh
Type: Weight – Domed
Issued: 1995 in a limited edition of 350
Status: Fully subscribed
Series: Limited – Modern Design
O.I.P.: U.K. £99.00
U.S. $310.00

U.K.: £100.00
U.S.: $200.00
Can.: $260.00

CT-1165
CARIBBEAN SUNRISE

Designer: Colin Terris
Type: Weight – Domed, quadruple overlay
Issued: 1995 in a limited edition of 25
Status: Fully subscribed
Series: Limited – Modern Design
O.I.P.: U.K. £495.00
U.S. $1,750.00

U.K.: £ 800.00
U.S.: $1,600.00
Can.: $2,100.00

CT-1166
CATCHING RAINDROPS

Designer: Colin Terris
Type: Weight – Spherical
Issued: 1995 in a limited edition of 650
Status: Closed at No. 622
Series: Limited – Modern Design
O.I.P.: U.K. £65.00
U.S. $225.00

U.K.: £ 65.00
U.S.: $130.00
Can.: $170.00

CT-1167
COCOON

Designer: Colin Terris
Type: Weight – Spherical
Issued: 1995 in a limited edition of 750
Status: Closed at No. 357
Series: Limited – Modern Design
O.I.P.: U.K. £60.00
U.S. $195.00

U.K.: £ 60.00
U.S.: $120.00
Can.: $155.00

CT-1168
TREBLE CHANCE

Designer: Helen MacDonald
Type: Weight – Spherical, facets
Issued: 1995 in a limited edition of 100
Status: Closed at No. 76
Series: Limited – Modern Design
O.I.P.: U.K. £150.00
U.S. $475.00

U.K.: £150.00
U.S.: $300.00
Can.: $400.00

CT-1169
EASTERN PROMISE

Designer: Colin Terris
Type: Weight – Spherical
Issued: 1995 in a limited edition of 75
Status: Closed at No. 68
Series: Limited – Modern Design
O.I.P.: U.K. £175.00
U.S. $550.00

U.K.: £175.00
U.S.: $350.00
Can.: $450.00

CT-1170
TROPICAL FANTASY

Designer: Colin Terris
Type: Weight – Spherical
Issued: 1995 in a limited edition of 75
Status: Fully subscribed
Series: Limited – Modern Design
O.I.P.: U.K. £195.00
U.S. $595.00

U.K.: £195.00
U.S.: $400.00
Can.: $525.00

CT-1171
ALLEY CAT

Designer: Helen MacDonald
Type: Weight – Domed
Issued: 1995 in a limited edition of 100
Status: Fully subscribed
Series: Limited – Modern Design
O.I.P.: U.K. £235.00
U.S. $725.00

U.K.: £250.00
U.S.: $500.00
Can.: $650.00

CT-1172
SMALL WORLD

Designer: Helen MacDonald
Type: Weight – Spherical
Issued: 1995 in a limited
edition of 75
Status: Fully subscribed
O.I.P.: U.K. £250.00
U.S. $750.00

U.K.: £250.00
U.S.: $500.00
Can.: $650.00

CT-1173
FAIRY LAND

Designer: Helen MacDonald
Type: Weight – Domed
Issued: 1995 in a limited
edition of 100
Status: Fully subscribed
Series: Limited – Modern
Design
O.I.P.: U.K. £235.00
U.S. $750.00

U.K.: £250.00
U.S.: $500.00
Can.: $650.00

CT-1174
TROPICAL VISION

Designer: Helen MacDonald
Type: Weight – Domed
Issued: 1995 in a limited
edition of 100
Status: Fully subscribed
Series: Limited – Modern
Design
O.I.P.: U.K. £235.00
U.S. $725.00

U.K.: £250.00
U.S.: $500.00
Can.: $650.00

CT-1175
ORIENTAL DAWN

Designer: Helen MacDonald
Type: Weight – Domed
Issued: 1995 in a limited
edition of 100
Status: Closed at No. 72
Series: Limited – Modern
Design
O.I.P.: U.K. £235.00
U.S. $725.00

U.K.: £250.00
U.S.: $500.00
Can.: $650.00

CT-1176
FANDANGO
Style Two

Designer: Colin Terris
Type: Weight – Spherical
Size: Magnum
Issued: 1995 in a limited
edition of 250
Status: Closed at No. 90
Series: Limited – Modern
Design
O.I.P.: U.K. £125.00
U.S. $395.00

U.K.: £125.00
U.S.: $250.00
Can.: $325.00

CT-1177
COVENANT

Designer: Helen MacDonald
Type: Weight – Spherical
Issued: 1995 in a limited
edition of 75
Status: Fully subscribed
Series: Limited – Modern
Design
O.I.P.: U.K. £195.00
U.S. $595.00

U.K.: £225.00
U.S.: $450.00
Can.: $575.00

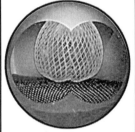

CT-1178
DOUBLE VISION

Designer: Alastair MacIntosh
Type: Weight – Spherical
Issued: 1995 in a limited
edition of 50
Status: Fully subscribed
Series: Limited – Modern
Design
O.I.P.: U.K. £225.00
U.S. $775.00

U.K.: £225.00
U.S.: $450.00
Can.: $575.00

CT-1179
LASER

Designer: Philip Chaplain
Type: Weight – Spherical
Issued: 1995 in a limited
edition of 750
Status: Closed at No. 453
Series: Limited – Modern
Design
O.I.P.: U.K. £60.00
U.S. $195.00

U.K.: £ 60.00
U.S.: $120.00
Can.: $160.00

CT-1180
JACK IN THE BOX

Designer: Margot Thomson
Type: Weight – Domed
Issued: 1995 in a limited
edition of 1,618
Status: Closed at No. 1,618
Series: Collectors' Society
O.I.P.: U.K. £80.00
U.S. $215.00

U.K.: £ 85.00
U.S.: $170.00
Can.: $225.00

CT-1181
ORCHID SPRAY

Designer: Allan Scott
Type: Weight – Spherical
Issued: 1995 in a limited
edition of 50
Status: Fully subscribed
Series: Whitefriars Collection
O.I.P.: U.K. £225.00
U.S. $695.00

U.K.: £225.00
U.S.: $450.00
Can.: $575.00

CT-1182
FRITILLARIA

Designer: Margot Thomson
Type: Weight – Spherical
Issued: 1995 in a limited
edition of 50
Status: Closed at No. 32
Series: Whitefriars Collection
O.I.P.: U.K. £175.00
U.S. $595.00

U.K.: £175.00
U.S.: $350.00
Can.: $450.00

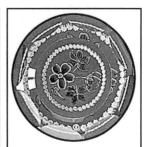

CT-1183
GERANIUM
Style One

Designer: Margot Thomson
Type: Weight – Spherical
Issued: 1995 in a limited
edition of 50
Status: Closed at No. 39
Series: Whitefriars Collection
O.I.P.: U.K. £175.00
U.S. $595.00

U.K.: £175.00
U.S.: $350.00
Can.: $450.00

CT-1184
MARIGOLDS

Designer: Margot Thomson
Type: Weight – Spherical
Issued: 1995 in a limited
edition of 50
Status: Fully subscribed
Series: Whitefriars Collection
O.I.P.: U.K. £185.00
U.S. $575.00

U.K.: £185.00
U.S.: $375.00
Can.: $475.00

CT-1185
PANSY PERFUME BOTTLE

Designer: Margot Thomson
Type: Perfume bottle
Issued: 1995 in a limited
edition of 50
Status: Closed at No. 36
Series: Whitefriars Collection
O.I.P.: U.K. £225.00
U.S. $750.00

U.K.: £225.00
U.S.: $450.00
Can.: $575.00

CT-1186
RHODODENDRON

Designer: Margot Thomson
Type: Weight – Spherical
Issued: 1995 in a limited
edition of 50
Status: Closed at No. 45
Series: Whitefriars Collection
O.I.P.: U.K. £215.00
U.S. $750.00

U.K.: £225.00
U.S.: $450.00
Can.: $575.00

CT-1187
IRIS BOUQUET

Designer: Colin Terris and
Allan Scott
Type: Weight – Spherical,
quadruple overlay
Issued: 1995 in a limited
edition of 25
Status: Fully subscribed
Series: Whitefriars Collection
O.I.P.: U.K. £595.00
U.S. $1,900.00

U.K.: £ 800.00
U.S.: $1,600.00
Can.: $2,100.00

CT-1188
MECONOPSIS

Designer: Margot Thomson
Type: Weight – Spherical
Issued: 1995 in a limited
edition of 50
Status: Closed at No. 45
Series: Whitefriars Collection
O.I.P.: U.K. £175.00
U.S. $595.00

U.K.: £175.00
U.S.: $350.00
Can.: $450.00

CT-1189
FREESIAS

Designer: Margot Thomson
Type: Weight – Spherical
Issued: 1995 in a limited
edition of 50
Status: Closed at No. 39
Series: Whitefriars Collection
O.I.P.: U.K. £225.00
U.S. $750.00

U.K.: £225.00
U.S.: $450.00
Can.: $600.00

CT-1190
CAPE PRIMROSE

Designer: Margot Thomson
Type: Weight – Spherical
Issued: 1995 in a limited
edition of 50
Status: Closed at No. 32
Series: Whitefriars Collection
O.I.P.: U.K. £165.00
U.S. $595.00

U.K.: £165.00
U.S.: $330.00
Can.: $430.00

CT-1191A
COSMOS
Style Two

Designer: Margot Thomson
Type: Weight – Spherical
Issued: 1995 in a limited
edition of 50
Status: Fully subscribed
Series: Whitefriars Collection
O.I.P.: U.K. £395.00/set
U.S. $1,350.00/set

U.K.: £225.00
U.S.: $450.00
Can.: $600.00

Note: CT-1191A and B were
issued and sold as a set.

CT-1191B
COSMOS PERFUME BOTTLE

Designer: Margot Thomson
Type: Perfume bottle
Issued: 1995 in a limited
edition of 50
Status: Fully subscribed
Series: Whitefriars Collection
O.I.P.: U.K. £395.00/set
U.S. $1,350.00/set

	Perfume	Set
U.K.:	£ 400.	625.
U.S.:	$ 800.	1,250.
Can.:	$1,050.	1,600.

CT-1192
YELLOW ROSE
Style Two

Designer: William Manson
Type: Weight – Spherical
Issued: 1995 in a limited
edition of 50
Status: Closed at No. 43
Series: Traditional Collection
O.I.P.: U.K. £250.00
U.S. $775.00

U.K.: £250.00
U.S.: $500.00
Can.: $650.00

CT-1193
BUMBLEBEE and BLUEBELLS

Designer: William Manson
Type: Weight – Spherical
Issued: 1995 in a limited
edition of 50
Status: Closed at No. 41
Series: Traditional Collection
O.I.P.: U.K. £250.00
U.S. $775.00

U.K.: £250.00
U.S.: $500.00
Can.: $650.00

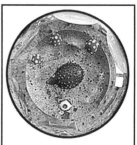

CT-1194
HEDGEHOG
Style Two

Designer: William Manson
Type: Weight – Spherical
Issued: 1995 in a limited
edition of 50
Status: Closed at No. 41
Series: Traditional Collection
O.I.P.: U.K. £250.00
U.S. $775.00

U.K.: £250.00
U.S.: $500.00
Can.: $650.00

CT-1195
TURTLE

Designer: William Manson
Type: Weight – Spherical
Issued: 1995 in a limited
edition of 50
Status: Closed at No. 37
Series: Traditional Collection
O.I.P.: U.K. £275.00
U.S. $850.00

U.K.: £300.00
U.S.: $600.00
Can.: $775.00

CT-1196
PYTHON

Designer: William Manson
Type: Weight – Spherical
Issued: 1995 in a limited
edition of 50
Status: Closed at No. 35
Series: Traditional Collection
O.I.P.: U.K. £295.00
U.S. $895.00

U.K.: £300.00
U.S.: $600.00
Can.: $775.00

CT-1197
CORAL REEF

Designer: William Manson
Type: Weight – Spherical
Issued: 1995 in a limited
edition of 50
Status: Closed at No. 38
Series: Traditional Collection
O.I.P.: U.K. £225.00
U.S. $695.00

U.K.: £300.00
U.S.: $600.00
Can.: $775.00

CT-1198
SEAHORSE
Style Two

Designer: William Manson
Type: Weight – Spherical
Issued: 1995 in a limited
edition of 50
Status: Fully subscribed
Series: Traditional Collection
O.I.P.: U.K. £275.00
U.S. $850.00

U.K.: £275.00
U.S.: $550.00
Can.: $725.00

CT-1199
BLUE LAGOON
Style One

Designer: William Manson
Type: Weight – Spherical
Issued: 1995 in a limited
edition of 50
Status: Fully subscribed
Series: Traditional Collection
O.I.P.: U.K. £225.00
U.S. $695.00

U.K.: £225.00
U.S.: $450.00
Can.: $600.00

CT-1200
IGUANA

Designer: William Manson
Type: Weight – Low Dome
Issued: 1995 in a limited
edition of 50
Status: Closed at No. 31
Series: Traditional Collection
O.I.P.: U.K. £295.00
U.S. $895.00

U.K.: £300.00
U.S.: $600.00
Can.: $775.00

CT-1201
KILLER WHALE

Designer: William Manson
Type: Weight – Low Dome
Issued: 1995 in a limited
edition of 50
Status: Closed at No. 41
Series: Traditional Collection
O.I.P.: U.K. £225.00
U.S. $695.00

U.K.: £300.00
U.S.: $600.00
Can.: $775.00

CT-1202
MARGUERITE
Style Two

Designer: William Manson
Type: Weight – Spherical
Size: Medium
Issued: 1995 in a limited
edition of 150
Status: Fully subscribed
Series: Traditional Collection
O.I.P.: U.K. £75.00
U.S. $225.00

U.K.: £ 75.00
U.S.: $150.00
Can.: $200.00

CT-1203
POINSETTIA
Style Two

Designer: William Manson
Type: Weight – Spherical
Size: Medium
Issued: 1995 in a limited
edition of 150
Status: Closed at No. 132
Series: Traditional Collection
O.I.P.: U.K. £75.00
U.S. $225.00

U.K.: £ 75.00
U.S.: $150.00
Can.: $200.00

CT-1204
DAHLIA
Style One

Designer: William Manson
Type: Weight – Spherical
Size: Medium
Issued: 1995 in a limited
edition of 150
Status: Closed at No. 124
Series: Traditional Collection
O.I.P.: U.K. £75.00
U.S. $225.00

U.K.: £ 75.00
U.S.: $150.00
Can.: $200.00

CT-1205
LILIUM
Style Two

Designer: William Manson
Type: Weight – Spherical
Size: Medium
Issued: 1995 in a limited
edition of 150
Status: Closed at No. 134
Series: Traditional Collection
O.I.P.: U.K. £75.00
U.S. $225.00

U.K.: £ 75.00
U.S.: $150.00
Can.: $200.00

CT-1206
DRAGONFLY – WHITE
FLOWER

Designer: Allan Scott
Type: Weight – Spherical
Issued: 1995 in a limited
edition of 50
Status: Fully subscribed
Series: Traditional Collection
Nature Study
O.I.P.: U.K. £125.00
U.S. $395.00

U.K.: £125.00
U.S.: $250.00
Can.: $325.00

CT-1207
DRAGONFLY – BLUE FLOWER

Designer: Allan Scott
Type: Weight – Spherical
Issued: 1995 in a limited
edition of 50
Status: Fully subscribed
Series: Traditional Collection
Nature Study
O.I.P.: U.K. £125.00
U.S. $395.00

U.K.: £125.00
U.S.: $250.00
Can.: $325.00

CT-1208
DRAGONFLY – LATTICINO
BASE

Designer: Allan Scott
Type: Weight – Spherical
Issued: 1995 in a limited
edition of 50
Status: Fully subscribed
Series: Traditional Collection
Nature Study
O.I.P.: U.K. £99.00
U.S. $325.00

U.K.: £100.00
U.S.: $200.00
Can.: $260.00

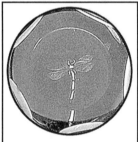

CT-1209
MINIATURE DRAGONFLY –
BLUE BASE

Designer: Allan Scott
Type: Weight – Spherical
Issued: 1995 in a limited
edition of 150
Status: Closed at No. 100
Series: Traditional Collection
Nature Study
O.I.P.: U.K. £70.00
U.S. $225.00

U.K.: £ 70.00
U.S.: $140.00
Can.: $180.00

CT-1210
MINIATURE DRAGONFLY –
GOLD BASE

Designer: Allan Scott
Type: Weight – Spherical
Issued: 1995 in a limited
edition of 150
Status: Closed at No. 87
Series: Traditional Collection
Nature Study
O.I.P.: U.K. £70.00
U.S. $225.00

U.K.: £ 70.00
U.S.: $140.00
Can.: $180.00

CT-1211
SCIMITAR

Designer:	Margot Thomson
Type:	Weight – Spherical
Issued:	1995
Status:	Closed
Series:	Unlimited – Modern Design
O.I.P.:	U.K. £28.50
	U.S. $95.00
U.K.:	£30.00
U.S.:	$60.00
Can.:	$80.00

CT-1212
SARACEN

Designer:	Alastair MacIntosh
Type:	Weight – Teardrop
Issued:	1995
Status:	Active
Series:	Unlimited – Modern Design
O.I.P.:	U.K. £27.00
	U.S. $87.50
U.K.:	£34.95
U.S.:	$95.00
Can.:	–

CT-1213
BRUSHSTROKES

Designer:	Alastair MacIntosh
Type:	Weight – Spherical
Issued:	1995
Status:	Closed
Series:	Unlimited – Modern Design
O.I.P.:	U.K. £28.50
	U.S. $95.00
U.K.:	£30.00
U.S.:	$60.00
Can.:	$80.00

CT-1214
CAULDRON RAINBOW

Designer:	Colin Terris
Type:	Weight – Spherical
Colour:	White, blue, green and yellow
Issued:	1995
Status:	Closed
Series:	Unlimited – Modern Design
O.I.P.:	U.K. £28.50
	U.S. $95.00
U.K.:	£30.00
U.S.:	$60.00
Can.:	$80.00

CT-1215
MAY DANCE MAGENTA

Designer:	Colin Terris
Type:	Weight – Spherical
Issued:	1995
Status:	Closed
Series:	Unlimited – Modern Design
O.I.P.:	U.K. £33.00
	U.S. $115.00
U.K.:	£35.00
U.S.:	$70.00
Can.:	$90.00

CT-1216
SEA GEMS

Designer:	Stuart Cumming
Type:	Weight – Spherical
Size:	Medium
Colour:	1. Azure
	2. Jade
	3. Magenta
	4. Rose
Issued:	1995
Status:	Closed
Series:	Medium and Miniature Size
O.I.P.:	U.K. £17.95
	U.S. $62.50
U.K.:	£20.00
U.S.:	$40.00
Can.:	$50.00

CT-1217
ETERNITY

Designer:	Colin Terris
Type:	Weight – Spherical
Colour:	1. Cobalt
	2. Gold
Issued:	1995
Status:	1. Closed
	2. Closed
Series:	Romance
O.I.P.:	U.K. £32.50
	U.S. $99.50
U.K.:	£35.00.
U.S.:	$70.00.
Can.:	$90.00.

CT-1218
ROMANCE
Style Two

Designer:	Alastair MacIntosh
Type:	Weight – Spherical
Issued:	1995
Status:	Closed
Series:	Romance
O.I.P.:	U.K. £32.50
	U.S. $95.00
U.K.:	£35.00
U.S.:	$70.00
Can.:	$90.00

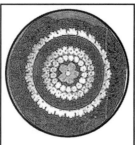

CT-1219
RED ROSE
Style Three

Designer: Allan Scott
Type: Weight – Spherical
Issued: 1995
Status: Closed
Series: Romance
O.I.P.: U.K. £34.50
U.S. $115.00

U.K.: £35.00
U.S.: $70.00
Can.: $90.00

CT-1220
RED ROSE PERFUME BOTTLE

Designer: Allan Scott
Type: Perfume bottle
Issued: 1995
Status: Closed
Series: Romance
O.I.P.: U.K. £57.70
U.S. $175.00

U.K.: £ 60.00
U.S.: $120.00
Can.: $155.00

CT-1221
TWO'S COMPANY

Designer: Alastair MacIntosh
Type: Weight – Spherical
Issued: 1995 in a limited
edition of 750
Status: Closed at No. 586
Series: Limited – Modern
Design
O.I.P.: U.K. £50.00
U.S. $150.00

U.K.: £ 50.00
U.S.: $100.00
Can.: $130.00

CT-1222
ROYALE

Designer: Helen MacDonald
Type: Weight – Domed
Issued: 1995 in a limited
edition of 650
Status: Closed at No. 469
Series: Limited – Modern
Design
O.I.P.: U.K. £75.00
U.S. $230.00

U.K.: £ 75.00
U.S.: $150.00
Can.: $200.00

CT-1223
PHARAOH

Designer: Philip Chaplain
Type: Weight – Spherical
Issued: 1995 in a limited
edition of 750
Status: Closed at No. 549
Series: Limited – Modern
Design
O.I.P.: U.K. £55.00
U.S. $165.00

U.K.: £ 55.00
U.S.: $110.00
Can.: $145.00

CT-1224
COLUMBINE

Designer: Helen MacDonald
Type: Weight – Spherical
Issued: 1995 in a limited
edition of 50
Status: Fully subscribed
Series: Limited – Modern
Design
O.I.P.: U.K. £250.00
U.S. $775.00

U.K.: £250.00
U.S.: $500.00
Can.: $650.00

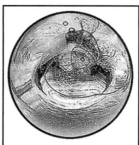

CT-1225
SOOTHSAYER

Designer: Philip Chaplain
Type: Weight – Spherical
Issued: 1995 in a limited
edition of 750
Status: Closed at No. 414
Series: Limited – Modern
Design
O.I.P.: U.K. £45.00
U.S. $140.00

U.K.: £ 45.00
U.S.: $ 90.00
Can.: $120.00

CT-1226
JOSEPH

Designer: Helen MacDonald
Type: Weight – Spherical
Issued: 1995 in a limited
edition of 75
Status: Fully subscribed
Series: Limited – Modern
Design
O.I.P.: U.K. £195.00
U.S. $675.00

U.K.: £325.00
U.S.: $650.00
Can.: $850.00

CT-1227
SAQQARA

Designer:	Helen MacDonald
Type:	Weight – Domed
Issued:	1995 in a limited edition of 50
Status:	Closed at No. 41
Series:	Limited – Modern Design
O.I.P.:	U.K. £225.00
	U.S. $695.00
U.K.:	£250.00
U.S.:	$500.00
Can.:	$650.00

CT-1228
SNOW DANCE

Designer:	Margot Thomson
Type:	Weight – Domed
Issued:	1995 in a limited edition of 350
Status:	Closed at No. 252
Series:	Limited – Modern Design
O.I.P.:	U.K. £99.00
	U.S. $300.00
U.K.:	£100.00
U.S.:	$200.00
Can.:	$260.00

CT-1229
NEW HORIZONS

Designer:	Alastair MacIntosh
Type:	Weight – Domed
Issued:	1995 in a limited edition of 100
Status:	Fully subscribed
Series:	Limited – Modern Design
O.I.P.:	U.K. £150.00
	U.S. $450.00
U.K.:	£150.00
U.S.:	$300.00
Can.:	$400.00

CT-1230
THREE TENORS

Designer:	Helen MacDonald
Type:	Weight – Domed
Issued:	1995 in a limited edition of 100
Status:	Fully subscribed
Series:	Limited – Modern Design
O.I.P.:	U.K. £235.00
	U.S. $725.00
U.K.:	£250.00
U.S.:	$500.00
Can.:	$650.00

Note: Issued to commemorate concerts given by José Carreras, Plácido Domingo and Luciano Pavarotti.

CT-1231
SPELLCASTER

Designer:	Alastair MacIntosh
Type:	Weight – Domed
Issued:	1995 in a limited edition of 650
Status:	Fully subscribed
Series:	Limited – Modern Design
O.I.P.:	U.K. £70.00
	U.S. $250.00
U.K.:	£ 70.00
U.S.:	$140.00
Can.:	$185.00

CT-1232
MEPHISTOPHELES

Designer:	Philip Chaplain
Type:	Weight – Domed
Issued:	1995 in a limited edition of 650
Status:	Closed at No. 562
Series:	Limited – Modern Design
O.I.P.:	U.K. £80.00
	U.S. $250.00
U.K.:	£ 80.00
U.S.:	$160.00
Can.:	$210.00

CT-1233
DAHLIA
Style Two

Designer:	Helen MacDonald
Type:	Weight – Spherical
Issued:	1995 in a limited edition of 50
Status:	Fully subscribed
Series:	Limited – Modern Design
O.I.P.:	U.K. £275.00
	U.S. $850.00
U.K.:	£275.00
U.S.:	$550.00
Can.:	$725.00

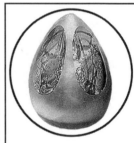

CT-1234
WISHING WELL

Designer:	Philip Chaplain
Type:	Weight – Domed
Issued:	1995 in a limited edition of 75
Status:	Fully subscribed
Series:	Limited – Modern Design
O.I.P.:	U.K. £175.00
	U.S. $550.00
U.K.:	£175.00
U.S.:	$350.00
Can.:	$450.00

CT-1235
MERMAID'S SECRET

Designer: Helen MacDonald
Type: Weight – Domed
Issued: 1995 in a limited
          edition of 100
Status: Fully subscribed
Series: Limited – Modern
          Design
O.I.P.:   U.K. £235.00
          U.S. $725.00

U.K.:   £250.00
U.S.: $500.00
Can.: $650.00

CT-1236
ADORATION

Designer: Colin Terris
Type: Weight – Spherical
Issued: 1995 in a limited
          edition of 50
Status: Fully subscribed
Series: Limited – Modern
          Design
O.I.P.:   U.K. £250.00
          U.S. $775.00

U.K.:   £250.00
U.S.: $500.00
Can.: $650.00

CT-1237
OMPHALOS

Designer: Philip Chaplain
Type: Weight – Domed
Issued: 1995 in a limited
          edition of 350
Status: Fully subscribed
Series: Limited – Modern
          Design
O.I.P.:   U.K. £85.00
          U.S. $260.00

U.K.:   £ 85.00
U.S.: $170.00
Can.: $225.00

CT-1238
LOVEBIRDS

Designer: Helen MacDonald
Type: Weight – Spherical,
          footed
Issued: 1995 in a limited
          edition of 15
Status: Fully subscribed
O.I.P.:   U.K. £795.00
          U.S. $2,500.00

U.K.:   £ 900.00
U.S.: $1,800.00
Can.: $2,350.00

CT-1239
DOG TOOTH VIOLET

Designer: Margot Thomson
Type: Weight – Spherical
Issued: 1995 in a limited
          edition of 50
Status: Closed at No. 33
Series: Whitefriars Collection
O.I.P.:   U.K. £175.00
          U.S. $550.00

U.K.:   £175.00
U.S.: $350.00
Can.: $450.00

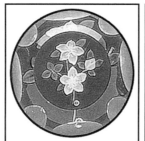

CT-1240
ROSE OF SHARON

Designer: Margot Thomson
Type: Weight – Spherical
Issued: 1995 in a limited
          edition of 50
Status: Closed at No. 35
Series: Whitefriars Collection
O.I.P.:   U.K. £165.00
          U.S. $495.00

U.K.:   £165.00
U.S.: $330.00
Can.: $430.00

CT-1241
MALLOW

Designer: Margot Thomson
Type: Weight – Spherical
Issued: 1994 in a limited
          edition of 50
Status: Closed at No. 39
Series: Whitefriars Collection
O.I.P.:   U.K. £175.00
          U.S. $550.00

U.K.:   £175.00
U.S.: $350.00
Can.: $450.00

CT-1242
PINK RHODODENDRON

Designer: Allan Scott
          Margot Thomson
Type: Weight – Spherical
Issued: 1994 in a limited
          edition of 25
Status: Fully subscribed
Series: Whitefriars Collection
O.I.P.:   U.K. £495.00
          U.S. $1,525.00

U.K.:   £ 500.00
U.S.: $1,000.00
Can.: $1,300.00

CT-1243
SWEET VIOLET

Designer: Margot Thomson
Type: Weight – Spherical
Issued: 1994 in a limited
edition of 50
Status: Closed at No. 49
Series: Whitefriars Collection
O.I.P.: U.K. £175.00
U.S. $550.00

U.K.: £175.00
U.S.: $350.00
Can.: $450.00

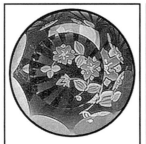

CT-1244A
SCARLET PIMPERNEL
Style Two

Designer: Margot Thomson
Type: Weight – Spherical
Issued: 1995 in a limited
edition of 50
Status: Fully subscribed
Series: Whitefriars Collection
O.I.P.: U.K. £395.00/set
U.S. $1,200.00/set

U.K.: £325.00
U.S.: $650.00
Can.: $850.00

Note: CT-1244A and B were
issued and sold as a set.

CT-1244B
SCARLET PIMPERNEL
PERFUME BOTTLE

Designer: Margot Thomson
Type: Perfume bottle
Issued: 1995 in a limited
edition of 50
Status: Fully subscribed
Series: Whitefriars Collection
O.I.P.: U.K. £395.00/set
U.S. $1,200.00/set

	Perfume	Set
U.K.:	£ 400.	725.
U.S.:	$ 800.	1,450.
Can.:	$1,050.	1,875.

CT-1245
SNAIL and BLOSSOM

Designer: William Manson
Type: Weight – Spherical
Issued: 1995 in a limited
edition of 50
Status: Closed at No. 39
Series: Traditional Collection
O.I.P.: U.K. £295.00
U.S. $895.00

U.K.: £300.00
U.S.: $600.00
Can.: $775.00

CT-1246
CATERPILLAR and CHERRY
BLOSSOM

Designer: William Manson
Type: Weight – Spherical
Issued: 1995 in a limited
edition of 50
Status: Closed at No. 38
Series: Traditional Collection
O.I.P.: U.K. £295.00
U.S. $895.00

U.K.: £300.00
U.S.: $600.00
Can.: $775.00

CT-1247
SUNSET FLIGHT

Designer: William Manson
Type: Weight – Spherical
Issued: 1995 in a limited
edition of 50
Status: Closed at No. 42
Series: Traditional Collection
O.I.P.: U.K. £250.00
U.S. $775.00

U.K.: £250.00
U.S.: $500.00
Can.: $650.00

CT-1248
TROPICAL PARAKEET

Designer: William Manson
Type: Weight – Spherical
Issued: 1995 in a limited
edition of 50
Status: Closed at No. 48
Series: Traditional Collection
O.I.P.: U.K. £275.00
U.S. $850.00

U.K.: £275.00
U.S.: $550.00
Can.: $700.00

CT-1249
AFRICAN CHAMELEON

Designer: William Manson
Type: Weight – Spherical
Issued: 1995 in a limited
edition of 50
Status: Closed at No. 43
Series: Traditional Collection
O.I.P.: U.K. £295.00
U.S. $895.00

U.K.: £300.00
U.S.: $600.00
Can.: $775.00

CT-1250
GOLD ROSE
Designer: William Manson
Type: Weight – Spherical
Size: Medium
Issued: 1995 in a limited edition of 150
Status: Closed at No. 112
Series: Traditional Collection
O.I.P.: U.K. £75.00
U.S. $230.00

U.K.: £ 75.00
U.S.: $150.00
Can.: $200.00

CT-1251
PINK ROSE
Designer: William Manson
Type: Weight – Spherical
Size: Medium
Issued: 1995 in a limited edition of 150
Status: Closed at No. 136
Series: Traditional Collection
O.I.P.: U.K. £75.00
U.S. $230.00

U.K.: £ 75.00
U.S.: $150.00
Can.: $200.00

CT-1252
PANSY
Style Three
Designer: William Manson
Type: Weight – Spherical
Size: Medium
Issued: 1995 in a limited edition of 150
Status: Closed at No. 135
Series: Traditional Collection
O.I.P.: U.K. £75.00
U.S. $230.00

U.K.: £ 75.00
U.S.: $150.00
Can.: $200.00

CT-1253
DELPHINIUM and LADYBIRD
Designer: William Manson
Type: Weight – Spherical
Size: Medium
Issued: 1995 in a limited edition of 150
Status: Closed at No. 90
Series: Traditional Collection
O.I.P.: U.K. £75.00
U.S. $230.00

U.K.: £ 75.00
U.S.: $150.00
Can.: $200.00

CT-1254
BUTTERFLY – PURPLE FLOWER
Designer: Allan Scott
Type: Weight – Spherical
Issued: 1995 in a limited edition of 50
Status: Closed at No. 41
Series: Traditional Collection Nature Study
O.I.P.: U.K. £195.00
U.S. $595.00

U.K.: £200.00
U.S.: $400.00
Can.: $525.00

CT-1255
BUTTERFLY – YELLOW FLOWER
Designer: Allan Scott
Type: Weight – Spherical
Issued: 1995 in a limited edition of 50
Status: Closed at No. 46
Series: Traditional Collection Nature Study
O.I.P.: U.K. £195.00
U.S. $595.00

U.K.: £200.00
U.S.: $400.00
Can.: $525.00

CT-1256
BUTTERFLY – LATTICINO BASE
Designer: Allan Scott
Type: Weight – Spherical
Issued: 1995 in a limited edition of 50
Status: Closed at No. 35
Series: Traditional Collection Nature Study
O.I.P.: U.K. £175.00
U.S. $550.00

U.K.: £175.00
U.S.: $350.00
Can.: $450.00

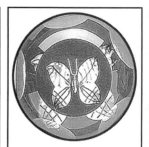

CT-1257
YELLOW BUTTERFLY – MINIATURE
Designer: Allan Scott
Type: Weight – Spherical
Issued: 1995 in a limited edition of 150
Status: Closed at No. 58
Series: Traditional Collection Nature Study
O.I.P.: U.K. £99.00
U.S. $295.00

U.K.: £100.00
U.S.: $200.00
Can.: $260.00

CT-1258
RED BUTTERFLY

Designer: Allan Scott
Type: Weight – Spherical
Size: Miniature
Issued: 1995 in a limited
edition of 150
Status: Closed at No. 62
Series: Traditional Collection
Nature Study
O.I.P.: U.K. £99.00
U.S. $295.00

U.K.: £100.00
U.S.: $200.00
Can.: $260.00

CT-1259
CAPRICORN

Designer: Philip Chaplain
Type: Weight – Spherical
Issued: 1995
Status: Closed
Series: Zodiac Collection
O.I.P.: U.K. £29.50
U.S. $95.00

U.K.: £30.00
U.S.: $60.00
Can.: $80.00

CT-1260
AQUARIUS
Style Two

Designer: Philip Chaplain
Type: Weight – Spherical
Issued: 1995
Status: Closed
Series: Zodiac Collection
O.I.P.: U.K. £29.50
U.S. $95.00

U.K.: £30.00
U.S.: $60.00
Can.: $80.00

CT-1261
PISCES

Designer: Philip Chaplain
Type: Weight – Spherical
Issued: 1995
Status: Closed
Series: Zodiac Collection
O.I.P.: U.K. £29.50
U.S. $95.00

U.K.: £30.00
U.S.: $60.00
Can.: $80.00

CT-1262
ARIES
Style Three

Designer: Philip Chaplain
Type: Weight – Spherical
Issued: 1995
Status: Closed
Series: Zodiac Collection
O.I.P.: U.K. £29.50
U.S. $95.00

U.K.: £30.00
U.S.: $60.00
Can.: $80.00

CT-1263
TAURUS

Designer: Philip Chaplain
Type: Weight – Spherical
Issued: 1995
Status: Closed
Series: Zodiac Collection
O.I.P.: U.K. £29.50
U.S. $95.00

U.K.: £30.00
U.S.: $60.00
Can.: $80.00

CT-1264
GEMINI
Style Two

Designer: Philip Chaplain
Type: Weight – Spherical
Issued: 1995
Status: Closed
Series: Zodiac Collection
O.I.P.: U.K. £29.50
U.S. $95.00

U.K.: £30.00
U.S.: $60.00
Can.: $80.00

CT-1265
CANCER

Designer: Philip Chaplain
Type: Weight – Spherical
Issued: 1995
Status: Closed
Series: Zodiac Collection
O.I.P.: U.K. £29.50
U.S. $95.00

U.K.: £30.00
U.S.: $60.00
Can.: $80.00

CT-1266
LEO
Designer: Philip Chaplain
Type: Weight – Spherical
Issued: 1995
Status: Closed
Series: Zodiac Collection
O.I.P.: U.K. £29.50
U.S. $95.00

U.K.: £30.00
U.S.: $60.00
Can.: $80.00

CT-1267
VIRGO
Designer: Philip Chaplain
Type: Weight – Spherical
Issued: 1995
Status: Closed
Series: Zodiac Collection
O.I.P.: U.K. £29.50
U.S. $95.00

U.K.: £30.00
U.S.: $60.00
Can.: $80.00

CT-1268
LIBRA
Style Two
Designer: Philip Chaplain
Type: Weight – Spherical
Issued: 1995
Status: Closed
Series: Zodiac Collection
O.I.P.: U.K. £29.50
U.S. $95.00

U.K.: £30.00
U.S.: $60.00
Can.: $80.00

CT-1269
SCORPIO
Designer: Philip Chaplain
Type: Weight – Spherical
Issued: 1995
Status: Closed
Series: Zodiac Collection
O.I.P.: U.K. £29.50
U.S. $95.00

U.K.: £30.00
U.S.: $60.00
Can.: $80.00

CT-1270
SAGITTARIUS
Style Two
Designer: Philip Chaplain
Type: Weight – Spherical
Issued: 1995
Status: Closed
Series: Zodiac Collection
O.I.P.: U.K. £29.50
U.S. $95.00

U.K.: £30.00
U.S.: $60.00
Can.: $80.00

CT-1271
GLAMIS ROSE PERFUME
BOTTLE
Designer: Colin Terris
Type: Perfume bottle
Issued: 1995 in a limited
edition of 95
Status: Fully subscribed
O.I.P.: U.K. £295.00
U.S. $850.00

U.K.: £300.00
U.S.: $600.00
Can.: $775.00

CT-1272
GLAMIS ROSE
Designer: Allan Scott
Type: Weight – Spherical
Issued: 1995 in a limited
edition of 95
Status: Fully subscribed
O.I.P.: U.K. £195.00
U.S. $575.00

U.K.: £200.00
U.S.: $400.00
Can.: $525.00

Note: CT-1272 and 1273
were issued to
commemorate HM The
Queen Mother's 95th
birthday.

CT-1273
CASTLE OF MEY
Style One
Designer: Caithness Engraving
Studios
Type: Weight – Spherical
Issued: 1995 in a limited
edition of 750
Status: Closed at No. 84
O.I.P.: U.K. £39.50
U.S. $115.00

U.K.: £ 40.00
U.S.: $ 80.00
Can.: $100.00

CT-1274
VICTORY IN EUROPE

Designer:	Philip Chaplain
Type:	Weight – Spherical
Issued:	1995 in a limited edition of 500
Status:	Closed at No. 140
O.I.P.:	U.K. £85.00
	U.S. $250.00
U.K.:	£ 85.00
U.S.:	$170.00
Can.:	$225.00

Note: This paperweight was issued to celebrate the 50th anniversary of the Allied Forces' victory in Europe.

ISSUES OF 1996

CT-1275
OSIRIS

Designer:	Philip Chaplain
Type:	Weight – Domed
Issued:	1996 in a limited edition of 350
Status:	Closed at No. 338
Series:	Limited – Modern Design
O.I.P.:	U.K. £85.00
	U.S. $275.00
U.K.:	£ 85.00
U.S.:	$170.00
Can.:	$225.00

CT-1276
WILDCARD

Designer:	Philip Chaplain
Type:	Weight – Spherical
Issued:	1996 in a limited edition of 750
Status:	Fully subscribed
Series:	Limited – Modern Design
O.I.P.:	U.K. £45.00
	U.S. $150.00
U.K.:	£ 45.00
U.S.:	$ 90.00
Can.:	$120.00

CT-1277
REACTOR

Designer:	Philip Chaplain
Type:	Weight – Spherical
Issued:	1996 in a limited edition of 750
Status:	Fully subscribed
Series:	Limited – Modern Design
O.I.P.:	U.K. £45.00
	U.S. $150.00
U.K.:	£ 45.00
U.S.:	$ 90.00
Can.:	$120.00

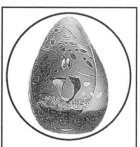

CT-1278
RIVER DANCERS

Designer:	Helen MacDonald
Type:	Weight – Domed
Issued:	1996 in a limited edition of 100
Status:	Fully subscribed
Series:	Limited – Modern Design
O.I.P.:	U.K. £235.00
	U.S. $725.00
U.K.:	£275.00
U.S.:	$550.00
Can.:	$725.00

CT-1279
SPACE ENCOUNTER

Designer:	Helen MacDonald
Type:	Weight – Spherical
Issued:	1996 in a limited edition of 75
Status:	Fully subscribed
Series:	Limited – Modern Design
O.I.P.:	U.K. £175.00
	U.S. $525.00
U.K.:	£175.00
U.S.:	$350.00
Can.:	$450.00

CT-1280
NOAH'S ARK

Designer:	Helen MacDonald
Type:	Weight – Teardrop
Issued:	1996 in a limited edition of 100
Status:	Fully subscribed
Series:	Limited – Modern Design
O.I.P.:	U.K. £235.00
	U.S. $795.00
U.K.:	£250.00
U.S.:	$500.00
Can.:	$650.00

CT-1281
JUGGLER

Designer:	Margot Thomson
Type:	Weight – Spherical
Issued:	1996 in a limited edition of 750
Status:	Closed at No. 717
Series:	Limited – Modern Design
O.I.P.:	U.K. £40.00
	U.S. $150.00
U.K.:	£ 40.00
U.S.:	$ 80.00
Can.:	$100.00

CT-1282
CHANNEL CROSSING

Designer:	Margot Thomson
Type:	Weight – Domed
Issued:	1996 in a limited edition of 650
Status:	Fully subscribed
Series:	Limited – Modern Design
O.I.P.:	U.K. £70.00
	U.S. $235.00
U.K.:	£ 70.00
U.S.:	$140.00
Can.:	$180.00

CT-1283
OCEANIC

Designer: John Spittal
Type: Weight – Pyramidal
Issued: 1996 in a limited
edition of 50
Status: Fully subscribed
Series: Limited – Modern
Design
O.I.P.: U.K. £295.00
U.S. $895.00

U.K.: £300.00
U.S.: $600.00
Can.: $775.00

CT-1284
FAR PAVILION

Designer: Helen MacDonald
Type: Weight – Domed
Issued: 1996 in a limited
edition of 100
Status: Closed at No. 82
Series: Limited – Modern
Design
O.I.P.: U.K. £235.00
U.S. $725.00

U.K.: £250.00
U.S.: $500.00
Can.: $650.00

CT-1285
VIVALDI

Designer: Margot Thomson
Type: Weight – Teardrop
Issued: 1996 in a limited
edition of 750
Status: Fully subscribed
Series: Limited – Modern
Design
O.I.P.: U.K. £60.00
U.S. $225.00

U.K.: £ 60.00
U.S.: $120.00
Can.: $155.00

CT-1286
CAPTOR

Designer: Alastair MacIntosh
Type: Weight – Spherical
Issued: 1996 in a limited
edition of 750
Status: Closed at No. 654
Series: Limited – Modern
Design
O.I.P.: U.K. £50.00
U.S. $150.00

U.K.: £ 50.00
U.S.: $100.00
Can.: $130.00

CT-1287
ALL THE FUN OF THE FAIR

Designer: Helen MacDonald
Type: Weight – Cylindrical
Issued: 1996 in a limited
edition of 25
Status: Fully subscribed
Series: Limited – Modern
Design
O.I.P.: U.K. £495.00
U.S. $1,500.00

U.K.: £ 500.00
U.S.: $1,000.00
Can.: $1,300.00

CT-1288
SING FOR YOUR SUPPER

Designer: Helen MacDonald
Type: Weight – Sculptural
Issued: 1996 in a limited
edition of 15
Status: Fully subscribed
Series: Limited – Modern
Design
O.I.P.: U.K. £795.00
U.S. $2,500.00

U.K.: £ 800.00
U.S.: $1,600.00
Can.: $2,100.00

CT-1289
PINK ANEMONE

Designer: Helen MacDonald
Type: Weight – Spherical
Issued: 1996 in a limited
edition of 50
Status: Fully subscribed
Series: Limited – Modern
Design
O.I.P.: U.K. £250.00
U.S. $750.00

U.K.: £250.00
U.S.: $500.00
Can.: $650.00

CT-1290
CORNFLOWER
Style One

Designer: Helen MacDonald
Type: Weight – Spherical
Issued: 1996 in a limited
edition of 50
Status: Fully subscribed
Series: Limited – Modern
Design
O.I.P.: U.K. £275.00
U.S. $825.00

U.K.: £275.00
U.S.: $550.00
Can.: $720.00

CT-1291
PROTEA

Designer: Jeneo Lewis
Type: Weight – Domed
Issued: 1996 in a limited
edition of 50
Status: Fully subscribed
Series: Limited – Modern
Design
O.I.P.: U.K. £225.00
U.S. $695.00

U.K.: £225.00
U.S.: $450.00
Can.: $575.00

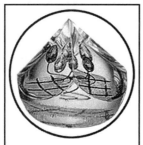

CT-1292
CHECKERS

Designer: Helen MacDonald
Type: Weight – Pyramid
facets
Issued: 1996 in a limited
edition of 350
Status: Closed at No. 294
Series: Limited – Modern
Design
O.I.P.: U.K. £85.00
U.S. $275.00

U.K.: £ 85.00
U.S.: $170.00
Can.: $225.00

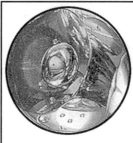

CT-1293
HALL OF MIRRORS

Designer: Shona Spittal
Type: Weight – Spherical
Issued: 1996 in a limited
edition of 75
Status: Fully subscribed
Series: Limited – Modern
Design
O.I.P.: U.K. £195.00
U.S. $595.00

U.K.: £200.00
U.S.: $400.00
Can.: $525.00

CT-1294
PINPOINT

Designer: Alastair MacIntosh
Type: Weight – Pyramid
Issued: 1996 in a limited
edition of 50
Status: Fully subscribed
Series: Limited – Modern
Design
O.I.P.: U.K. £225.00
U.S. $695.00

U.K.: £225.00
U.S.: $450.00
Can.: $580.00

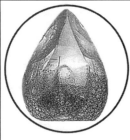

CT-1295
DEVIL'S ADVOCATE

Designer: Philip Chaplain
Type: Weight – Domed
Issued: 1996 in a limited
edition of 150
Status: Fully subscribed
Series: Limited – Modern
Design
O.I.P.: U.K. £110.00
U.S. $330.00

U.K.: £110.00
U.S.: $220.00
Can.: $285.00

CT-1296
ABYSS

Designer: Philip Chaplain
Type: Weight – Domed
Issued: 1996 in a limited
edition of 650
Status: Fully subscribed
Series: Limited – Modern
Design
O.I.P.: U.K. £65.00
U.S. $195.00

U.K.: £ 65.00
U.S.: $130.00
Can.: $170.00

CT-1297
SNOWY OWL

Designer: Alastair MacIntosh
Type: Weight – Spherical
Issued: 1996 in a limited
edition of 650
Status: Fully subscribed
Series: Limited – Modern
Design
O.I.P.: U.K. £75.00
U.S. $225.00

U.K.: £ 75.00
U.S.: $150.00
Can.: $200.00

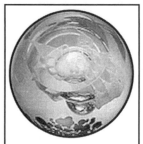

CT-1298
SPOOKY HANDS

Designer: Philip Chaplain
Type: Weight – Spherical
Issued: 1996 in a limited
edition of 650
Status: Closed at No. 605
Series: Limited – Modern
Design
O.I.P.: U.K. £65.00
U.S. $195.00

U.K.: £ 65.00
U.S.: $130.00
Can.: $170.00

CT-1299
ENCHANTMENT
Designer: Colin Terris
Type: Weight – Spherical
Size: Magnum
Issued: 1996 in a limited
         edition of 75
Status: Fully subscribed
Series: Limited – Modern
         Design
O.I.P.: U.K. £350.00
         U.S. $1,050.00

U.K.:   £375.00
U.S.: $750.00
Can.: $975.00

CT-1300
MOSES
Designer: Helen MacDonald
Type: Weight – Spherical
Issued: 1996 in a limited
         edition of 75
Status: Fully subscribed
Series: Limited – Modern
         Design
O.I.P.: U.K. £195.00
         U.S. $595.00

U.K.:   £200.00
U.S.: $400.00
Can.: $525.00

CT-1301
INCA GOLD
Designer: Alastair MacIntosh
Type: Weight – Domed
Issued: 1996 in a limited
         edition of 150
Status: Fully subscribed
Series: Limited – Modern
         Design
O.I.P.: U.K. £110.00
         U.S. $330.00

U.K.:   £110.00
U.S.: $220.00
Can.: $290.00

CT-1302A
NIGHT
Designer: Colin Terris
Type: Weight – Spherical
Issued: 1996 in a limited
         edition of 250
Status: Fully subscribed
Series: Limited – Modern
         Design
O.I.P.: U.K. £195.00/set
         U.S. $595.00/set

	Night	Set
U.K.:	£100.	200.
U.S.:	$200.	400.
Can.:	$260.	525.

Note: CT-1302A and B were
issued and sold as a set.

CT-1302B
DAY
Designer: Colin Terris
Type: Weight – Spherical
Issued: 1996 in a limited
         edition of 250
Status: Fully subscribed
Series: Limited – Modern
         Design
O.I.P.: U.K. £195.00/set
         U.S. $595.00/set

U.K.:   £100.00
U.S.: $200.00
Can.: $260.00

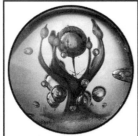

CT-1303
DOUBLE MAGNUM '96
Designer: Franco Toffolo
Type: Weight – Spherical,
         double magnum
Issued: 1996 in a limited
         edition of 150
Status: Closed at No. 126
Series: Limited – Modern
         Design
O.I.P.: U.K. £195.00
         U.S. $595.00

U.K.:   £200.00
U.S.: $400.00
Can.: $525.00

CT-1304
TROPICANA
Style Two
Designer: Helen MacDonald
Type: Weight – Spherical
Issued: 1996 in a limited
         edition of 1,765
Status: Closed at No. 1,765
Series: Collectors' Society
O.I.P.: U.K. £80.00
         U.S. $215.00

U.K.:   £ 80.00
U.S.: $160.00
Can.: $210.00

CT-1305
TWILIGHT ZONE
Designer: Philip Chaplain
Type: Weight – Spherical
Issued: 1996 in a limited
         edition of 750
Status: Closed at No. 441
Series: Limited – Modern
         Design
O.I.P.: U.K. £55.00
         U.S. $165.00

U.K.:   £ 55.00
U.S.: $110.00
Can.: $145.00

CT-1306
SALOMÉ

Designer:	Alastair MacIntosh
Type:	Weight – Spherical
Issued:	1996 in a limited edition of 350
Status:	Fully subscribed
Series:	Limited – Modern Design
O.I.P.:	U.K. £85.00
	U.S. $275.00
U.K.:	£ 85.00
U.S.:	$170.00
Can.:	$225.00

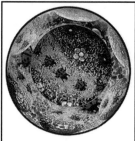

CT-1307
FOLLOW MY LEADER

Designer:	Colin Terris and William Manson
Type:	Weight – Spherical
Issued:	1996 in a limited edition of 50
Status:	Fully subscribed
Series:	Traditional Collection
O.I.P.:	U.K. £275.00
	U.S. $850.00
U.K.:	£275.00
U.S.:	$550.00
Can.:	$725.00

CT-1308
TEDDY BEAR

Designer:	William Manson
Type:	Weight – Spherical
Issued:	1996 in a limited edition of 50
Status:	Fully subscribed
Series:	Traditional Collection
O.I.P.:	U.K. £295.00
	U.S. $895.00
U.K.:	£300.00
U.S.:	$600.00
Can.:	$775.00

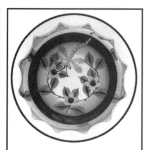

CT-1309
DAMSEL FLY

Designer:	William Manson
Type:	Weight – Spherical, faceted
Issued:	1996 in a limited edition of 50
Status:	Closed at No. 37
Series:	Traditional Collection
O.I.P.:	U.K. £350.00
	U.S. $1,075.00
U.K.:	£350.00
U.S.:	$700.00
Can.:	$900.00

CT-1310
LAGOON LIFE

Designer:	William Manson
Type:	Weight – Spherical
Issued:	1996 in a limited edition of 50
Status:	Fully subscribed
Series:	Traditional Collection
O.I.P.:	U.K. £295.00
	U.S. $895.00
U.K.:	£300.00
U.S.:	$600.00
Can.:	$775.00

CT-1311
OCEAN ENCOUNTER

Designer:	William Manson
Type:	Weight – Spherical
Issued:	1996 in a limited edition of 50
Status:	Closed at No. 36
Series:	Traditional Collection
O.I.P.:	U.K. £295.00
	U.S. $895.00
U.K.:	£300.00
U.S.:	$600.00
Can.:	$775.00

CT-1312
EGRET

Designer:	William Manson
Type:	Weight – Spherical
Issued:	1996 in a limited edition of 50
Status:	Closed at No. 47
Series:	Traditional Collection
O.I.P.:	U.K. £275.00
	U.S. $850.00
U.K.:	£275.00
U.S.:	$550.00
Can.:	$725.00

CT-1313
NEPTUNE'S KINGDOM
Style Two

Designer:	William Manson
Type:	Weight – Spherical
Size:	Magnum
Issued:	1996 in a limited edition of 10
Status:	Fully subscribed
Series:	Traditional Collection
O.I.P.:	U.K. £795.00
	U.S. $2,500.00
U.K.:	£ 850.00
U.S.:	$1,700.00
Can.:	$2,250.00

CT-1314
ORCHID
Style One

Designer:	William Manson
Type:	Weight – Spherical
Issued:	1996 in a limited edition of 150
Status:	Fully subscribed
Series:	Traditional Collection
O.I.P.:	U.K. £75.00
	U.S. $230.00
U.K.:	£ 75.00
U.S.:	$150.00
Can.:	$200.00

CT-1315
GOLDEN SPLENDOUR

Designer:	William Manson
Type:	Weight – Spherical
Issued:	1996 in a limited edition of 150
Status:	Closed at No. 106
Series:	Traditional Collection
O.I.P.:	U.K. £75.00
	U.S. $230.00
U.K.:	£ 75.00
U.S.:	$150.00
Can.:	$200.00

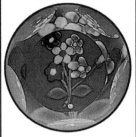

CT-1316
SUMMER POSY
Style Two

Designer:	William Manson
Type:	Weight – Spherical
Issued:	1996 in a limited edition of 150
Status:	Closed at No. 118
Series:	Traditional Collection
O.I.P.:	U.K. £75.00
	U.S. $230.00
U.K.:	£ 75.00
U.S.:	$150.00
Can.:	$200.00

CT-1317
PINK BLOSSOM

Designer:	William Manson
Type:	Weight – Spherical
Issued:	1996 in a limited edition of 150
Status:	Closed at No. 108
Series:	Traditional Collection
O.I.P.:	U.K. £75.00
	U.S. $230.00
U.K.:	£ 75.00
U.S.:	$150.00
Can.:	$200.00

CT-1318
PINK BUTTERFLY

Designer:	Allan Scott
Type:	Weight – Spherical
Size:	Miniature
Issued:	1996 in a limited edition of 150
Status:	Closed at No. 63
Series:	Traditional Collection Nature Study
O.I.P.:	U.K. £99.00
	U.S. $295.00
U.K.:	£100.00
U.S.:	$200.00
Can.:	$260.00

CT-1319
BLUE BUTTERFLY

Designer:	Allan Scott
Type:	Weight – Spherical
Size:	Miniature
Issued:	1996 in a limited edition of 150
Status:	Closed at No. 62
Series:	Traditional Collection Nature Study
O.I.P.:	U.K. £99.00
	U.S. $295.00
U.K.:	£100.00
U.S.:	$200.00
Can.:	$260.00

CT-1320
EMERALD SPRAY

Designer:	Allan Scott
Type:	Weight – Spherical
Issued:	1996 in a limited edition of 25
Status:	Fully subscribed
Series:	Traditional Collection Nature Study
O.I.P.:	U.K. £495.00
	U.S. $1,500.00
U.K.:	£ 500.00
U.S.:	$1,000.00
Can.:	$1,300.00

CT-1321A
SPRING
Style Two

Designer:	Rosette Fleming
Type:	Weight – Spherical
Issued:	1996 in a limited edition of 25
Status:	Fully subscribed
Series:	Four Seasons Set
O.I.P.:	U.K. £750.00/set
	U.S. $2,500.00/set

	Spring	Set
U.K.:	£200.	800.
U.S.:	$400.	1,600.
Can.:	$525.	2,100.

Note: CT-1321A, B, C and D were issued and sold as a set.

CT-1321B
SUMMER
Style Two

Designer: Rosette Fleming
Type: Weight – Spherical
Issued: 1996 in a limited
edition of 25
Status: Fully subscribed
Series: Four Seasons Set
O.I.P.: U.K. £750.00/set
U.S. $2,500.00/set

U.K.: £200.00
U.S.: $400.00
Can.: $525.00

CT-1321C
AUTUMN
Style Two

Designer: Rosette Fleming
Type: Weight – Spherical
Issued: 1996 in a limited
edition of 25
Status: Fully subscribed
Series: Four Seasons Set
O.I.P.: U.K. £750.00/set
U.S. $2,500.00/set

U.K.: £200.00
U.S.: $400.00
Can.: $525.00

CT-1321D
WINTER
Style Two

Designer: Rosette Fleming
Type: Weight – Spherical
Issued: 1996 in a limited
edition of 25
Status: Fully subscribed
Series: Four Seasons Set
O.I.P.: U.K. £750.00/set
U.S. $2,500.00/set

U.K.: £200.00
U.S.: $400.00
Can.: $525.00

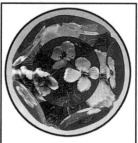

CT-1322
POPPIES
Style Three

Designer: Allan Scott
Type: Weight – Spherical
Issued: 1996 in a limited
edition of 25
Status: Fully subscribed
Series: Traditional Collection
Nature Study
O.I.P.: U.K. £595.00
U.S. $1,795.00

U.K.: £ 600.00
U.S.: $1,200.00
Can.: $1,550.00

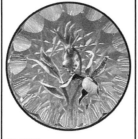

CT-1323
WILD ORCHIDS

Designer: Allan Scott
Type: Weight – Spherical
Issued: 1996 in a limited
edition of 25
Status: Fully subscribed
Series: Traditional Collection
Nature Study
O.I.P.: U.K. £550.00
U.S. $1,795.00

U.K.: £ 600.00
U.S.: $1,200.00
Can.: $1,550.00

CT-1324
BLUE BUTTERFLY – GOLD
FLOWER

Designer: Allan Scott
Type: Weight – Spherical
Issued: 1996 in a limited
edition of 50
Status: Closed at No. 39
Series: Traditional Collection
Nature Study
O.I.P.: U.K. £195.00
U.S. $595.00

U.K.: £200.00
U.S.: $400.00
Can.: $525.00

CT-1325
PINK BUTTERFLY – BLUE
FLOWER

Designer: Allan Scott
Type: Weight – Spherical
Issued: 1996 in a limited
edition of 50
Status: Closed at No. 46
Series: Traditional Collection
Nature Study
O.I.P.: U.K. £195.00
U.S. $595.00

U.K.: £200.00
U.S.: $400.00
Can.: $525.00

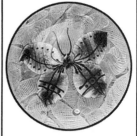

CT-1326
BLUE BUTTERFLY – LATTICINO
BASE

Designer: Allan Scott
Type: Weight – Spherical
Issued: 1996 in a limited
edition of 50
Status: Fully subscribed
Series: Traditional Collection
Nature Study
O.I.P.: U.K. £175.00
U.S. $525.00

U.K.: £175.00
U.S.: $350.00
Can.: $450.00

CT-1327
FLAME NASTURTIUM

Designer:	Margot Thomson
Type:	Weight – Spherical
Issued:	1996 in a limited edition of 50
Status:	Closed at No. 36
Series:	Whitefriars Collection
O.I.P.:	U.K. £215.00
	U.S. $750.00
U.K.:	£225.00
U.S.:	$450.00
Can.:	$600.00

CT-1328
PANSY
Style Four

Designer:	Margot Thomson
Type:	Weight – Spherical
Issued:	1996 in a limited edition of 50
Status:	Closed at No. 25
Series:	Whitefriars Collection
O.I.P.:	U.K. £295.00
	U.S. $895.00
U.K.:	£300.00
U.S.:	$600.00
Can.:	$775.00

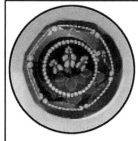

CT-1329
HOSTA

Designer:	Margot Thomson
Type:	Weight – Spherical
Issued:	1996 in a limited edition of 50
Status:	Closed at No. 30
Series:	Whitefriars Collection
O.I.P.:	U.K. £165.00
	U.S. $550.00
U.K.:	£175.00
U.S.:	$350.00
Can.:	$450.00

CT-1330
ROCK ROSE

Designer:	Margot Thomson
Type:	Weight – Spherical
Issued:	1996 in a limited edition of 50
Status:	Closed at No. 30
Series:	Whitefriars Collection
O.I.P.:	U.K. £175.00
	U.S. $550.00
U.K.:	£175.00
U.S.:	$350.00
Can.:	$450.00

CT-1331
FUCHSIA
Style Three

Designer:	Margot Thomson
Type:	Weight – Spherical
Issued:	1996 in a limited edition of 50
Status:	Fully subscribed
Series:	Whitefriars Collection
O.I.P.:	U.K. £135.00
	U.S. $450.00
U.K.:	£135.00
U.S.:	$270.00
Can.:	$350.00

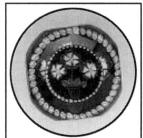

CT-1332
AURICULA

Designer:	Margot Thomson
Type:	Weight – Spherical
Issued:	1996 in a limited edition of 50
Status:	Closed at No. 29
Series:	Whitefriars Collection
O.I.P.:	U.K. £165.00
	U.S. $550.00
U.K.:	£200.00
U.S.:	$400.00
Can.:	$525.00

CT-1333
CAMOMILE

Designer:	Margot Thomson
Type:	Weight – Spherical
Issued:	1996 in a limited edition of 50
Status:	Closed at No. 30
Series:	Whitefriars Collection
O.I.P.:	U.K. £195.00
	U.S. $595.00
U.K.:	£200.00
U.S.:	$400.00
Can.:	$525.00

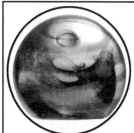

CT-1334
TITANIA

Designer:	Colin Terris
Type:	Weight – Spherical
Issued:	1996
Status:	Closed
Series:	Unlimited – Modern Design
O.I.P.:	U.K. £26.00
	U.S. $87.50
U.K.:	£30.00
U.S.:	$60.00
Can.:	$80.00

CT-1335
TARTAN TWIRL
Designer: Alastair MacIntosh
Type: Weight – Spherical
Issued: 1996
Status: Closed
Series: Unlimited – Modern Design
O.I.P.: U.K. £27.00
U.S. $87.50
U.K.: £30.00
U.S.: $60.00
Can.: $80.00

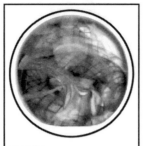

CT-1336
SORCERER'S APPRENTICE
Style One
Designer: Alastair MacIntosh
Type: Weight – Spherical
Issued: 1996
Status: Closed
Series: Unlimited – Modern Design
O.I.P.: U.K. £23.00
U.S. $72.50
U.K.: £25.00
U.S.: $50.00
Can.: $65.00

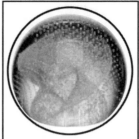

CT-1337
HARMONICS
Style One
Designer: Alastair MacIntosh
Type: Weight – Spherical
Colour: Pink
Issued: 1996
Status: Closed
Series: Unlimited – Modern Design
O.I.P.: U.K. £20.00
U.S. $72.50
U.K.: £25.00
U.S.: $50.00
Can.: $65.00

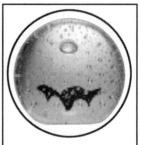

CT-1338
DEW DROPS
Designer: Colin Terris
Type: Weight – Spherical
Issued: 1996
Status: Closed
Series: Unlimited – Modern Design
O.I.P.: U.K. £25.00
U.S. $87.50
U.K.: £25.00
U.S.: $50.00
Can.: $65.00

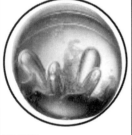

CT-1339
MOONFLOWER GREEN
Designer: Colin Terris
Type: Weight – Spherical
Issued: 1996
Status: Closed
Series: Unlimited – Modern Design
O.I.P.: U.K. £34.50
U.S. $110.00
U.K.: £35.00
U.S.: $70.00
Can.: $90.00

CT-1340
BAMBOOZLED
Designer: Helen MacDonald
Type: Weight – Domed
Issued: 1996 in a limited edition of 25
Status: Fully subscribed
Series: Limited – Modern Design
O.I.P.: U.K. £495.00
U.S. $1,600.00
U.K.: £ 500.00
U.S.: $1,000.00
Can.: $1,300.00

CT-1341
RING OF FIRE
Designer: Helen MacDonald
Type: Weight – Spherical
Issued: 1996 in a limited edition of 75
Status: Fully subscribed
Series: Limited – Modern Design
O.I.P.: U.K. £195.00
U.S. $575.00
U.K.: £200.00
U.S.: $400.00
Can.: $525.00

CT-1342
NORTHERN EXPOSURE
Designer: Helen MacDonald
Type: Weight – Sculptural
Issued: 1996 in a limited edition of 25
Status: Fully subscribed
Series: Limited – Modern Design
O.I.P.: U.K. £650.00
U.S. $2,000.00
U.K.: £ 650.00
U.S.: $1,300.00
Can.: $1,700.00

CT-1343
SHOWTIME

Designer: Helen MacDonald
Type: Weight – Domed
Issued: 1996 in a limited edition of 50
Status: Fully subscribed
Series: Limited – Modern Design
O.I.P.: U.K. £225.00
U.S. $650.00

U.K.: £225.00
U.S.: $450.00
Can.: $600.00

CT-1344
TRANQUIL POOL

Designer: Colin Terris
Type: Weight – Spherical
Issued: 1996 in a limited edition of 50
Status: Fully subscribed
Series: Limited – Modern Design
O.I.P.: U.K. £275.00
U.S. $795.00

U.K.: £275.00
U.S.: $550.00
Can.: $725.00

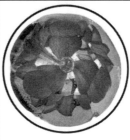

CT-1345
MASQUERADE

Designer: Colin Terris
Type: Weight – Spherical
Issued: 1996 in a limited edition of 75
Status: Fully subscribed
Series: Limited – Modern Design
O.I.P.: U.K. £195.00
U.S. $575.00

U.K.: £200.00
U.S.: $400.00
Can.: $525.00

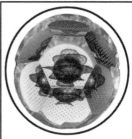

CT-1346
CONQUISTADOR

Designer: Colin Terris
Type: Weight – Spherical
Issued: 1996 in a limited edition of 50
Status: Fully subscribed
Series: Limited – Modern Design
O.I.P.: U.K. £250.00
U.S. $750.00

U.K.: £250.00
U.S.: $500.00
Can.: $650.00

CT-1347
SERENDIPITY

Designer: Colin Terris
Type: Weight – Spherical
Issued: 1996 in a limited edition of 50
Status: Fully subscribed
Series: Limited – Modern Design
O.I.P.: U.K. £295.00
U.S. $850.00

U.K.: £300.00
U.S.: $600.00
Can.: $775.00

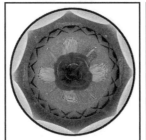

CT-1348
RAPTURE

Designer: Alastair MacIntosh
Type: Weight – Spherical
Size: Magnum
Issued: 1996 in a limited edition of 75
Status: Closed at No. 53
Series: Limited – Modern Design
O.I.P.: U.K. £350.00
U.S. $995.00

U.K.: £350.00
U.S.: $700.00
Can.: $900.00

CT-1349
KINGDOM OF THE DEEP

Designer: Colin Terris
Type: Weight – Spherical
Size: Magnum
Issued: 1996 in a limited edition of 100
Status: Closed at No. 59
Series: Limited – Modern Design
O.I.P.: U.K. £250.00
U.S. $750.00

U.K.: £250.00
U.S.: $500.00
Can.: $650.00

CT-1350
SILKEN STRANDS

Designer: Helen MacDonald
Type: Weight – Spherical
Issued: 1996 in a limited edition of 350
Status: Fully subscribed
Series: Limited – Modern Design
O.I.P.: U.K. £85.00
U.S. $250.00

U.K.: £ 85.00
U.S.: $170.00
Can.: $225.00

CT-1351
ALLURE

Designer: Helen MacDonald
Type: Weight – Teardrop
Issued: 1996 in a limited
edition of 100
Status: Fully subscribed
Series: Limited – Modern
Design
O.I.P.: U.K. £235.00
U.S. $695.00

U.K.: £250.00
U.S.: $500.00
Can.: $650.00

CT-1352
PHANTOM

Designer: Helen MacDonald
Type: Weight – Domed
Issued: 1996 in a limited
edition of 100
Status: Fully subscribed
Series: Limited – Modern
Design
O.I.P.: U.K. £250.00
U.S. $750.00

U.K.: £250.00
U.S.: $500.00
Can.: $650.00

CT-1353
SPRING CROCUS

Designer: Helen MacDonald
Type: Weight – Domed
Issued: 1996 in a limited
edition of 350
Status: Fully subscribed
Series: Limited – Modern
Design
O.I.P.: U.K. £99.00
U.S. $295.00

U.K.: £100.00
U.S.: $200.00
Can.: $260.00

CT-1354
COSMIC COLLISION

Designer: Colin Terris
Type: Weight – Spherical
Issued: 1996 in a limited
edition of 650
Status: Closed at No. 397
Series: Limited – Modern
Design
O.I.P.: U.K. £75.00
U.S. $225.00

U.K.: £ 75.00
U.S.: $150.00
Can.: $200.00

CT-1355
AVENTURINE

Designer: Caithness Design
Studio
Type: Weight – Spherical
Issued: 1996 in a limited
edition of 750
Status: Fully subscribed
Series: Limited – Modern
Design
O.I.P.: U.K. £50.00
U.S. $150.00

U.K.: £ 50.00
U.S.: $100.00
Can.: $130.00

CT-1356
HIBERNATION

Designer: Colin Terris
Type: Weight – Ovoid
Issued: 1996 in a limited
edition of 650
Status: Closed at No. 544
Series: Limited – Modern
Design
O.I.P.: U.K. £75.00
U.S. $225.00

U.K.: £ 75.00
U.S.: $150.00
Can.: $200.00

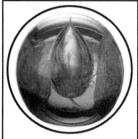

CT-1357
HYPNOSIS

Designer: Philip Chaplain
Type: Weight – Spherical
Issued: 1996 in a limited
edition of 750
Status: Closed at No. 473
Series: Limited – Modern
Design
O.I.P.: U.K. £60.00
U.S. $175.00

U.K.: £ 60.00
U.S.: $120.00
Can.: $155.00

CT-1358
KATMANDU

Designer: Philip Chaplain
Type: Weight – Domed
Issued: 1996 in a limited
edition of 750
Status: Fully subscribed
Series: Limited – Modern
Design
O.I.P.: U.K. £60.00
U.S. $175.00

U.K.: £ 60.00
U.S.: $120.00
Can.: $155.00

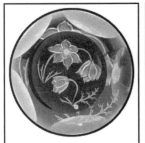

CT-1359
PASQUE FLOWER
Designer: Margot Thomson
Type: Weight – Spherical
Issued: 1996 in a limited edition of 50
Status: Fully subscribed
Series: Whitefriars Collection
O.I.P.: U.K. £110.00
U.S. $325.00

U.K.: £150.00
U.S.: $300.00
Can.: $400.00

CT-1360
DAFFODIL SPRAY
Designer: Allan Scott
Type: Weight – Spherical
Issued: 1996 in a limited edition of 50
Status: Fully subscribed
Series: Whitefriars Collection
O.I.P.: U.K. £135.00
U.S. $395.00

U.K.: £150.00
U.S.: $300.00
Can.: $400.00

CT-1361
SPRING POSY
Designer: Allan Scott
Type: Weight – Spherical
Issued: 1996 in a limited edition of 25
Status: Closed at No. 22
Series: Traditional Collection Nature Study
O.I.P.: U.K. £595.00
U.S. $1,700.00

U.K.: £ 600.00
U.S.: $1,200.00
Can.: $1,550.00

CT-1362
TERRARIUM
Designer: Allan Scott
Type: Weight – Spherical
Issued: 1996 in a limited edition of 25
Status: Fully subscribed
Series: Traditional Collection Nature Study
O.I.P.: U.K. £595.00
U.S. $1,700.00

U.K.: £ 600.00
U.S.: $1,200.00
Can.: $1,550.00

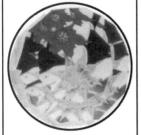

CT-1363
TROPICAL BOUQUET
Designer: Allan Scott
Type: Weight – Spherical
Issued: 1996 in a limited edition of 25
Status: Fully subscribed
Series: Traditional Collection Nature Study
O.I.P.: U.K. £595.00
U.S. $1,700.00

U.K.: £ 600.00
U.S.: $1,200.00
Can.: $1,550.00

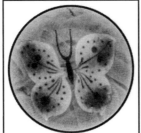

CT-1364
PURPLE BUTTERFLY – LATTICINO BASE
Designer: Allan Scott
Type: Weight – Spherical
Issued: 1996 in a limited edition of 50
Status: Closed at No. 39
Series: Traditional Collection Nature Study
O.I.P.: U.K. £175.00
U.S. $575.00

U.K.: £175.00
U.S.: $350.00
Can.: $450.00

CT-1365
WHITE BUTTERFLY – YELLOW FLOWER
Designer: Allan Scott
Type: Weight – Spherical
Issued: 1996 in a limited edition of 50
Status: Closed at No. 26
Series: Traditional Collection Nature Study
O.I.P.: U.K. £195.00
U.S. $575.00

U.K.: £200.00
U.S.: $400.00
Can.: $525.00

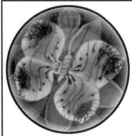

CT-1366
GOLD BUTTERFLY – PINK FLOWER
Designer: Allan Scott
Type: Weight – Spherical
Issued: 1996 in a limited edition of 50
Status: Closed at No. 33
Series: Traditional Collection Nature Study
O.I.P.: U.K. £195.00
U.S. $575.00

U.K.: £200.00
U.S.: $400.00
Can.: $525.00

CT-1367
BOYHOOD MEMORIES

Designer: William Manson
Type: Weight – Cylindrical
Issued: 1996 in a limited
          edition of 50
Status: Closed at No. 36
Series: Traditional Collection
O.I.P.:   U.K. £395.00
          U.S. $1,200.00

U.K.:   £   400.00
U.S.: $ 800.00
Can.: $1,050.00

CT-1368
SCARECROW

Designer: Colin Terris and
          William Manson
Type: Weight – Spherical
Issued: 1996 in a limited
          edition of 50
Status: Closed at No. 41
Series: Traditional Collection
O.I.P.:   U.K. £275.00
          U.S. $775.00

U.K.:   £275.00
U.S.: $550.00
Can.: $725.00

CT-1369
MEADOW POOL

Designer: William Manson
Type: Weight – Spherical
Size: Magnum
Issued: 1996 in a limited
          edition of 25
Status: Closed at No. 18
Series: Traditional Collection
O.I.P.:   U.K. £850.00
          U.S. $2,750.00

U.K.:   £   850.00
U.S.: $1,700.00
Can.: $2,200.00

CT-1370
DEEP SEA DIVER

Designer: William Manson
Type: Weight – Spherical
Issued: 1996 in a limited
          edition of 50
Status: Closed at No. 36
Series: Traditional Collection
O.I.P.:   U.K. £295.00
          U.S. $995.00

U.K.:   £300.00
U.S.: $600.00
Can.: $775.00

CT-1371
WHIZZ

Designer: Alastair MacIntosh
Type: Weight – Spherical
Issued: 1996
Status: Closed
Series: Unlimited – Modern
          Design
O.I.P.:   U.K. £26.00
          U.S. $79.50

U.K.:   £30.00
U.S.: $60.00
Can.: $80.00

CT-1372
CASCADE
Style Two

Designer: Helen MacDonald
Type: Weight – Spherical
Issued: 1996
Status: Closed
Series: Unlimited – Modern
          Design
O.I.P.:   U.K. £30.00
          U.S. $95.00

U.K.:   £30.00
U.S.: $60.00
Can.: $80.00

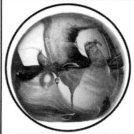

CT-1373
DEBUTANTE

Designer: Colin Terris
Type: Weight – Spherical
Colour: 1. Azure
          2. Emerald
          3. Ruby
Issued: 1996
Status: Closed
Series: Unlimited – Modern
          Design
O.I.P.:   U.K. £25.00
          U.S. $79.50

U.K.:   £25.00
U.S.: $50.00
Can.: $65.00

CT-1374
FOURSOME

Designer: Alastair MacIntosh
Type: Weight – Spherical
Issued: 1996
Status: Closed
Series: Unlimited – Modern
          Design
O.I.P.:   U.K. £27.00
          U.S. $79.50

U.K.:   £30.00
U.S.: $60.00
Can.: $80.00

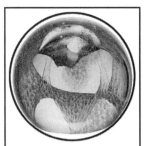

CT-1375
BIG TOP

Designer:	Alastair MacIntosh
Type:	Weight – Spherical
Issued:	1996
Status:	Closed
Series:	Unlimited – Modern Design
O.I.P.:	U.K. £28.00
	U.S. $87.50
U.K.:	£30.00
U.S.:	$60.00
Can.:	$80.00

CT-1376
EXTRAVAGANZA

Designer:	Colin Terris
Type:	Weight – Spherical
Colour:	1. Black
	2. Blue
	3. Green
Issued:	1996
Status:	Closed
Series:	Unlimited – Modern Design
O.I.P.:	U.K. £24.00
	U.S. $72.50
U.K.:	£30.00
U.S.:	$60.00
Can.:	$80.00

CT-1377
HM QUEEN ELIZABETH II 70TH BIRTHDAY CROWN OVERLAY

Designer:	Colin Terris
Type:	Weight – Spherical
Issued:	1996 in a limited edition of 70
Status:	Closed at No. 34
O.I.P.:	£200.00
U.K.:	£200.00
U.S.:	$400.00
Can.:	$525.00

Note: The 70th birthday weights and perfume bottle were not issued in the U.S.

CT-1378
HM QUEEN ELIZABETH II 70TH BIRTHDAY CROWN

Designer:	Colin Terris
Type:	Weight – Spherical
Issued:	1996 in a limited edition of 250
Status:	Closed at No. 69
O.I.P.:	£125.00
U.K.:	£125.00
U.S.:	$250.00
Can.:	$325.00

CT-1379
HM QUEEN ELIZABETH II 70TH BIRTHDAY ROSE

Designer:	Colin Terris
Type:	Weight – Spherical
Issued:	1996 in a limited edition of 70
Status:	Closed at No. 42
O.I.P.:	£195.00
U.K.:	£200.00
U.S.:	$400.00
Can.:	$525.00

CT-1380
HM QUEEN ELIZABETH II 70TH BIRTHDAY ROSE PERFUME BOTTLE

Designer:	Colin Terris
Type:	Perfume bottle
Issued:	1996 in a limited edition of 70
Status:	Closed at No. 37
O.I.P.:	£250.00
U.K.:	£250.00
U.S.:	$500.00
Can.:	$650.00

THREE GENTIANS

Designer:	Alastair MacIntosh
Type:	Weight – Spherical
Issued:	1996 in a limited edition of 750
Status:	Closed
Series:	Unknown
U.K.:	£ 55.00
U.S.:	$110.00
Can.:	$145.00

Photograph not available at press time

SEA SHANTY

Designer:	Unknown
Type:	Weight – Unknown
Issued:	1996
Status:	Closed
Series:	Special Event
U.K.:	£ 55.00
U.S.:	$110.00
Can.:	$145.00

ISSUES OF 1997

CT-1381
TARANTELLA

Designer: Philip Chaplain
Type: Weight – Spherical
Issued: 1997 in a limited edition of 650
Status: Closed at No. 499
Series: Limited – Modern Design
O.I.P.: U.K. £70.00
U.S. $225.00

U.K.: £ 75.00
U.S.: $150.00
Can.: $200.00

CT-1382
IT'S LIFE JIM

Designer: Helen MacDonald
Type: Weight – Spherical with plinth
Issued: 1997 in a limited edition of 25
Status: Closed at No. 23
Series: Limited – Modern Design
O.I.P.: U.K. £650.00
U.S. $2,125.00

U.K.: £ 650.00
U.S.: $1,300.00
Can.: $1,700.00

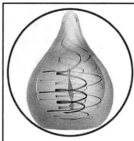

CT-1383
TWISTER

Designer: Simon Langdon
Type: Weight – Teardrop
Issued: 1997 in a limited edition of 650
Status: Closed at No. 249
Series: Limited – Modern Design
O.I.P.: U.K. £80.00
U.S. $265.00

U.K.: £ 85.00
U.S.: $170.00
Can.: $225.00

CT-1384
NORSE LEGEND

Designer: Philip Chaplain
Type: Weight – Spherical
Issued: 1997 in a limited edition of 750
Status: Fully subscribed
Series: Limited – Modern Design
O.I.P.: U.K. £60.00
U.S. $195.00

U.K.: £ 65.00
U.S.: $130.00
Can.: $170.00

CT-1385
HOMEWARD BOUND

Designer: Colin Terris
Type: Weight – Spherical
Issued: 1997 in a limited edition of 750
Status: Closed at No. 462
Series: Limited – Modern Design
O.I.P.: U.K. £55.00
U.S. $175.00

U.K.: £ 60.00
U.S.: $120.00
Can.: $155.00

CT-1386
FRAMBOISE

Designer: Philip Chaplain
Type: Weight – Spherical
Issued: 1997 in a limited edition of 650
Status: Fully subscribed
Series: Limited – Modern Design
O.I.P.: U.K. £70.00
U.S. $225.00

U.K.: £ 70.00
U.S.: $140.00
Can.: $180.00

CT-1387
DOUBLE MAGNUM 97

Designer: Franco Toffolo
Type: Weight – Spherical
Size: Double magnum
Issued: 1997 in a limited edition of 150
Status: Closed at No. 79
Series: Limited – Modern Design
O.I.P.: U.K. £195.00
U.S. $595.00

U.K.: £200.00
U.S.: $400.00
Can.: $525.00

CT-1388
GOLDEN MITRE

Designer: Alastair MacIntosh
Type: Weight – Domed
Issued: 1997 in a limited edition of 50
Status: Fully subscribed
Series: Limited – Modern Design
O.I.P.: U.K. £275.00
U.S. $895.00

U.K.: £275.00
U.S.: $550.00
Can.: $725.00

CT-1389
AZTEC RAINFLOWER

Designer:	Alastair MacIntosh
Type:	Weight – Domed
Issued:	1997 in a limited edition of 350
Status:	Fully subscribed
Series:	Limited – Modern Design
O.I.P.:	U.K. £125.00 U.S. $395.00
U.K.:	£125.00
U.S.:	$250.00
Can.:	$325.00

CT-1390
HERMITAGE

Designer:	Alastair MacIntosh
Type:	Weight – Sculptural
Issued:	1997 in a limited edition of 50
Status:	Fully subscribed
Series:	Limited – Modern Design
O.I.P.:	U.K. £275.00 U.S. $895.00
U.K.:	£275.00
U.S.:	$550.00
Can.:	$725.00

CT-1391
WHITE NARCISSUS

Designer:	Helen MacDonald
Type:	Weight – Spherical
Issued:	1997 in a limited edition of 75
Status:	Fully subscribed
Series:	Limited – Modern Design
O.I.P.:	U.K. £250.00 U.S. $825.00
U.K.:	£250.00
U.S.:	$500.00
Can.:	$650.00

CT-1392
OUT OF THE BLUE

Designer:	Philip Chaplain
Type:	Weight – Spherical
Issued:	1997 in a limited edition of 650
Status:	Closed at No. 618
Series:	Limited – Modern Design
O.I.P.:	U.K. £70.00 U.S. $225.00
U.K.:	£ 70.00
U.S.:	$140.00
Can.:	$180.00

CT-1393
HICKORY DICKORY DOCK

Designer:	Helen MacDonald
Type:	Weight – Domed
Issued:	1997 in a limited edition of 100
Status:	Closed at No. 78
Series:	Limited – Modern Design
O.I.P.:	U.K. £300.00 U.S. $950.00
U.K.:	£300.00
U.S.:	$600.00
Can.:	$775.00

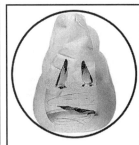

CT-1394
SOUTHERN EXPOSURE

Designer:	Helen MacDonald
Type:	Weight – Sculptural
Issued:	1997 in a limited edition of 25
Status:	Fully subscribed
Series:	Limited – Modern Design
O.I.P.:	U.K. £650.00 U.S. $2,125.00
U.K.:	£ 650.00
U.S.:	$1,300.00
Can.:	$1,700.00

CT-1395
DREAM WEAVER

Designer:	Philip Chaplain
Type:	Weight – Domed
Issued:	1997 in a limited edition of 750
Status:	Fully subscribed
Series:	Limited – Modern Design
O.I.P.:	U.K. £60.00 U.S. $195.00
U.K.:	£ 60.00
U.S.:	$120.00
Can.:	$155.00

CT-1396
INNOCENCE

Designer:	Colin Terris
Type:	Weight – Spherical, facets
Issued:	1997 in a limited edition of 75
Status:	Fully subscribed
Series:	Limited – Modern Design
O.I.P.:	U.K. £250.00 U.S. $825.00
U.K.:	£250.00
U.S.:	$500.00
Can.:	$650.00

CT-1397
CACTUS CITY

Designer: Alastair MacIntosh
Type: Weight – Spherical, facets
Issued: 1997 in a limited edition of 50
Status: Fully subscribed
Series: Limited – Modern Design
O.I.P.: U.K. £295.00
U.S. $975.00

U.K.: £300.00
U.S.: $600.00
Can.: $775.00

CT-1398
AULD LANG SYNE

Designer: Helen MacDonald
Type: Weight – Domed
Issued: 1997 in a limited edition of 125
Status: Closed at No. 96
Series: Limited – Modern Design
O.I.P.: U.K. £250.00
U.S. $795.00

U.K.: £250.00
U.S.: $500.00
Can.: $650.00

CT-1399
ADMIRATION

Designer: Colin Terris
Type: Weight – Teardrop, facets
Size: Magnum
Issued: 1997 in a limited edition of 75
Status: Fully subscribed
Series: Limited – Modern Design
O.I.P.: U.K. £300.00
U.S. $975.00

U.K.: £300.00
U.S.: $600.00
Can.: $775.00

CT-1400
SPIRIT DANCER

Designer: Jason Green
Type: Weight – Teardrop
Issued: 1997 in a limited edition of 650
Status: Fully subscribed
Series: Limited – Modern Design
O.I.P.: U.K. £75.00
U.S. $250.00

U.K.: £ 75.00
U.S.: $150.00
Can.: $200.00

CT-1401
SPRING SENTINEL

Designer: Helen MacDonald
Type: Weight – Teardrop
Issued: 1997 in a limited edition of 125
Status: Closed at No. 102
Series: Limited – Modern Design
O.I.P.: U.K. £250.00
U.S. $795.00

U.K.: £250.00
U.S.: $500.00
Can.: $650.00

CT-1402
NORMAN CONQUEST

Designer: Colin Terris
Type: Weight – Domed
Issued: 1997 in a limited edition of 100
Status: Fully subscribed
Series: Limited – Modern Design
O.I.P.: U.K. £275.00
U.S. $875.00

U.K.: £275.00
U.S.: $550.00
Can.: $725.00

CT-1403
MAGIC POTION

Designer: Alastair MacIntosh
Type: Weight – Spherical
Issued: 1997 in a limited edition of 750
Status: Fully subscribed
Series: Limited – Modern Design
O.I.P.: U.K. £45.00
U.S. $150.00

U.K.: £ 45.00
U.S.: $ 90.00
Can.: $120.00

CT-1404
TEMPTATION

Designer: Helen MacDonald
Type: Weight – Spherical
Issued: 1997 in a limited edition of 100
Status: Closed at No. 62
Series: Limited – Modern Design
O.I.P.: U.K. £275.00
U.S. $875.00

U.K.: £275.00
U.S.: $550.00
Can.: $725.00

CT-1405
ACQUIESCENCE

Designer: Colin Terris
Type: Weight – Spherical
Issued: 1997 in a limited
edition of 650
Status: Fully subscribed
Series: Limited – Modern
Design
O.I.P.: U.K. £65.00
U.S. $210.00

U.K.: £ 65.00
U.S.: $130.00
Can.: $170.00

CT-1406
TRINCULO

Designer: Alan Scrimgeour
Type: Weight – Domed
Issued: 1997 in a limited
edition of 150
Status: Fully subscribed
Series: Limited – Modern
Design
O.I.P.: U.K. £195.00
U.S. $625.00

U.K.: £200.00
U.S.: $400.00
Can.: $525.00

CT-1407
IMPRINT

Designer: Alastair MacIntosh
Type: Weight – Pyramid
facets
Issued: 1997 in a limited
edition of 200
Status: Closed at No. 107
Series: Limited – Modern
Design
O.I.P.: U.K. £160.00
U.S. $525.00

U.K.: £175.00
U.S.: $350.00
Can.: $450.00

CT-1408
CRITICAL MASS

Designer: Philip Chaplain
Type: Weight – Spherical
Issued: 1997 in a limited
edition of 750
Status: Closed at No. 678
Series: Limited – Modern
Design
O.I.P.: U.K. £55.00
U.S. $175.00

U.K.: £ 60.00
U.S.: $120.00
Can.: $155.00

CT-1409
LIFE'S A BEACH

Designer: Allan Scott
Type: Weight – Spherical
Issued: 1997 in a limited
edition of 75
Status: Fully subscribed
Series: Limited – Modern
Design
O.I.P.: U.K. £295.00
U.S. $975.00

U.K.: £300.00
U.S.: $600.00
Can.: $775.00

CT-1410
AMMADORA

Designer: Caithness Design
Studio
Type: Weight – Hexagonal
column
Issued: 1997 in a limited
edition of 50
Status: Fully subscribed
Series: Limited – Modern
Design
O.I.P.: U.K. £275.00
U.S. $895.00

U.K.: £275.00
U.S.: $550.00
Can.: $725.00

CT-1411
LOS TRES AMIGOS

Designer: Neil Allan
Jason Green
Type: Weight – Domed
Issued: 1997 in a limited
edition of 350
Status: Closed at No. 304
Series: Limited – Modern
Design
O.I.P.: U.K. £115.00
U.S. $375.00

U.K.: £125.00
U.S.: $250.00
Can.: $325.00

CT-1412
SACRED SPIRIT

Designer: Helen MacDonald
Type: Weight – Sculptural
Issued: 1997 in a limited
edition of 250
Status: Closed at No. 237
Series: Limited – Modern
Design
O.I.P.: U.K. £150.00
U.S. $475.00

U.K.: £150.00
U.S.: $300.00
Can.: $400.00

CT-1413
INCOGNITO

Designer: Alastair MacIntosh
Type: Weight – Spherical
Issued: 1997 in a limited
edition of 650
Status: Closed at No. 250
Series: Limited – Modern
Design
O.I.P.: U.K. £70.00
U.S. $225.00

U.K.: £ 75.00
U.S.: $150.00
Can.: $200.00

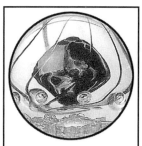

CT-1414
METAMORPHOSIS

Designer: Philip Chaplain
Type: Weight – Spherical
Issued: 1997 in a limited
edition of 650
Status: Closed at No. 484
Series: Limited – Modern
Design
O.I.P.: U.K. £70.00
U.S. $225.00

U.K.: £ 75.00
U.S.: $150.00
Can.: $200.00

CT-1415
NEMESIS

Designer: Philip Chaplain
Type: Weight – Spherical
Issued: 1997 in a limited
edition of 750
Status: Closed at no. 671
Series: Limited – Modern
Design
O.I.P.: U.K. £60.00
U.S. $195.00

U.K.: £ 60.00
U.S.: $120.00
Can.: $155.00

CT-1416
PENTECOST

Designer: Helen MacDonald
Type: Weight – Domed
Issued: 1997 in a limited
edition of 75
Status: Fully subscribed
Series: Limited – Modern
Design
O.I.P.: U.K. £250.00
U.S. $825.00

U.K.: £250.00
U.S.: $500.00
Can.: $650.00

CT-1417
GLADIATORS

Designer: Garry Kean
Type: Weight – Domed
Issued: 1997 in a limited
edition of 150
Status: Closed at No. 130
Series: Limited – Modern
Design
O.I.P.: U.K. £175.00
U.S. $575.00

U.K.: £175.00
U.S.: $350.00
Can.: $450.00

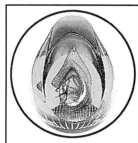

CT-1418
SALADIN

Designer: Colin Terris
Type: Weight – Domed
Issued: 1997 in a limited
edition of 1,995
Status: Closed at No. 1,995
Series: Collectors' Society
O.I.P.: U.K. £75.00
U.S. $215.00

U.K.: £ 85.00
U.S.: $170.00
Can.: $225.00

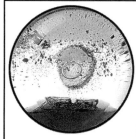

CT-1419
VISITATION

Designer: Colin Terris
Type: Weight – Spherical
magnum size
Issued: 1997 in a limited
edition of 100
Status: Closed at No. 61
Series: Limited – Modern
Design
O.I.P.: U.K. £225.00
U.S. $875.00

U.K.: £225.00
U.S.: $450.00
Can.: $600.00

CT-1420
BIOSPHERE

Designer: Alastair MacIntosh
Type: Weight – Spherical
Issued: 1997 in a limited
edition of 500
Status: Fully subscribed
Series: Limited – Modern
Design
O.I.P.: U.K. £90.00
U.S. $295.00

U.K.: £ 90.00
U.S.: $180.00
Can.: $240.00

CT-1421
DOWN ON THE FARM

Designer:	William Manson
Type:	Weight – Spherical
Issued:	1997 in a limited edition of 50
Status:	Closed at No. 30
Series:	Traditional Collection
O.I.P.:	U.K. £325.00
	U.S. $1,050.00
U.K.:	£325.00
U.S.:	$650.00
Can.:	$850.00

CT-1422
RED ADMIRAL

Designer:	William Manson
Type:	Weight – Spherical
Issued:	1997 in a limited edition of 50
Status:	Closed at No. 28
Series:	Traditional Collection
O.I.P.:	U.K. £395.00
	U.S. $1,295.00
U.K.:	£ 400.00
U.S.:	$ 800.00
Can.:	$1,050.00

CT-1423
WALKABOUT

Designer:	William Manson
Type:	Weight – Spherical
Issued:	1997 in a limited edition of 50
Status:	Closed at No. 34
Series:	Traditional Collection
O.I.P.:	U.K. £325.00
	U.S. $1,050.00
U.K.:	£325.00
U.S.:	$650.00
Can.:	$850.00

Note: This paperweight features surface lampwork.

CT-1424
FLAMINGO

Designer:	William Manson
Type:	Weight – Spherical
Size:	Medium
Issued:	1997 in a limited edition of 150
Status:	Closed at No. 112
Series:	Traditional Collection
O.I.P.:	U.K. £85.00
	U.S. $265.00
U.K.:	£ 85.00
U.S.:	$170.00
Can.:	$225.00

CT-1425
KINGFISHER
Style Two

Designer:	William Manson
Type:	Weight – Spherical
Size:	Medium
Issued:	1997 in a limited edition of 150
Status:	Closed at No. 90
Series:	Traditional Collection
O.I.P.:	U.K. £85.00
	U.S. $265.00
U.K.:	£ 85.00
U.S.:	$170.00
Can.:	$225.00

CT-1426
HERON

Designer:	William Manson
Type:	Weight – Spherical
Size:	Medium
Issued:	1997 in a limited edition of 150
Status:	Closed at No. 112
Series:	Traditional Collection
O.I.P.:	U.K. £85.00
	U.S. $265.00
U.K.:	£ 85.00
U.S.:	$170.00
Can.:	$225.00

CT-1427
SWAN
Style Two

Designer:	William Manson
Type:	Weight – Spherical
Size:	Medium
Issued:	1997 in a limited edition of 150
Status:	Fully subscribed
Series:	Traditional Collection
O.I.P.:	U.K. £85.00
	U.S. $265.00
U.K.:	£ 85.00
U.S.:	$170.00
Can.:	$225.00

CT-1428
SNAKE BASKET

Designer:	Colin Terris
	William Manson
Type:	Weight – Spherical
Issued:	1997 in a limited edition of 50
Status:	Closed at No. 29
Series:	Traditional Collection
O.I.P.:	U.K. £350.00
	U.S. $1,150.00
U.K.:	£350.00
U.S.:	$700.00
Can.:	$900.00

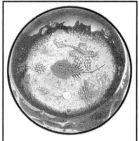

CT-1429
ROCK POOL

Designer: William Manson
Type: Weight – Spherical
Issued: 1997 in a limited
edition of 50
Status: Closed at No. 40
Series: Traditional Collection
O.I.P.: U.K. £360.00
U.S. $1,175.00

U.K.: £ 500.00
U.S.: $1,000.00
Can.: $1,300.00

CT-1430
DESTINATION MARS

Designer: Colin Terris
Type: Weight – Spherical
Issued: 1997 in a limited
edition of 500
Status: Closed
Series: Traditional Collection
O.I.P.: U.K. £70.00
U.S. $225.00

U.K.: £ 70.00
U.S.: $140.00
Can.: $180.00

CT-1431
DRIFTING BY

Designer: William Manson
Type: Weight – Spherical
Issued: 1997 in a limited
edition of 50
Status: Closed at No. 36
Series: Traditional Collection
O.I.P.: U.K. £315.00
U.S. $975.00

U.K.: £325.00
U.S.: $650.00
Can.: $850.00

CT-1432
TREASURE TROVE

Designer: William Manson
Type: Weight – Spherical
Issued: 1997 in a limited
edition of 50
Status: Closed at No. 31
Series: Traditional Collection
O.I.P.: U.K. £395.00
U.S. $1,295.00

U.K.: £ 400.00
U.S.: $ 800.00
Can.: $1,050.00

CT-1433
CRAB APPLE

Designer: Allan Scott
Type: Weight – Spherical
Issued: 1997 in a limited
edition of 50
Status: Closed at No. 31
Series: Traditional Collection
Nature Study
O.I.P.: U.K. £350.00
U.S. $1,125.00

U.K.: £350.00
U.S.: $700.00
Can.: $900.00

CT-1434
SUNSET DUET

Designer: Allan Scott
Type: Weight – Spherical
Issued: 1997 in a limited
edition of 25
Status: Closed at No. 20
Series: Traditional Collection
Nature Study
O.I.P.: U.K. £595.00
U.S. $1,925.00

U.K.: £ 600.00
U.S.: $1,200.00
Can.: $1,550.00

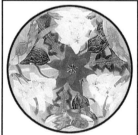

CT-1435
FLEUR ROUGE

Designer: Allan Scott
Type: Weight – Spherical
Issued: 1997 in a limited
edition of 25
Status: Closed at No. 23
Series: Traditional Collection
Nature Study
O.I.P.: U.K. £595.00
U.S. $1,925.00

U.K.: £ 600.00
U.S.: $1,200.00
Can.: $1,550.00

CT-1436
TOKEN OF LOVE

Designer: Allan Scott
Type: Weight – Spherical
Issued: 1997 in a limited
edition of 25
Status: Fully subscribed
Series: Traditional Collection
Nature Study
O.I.P.: U.K. £595.00
U.S. $1,925.00

U.K.: £ 600.00
U.S.: $1,200.00
Can.: $1,550.00

CT-1437
CASTLE GARDEN

Designer: Harry McKay
Type: Weight – Pyramid, facets
Issued: 1997 in a limited edition of 50
Status: Closed at No. 47
Series: Traditional Collection Nature Study
O.I.P.: U.K. £400.00
U.S. $1,300.00

U.K.: £ 400.00
U.S.: $ 800.00
Can.: $1,050.00

CT-1438A
FRUIT

Designer: Margot Thomson
Type: Weight – Spherical
Issued: 1997 in a limited edition of 25
Status: Fully subscribed
Series: Traditional Collection Nature Study
O.I.P.: U.K. £850.00/set
U.S. $2,775.00/set

	Fruit	Set
U.K.:	£ 425.	850.
U.S.:	$ 850.	1,700.
Can.:	$1,100.	2,200.

Note: CT-1438A and B were issued and sold as a set.

CT-1438B
VEG

Designer: Margot Thomson
Type: Weight - Spherical
Issued: 1997 in a limited edition of 25
Status: Fully subscribed
Series: Traditional Collection Nature Study
O.I.P.: U.K. £850.00/set
U.S. $2,775.00/set

U.K.: £ 425.00
U.S.: $ 850.00
Can.: $1,100.00

CT-1439
SPRING BOTANICAL

Designer: Rosette Fleming
Type: Weight – Spherical, facets
Issued: 1997 in a limited edition of 50
Status: Fully subscribed
Series: Whitefriars Collection
O.I.P.: U.K. £175.00
U.S. $575.00

U.K.: £175.00
U.S.: $350.00
Can.: $450.00

CT-1440
AUTUMN GOLD

Designer: Rosette Fleming
Type: Weight – Spherical
Issued: 1997 in a limited edition of 50
Status: Fully subscribed
Series: Whitefriars Collection
O.I.P.: U.K. £150.00
U.S. $495.00

U.K.: £150.00
U.S: $300.00
Can.: $400.00

CT-1441
DIAMOND BOUQUET

Designer: Rosette Fleming
Type: Weight – Spherical
Issued: 1997 in a limited edition of 50
Status: Closed at No. 41
Series: Whitefriars Collection
O.I.P.: U.K. £195.00
U.S. $650.00

U.K.: £200.00
U.S.: $400.00
Can.: $525.00

CT-1442
FESTIVE DELIGHT

Designer: Rosette Fleming
Type: Weight – Spherical
Issued: 1997 in a limited edition of 50
Status: Closed at No. 40
Series: Whitefriars Collection
O.I.P.: U.K. £175.00
U.S. $575.00

U.K.: £175.00
U.S.: $350.00
Can.: $450.00

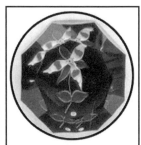

CT-1443
TRILLIUM

Designer: Rosette Fleming
Type: Weight – Spherical
Issued: 1997 in a limited edition of 50
Status: Closed at No. 30
Series: Whitefriars Collection
O.I.P.: U.K. £150.00
U.S. $495.00

U.K.: £175.00
U.S.: $350.00
Can.: $450.00

CT-1444
BRIGHT NEW DAY

Designer: Rosette Fleming
Type: Weight – Spherical
Issued: 1997 in a limited
edition of 50
Status: Fully subscribed
Series: Whitefriars Collection
O.I.P.: U.K. £135.00
U.S. $475.00

U.K.: £135.00
U.S.: $270.00
Can.: $350.00

CT-1445
TRADITIONAL TRIBUTE

Designer: Allan Scott
Type: Weight – Spherical
Issued: 1997 in a limited
edition of 50
Status: Fully subscribed
Series: Whitefriars Collection
O.I.P.: U.K. £110.00
U.S. $375.00

U.K.: £110.00
U.S.: $220.00
Can.: $290.00

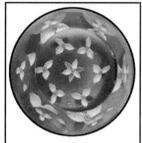

CT-1446
EMERALD DANCERS

Designer: Rosette Fleming
Type: Weight – Spherical
Issued: 1997 in a limited
edition of 50
Status: Fully subscribed
Series: Whitefriars Collection
O.I.P.: U.K. £175.00
U.S. $575.00

U.K.: £175.00
U.S.: $350.00
Can.: $450.00

CT-1447
VICTORIAN MEMORIES

Designer: Allan Scott
Type: Weight – Spherical
Issued: 1997 in a limited
edition of 50
Status: Fully subscribed
Series: Whitefriars Collection
O.I.P.: U.K. £110.00
U.S. $395.00

U.K.: £110.00
U.S.: $220.00
Can.: $290.00

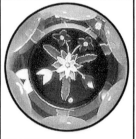

CT-1448
BURGUNDY BLOOM

Designer: Rosette Fleming
Type: Weight – Spherical
Issued: 1997 in a limited
edition of 50
Status: Closed at No. 40
Series: Whitefriars Collection
O.I.P.: U.K. £135.00
U.S. $450.00

U.K.: £135.00
U.S.: $270.00
Can.: $350.00

CT-1449
**SWEET SENSATION
KINGFISHER**

Designer: Rosette Fleming
Type: Weight – Spherical
Size: Medium
Issued: 1997 in a limited
edition of 150
Status: Closed at No. 55
Series: Whitefriars Collection
O.I.P.: U.K. £80.00
U.S. $250.00

U.K.: £ 80.00
U.S.: $160.00
Can.: $210.00

CT-1450
SWEET SENSATION COBALT

Designer: Rosette Fleming
Type: Weight – Spherical
Size: Medium
Issued: 1997 in a limited
edition of 150
Status: Closed at No. 60
Series: Whitefriars Collection
O.I.P.: U.K. £80.00
U.S. $250.00

U.K.: £ 80.00
U.S.: $160.00
Can.: $210.00

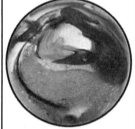

CT-1451
CHERRY PIE

Designer: Stuart Cumming
Type: Weight – Spherical
Issued: 1997
Status: Closed
Series: Unlimited – Modern
Design
O.I.P.: U.K. £28.50
U.S. $95.00

U.K.: £30.00
U.S.: $60.00
Can.: $80.00

CT-1452
RHYTHM 'N BLUES

Designer:	Helen MacDonald
Type:	Weight – Spherical
Issued:	1997
Status:	Closed
Series:	Unlimited – Modern Design
O.I.P.:	U.K. £30.00
	U.S. $95.00
U.K.:	£ 40.00
U.S.:	$ 80.00
Can.:	$100.00

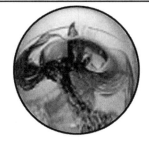

CT-1453
MOONCRYSTAL
Style Two

Designer:	Colin Terris		
Type:	Weight – Spherical		
Size:	Medium		
Colour:	1. Black	4.	Hyacinth
	2. Blue	5.	Pink
	3. Green	6.	Yellow
Issued:	1997		
Status:	Active		
Series:	Medium and Miniature Size		
O.I.P.:	U.K. £14.95		
	U.S. $49.50		
U.K.:	£14.95		
U.S.:	$37.50		
Can.:	–		

CT-1454
OPTIX

Designer:	Philip Chaplain
Type:	Weight – Spherical
Colour:	1. Gold and aqua
	2. Green and blue
	3. Purple and violet
Issued:	1997
Status:	Closed
Series:	Unlimited – Modern Design
O.I.P.:	U.K. £20.00
	U.S. $65.00
U.K.:	£20.00
U.S.:	$40.00
Can.:	$50.00

Note: This paperweight has a ribbed finish.

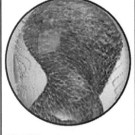

CT-1455
HARMONICS
Style Two

Designer:	Alastair MacIntosh
Type:	Weight – Spherical
Colour:	1. Blue
	2. Emerald
	3. Purple
Issued:	1997
Status:	Closed
Series:	Unlimited – Modern Design
O.I.P.:	U.K. £24.00
	U.S. $79.50
U.K.:	£25.00
U.S.:	$50.00
Can.:	$65.00

CT-1456
SUGAR FRUITS

Designer:	Philip Chaplain
	Stuart Cumming
Type:	Weight – Spherical
Colour:	1. Blackberry (fuchsia)
	2. Blueberry (blue)
	3. Gooseberry (green)
	4. Raspberry (red)
Issued:	1997
Status:	Closed
Series:	Unlimited – Modern Design
O.I.P.:	U.K. £29.00
	U.S. $95.00
U.K.:	£30.00
U.S.:	$60.00
Can.:	$80.00

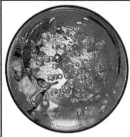

CT-1457
STRANGE BREW

Designer:	Franco Toffolo
Type:	Weight – Spherical
Size:	Magnum
Issued:	1997
Status:	Closed
Series:	Unlimited – Modern Design
O.I.P.:	U.K. £60.00
	U.S. $195.00
U.K.:	£ 75.00
U.S.:	$150.00
Can.:	$200.00

CT-1458
APPARITION

Designer: Alastair MacIntosh
Type: Weight – Domed
Issued: 1997 in a limited
edition of 500
Status: Closed at No. 137
Series: Premier Stockist
Paperweight
Collection
O.I.P.: £104.00

U.K.: £100.00
U.S.: $200.00
Can.: $260.00

Note: Weights CR-1458 to
1463 were offered only
through U.K. Premier
Stockists.

CT-1459
GOLDEN SANCTUARY

Designer: Alastair MacIntosh
Type: Weight – Pyramid
facets
Issued: 1997 in a limited
edition of 200
Status: Closed at No. 69
Series: Premier Stockist
Paperweight
Collection
O.I.P.: £165.00

U.K.: £175.00
U.S.: $350.00
Can.: $450.00

CT-1460
KNOSSOS

Designer: Alastair MacIntosh
Type: Weight – Domed
Issued: 1997 in a limited
edition of 100
Status: Closed at No. 41
Series: Premier Stockist
Paperweight
Collection
O.I.P.: £258.00

U.K.: £275.00
U.S.: $550.00
Can.: $725.00

CT-1461
STELLA MARIS

Designer: Colin Terris
Type: Weight – Spherical
Issued: 1997 in a limited
edition of 75
Status: Closed at No. 57
Series: Premier Stockist
Paperweight
Collection
O.I.P.: £250.00

U.K.: £250.00
U.S.: $500.00
Can.: $650.00

CT-1462
REINCARNATION

Designer: Alastair MacIntosh
Type: Weight – Domed
multifaceted
Issued: 1997 in a limited
edition of 50
Status: Closed at No. 42
Series: Premier Stockist
Paperweight
Collection
O.I.P.: £275.00

U.K.: £275.00
U.S.: $550.00
Can.: $725.00

CT-1463
FRIVOLITY

Designer: Philip Chaplain
Type: Weight – Spherical
Issued: 1997 in a limited
edition of 350
Status: Closed at No. 57
Series: Premier Stockist
Paperweight
Collection
O.I.P.: £105.00

U.K.: £100.00
U.S.: $200.00
Can.: $260.00

CT-1464
CARNIVAL CASCADE

Designer: Colin Terris
Type: Weight – Domed
Issued: 1997 in a limited
edition of 650
Status: Fully subscribed
Series: Colin Terris
Designer Collection
O.I.P.: U.K. £60.00
U.S. $195.00

U.K.: £ 60.00
U.S.: $120.00
Can.: $160.00

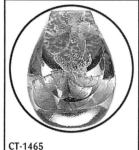

CT-1465
CACTUS REFLECTION

Designer: Colin Terris
Type: Weight – Domed
Issued: 1997 in a limited
edition of 350
Status: Fully subscribed
Series: Colin Terris
Designer Collection
O.I.P.: U.K. £125.00
U.S. $395.00

U.K.: £125.00
U.S.: $250.00
Can.: $325.00

CT-1466
BLUE LAGOON
Style Two
Designer:	Colin Terris
Type:	Weight – Domed
Issued:	1997 in a limited edition of 100
Status:	Fully subscribed
Series:	Colin Terris Designer Collection
O.I.P.:	U.K. £225.00 U.S. $695.00
U.K.:	£225.00
U.S.:	$450.00
Can.:	$600.00

CT-1467
EMERALD GROTTO
Designer:	Colin Terris
Type:	Weight – Domed
Issued:	1997 in a limited edition of 100
Status:	Fully subscribed
Series:	Colin Terris Designer Collection
O.I.P.:	U.K. £250.00 U.S. $795.00
U.K.:	£250.00
U.S.:	$500.00
Can.:	$650.00

CT-1468
CHUCKIE STANE
Designer:	Colin Terris
Type:	Weight – Ovoid
Issued:	1997 in a limited edition of 150
Status:	Closed at No. 146
Series:	Colin Terris Designer Collection
O.I.P.:	U.K. £175.00 U.S. $550.00
U.K.:	£175.00
U.S.:	$350.00
Can.:	$450.00

Note: "Chuckie stane" is a Scottish expression for a pebble or stone.

CT-1469
CORAL GARDEN
Designer:	Colin Terris
Type:	Weight – Spherical
Issued:	1997 in a limited edition of 500
Status:	Fully subscribed
Series:	Colin Terris Designer Collection
O.I.P.:	U.K. £80.00 U.S. $250.00
U.K.:	£ 80.00
U.S.:	$160.00
Can.:	$210.00

CT-1470
PINK BEAUTY
Designer:	Colin Terris
Type:	Weight – Spherical
Issued:	1997 in a limited edition of 650
Status:	Fully subscribed
Series:	Colin Terris Designer Collection
O.I.P.:	U.K. £60.00 U.S. $195.00
U.K.:	£ 60.00
U.S.:	$120.00
Can.:	$160.00

CT-1471
CAMELOT II
Designer:	Colin Terris
Type:	Weight – Domed
Issued:	1997 in a limited edition of 250
Status:	Closed at No. 228
Series:	Colin Terris Designer Collection
O.I.P.:	U.K. £150.00 U.S. $475.00
U.K.:	£150.00
U.S.:	$300.00
Can.:	$400.00

CT-1472
ROYAL GOLDEN WEDDING
Designer:	Colin Terris
Type:	Weight – Spherical engraved
Issued:	1997
Status:	Closed
Series:	HM The Queen's 50th Wedding Anniversary Collection
O.I.P.:	£40.00
U.K.:	£ 40.00
U.S.:	$ 80.00
Can.:	$100.00

Note: Weights CT-1472, 1473 and 1475 were not issued in the U.S.

CT-1473
ROYAL GOLDEN WEDDING CROWN
Designer:	Colin Terris
Type:	Weight – Spherical
Issued:	1997 in a limited edition of 50
Status:	Fully subscribed
Series:	HM The Queen's 50th Wedding Anniversary Collection
O.I.P.:	£350.00
U.K.:	£350.00
U.S.:	$700.00
Can.:	$900.00

CT-1474
ROYAL GOLDEN WEDDING PERFUME BOTTLE

Designer:	Colin Terris
Type:	Perfume bottle
Issued:	1997 in a limited edition of 50
Status:	Fully subscribed
Series:	HM The Queen's 50th Wedding Anniversary Collection
O.I.P.:	£350.00
U.K.:	£350.00
U.S.:	$700.00
Can.:	$900.00

Note: This perfume bottle was not issued in the U.S.

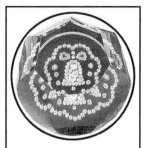

CT-1475
ROYAL GOLDEN WEDDING BELL

Designer:	Colin Terris
Type:	Weight – Spherical
Issued:	1997 in a limited edition of 50
Status:	Fully subscribed
Series:	HM The Queen's 50th Wedding Anniversary Collection
O.I.P.:	£275.00
U.K.:	£275.00
U.S.:	$550.00
Can.:	$725.00

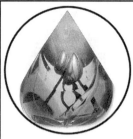

CT-1476
SEA NYMPHS

Designer:	Helen MacDonald
Type:	Weight – Pyramid facets
Issued:	1997 in a limited edition of 350
Status:	Fully subscribed
Series:	Limited – Modern Design
O.I.P.:	U.K. £125.00 U.S. $395.00
U.K.:	£125.00
U.S.:	$250.00
Can.:	$325.00

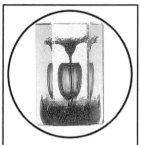

CT-1477
AMAZONIA

Designer:	Colin Terris
Type:	Weight – Hexagonal column
Issued:	1997 in a limited edition of 50
Status:	Fully subscribed
Series:	Limited – Modern Design
O.I.P.:	U.K. £325.00 U.S. $1,050.00
U.K.:	£325.00
U.S.:	$650.00
Can.:	$850.00

CT-1478
SHE

Designer:	Helen MacDonald
Type:	Weight – Domed, faceted
Issued:	1997 in a limited edition of 75
Status:	Fully subscribed
Series:	Limited – Modern Design
O.I.P.:	U.K. £295.00 U.S. $950.00
U.K.:	£300.00
U.S.:	$600.00
Can.:	$775.00

CT-1479
FUJIYAMA

Designer:	Alastair MacIntosh
Type:	Weight – Domed
Issued:	1997 in a limited edition of 650
Status:	Closed at No. 412
Series:	Limited – Modern Design
O.I.P.:	U.K. £80.00 U.S. $250.00
U.K.:	£ 80.00
U.S.:	$160.00
Can.:	$210.00

CT-1480
IONIAN VOYAGER

Designer:	Colin Terris
Type:	Weight – Spherical
Issued:	1997 in a limited edition of 750
Status:	Closed at No. 530
Series:	Limited – Modern Design
O.I.P.:	U.K. £65.00 U.S. $210.00
U.K.:	£ 65.00
U.S.:	$130.00
Can.:	$170.00

CT-1481
SWEET DREAMS

Designer:	Colin Terris
Type:	Weight – Spherical
Issued:	1997 in a limited edition of 750
Status:	Closed at No. 199
Series:	Limited – Modern Design
O.I.P.:	U.K. £80.00 U.S. $250.00
U.K.:	£ 80.00
U.S.:	$160.00
Can.:	$210.00

CT-1482
MAGIC ROUNDABOUT

Designer:	Colin Terris
Type:	Weight – Spherical
Issued:	1997 in a limited edition of 750
Status:	Closed at No. 610
Series:	Limited – Modern Design
O.I.P.:	U.K. £65.00 U.S. $210.00
U.K.:	£ 65.00
U.S.:	$130.00
Can.:	$170.00

CT-1483
THE RED SEA

Designer:	Helen MacDonald
Type:	Weight – Spherical
Issued:	1997 in a limited edition of 75
Status:	Fully subscribed
Series:	Limited – Modern Design
O.I.P.:	U.K. £295.00 U.S. $950.00
U.K.:	£300.00
U.S.:	$600.00
Can.:	$775.00

CT-1484
ABRACADABRA

Designer:	Helen MacDonald
Type:	Weight – Sculptural
Issued:	1997 in a limited edition of 25
Status:	Fully subscribed
Series:	Limited – Modern Design
O.I.P.:	U.K. £650.00 U.S. $2,125.00
U.K.:	£ 650.00
U.S.:	$1,300.00
Can.:	$1,700.00

CT-1485
HALLUCINATION

Designer:	Philip Chaplain
Type:	Weight – Spherical
Issued:	1997 in a limited edition of 350
Status:	Closed at No. 254
Series:	Limited – Modern Design
O.I.P.:	U.K. £99.00 U.S. $310.00
U.K.:	£100.00
U.S.:	$200.00
Can.:	$260.00

CT-1486
FIREWORK FIESTA

Designer:	Colin Terris
Type:	Weight – Spherical
Issued:	1997 in a limited edition of 50
Status:	Fully subscribed
Series:	Limited – Modern Design
O.I.P.:	U.K. £325.00 U.S. $1,050.00
U.K.:	£325.00
U.S.:	$650.00
Can.:	$850.00

CT-1487
GOLDEN CITADEL

Designer:	Colin Terris
Type:	Weight – Domed
Issued:	1997 in a limited edition of 650
Status:	Closed at No. 424
Series:	Limited – Modern Design
O.I.P.:	U.K. £80.00 U.S. $250.00
U.K.:	£ 80.00
U.S.:	$160.00
Can.:	$210.00

CT-1488
FINALE

Designer:	Helen MacDonald
Type:	Weight – Teardrop
Issued:	1997 in a limited edition of 50
Status:	Fully subscribed
Series:	Limited – Modern Design
O.I.P.:	U.K. £325.00 U.S. $1,050.00
U.K.:	£325.00
U.S.:	$650.00
Can.:	$850.00

CT-1489
ORATION

Designer:	Colin Terris
Type:	Weight – Spherical
Issued:	1997 in a limited edition of 750
Status:	Closed at No. 264
Series:	Limited – Modern Design
O.I.P.:	U.K. £70.00 U.S. $225.00
U.K.:	£ 70.00
U.S.:	$140.00
Can.:	$180.00

CT-1490
FIRE BIRDS

Designer: Helen MacDonald
Type: Weight – Spherical
Issued: 1997 in a limited
edition of 500
Status: Closed at No. 438
Series: Limited – Modern
Design
O.I.P.: U.K. £90.00
U.S. $275.00

U.K.: £ 90.00
U.S.: $180.00
Can.: $235.00

CT-1491
ROUND THE TWIST

Designer: Alastair MacIntosh
Type: Weight – Spherical
Issued: 1997 in a limited
edition of 750
Status: Closed at No. 297
Series: Limited – Modern
Design
O.I.P.: U.K. £55.00
U.S. $175.00

U.K.: £ 55.00
U.S.: $110.00
Can.: $145.00

CT-1492
ICE FOREST

Designer: Colin Terris
Type: Weight – Spherical
Issued: 1997 in a limited
edition of 750
Status: Fully subscribed
Series: Limited – Modern
Design
O.I.P.: U.K. £60.00
U.S. $195.00

U.K.: £ 60.00
U.S.: $120.00
Can.: $155.00

CT-1493
EMERALD CITY

Designer: Colin Terris
Type: Weight – Sculptural
Issued: 1997 in a limited
edition of 50
Status: Fully subscribed
Series: Limited – Modern
Design
O.I.P.: U.K. £350.00
U.S. $1,100.00

U.K.: £350.00
U.S.: $700.00
Can.: $900.00

CT-1494
PURITY

Designer: Alastair MacIntosh
Stuart Cumming
Type: Weight – Domed
Issued: 1997 in a limited
edition of 350
Status: Fully subscribed
Series: Limited – Modern
Design
O.I.P.: U.K. £115.00
U.S. $350.00

U.K.: £115.00
U.S.: $230.00
Can.: $300.00

CT-1495
ANOUSHKA

Designer: Philip Chaplain
Type: Weight – Spherical
Issued: 1997 in a limited
edition of 650
Status: Closed at No. 435
Series: Limited – Modern
Design
O.I.P.: U.K. £75.00
U.S. $250.00

U.K.: £ 75.00
U.S.: $150.00
Can.: $200.00

CT-1496
PASSION FLOWER

Designer: Helen MacDonald
Type: Weight – Spherical
Issued: 1997 in a limited
edition of 125
Status: Closed at No. 55
Series: Limited – Modern
Design
O.I.P.: U.K. £275.00
U.S. $875.00

U.K.: £275.00
U.S.: $550.00
Can.: $725.00

CT-1497
WINTER PALACE

Designer: Helen MacDonald
Type: Weight – Domed
Issued: 1997 in a limited
edition of 125
Status: Closed at No. 106
Series: Limited – Modern
Design
O.I.P.: U.K. £275.00
U.S. $875.00

U.K.: £275.00
U.S.: $550.00
Can.: $725.00

CT-1498
THE AGE OF CHIVALRY

Designer:	Helen MacDonald
Type:	Weight – Sculptural
Issued:	1997 in a limited edition of 25
Status:	Closed at No. 21
Series:	Limited – Modern Design
O.I.P.:	U.K. £650.00
	U.S. $2,125.00
U.K.:	£ 650.00
U.S.:	$1,300.00
Can.:	$1,700.00

CT-1499
TEMPUS FUGIT

Designer:	Helen MacDonald
Type:	Weight – Spherical
Issued:	1997 in a limited edition of 125
Status:	Closed at No. 91
Series:	Limited – Modern Design
O.I.P.:	U.K. £275.00
	U.S. $875.00
U.K.:	£275.00
U.S.:	$550.00
Can.:	$725.00

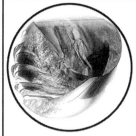

CT-1500
ASTRAL NAVIGATOR

Designer:	Colin Terris
Type:	Weight – Sculptural ovoid
Issued:	1997 in a limited edition of 75
Status:	Closed at No. 70
Series:	Limited – Modern Design
O.I.P.:	U.K. £295.00
	U.S. $950.00
U.K.:	£300.00
U.S.:	$600.00
Can.:	$775.00

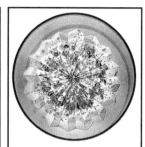

CT-1501
KALEIDOSCOPE '97

Designer:	Colin Terris
Type:	Weight – Spherical
Issued:	1997 in a limited edition of 200
Status:	Closed at No. 111
Series:	Limited – Modern Design
O.I.P.:	U.K. £150.00
	U.S. $475.00
U.K.:	£150.00
U.S.:	$300.00
Can.:	$400.00

Note: This paperweight is supplied with a stand.

CT-1502
DIVINITY

Designer:	Colin Terris
Type:	Weight – Spherical, facets
Issued:	1997 in a limited edition of 75
Status:	Closed at No. 62
Series:	Limited – Modern Design
O.I.P.:	U.K. £295.00
	U.S. $950.00
U.K.:	£300.00
U.S.:	$600.00
Can.:	$775.00

CT-1503
MOONLIGHT BLOSSOM

Designer:	Philip Chaplain
Type:	Weight – Spherical
Issued:	1997 in a limited edition of 250
Status:	Closed at No. 68
Series:	Limited – Modern Design
O.I.P.:	U.K. £125.00
	U.S. $395.00
U.K.:	£125.00
U.S.:	$250.00
Can.:	$325.00

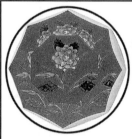

CT-1504
COMPASSION

Designer:	Rosette Fleming
Type:	Weight – Spherical, facets
Issued:	1997 in a limited edition of 50
Status:	Closed at No. 27
Series:	Traditional Collection Nature Study
O.I.P.:	U.K. £350.00
	U.S. $1,100.00
U.K.:	£350.00
U.S.:	$700.00
Can.:	$900.00

CT-1505
WOOD VIOLET

Designer:	Allan Scott
Type:	Weight – Spherical
Issued:	1997 in a limited edition of 50
Status:	Closed at No. 34
Series:	Traditional Collection Nature Study
O.I.P.:	U.K. £395.00
	U.S. $1,250.00
U.K.:	£ 400.00
U.S.:	$ 800.00
Can.:	$1,050.00

CT-1506
OCEAN SERENADE
Designer: Helen MacDonald
Type: Weight – Domed
Issued: 1997 in a limited edition of 25
Status: Fully subscribed
Series: Traditional Collection Nature Study
O.I.P.: U.K. £595.00
U.S. $1,850.00

U.K.: £ 600.00
U.S.: $1,200.00
Can.: $1,550.00

CT-1507
SUMMER LILIES
Designer: Rosette Fleming
Type: Weight – Domed
Issued: 1997 in a limited edition of 75
Status: Closed at No. 40
Series: Traditional Collection Nature Study
O.I.P.: U.K. £350.00
U.S. $1,100.00

U.K.: £350.00
U.S.: $700.00
Can.: $900.00

CT-1508
BRANCHING OUT
Designer: Allan Scott
Type: Weight – Spherical
Issued: 1997 in a limited edition of 25
Status: Closed at No. 22
Series: Traditional Collection Nature Study
O.I.P.: U.K. £595.00
U.S. $1,850.00

U.K.: £ 600.00
U.S.: $1,200.00
Can.: $1,550.00

CT-1509
SWISH
Designer: Philip Chaplain
Type: Weight – Domed
Colour: 1. Cerise
2. Cobalt
3. Emerald
Issued: 1997
Status: Closed
Series: Unlimited – Modern Design
O.I.P.: U.K. £25.00
U.S. $79.50

U.K.: £25.00
U.S.: $50.00
Can.: $65.00

CT-1510
WHIRLPOOL
Designer: Alastair MacIntosh
Type: Weight – Domed
Issued: 1997
Status: Closed
Series: Unlimited – Modern Design
O.I.P.: U.K. £29.50
U.S. $95.00

U.K.: £30.00
U.S.: $60.00
Can.: $80.00

CT-1511
MOONFLOWER CARNIVAL
Designer: Colin Terris
Type: Weight – Spherical
Colour: Yellow, orange, red, pink and blue
Issued: 1997
Status: Closed
Series: Unlimited – Modern Design
O.I.P.: U.K. £34.50
U.S. $110.00

U.K.: £35.00
U.S.: $70.00
Can.: $90.00

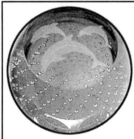

CT-1512
JUMPING FOR JOY
Designer: Helen MacDonald
Type: Weight – Spherical
Issued: 1997
Status: Active
Series: Unlimited – Modern Design
O.I.P.: U.K. £30.00
U.S. $79.50

U.K.: £37.50
U.S.: $95.00
Can.: –

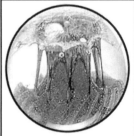

CT-1513
MARQUEE
Designer: Philip Chaplain
Type: Weight – Spherical
Colour: 1. Amethyst
2. Cobalt
3. Kingfisher
Issued: 1997
Status: Closed
Series: Unlimited – Modern Design
O.I.P.: U.K. £28.00
U.S. $87.50

U.K.: £30.00
U.S.: $60.00
Can.: $80.00

CT-1514
DOLPHINARIUM

Designer:	Helen MacDonald
Type:	Weight – Spherical
Size:	Magnum
Issued:	1997
Status:	Closed
Series:	Unlimited – Modern Design
O.I.P.:	U.K. £60.00
	U.S. $195.00
U.K.:	£ 60.00
U.S.:	$120.00
Can.:	$155.00

CT-1515
ETERNAL LOVE

Designer:	Rosette Fleming
Type:	Weight – Spherical
Issued:	1997 in a limited edition of 50
Status:	Closed at No. 44
Series:	Whitefriars Collection
O.I.P.:	U.K. £135.00
	U.S. $450.00
U.K.:	£135.00
U.S.:	$270.00
Can.:	$350.00

CT-1516
CLASSICAL MOMENT

Designer:	Rosette Fleming
Type:	Weight – Spherical
Issued:	1997 in a limited edition of 50
Status:	Closed at No. 31
Series:	Whitefriars Collection
O.I.P.:	U.K. £175.00
	U.S. $550.00
U.K.:	£175.00
U.S.:	$350.00
Can.:	$450.00

CT-1517
SPOILT FOR CHOICE

Designer:	Rosette Fleming
Type:	Weight – Spherical
Issued:	1997 in a limited edition of 50
Status:	Closed at No. 31
Series:	Whitefriars Collection
O.I.P.:	U.K. £195.00
	U.S. $595.00
U.K.:	£200.00
U.S.:	$400.00
Can.:	$525.00

CT-1518
FRENCH FANCY

Designer:	Rosette Fleming
Type:	Weight – Spherical
Issued:	1997 in a limited edition of 50
Status:	Closed at No. 39
Series:	Whitefriars Collection
O.I.P.:	U.K. £150.00
	U.S. $475.00
U.K.:	£150.00
U.S.:	$300.00
Can.:	$400.00

CT-1519
PRETTY IN PINK

Designer:	Rosette Fleming
Type:	Weight – Spherical
Issued:	1997 in a limited edition of 50
Status:	Closed at No. 35
Series:	Whitefriars Collection
O.I.P.:	U.K. £250.00
	U.S. $795.00
U.K.:	£250.00
U.S.:	$500.00
Can.:	$650.00

CT-1520
ALPINE GLORY

Designer:	Rosette Fleming
Type:	Weight – Spherical
Issued:	1997 in a limited edition of 50
Status:	Closed at No. 44
Series:	Whitefriars Collection
O.I.P.:	U.K. £175.00
	U.S. $550.00
U.K.:	£175.00
U.S.:	$350.00
Can.:	$450.00

CT-1521
MOONWALK

Designer:	William Manson
Type:	Weight – Spherical
Issued:	1997 in a limited edition of 50
Status:	Closed at No. 28
Series:	William Manson Traditionals
O.I.P.:	U.K. £295.00
	U.S. $895.00
U.K.:	£300.00
U.S.:	$600.00
Can.:	$775.00

CT-1522
THE LOST CITY

Designer:	William Manson
Type:	Weight – Spherical
Issued:	1997 in a limited edition of 50
Status:	Closed at No. 24
Series:	William Manson Traditionals
O.I.P.:	U.K. £295.00 U.S. $895.00
U.K.:	£300.00
U.S.:	$600.00
Can.:	$775.00

CT-1523
AQUARIUM

Designer:	William Manson
Type:	Weight – Spherical
Issued:	1997 in a limited edition of 50
Status:	Closed at No. 29
Series:	William Manson Traditionals
O.I.P.:	U.K. £295.00 U.S. $895.00
U.K.:	£300.00
U.S.:	$600.00
Can.:	$775.00

ISSUES OF 1998

ABERRATION
Designer: Helen MacDonald
Type: Weight – Pyramid facets
Issued: 1998 in a limited edition of 150
Status: Closed at No. 100
Series: Limited – Modern Design
O.I.P.: U.K. £175.00
U.S. $550.00

U.K.: £175.00
U.S.: $350.00
Can.: $450.00

AEGEAN PEARL
Designer: Colin Terris
Type: Weight – Spherical
Issued: 1998 in a limited edition of 50
Status: Closed at No. 38
Series: Premier Stockist Paperweight Collection
O.I.P.: U.K. £275.00
U.S. $875

U.K.: £375.00
U.S.: $750.00
Can.: $975.00

AFRICAN ADVENTURE
Designer: Helen MacDonald
Type: Weight – Sculptural
Issued: 1998 in a limited edition of 25
Status: Fully subscribed
Series: Limited – Modern Design
O.I.P.: U.K. £650.00
U.S. $2,100.00

U.K.: £ 650.00
U.S.: $1,300.00
Can.: $1,700.00

ALCHEMIST
Designer: Alastair MacIntosh
Type: Weight – Domed
Issued: 1998 in a limited edition of 750
Status: Closed at No. 488
Series: Limited – Modern Design
O.I.P.: U.K. £75.00
U.S. $225.00

U.K.: £ 75.00
U.S.: $150.00
Can.: $200.00

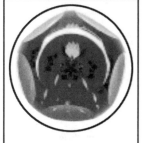
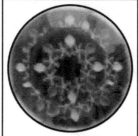

ALPINE SUMMER
Designer: Rosette Fleming
Type: Weight – Spherical
Issued: 1998 in a limited edition of 50
Status: Closed at No. 28
Series: Whitefriars Collection
O.I.P.: U.K. £135.00
U.S. $425.00

U.K.: £135.00
U.S.: $270.00
Can.: $350.00

AMETHYST GARLAND
Designer: Rosette Fleming
Type: Weight – Spherical
Issued: 1998 in a limited edition of 50
Status: Closed at No. 29
Series: Whitefriars Collection
O.I.P.: U.K. £150.00
U.S. $485.00

U.K.: £150.00
U.S.: $300.00
Can.: $400.00

AMOROSO
Designer: Colin Terris
Type: Weight – Domed
Issued: 1998 in a limited edition of 100
Status: Fully subscribed
Series: Collectable Eggs – Limited
O.I.P.: U.K. £70.00
U.S. $225.00

U.K.: £ 70.00
U.S.: $140.00
Can.: $180.00

ANASTASIA
Designer: Colin Terris
Type: Weight – Domed
Issued: 1998 in a limited edition of 100
Status: Fully subscribed
Series: Collectable Eggs – Limited
O.I.P.: U.K. £150.00
U.S. $475.00

U.K.: £150.00
U.S.: $300.00
Can.: $400.00

APERTURE

Designer: Alastair MacIntosh
Type: Weight – Spherical
Issued: 1998 in a limited edition of 50
Status: Fully subscribed
Series: Limited – Modern Design
O.I.P.: U.K. £295.00
U.S. $950.00

U.K.: £300.00
U.S.: $600.00
Can.: $775.00

AQUAFLORA

Designer: Helen MacDonald
Type: Weight – Spherical
Size: Magnum
Issued: 1998 in a limited edition of 75
Status: Fully subscribed
Series: Limited – Modern Design
O.I.P.: U.K. £275.00
U.S. $875.00

U.K.: £275.00
U.S.: $550.00
Can.: $725.00

AQUAMARINA

Designer: Philip Chaplain
Type: Weight – Spherical
Issued: 1998 in a limited edition of 2,092
Status: Closed at No. 2,092
Series: Collectors' Society
O.I.P.: U.K. £85.00
U.S. $225.00

U.K.: £ 85.00
U.S.: $170.00
Can.: $225.00

ARCTIC CROCUS

Designer: Colin Terris
Type: Weight – Domed
Issued: 1998 in a limited edition of 100
Status: Fully subscribed
Series: Collectable Eggs – Limited
O.I.P.: U.K. £120.00
U.S. $385.00

U.K.: £120.00
U.S.: $240.00
Can.: $315.00

Note: This weight is supplied with a stand.

ARCTIC CRYSTAL

Designer: Colin Terris
Type: Weight – Domed
Issued: 1998 in a limited edition of 50
Status: Fully subscribed
Series: Limited – Modern Design
O.I.P.: U.K. £295.00
U.S. $950.00

U.K.: £295.00
U.S.: $600.00
Can.: $775.00

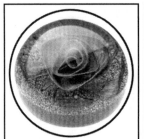

ARIA

Designer: Helen MacDonald
Type: Weight – Spherical
Issued: 1998 in a limited edition of 500
Status: Closed at No. 295
Series: Limited – Modern Design
O.I.P.: U.K. £90.00
U.S. $295.00

U.K.: £ 90.00
U.S.: $180.00
Can.: $235.00

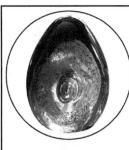

ASTRA DANCE

Designer: Caithness Design Studios
Type: Weight – Domed
Issued: 1998
Status: Closed
Series: Unlimited – Modern Design
O.I.P.: U.K. £30.00
U.S. $95.00

U.K.: £30.00
U.S.: $60.00
Cam.: $80.00

AUTUMN HEDGEROW

Designer: Allan Scott
Type: Weight – Sculptural
Issued: 1998 in a limited edition of 25
Status: Closed at No. 17
Series: Traditional Collection Nature Study
O.I.P.: U.K. £595.00
U.S. $1,925.00

U.K.: £ 600.00
U.S.: $1,200.00
Can.: $1,550.00

AZURINA

Designer: Philip Chaplain
Type: Weight – Domed
Issued: 1998 in a limited edition of 150
Status: Closed at No. 119
Series: Collectable Eggs – Limited
O.I.P.: U.K. £125.00
U.S. $385.00

U.K.: £125.00
U.S.: $250.00
Can.: $325.00

Note: This weight is supplied with a stand.

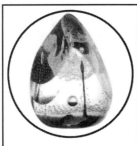

BANSHEE

Designer: Philip Chaplain
Type: Weight – Domed
Issued: 1998 in a limited edition of 350
Status: Fully subscribed
Series: Limited – Modern Design
O.I.P.: U.K. £99.00
U.S. $325.00

U.K.: £100.00
U.S.: $200.00
Can.: $260.00

BLUE MOON

Designer: Colin Terris
Type: Weight – Spherical, dichroic
Issued: 1998 in a limited edition of 650
Status: Closed at No. 469
Series: Colin Terris Designer Collection II
O.I.P.: U.K. £85.00
U.S. $265.00

U.K.: £ 85.00
U.S.: $170.00
Can.: $225.00

BOUNTEOUS

Designer: Philip Chaplain
Type: Weight – Cylindrical
Issued: 1998 in a limited edition of 50
Status: Closed at No. 40
Series: Limited – Modern Design
O.I.P.: U.K. £350.00
U.S. $1,125.00

U.K.: £350.00
U.S.: $700.00
Can.: $900.00

BRACHIOSAURUS

Designer: Colin Terris
Type: Weight – Spherical
Size: Medium
Colour: Pink
Issued: 1998
Status: Closed
Series: Medium and Miniature Size
O.I.P.: U.K. £20.00
U.S. $62.50

U.K.: £20.00
U.S.: $40.00
Can.: $50.00

BUCCANEER

Designer: Philip Chaplain
Type: Weight – Spherical
Issued: 1998 in a limited edition of 750
Status: Fully subscribed
Series: Limited – Modern Design
O.I.P.: U.K. £60.00
U.S. $195.00

U.K.: £ 60.00
U.S.: $120.00
Can.: $155.00

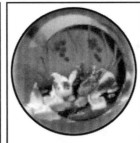

BUNNIES

Designer: Allan Scott
Type: Weight – Spherical
Issued: 1998 in a limited edition of 25
Status: Closed at No. 23
Series: Traditional Collection Nature Study
O.I.P.: U.K. £595.00
U.S. $1,925.00

U.K.: £ 600.00
U.S.: $1,200.00
Can.: $1,550.00

BURNING BUSH

Designer: Helen MacDonald
Type: Weight – Spherical
Issued: 1998 in a limited edition of 75
Status: Fully subscribed
Series: Limited – Modern Design
O.I.P.: U.K. £250.00
U.S. $795.00

U.K.: £250.00
U.S.: $500.00
Can.: $650.00

BUSY BEES
Designer: Helen MacDonald
Type: Weight – Spherical
Issued: 1998 in a limited edition of 350
Status: Closed at No. 234
Series: Limited – Modern Design
O.I.P.: U.K. £99.00
U.S. $350.00

U.K.: £100.00
U.S.: $200.00
Can.: $260.00

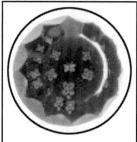

BUTTERCUPS and BUTTERFLY
Designer: Rosette Fleming
Type: Weight – Spherical
Issued: 1998 in a limited edition of 50
Status: Closed at No. 22
Series: Whitefriars Collection
O.I.P.: U.K. £225.00
U.S. $725.00

U.K.: £225.00
U.S.: $450.00
Can.: $575.00

CASTLES IN THE AIR
Designer: Colin Terris
Type: Weight – Spherical
Issued: 1998 in a limited edition of 750
Status: Closed at No. 592
Series: Limited – Modern Design
O.I.P.: U.K. £65.00
U.S. $210.00

U.K.: £ 65.00
U.S.: $130.00
Can.: $170.00

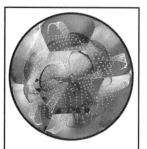

CAVATINA
Designer: Colin Terris
Type: Weight – Spherical, dichroic
Issued: 1998 in a limited edition of 75
Status: Fully subscribed
Series: Colin Terris Designer Collection II
O.I.P.: U.K. £250.00
U.S. $775.00

U.K.: £250.00
U.S.: $500.00
Can.: $650.00

CELTIC KNOT
Designer: Helen MacDonald
Type: Weight – Spherical
Issued: 1998 in a limited edition of 750
Status: Closed at No. 680
Series: Limited – Modern Design
O.I.P.: U.K. £50.00
U.S. $165.00

U.K.: £ 50.00
U.S.: $100.00
Can.: $130.00

CHARTREUSE
Designer: Helen MacDonald
Type: Weight – Spherical
Issued: 1998 in a limited edition of 500
Status: Closed at No. 293
Series: Limited – Modern Design
O.I.P.: U.K. £90.00
U.S. $295.00

U.K.: £ 90.00
U.S.: $180.00
Can.: $235.00

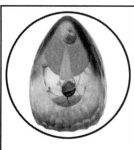

CHASM
Designer: Philip Chaplain
Type: Weight – Domed
Issued: 1998 in a limited edition of 125
Status: Closed at No. 94
Series: Limited – Modern Design
O.I.P.: U.K. £250.00
U.S. $795.00

U.K.: £250.00
U.S.: $500.00
Can.: $650.00

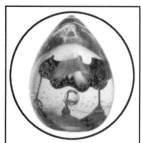

CINNABAR
Designer: Philip Chaplain
Type: Weight – Domed
Issued: 1998 in a limited edition of 750
Status: Fully subscribed
Series: Limited – Modern Design
O.I.P.: U.K. £60.00
U.S. $195.00

U.K.: £ 60.00
U.S.: $120.00
Can.: $155.00

CLEMATIS and TRELLIS
Designer: Rosette Fleming
Type: Weight – Spherical
Issued: 1998 in a limited
          edition of 50
Status: Closed at No. 21
Series: Traditional
          Collection –
          Nature Study
O.I.P.:   U.K. £350.00
          U.S. $1,125.00

U.K.:   £350.00
U.S.: $700.00
Can.: $900.00

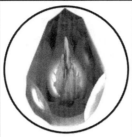

COBALT SPLENDOUR
Designer: Alastair MacIntosh
Type: Weight – Domed
Issued: 1998 in a limited
          edition of 50
Status: Fully subscribed
Series: Limited – Modern
          Design
O.I.P.:   U.K. £325.00
          U.S. $1,050.00

U.K.:   £325.00
U.S.: $650.00
Can.: $850.00

COLOUR POOL
Designer: Colin Terris
Type: Weight – Domed
Colour: 1. Blue
          2. Green
          3. Magenta
Issued: 1998
Status: Closed
Series: Collectable Eggs –
          Unlimited
O.I.P.:   U.K. £37.50
          U.S. $125.00

U.K.:   £ 40.00
U.S.: $ 80.00
Can.: $100.00

CONCENTRIX
Designer: Philip Chaplain
Type: Weight – Domed
Colour: 1. Cobalt
          2. Gold
          3. Kingfisher
Issued: 1998
Status: Closed
Series: Unlimited –
          Modern Design
O.I.P.:   U.K. £35.00
          U.S. $110.00

U.K.:   £35.00
U.S.: $70.00
Can.: $90.00

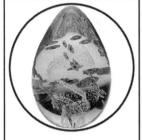

CONFETTI CASCADE
Designer: Helen MacDonald
Type: Weight – Domed
Issued: 1998 in a limited
          edition of 100
Status: Fully subscribed
Series: Collectable Eggs –
          Limited
O.I.P.:   U.K. £65.00
          U.S. $225.00

U.K.:   £ 65.00
U.S.: $130.00
Can.: $170.00

COSMIC VISION
Designer: Colin Terris
Type: Weight – Spherical
Size: Magnum
Issued: 1998 in a limited
          edition of 250
Status: Closed at No. 153
Series: Colin Terris
          Designer Collection II
O.I.P.:   U.K. £150.00
          U.S. $475.00

U.K.:   £150.00
U.S.: $300.00
Can.: $400.00

COTTAGE GARDEN
Designer: Helen MacDonald
Type: Weight – Spherical
Issued: 1998 in a limited
          edition of 150
Status: Closed at No. 104
Series: Limited – Modern
          Design
O.I.P.:   U.K. £195.00
          U.S. $675.00

U.K.:   £200.00
U.S.: $400.00
Can.: $525.00

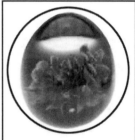

COUNTRY POSY
Designer: Allan Scott
Type: Weight – Domed
Issued: 1998 in a limited
          edition of 150
Status: Closed at No. 74
Series: Traditional Collection
          Nature Study
O.I.P.:   U.K. £125.00
          U.S. $395.00

U.K.:   £125.00
U.S.: $250.00
Can.: $325.00

CRYSTAL VOYAGER
Designer: Helen MacDonald
Type: Weight – Ovoid
Issued: 1998 in a limited edition of 125
Status: Closed at No. 100
Series: Limited – Modern Design
O.I.P.: U.K. £250.00
U.S. $795.00

U.K.: £250.00
U.S.: $500.00
Can.: $650.00

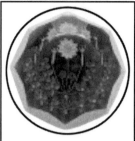

DAISY and FORGET-ME-NOT
Designer: Rosette Fleming
Type: Weight – Spherical, facets
Issued: 1998 in a limited edition of 50
Status: Closed at No. 27
Series: Whitefriars Collection
O.I.P.: U.K. £195.00
U.S. $625.00

U.K.: £200.00
U.S.: $400.00
Can.: $525.00

DAISY BOUQUET
Designer: Allan Scott
Type: Weight – Spherical
Issued: 1998 in a limited edition of 75
Status: Closed at No. 39
Series: Whitefriars Collection
O.I.P.: U.K. £120.00
U.S. $385.00

U.K.: £120.00
U.S.: $250.00
Can.: $325.00

DEEP ENDEAVOUR
Designer: Philip Chaplain
Type: Weight – Sculptural
Issued: 1998 in a limited edition of 250
Status: Closed at No. 113
Series: Limited – Modern Design
O.I.P.: U.K. £125.00
U.S. $395.00

U.K.: £125.00
U.S.: $250.00
Can.: $325.00

DEITY
Designer: Alastair MacIntosh
Type: Weight – Spherical, facets
Issued: 1998 in a limited edition of 50
Status: Fully subscribed
Series: Limited – Modern Design
O.I.P.: U.K. £295.00
U.S. $950.00

U.K.: £300.00
U.S.: $600.00
Can.: $775.00

DESTINATION DEIMOS
Designer: Philip Chaplain
Type: Weight – Domed
Issued: 1998 in a limited edition of 75
Status: Fully subscribed
Series: Limited – Modern Design
O.I.P.: U.K. £250.00
U.S. $795.00

U.K.: £250.00
U.S.: $500.00
Can.: $650.00

DEVOTION
Designer: Helen MacDonald
Type: Weight – Teardrop
Issued: 1998 in a limited edition of 250
Status: Fully subscribed
Series: Limited – Modern Design
O.I.P.: U.K. £125.00
U.S. $395.00

U.K.: £125.00
U.S.: $250.00
Can.: $325.00

DIAMOND LILY
Designer: Allan Scott
Type: Weight – Spherical, facets
Issued: 1998 in a limited edition of 25
Status: Fully subscribed
Series: Traditional Collection - Nature Study
O.I.P.: U.K. £595.00
U.S. $1,925.00

U.K.: £ 600.00
U.S.: $1,200.00
Can.: $1,550.00

DOUBLE HELIX

Designer: Alastair MacIntosh
Type: Weight – Cylindrical
Issued: 1998 in a limited
        edition of 250
Status: Closed at No. 130
Series: Limited – Modern
        Design
O.I.P.: U.K. £150.00
        U.S. $485.00

U.K.: £150.00
U.S.: $300.00
Can.: $400.00

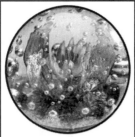

DOUBLE MAGNUM '98

Designer: Franco Toffolo
Type: Weight – Spherical
Size: Double magnum
Colour: Pink, blue, green
        and gold
Issued: 1998 in a limited
        edition of 100
Status: Closed at No. 51
Series: Limited – Modern
        Design
O.I.P.: U.K. £350.00
        U.S. $1,125.00

U.K.: £350.00
U.S.: $700.00
Can.: $900.00

EFFERVESCENCE

Designer: Philip Chaplain
Type: Weight – Domed
Colour: 1. Aqua
        2. Emerald
        3. Sable
Issued: 1998
Status: Closed
Series: Collectable Eggs –
        Unlimited
O.I.P.: U.K. £37.50
        U.S. $125.00

U.K.: £ 40.00
U.S.: $ 80.00
Can.: $100.00

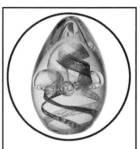

EGGSTRAVAGANZA

Designer: Helen MacDonald
Type: Weight – Domed
Colour: 1. Blue, Green, Pink
        2. Yellow, Orange,
           Red
        3. Blue, Purple, Lime
Issued: 1998
Status: Closed
Series: Collectable Eggs –
        Unlimited
O.I.P.: U.K. £40.00
        U.S. $79.50

U.K.: £ 40.00
U.S.: $ 80.00
Can.: $100.00

ELSINORE

Designer: Philip Chaplain
Type: Weight – Domed
Issued: 1998 in a limited
        edition of 75
Status: Closed at No. 52
Series: Premier Stockist
        Paperweight
        Collection
O.I.P.: U.K. £250.00
        U.S. $795.00

U.K.: £250.00
U.S.: $500.00
Can.: $650.00

EMERALD POPPY

Designer: Helen MacDonald
Type: Weight – Spherical
Issued: 1998 in a limited
        edition of 150
Status: Closed at No. 114
Series: Limited – Modern
        Design
O.I.P.: U.K. £195.00
        U.S. $625.00

U.K.: £200.00
U.S.: $400.00
Can.: $525.00

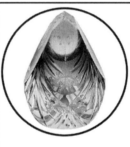

ENCORE

Designer: Helen MacDonald
Type: Weight – Domed
Issued: 1998 in a limited
        edition of 50
Status: Fully subscribed
Series: Limited – Modern
        Design
O.I.P.: U.K. £325.00
        U.S. $995.00

U.K.: £325.00
U.S.: $650.00
Can.: $850.00

ENERGIZE

Designer: Philip Chaplain
Type: Weight – Spherical
Issued: 1998 in a limited
        edition of 750
Status: Fully subscribed
O.I.P.: U.K. £65.00
        U.S. $210.00

U.K.: £ 65.00
U.S.: $130.00
Can.: $170.00

ETERNAL FLAME
Designer: Helen MacDonald
Type: Weight – Sculptural
Issued: 1998 in a limited
edition of 100
Status: Closed at No. 74
Series: Limited – Modern
Design
O.I.P.: U.K. £275.00
U.S. $875.00

U.K.: £275.00
U.S.: $550.00
Can.: $725.00

ETERNAL PASSION
Designer: Helen MacDonald
Type: Weight – Domed
Issued: 1998 in a limited
edition of 500
Status: Closed at No. 452
Series: Limited – Modern
Design
O.I.P.: U.K. £90.00
U.S. $275.00

U.K.: £ 90.00
U.S.: $180.00
Can.: $235.00

EYE OF THE STORM
Designer: Alastair MacIntosh
Type: Weight – Spherical
Issued: 1998 in a limited
edition of 750
Status: Closed at No. 726
Series: Limited – Modern
Design
O.I.P.: U.K. £70.00
U.S. $225.00

U.K.: £ 70.00
U.S.: $140.00
Can.: $180.00

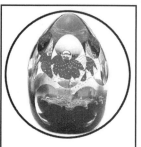

FAERIE DANCE
Designer: Colin Terris
Type: Weight – Domed
Issued: 1998 in a limited
edition of 200
Status: Closed at No. 101
Series: Colin Terris
Designer Collection II
O.I.P.: U.K. £165.00
U.S. $525.00

U.K.: £165.00
U.S.: $330.00
Can.: $430.00

FESTIVE WINDOW
Designer: William Manson
Type: Weight – Spherical
Issued: 1998 in a limited
edition of 50
Status: Fully subscribed
Series: William Manson
Traditionals
O.I.P.: U.K. £350.00
U.S. $1,100.00

U.K.: £350.00
U.S.: $700.00
Can.: $900.00

FIRST LOVE
Designer: Colin Terris
Type: Weight – Spherical
Issued: 1998 in a limited
edition of 650
Status: Closed at No. 524
Series: Limited – Modern
Design
O.I.P.: U.K. £85.00
U.S. $260.00

U.K.: £ 85.00
U.S.: $170.00
Can.: $225.00

FLAMBOYANCE
Designer: Helen MacDonald
Type: Weight – Sculptural
Issued: 1998 in a limited
edition of 125
Status: Closed at No. 102
Series: Limited – Modern
Design
O.I.P.: U.K. £250.00
U.S. $795.00

U.K.: £250.00
U.S.: $500.00
Can.: $650.00

FLORAL CAROUSEL
Designer: Colin Terris
Type: Weight – Spherical
Facets
Issued: 1998 in a limited
edition of 75
Status: Closed at 55
O.I.P.: U.K. £275.00
U.S. $875.00

U.K.: £250.00
U.S.: $500.00
Can.: $650.00

FLORAL DIAMOND

Designer:	Rosette Fleming
Type:	Weight – Spherical
Issued:	1998 in a limited edition of 50
Status:	Fully subscribed
Series:	Whitefriars Collection
O.I.P.:	U.K. £125.00
	U.S. $385.00
U.K.:	£125.00
U.S.:	$250.00
Can.:	$325.00

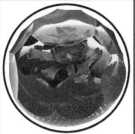

FLORIBUNDA

Designer:	Colin Terris
Type:	Weight – Facetted
Issued:	1998 in a limited edition of 75
Status:	Closed at No. 46
O.I.P.:	U.K. £275.00
	U.S. $875.00
U.K.:	£275.00
U.S.:	$550.00
Can.:	$725.00

FLOWERPOT PEOPLE – ONE

Designer:	Rosette Fleming
Type:	Weight – Cylindrical
Issued:	1998 in a limited edition of 25
Status:	Closed at No. 15
Series:	Traditional Collection Nature Study
O.I.P.:	U.K. £795.00/set
	U.S. $2,550.00/set

	Flowerpot	Set
U.K.:	£ 400.	800.
U.S.:	$ 800.	1,200.
Can.:	$1,050.	1,550.

Note: CT-158A and B were issued and sold as a set.

FLOWERPOT PEOPLE – TWO

Designer:	Rosette Fleming
Type:	Weight – Cylindrical
Issued:	1998 in a limited edition of 25
Status:	Closed at No. 15
Series:	Traditional Collection Nature Study
O.I.P.:	U.K. £795.00/set
	U.S. $2,550.00/set
U.K.:	£ 400.00
U.S.:	$ 800.00
Can.:	$1,050.00

40 FATHOMS

Designer:	Alastair MacIntosh
Type:	Weight – Spherical
Issued:	1998 in a limited edition of 750
Status:	Closed at No. 585
Series:	Limited – Modern Design
O.I.P.:	U.K. £50.00
	U.S. $150.00
U.K.:	£ 50.00
U.S.:	$100.00
Can.:	$130.00

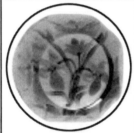

FRAGRANT ORCHID

Designer:	Allan Scott
Type:	Weight – Spherical
Issued:	1998 in a limited edition of 50
Status:	Closed at No. 35
Series:	Whitefriars Collection
O.I.P.:	U.K. £135.00
	U.S. $425.00
U.K.:	£135.00
U.S.:	$270.00
Can.:	$350.00

FROM THE FLAMES

Designer:	Colin Terris
Type:	Weight – Domed
Issued:	1998 in a limited edition of 100
Status:	Closed at No. 66
Series:	Collectable Eggs – Limited
O.I.P.:	U.K. £150.00
	U.S. $485.00
U.K.:	£150.00
U.S.:	$300.00
Can.:	$400.00

Note: This weight is supplied with a stand.

GARDEN POSY

Designer:	Allan Scott
Type:	Weight – Domed
Issued:	1998 in a limited edition of 150
Status:	Closed at No. 97
Series:	Traditional Collection Nature Study
O.I.P.:	U.K. £125.00
	U.S. $395.00
U.K.:	£125.00
U.S.:	$250.00
Can.:	$325.00

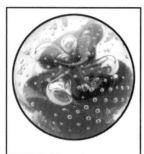

GOLD RUSH

Designer:	Philip Chaplain
Type:	Weight – Spherical
Colour:	1. Cobalt
	2. Emerald
	3. Heather
	4. Kingfisher
Issued:	1998
Status:	Closed
Series:	Unlimited – Modern Design
O.I.P.:	U.K. £25.00
	U.S. $79.50
U.K.:	£25.00
U.S.:	$50.00
Can.:	$65.00

GOLDEN AWAKENING

Designer:	Allan Scott
Type:	Weight – Spherical
Issued:	1998 in a limited edition of 50
Status:	Fully subscribed
Series:	Whitefriars Collection
O.I.P.:	U.K. £135.00
	U.S. $425.00
U.K.:	£150.00
U.S.:	$300.00
Can.:	$400.00

HEATHER CORSAGE

Designer:	Rosette Fleming
Type:	Weight – Spherical
Issued:	1998 in a limited edition of 25
Status:	Fully subscribed
Series:	Traditional Collection Nature Study
O.I.P.:	U.K. £595.00
	U.S. $1,295.00
U.K.:	£ 600.00
U.S.:	$1,200.00
Can.:	$1,550.00

HIDDEN IN TIME

Designer:	Helen MacDonald
Type:	Weight – Domed, Engraved
Issued:	1998 in a limited edition of 100
Status:	Fully subscribed
Series:	Limited – Modern Design
O.I.P.:	U.K. £295.00
	U.S. $950.00
U.K.:	£300.00
U.S.:	$600.00
Can.:	$775.00

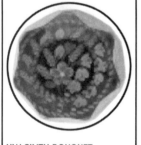

HYACINTH BOUQUET

Designer:	Rosette Fleming
Type:	Weight – Spherical
Issued:	1998 in a limited edition of 50
Status:	Closed at No. 35
Series:	Whitefriars Collection
O.I.P.:	U.K. £250.00
	U.S. $795.00
U.K.:	£250.00
U.S.:	$500.00
Can.:	$650.00

INCANDESCENCE

Designer:	Philip Chaplain
Type:	Weight – Domed
Issued:	1998 in a limited edition of 500
Status:	Closed at No. 486
Series:	Limited – Modern Design
O.I.P.:	U.K. £90.00
	U.S. $295.00
U.K.:	£ 90.00
U.S.:	$180.00
Can.:	$235.00

INNER SANCTUM

Designer:	Philip Chaplain
Type:	Weight – Domed
Issued:	1998 in a limited edition of 150
Status:	Closed at No. 132
Series:	Limited – Modern Design
O.I.P.:	U.K. £225.00
	U.S. $695.00
U.K.:	£225.00
U.S.:	$450.00
Can.:	$600.00

INVINCIBLE

Designer:	Philip Chaplain
Type:	Weight – Spherical
Issued:	1998 in a limited edition of 75
Status:	Closed at No. 41
Series:	Premier Stockist Paperweight Collection
O.I.P.:	U.K. £250.00
	U.S. $795.00
U.K.:	£250.00
U.S.:	$500.00
Can.:	$650.00

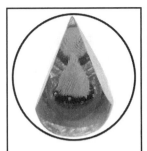

JALAL
Designer: Alastair MacIntosh
Type: Weight – Pyramid, facets
Issued: 1998 in a limited edition of 350
Status: Fully subscribed
Series: Limited – Modern Design
O.I.P.: U.K. £99.00
U.S. $325.00

U.K.: £100.00
U.S.: $200.00
Can.: $260.00

KHAMSIN
Designer: Philip Chaplain
Type: Weight – Domed
Issued: 1998 in a limited edition of 100
Status: Fully subscribed
Series: Collectable Eggs – Limited
O.I.P.: U.K. £70.00
U.S. $225.00

U.K.: £ 70.00
U.S.: $140.00
Can.: $180.00

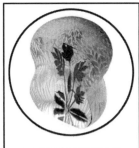

LATE SUMMER SPLENDOUR
Designer: Helen MacDonald
Type: Weight – Sculptural
Issued: 1998 in a limited edition of 25
Status: Fully subscribed
Series: Limited – Modern Design
O.I.P.: U.K. £595.00
U.S. $1,925.00

U.K.: £ 600.00
U.S.: $1,200.00
Can.: $1,550.00

LILY POOL
Designer: Colin Terris
Type: Weight – Spherical
Issued: 1998 in a limited edition of 350
Status: Closed at No. 94
Series: Colin Terris Water Lily Collection
O.I.P.: U.K. £150.00
U.S. $485.00

U.K.: £150.00
U.S.: $300.00
Can.: $400.00

LIVE WIRE
Designer: Alastair MacIntosh
Type: Weight – Domed
Issued: 1998 in a limited edition of 150
Status: Closed at No. 64
Series: Limited – Modern Design
O.I.P.: U.K. £195.00
U.S. $625.00

U.K.: £200.00
U.S.: $400.00
Can.: $525.00

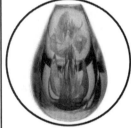

LOST WORLD
Designer: Alastair MacIntosh
Type: Weight – Domed
Issued: 1998 in a limited edition of 350
Status: Fully subscribed
Series: Limited – Modern Design
O.I.P.: U.K. £99.00
U.S. $225.00

U.K.: £100.00
U.S.: $200.00
Can.: $260.00

MALAYSIAN MELODY
Designer: Helen MacDonald
Type: Weight – Spherical
Size: Magnum
Issued: 1998 in a limited edition of 25
Status: Fully subscribed
Series: Limited – Modern Design
O.I.P.: U.K. £650.00
U.S. $2,100.00

U.K.: £ 650.00
U.S.: $1,300.00
Can.: $1,700.00

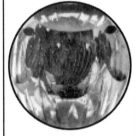

MARINE FANTASY
Designer: Colin Terris
Type: Weight – Spherical
Issued: 1998 in a limited edition of 75
Status: Closed at No. 65
Series: Limited – Modern Design
O.I.P.: U.K. £250.00
U.S. $795.00

U.K.: £250.00
U.S.: $500.00
Can.: $650.00

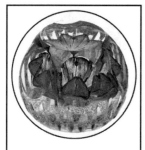

MORELLO

Designer: Colin Terris
Type: Weight: Spherical, facets
Issued: 1998 in a limited edition of 150
Status: Closed at No. 84
O.I.P.: U.K. £275.00/set
U.S. $875.00/set

U.K.: £275.00
U.S.: $550.00
Can.: $725.00

Note: The Morello Paperweight and Perfume Bottle were issued and sold as a set.

MORELLO PERFUME BOTTLE

Designer: Colin Terris
Type: Perfume Bottle
Issued: 1998 in a limited edition of 150
Status: Closed at No. 84
O.I.P.: U.K. £275.00/set
U.S. $875.00/set

U.K.: £275.00
U.S.: $550.00
Can.: $725.00

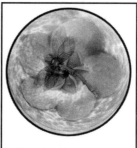

MORNING FLIGHT

Designer: Colin Terris
Type: Weight – Spherical
Size: Medium
Issued: 1998 in a limited edition of 500
Status: Fully subscribed
Series: Colin Terris Water Lily Collection
O.I.P.: U.K. £70.00
U.S. $225.00

U.K.: £ 70.00
U.S.: $140.00
Can.: $180.00

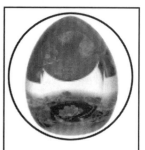

MORNING REFLECTIONS

Designer: Rosette Fleming
Type: Weight – Domed
Issued: 1998 in a limited edition of 75
Status: Closed at No. 37
Series: Traditional Collection - Nature Study
O.I.P.: U.K. £295.00
U.S. $950.00

U.K.: £300.00
U.S.: $600.00
Can.: $775.00

MYSTIC SHRINE

Designer: Colin Terris
Type: Weight – Domed
Issued: 1998 in a limited edition of 650
Status: Closed at No. 473
Series: Limited – Modern Design
O.I.P.: U.K. £85.00
U.S. $260.00

U.K.: £ 85.00
U.S.: $170.00
Can.: $225.00

NATIONAL QUARTET – ONE

Designer: Rosette Fleming
Type: Weight – Spherical, facets
Issued: 1998 in a limited edition of 25
Status: Closed at No. 18
Series: National Quartet Set
O.I.P.: U.K. £695.00/set
U.S. $2,250.00/set

	Quartet	Set
U.K.:	£200.	800.
U.S.:	$400.	1,600.
Can.:	$525.	2,100.

Note: CT-1667a, b, c, and d were issued and sold as a set.

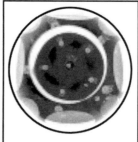

NATIONAL QUARTET – TWO

Designer: Rosette Fleming
Type: Weight – Spherical, facets
Issued: 1998 in a limited edition of 25
Status: Closed at No. 18
Series: National Quartet Set
O.I.P.: U.K. £695.00/set
U.S. $2,250.00/set

U.K.: £200.00
U.S.: $400.00
Can.: $525.00

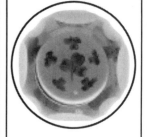

NATIONAL QUARTET – THREE

Designer: Rosette Fleming
Type: Weight – Spherical, facets
Issued: 1998 in a limited edition of 25
Status: Closed at No. 18
Series: National Quartet Set
O.I.P.: U.K. £695.00/set
U.S. $2,250.00/set

U.K.: £200.00
U.S.: $400.00
Can.: $525.00

GIFT OCCASIONS

Bridal Waltz
(Weddings)

Wise Owl
(Graduation)

Wedding Day
(Weddings and Anniversaries)

MODERN DESIGNS

Polynesian Paradise
(Magnum)

Coral Fantasy '99
(Magnum)

Coral City
(Magnum)

PAPERWEIGHT LOVERS SERIES

Fair Juliet

Romeo

NATURAL ENVIRONMENTS SERIES

Coral Paradise

Polar Ice Flow

Desert Dreams

Rainforest

PICTORIAL SERIES

Home Coming

Eve

Titanic

FOUR SEASONS IMPRESSIONIST COLLECTION

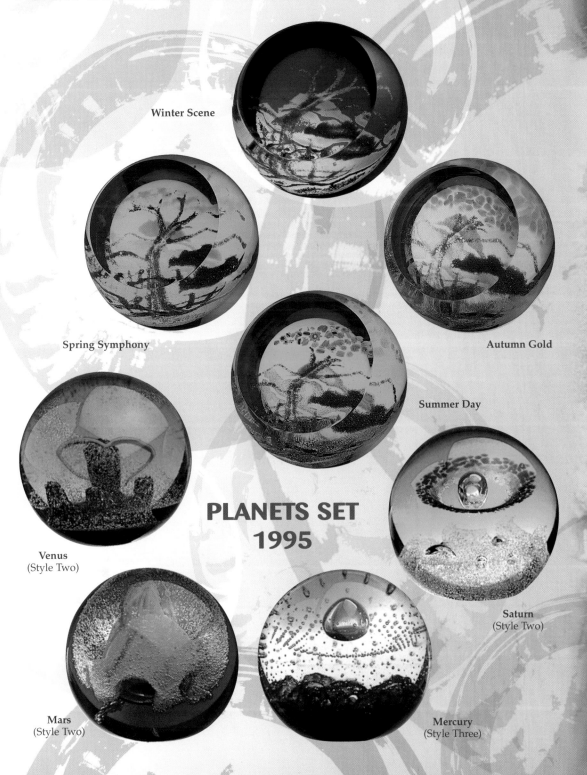

Winter Scene

Spring Symphony

Autumn Gold

Summer Day

Venus
(Style Two)

**PLANETS SET
1995**

Saturn
(Style Two)

Mars
(Style Two)

Mercury
(Style Three)

THE QUEEN'S GOLDEN JUBILEE

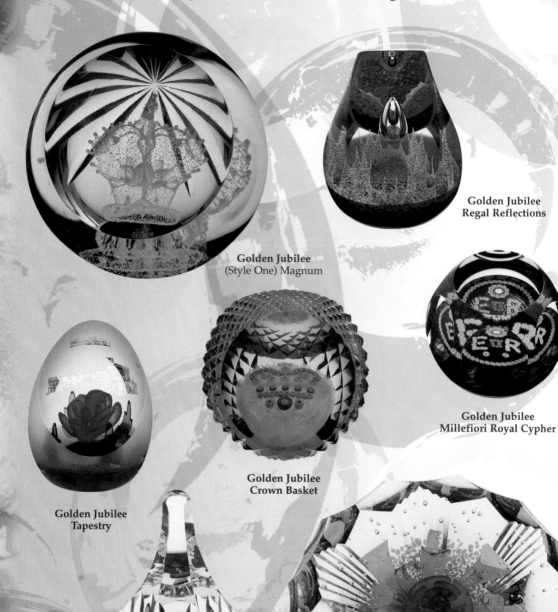

Golden Jubilee
(Style One) Magnum

Golden Jubilee
Regal Reflections

Golden Jubilee
Millefiori Royal Cypher

Golden Jubilee
Tapestry

Golden Jubilee
Crown Basket

Golden Jubilee
Reflections

Golden Jubilee
Majesty
(Centre Piece)

FESTIVE COLLECTION

Festive Beauty

Festive Kisses

Festive Reflections

WE THREE KINGS

Gold

Frankincense

Myrrh

FROSTED CHRISTMAS

Frosty's Night Out (2001)

Hey You, Get Off My Cloud (2002)

Now, Where is Rudolph? (2003)

Miniature Forget-Me-Not

MILLEFIORI MINIATURES SERIES

Miniature Daffodil

Miniature Heart
(Style One, Second Version)

Miniature Scots Thistle

Miniature Shamrock

Christmas Lantern

FLORAL CHARMS SERIES

Yellow Carnation

Red Poppy
(Style One)

Blue Anemone

MAGNUMS

Perfect Storm

Magnum Opus '88
(Treble Magnum)

Double Magnum Emerald

Another World
(Magnum)

ELEMENTS, SET TWO, 1989

Air
(Style Two)

Water
(Style Two)

Fire
(Style Three)

Earth
(Style Three)

VAN GOGH INSPIRATIONS

The Iris
(Style Three)

Vincent's Chair

One Starry Night

NATIONAL QUARTET – FOUR

Designer: Rosette Fleming
Type: Weight – Spherical, facets
Issued: 1998 in a limited edition of 25
Status: Closed at No. 18
Series: National Quartet Set
O.I.P.: U.K. £695.00/set
U.S. $2,250.00/set

U.K.: £200.00
U.S.: $400.00
Can.: $525.00

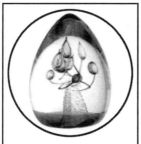

ONCE UPON A TIME

Designer: Colin Terris
Type: Weight – Domed
Issued: 1998 in a limited edition of 650
Status: Closed at No. 449
Series: Limited – Modern Design
O.I.P.: U.K. £75.00
U.S. $250.00

U.K.: £ 75.00
U.S.: $150.00
Can.: $200.00

OPULENCE

Designer: Colin Terris
Type: Weight – Spherical, dichroic .
Issued: 1998 in a limited edition of 500
Status: Closed at No. 328
Series: Colin Terris Designer Collection II
O.I.P.: U.K. £95.00
U.S. $295.00

U.K.: £ 95.00
U.S.: $190.00
Can.: $250.00

ORIENTAL LILY

Designer: Helen MacDonald
Type: Weight – Domed
Issued: 1998 in a limited edition of 150
Status: Closed at No. 99
Series: Limited – Modern Design
O.I.P.: U.K. £225.00
U.S. $695.00

U.K.: £225.00
U.S.: $450.00
Can.: $575.00

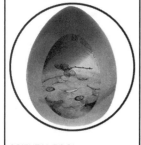

ORIENTAL POOL

Designer: Colin Terris
Type: Weight – Domed
Issued: 1998 in a limited edition of 100
Status: Closed at No. 89
Series: Colin Terris Water Lily Collection
O.I.P.: U.K. £225.00
U.S. $950.00

U.K.: £250.00
U.S.: $500.00
Can.: $650.00

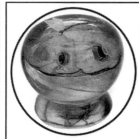

ORNAMENTAL POOL

Designer: Colin Terris
Type: Weight – Spherical
Issued: 1998 in a limited edition of 150
Status: Closed at No. 68
Series: Colin Terris Water Lilly Collection
O.I.P.: U.K. £225.00
U.S. $725.00

U.K.: £225.00
U.S.: $450.00
Can.: $575.00

PACHYRHNOSAURUS

Designer: Colin Terris
Type: Weight – Spherical
Size: Medium
Colour: Violet
Issued: 1998
Status: Closed
Series: Medium and Miniature Size
O.I.P.: U.K. £20.00
U.S. $62.50

U.K.: £20.00
U.S.: $40.00
Can.: $50.00

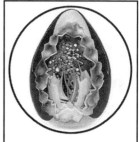

PAGAN RITUAL

Designer: Colin Terris
Type: Weight – Domed
Issued: 1998 in a limited edition of 150
Status: Closed at No. 109
Series: Colin Terris Designer Collection II
O.I.P.: U.K. £195.00
U.S. $595.00

U.K.: £200.00
U.S.: $400.00
Can.: $525.00

PANSY LATTICINO

Designer: Allan Scott
Type: Weight – Spherical
Issued: 1998 in a limited edition of 75
Status: Closed at No. 34
Series: Whitefriars Collection
O.I.P.: U.K. £120.00
U.S. $425.00

U.K.: £125.00
U.S.: $250.00
Can.: $325.00

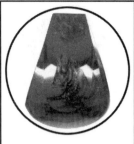

PARADISE LOST

Designer: Alastair MacIntosh
Type: Weight – Domed
Issued: 1998 in a limited edition of 350
Status: Fully subscribed
Series: Limited – Modern Design
O.I.P.: U.K. £99.00
U.S. $325.00

U.K.: £100.00
U.S.: $200.00
Can.: $260.00

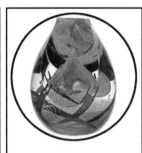

PARADOX

Designer: Colin Terris
Type: Weight – Domed
Issued: 1998 in a limited edition of 250
Status: Closed at No. 46
Series: Premier Stockist Paperweight Collection
O.I.P.: U.K. £150.00
U.S. $475.00

U.K.: £150.00
U.S.: $300.00
Can.: $400.00

PATRIOT

Designer: Colin Terris
Type: Weight – Spherical
Issued: 1998 in a limited edition of 750
Status: Closed at No. 215
Series: Colin Terris Designer Collection II
O.I.P.: U.K. £75.00
U.S. $240.00

U.K.: £ 75.00
U.S.: $150.00
Can.: $200.00

PERIWINKLES
Style Two

Designer: Helen MacDonald
Type: Weight – Spherical
Size: Magnum
Issued: 1998
Status: Closed
Series: Unlimited – Modern Design
O.I.P.: U.K. £65.00
U.S. $210.00

U.K.: £ 65.00
U.S.: $130.00
Can.: $170.00

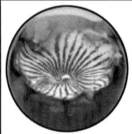

PETUNIAS

Designer: Colin Terris
Type: Weight – Spherical
Colour: 1. Pink
2. Purple
3. Red
4. Sky
5. White
Issued: 1998
Status: Closed
Series: Unlimited – Modern Design
O.I.P.: U.K. £18.50
U.S. $58.50
U.K.: £20.00
U.S.: $40.00
Can.: $50.00

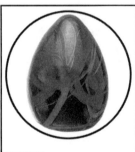

PHAEDRA

Designer: Philip Chaplain Stuart Cumming
Type: Weight – Domed
Issued: 1998 in a limited edition of 750
Status: Closed at No. 156
Series: Limited – Modern Design
O.I.P.: U.K. £55.00
U.S. $175.00

U.K.: £ 55.00
U.S.: $110.00
Can.: $145.00

PINK CONFETTI

Designer: Helen MacDonald
Type: Weight – Domed
Issued: 1998
Status: Closed
Series: Collectable Eggs – Unlimited
O.I.P.: U.K. £45.00
U.S. $150.00

U.K.: £ 45.00
U.S.: $ 90.00
Can.: $120.00

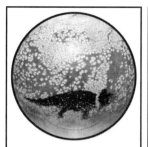

PTEROSAURUS
Designer: Colin Terris
Type: Weight – Spherical
Size: Medium
Colour: Blue
Issued: 1998
Status: Closed
Series: Medium and
Miniature Size
O.I.P.: U.K. £20.00
U.S. $62.50

U.K.: £20.00
U.S.: $40.00
Can.: $50.00

RAJ
Designer: Helen MacDonald
Type: Weight – Teardrop
Issued: 1998 in a limited
edition of 50
Status: Fully subscribed
Series: Limited – Modern
Design
O.I.P.: U.K. £425.00
U.S. $1,375.00

U.K.: £ 425.00
U.S.: $ 850.00
Can.: $1,100.00

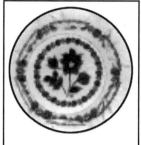

RED ROSE BOUQUET
Designer: Allan Scott
Type: Weight – Spherical
Issued: 1998 in a limited
edition of 50
Status: Closed at No. 26
Series: Whitefriars Collection
O.I.P.: U.K. £175.00
U.S. $575.00

U.K.: £175.00
U.S.: $350.00
Can.: $450.00

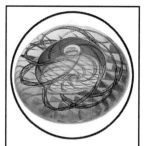

REFRACTOR
Designer: Philip Chaplain
Type: Weight – Spherical
Issued: 1998 in a limited
edition of 50
Status: Closed at No. 46
Series: Limited – Modern
Design
O.I.P.: U.K. £295.00
U.S. $895.00

U.K.: £300.00
U.S.: $600.00
Can.: $775.00

REGAL IRIS
Designer: Helen MacDonald
Type: Weight – Domed
Issued: 1998 in a limited
edition of 100
Status: Fully subscribed
Series: Limited – Modern
Design
O.I.P.: U.K. £295.00
U.S. $925.00

U.K.: £300.00
U.S.: $600.00
Can.: $775.00

RETICELLO ROSE
Designer: Rosette Fleming
Type: Weight – Spherical,
facets
Issued: 1998 in a limited
edition of 50
Status: Closed at No. 45
Series: Whitefriars Collection
O.I.P.: U.K. £150.00
U.S. $495.00

U.K.: £150.00
U.S.: $300.00
Can.: $400.00

REVIVAL
Designer: Alastair MacIntosh
Type: Weight – Spherical
Issued: 1998 in a limited
edition of 650
Status: Closed at No. 211
O.I.P.: U.K. £80.00
U.S. $275.00

U.K.: £ 80.00
U.S.: $160.00
Can.: $210.00

RITES OF SPRING
Designer: Helen MacDonald
Type: Weight – Domed,
facets
Issued: 1998 in a limited
edition of 250
Status: Closed at No. 198
Series: Limited – Modern
Design
O.I.P.: U.K. £175.00
U.S. $550.00

U.K.: £175.00
U.S.: $350.00
Can.: $450.00

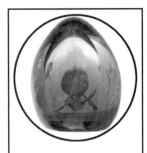

SCOTIA
Designer: Philip Chaplain
Type: Weight – Domed
Issued: 1998 in a limited edition of 650
Status: Fully subscribed
Series: Limited – Modern Design
O.I.P.: U.K. £80.00
U.S. $250.00

U.K.: £ 80.00
U.S.: $160.00
Can.: $210.00

Photograph not available at press time

SCOTS THISTLE
Style Two
Designer: Philip Chaplain
Type: Weight –
Issued: 1998 in a limited edition of 650
Status: Fully subscribed
Series: Visitor Centre
O.I.P.: U.K. £70.00
U.S. $225.00

U.K.: £ 70.00
U.S.: $140.00
Can.: $180.00

SCULPTURED POOL
Designer: Colin Terris
Type: Weight – Spherical sculpture
Issued: 1998 in a limited edition of 75
Status: Fully subscribed
Series: Colin Terris Water Lily Collection
O.I.P.: U.K. £350.00
U.S. $1,125.00

U.K.: £350.00
U.S.: $700.00
Can.: $900.00

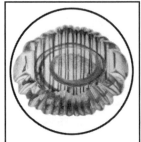

SEA PEARLS
Designer: Alastair MacIntosh
Type: Weight – Sculptural
Colour: 1. Gold
2. Heather
3. Kingfisher
Issued: 1998
Status: Closed
Series: Unlimited – Modern Design
O.I.P.: U.K. £30.00
U.S. $95.00

U.K.: £30.00
U.S.: $60.00
Can.: $80.00

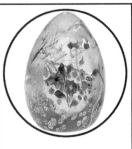

SECRET GARDEN '98
Designer: Colin Terris
Type: Weight – Domed
Colour: Blue, purple, pink, yellow and green
Issued: 1998 in a limited edition of 100
Status: Fully subscribed
Series: Colin Terris Designer Collection II
O.I.P.: U.K. £295.00
U.S. $925.00

U.K.: £300.00
U.S.: $600.00
Can.: $775.00

SENSATIONS
Designer: Helen MacDonald
Type: Weight – Spherical
Issued: 1998 in a limited| edition of 750
Status: Closed at No. 603
O.I.P.: U.K. £45.00
U.S. $150.00

U.K.: £175.00
U.S.: $350.00
Can.: $450.00

SHAMBALAH
Designer: Philip Chaplain
Type: Weight – Domed
Issued: 1998 in a limited edition of 250
Status: Closed at No. 132
Series: Collectable Eggs – Limited
O.I.P.: U.K. £99.00
U.S. $310.00

U.K.: £100.00
U.S.: $200.00
Can.: $260.00

Note: This weight is supplied with a stand.

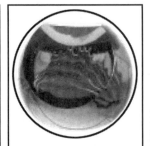

SHOCKWAVE
Designer: Alastair MacIntosh
Type: Weight – Spherical
Issued: 1998 in a limited edition of 500
Status: Closed at No. 122
Series: Limited – Modern Design
O.I.P.: U.K. £90.00
U.S. $295.00

U.K.: £ 90.00
U.S.: $180.00
Can.: $235.00

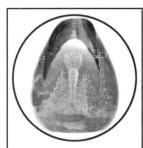

SIR PERCIVAL'S QUEST
Designer: Colin Terris
Type: Weight – Domed
Issued: 1998 in a limited edition of 650
Status: Closed at No. 538
Series: Limited – Modern Design
O.I.P.: U.K. £80.00
U.S. $250.00

U.K.: £ 80.00
U.S.: $160.00
Can.: $210.00

SNOW ORCHID
Designer: Colin Terris
Type: Weight – Spherical
Issued: 1998 in a limited edition of 750
Status: Fully subscribed
Series: Limited – Modern Design
O.I.P.: U.K. £65.00
U.S. $210.00

U.K.: £ 65.00
U.S.: $130.00
Can.: $170.00

SOLITUDE
Designer: Alastair MacIntosh
Type: Weight – Sculptural, facets
Issued: 1998 in a limited edition of 50
Status: Fully subscribed
Series: Limited – Modern Design
O.I.P.: U.K. £295.00
U.S. $950.00

U.K.: £300.00
U.S.: $600.00
Can.: $775.00

SPACE HIBISCUS
Designer: Helen MacDonald
Type: Weight – Domed
Issued: 1998 in a limited edition of 350
Status: Closed
Series: Limited – Modern Design
O.I.P.: U.K. £99.00
U.S. $310.00

U.K.: £100.00
U.S.: $200.00
Can.: $260.00

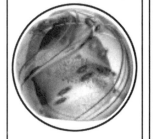

SPRING FESTIVAL
Designer: Helen MacDonald
Type: Weight – Spherical
Issued: 1998
Status: Closed
Series: Unlimited – Modern Design
O.I.P.: U.K. £33.50
U.S. $115.00

U.K.: £35.00
U.S.: $70.00
Can.: $90.00

SPRING FLORETTE, COBALT
Designer: Rosette Fleming
Type: Weight – Domed
Issued: 1998 in a limited edition of 150
Status: Closed at No. 80
Series: Whitefriars Collection
O.I.P.: U.K. £70.00
U.S. $250.00

U.K.: £ 70.00
U.S.: $140.00
Can.: $180.00

SPRING FLORETTE, KINGFISHER
Designer: Rosette Fleming
Type: Weight – Domed
Issued: 1998 in a limited edition of 150
Status: Closed at No. 64
Series: Whitefriars Collection
O.I.P.: U.K. £70.00
U.S. $250.00

U.K.: £ 70.00
U.S.: $140.00
Can.: $180.00

STAR CRYSTAL
Designer: Helen MacDonald
Type: Weight – Sculptural
Issued: 1998 in a limited edition of 50
Status: Fully subscribed
Series: Limited – Modern Design
O.I.P.: U.K. £325.00
U.S. $1,050.00

U.K.: £325.00
U.S.: $650.00
Can.: $850.00

STARSTRUCK

Designer:	Helen MacDonald
Type:	Weight – Diamond
Issued:	1998 in a limited edition of 50
Status:	Fully subscribed
Series:	Limited – Modern Design
O.I.P.:	U.K. £325.00
	U.S. $1,050.00
U.K.:	£325.00
U.S.:	$650.00
Can.:	$850.00

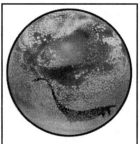

STEGOSAURUS

Designer:	Colin Terris
Type:	Weight – Spherical
Size:	Medium
Colour:	Tabac
Issued:	1998
Status:	Closed
Series:	Medium and Miniature Size
O.I.P.:	U.K. £20.00
	U.S. $62.50
U.K.:	£20.00
U.S.:	$40.00
Can.:	$50.00

SUMMER FAIR

Designer:	Helen MacDonald
Type:	Weight – Domed
Issued:	1998
Status:	Closed
Series:	Unlimited – Modern Design
O.I.P.:	U.K. £33.50
	U.S. $115.00
U.K.:	£35.00
U.S.:	$70.00
Can.:	$90.00

SUNFLOWERS

Designer:	Rosette Fleming
Type:	Weight – Spherical, facets
Issued:	1998 in a limited edition of 50
Status:	Closed at No. 37
Series:	Traditional Collection Nature Study
O.I.P.:	U.K. £350.00
	U.S. $1,125.00
U.K.:	£350.00
U.S.:	$700.00
Can.:	$900.00

SUNNY DAYS PERFUME BOTTLE

Designer:	Allan Scott
Type:	Perfume Bottle
Issued:	1998 in a limited edition of 50
Status:	Closed at No. 36
Series:	Whitefriars Collection
O.I.P.:	U.K. £250.00
	U.S. $875.00
U.K.:	£250.00
U.S.:	$500.00
Can.:	$650.00

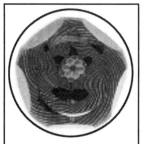

SWAN VISTA

Designer:	Helen MacDonald
Type:	Weight – Domed, engraved
Issued:	1998 in a limited edition of 125
Status:	Closed at No. 69
Series:	Limited – Modern Design
O.I.P.:	U.K. £285.00
	U.S. $875.00
U.K.:	£300.00
U.S.:	$600.00
Can.:	$775.00

SYMPHONY IN BLUE

Designer:	Rosette Fleming
Type:	Weight – Spherical, facets
Issued:	1998 in a limited edition of 50
Status:	Closed at No. 23
Series:	Whitefriars Collection
O.I.P.:	U.K. £150.00
	U.S. $485.00
U.K.:	£150.00
U.S.:	$300.00
Can.:	$400.00

TEARS OF JOY
Designer: Helen MacDonald
Type: Weight – Teardrop
Issued: 1998 in a limited
edition of 750
Status: Closed at No. 624
Series: Limited – Modern
Design
O.I.P.: U.K. £60.00
U.S. $185.00

U.K.: £ 60.00
U.S.: $120.00
Can.: $160.00

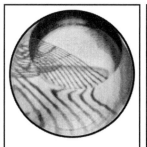

TECHNO-TRIP
Designer: Alastair MacIntosh
Type: Weight – Spherical
Issued: 1998 in a limited
edition of 750
Status: Closed at No. 218
Series: Limited – Modern
Design
O.I.P.: U.K. £70.00
U.S. $225.00

U.K.: £ 70.00
U.S.: $140.00
Can.: $180.00

TIJUANA
Designer: Alastair MacIntosh
Type: Weight – Domed
Issued: 1998 in a limited
edition of 750
Status: Closed at No. 463
Series: Limited – Modern
Design
O.I.P.: U.K. £75.00
U.S. $235.00

U.K.: £ 75.00
U.S.: $150.00
Can.: $200.00

TIME TUNNEL
Designer: Helen MacDonald
Type: Weight – Spherical
Issued: 1998 in a limited
edition of 750
Status: Fully subscribed
Series: Limited – Modern
Design
O.I.P.: U.K. £55.00
U.S. $175.00

U.K.: £ 55.00
U.S.: $110.00
Can.: $145.00

TO BOLDLY GO...
Designer: Colin Terris
Type: Weight – Domed
Issued: 1998 in a limited
edition of 750
Status: Closed at No. 361
Series: Colin Terris
Designer Collection II
O.I.P.: U.K. £70.00
U.S. $225.00

U.K.: £ 70.00
U.S.: $140.00
Can.: $180.00

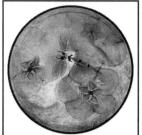

TRADITIONAL POOL
Designer: Colin Terris
Type: Weight – Spherical
Issued: 1998 in a limited
edition of 350
Status: Fully subscribed
Series: Colin Terris Water
Lily Collection
O.I.P.: U.K. £99.00
U.S. $325.00

U.K.: £100.00
U.S.: $200.00
Can.: $260.00

TRANQUIL POND
Designer: Colin Terris
Type: Weight – Sculptural
Issued: 1998 in a limited
edition of 100
Status: Closed at No. 54
Series: Colin Terris Water
Lily Collection
O.I.P.: U.K. £250.00
U.S. $795.00

U.K.: £250.00
U.S.: $500.00
Can.: $650.00

TURQUOISE DELIGHT
Designer: Philip Chaplain
Type: Weight – Domed
Issued: 1998 in a limited
edition of 100
Status: Fully subscribed
Series: Collectable Eggs –
Limited
O.I.P.: U.K. £99.00
U.S. $325.00

U.K.: £100.00
U.S.: $200.00
Can.: $260.00

Note: This weight is supplied
with a stand.

TWILIGHT MYSTERY

Designer: Allan Scott
Type: Weight – Spherical, facets
Issued: 1998 in a limited edition of 25
Status: Fully subscribed
Series: Traditional Collection Nature Study
O.I.P.: U.K. £595.00
U.S. $1,925.00

U.K.: £ 600.00
U.S.: $1,200.00
Can.: $1,550.00

TYRANNOSAURUS

Designer: Colin Terris
Type: Weight – Spherical
Size: Medium
Colour: Green
Issued: 1998
Status: Closed
Series: Medium and Miniature Size
O.I.P.: U.K. £20.00
U.S. $62.50

U.K.: £20.00
U.S.: $40.00
Can.: $50.00

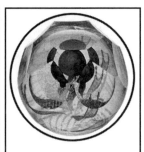

ULTRAMARINE

Designer: Philip Chaplain
Type: Weight – Spherical, facets
Issued: 1998 in a limited edition of 75
Status: Closed at No. 74
Series: Limited – Modern Design
O.I.P.: U.K. £275.00
U.S. $850.00

U.K.: £275.00
U.S.: $550.00
Can.: $725.00

VALENTINO

Designer: Rosette Fleming
Type: Weight – Spherical
Issued: 1998 in a limited edition of 50
Status: Closed at No. 36
Series: Whitefriars Collection
O.I.P.: U.K. £200.00
U.S. $595.00

U.K.: £200.00
U.S.: $400.00
Can.: $525.00

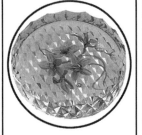

VICTORIANA

Designer: Allan Scott
Type: Weight – Disk, faceted
Issued: 1998 in a limited edition of 50
Status: Closed at No. 43
Series: Traditional Collection Nature Study
O.I.P.: U.K. £350.00
U.S. $1,125.00

U.K.: £350.00
U.S.: $700.00
Can.: $900.00

VIOLETTA

Designer: Helen MacDonald
Type: Weight – Low Dome
Issued: 1998 in a limited edition of 500
Status: Closed at No. 397
Series: Limited – Modern Design
O.I.P.: U.K. £90.00
U.S. $275.00

U.K.: £ 90.00
U.S.: $180.00
Can.: $235.00

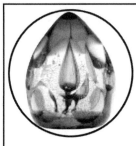

VIRIDIAN

Designer: Philip Chaplain
Type: Weight – Domed
Issued: 1998 in a limited edition of 75
Status: Closed at No. 69
Series: Limited – Modern Design
O.I.P.: U.K. £295.00
U.S. $950.00

U.K.: £300.00
U.S.: $600.00
Can.: $775.00

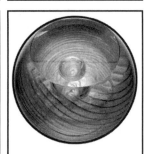

VORTICE

Designer: Helen MacDonald
Type: Weight – Spherical
Colour: 1. Green
2. Purple
3. Red
Issued: 1998
Status: Closed
Series: Unlimited – Modern Design
O.I.P.: U.K. £33.50
U.S. $99.50

U.K.: £35.00
U.S.: $70.00
Can.: $90.00

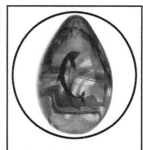

WALLS OF JERICHO

Designer:	Helen MacDonald
Type:	Weight – Spherical
Issued:	1998 in a limited edition of 75
Status:	Closed at No. 38
Series:	Limited – Modern Design
O.I.P.:	U.K. £250.00
	U.S. $795.00
U.K.:	£250.00
U.S.:	$500.00
Can.:	$650.00

WATER GARDEN

Designer:	Colin Terris
Type:	Weight – Domed
Issued:	1998 in a limited edition of 250
Status:	Closed at No. 243
Series:	Colin Terris Water Lily Collection
O.I.P.:	U.K. £125.00
	U.S. $395.00
U.K.:	£125.00
U.S.:	$250.00
Can.:	$325.00

WAVEDANCERS

Designer:	Helen MacDonald
	Stuart Cumming
Type:	Weight – Domed
Issued:	1998
Status:	Closed
Series:	Collectable Eggs – Unlimited
O.I.P.:	U.K. £40.00
	U.S. $125.00
U.K.:	£ 40.00
U.S.:	$ 80.00
Can.:	$100.00

ISSUES OF 1999

AERONAUT

Designer: Colin Terris
Type: Weight – Spherical
Issued: 1999 in a limited edition of 500
Status: Closed at No. 195
O.I.P.: U.K. £80.00
U.S. $250.00

U.K.: £ 80.00
U.S.: $160.00
Can.: $210.00

ALBA GOLD

Designer: Helen MacDonald
Type: Weight – Spherical
Issued: 1999
Status: Closed
Series: Unlimited – Modern Design
O.I.P.: U.K. £45.00
U.S. $110.00

U.K.: £ 45.00
U.S.: $ 90.00
Can.: $120.00

ALBA KINGFISHER

Designer: Helen MacDonald
Type: Weight – Spherical
Issued: 1999
Status: Closed
Series: Unlimited – Scottish Inspirations
O.I.P.: U.K. £45.00
U.S. $110.00

U.K.: £ 45.00
U.S.: $ 90.00
Can.: $120.00

AMBER GAMBLER

Designer: Philip Chaplain
Type: Weight – Domed
Issued: 1999 in a limited edition of 750
Status: Closed at No. 615
Series: Limited – Modern Design
O.I.P.: U.K. £75.00
U.S. $250.00

U.K.: £ 75.00
U.S.: $150.00
Can.: $200.00

AMETHYST POPPY

Designer: Helen MacDonald
Type: Weight – Spherical, facets
Issued: 1999 in a limited edition of 100
Status: Closed at No. 49
O.I.P.: U.K. £235.00
U.S. $695.00

U.K.: £235.00
U.S.: $470.00
Can.: $600.00

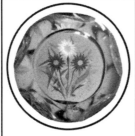

APRIL SHOWERS

Designer: Allan Scott
Type: Weight – Spherical, facets
Issued: 1999 in a limited edition of 50
Status: Closed at No. 42
O.I.P.: U.K. £155.00
U.S. $495.00

U.K.: £150.00
U.S.: $300.00
Can.: $400.00

ART DECO

Designer: Alastair MacIntosh
Type: Weight – Cylindrical, facets
Issued: 1999 in a limited edition of 250
Status: Closed at No. 92
Series: Limited – Modern Design
O.I.P.: U.K. £150.00
U.S. $475.00

U.K.: £150.00
U.S.: $300.00
Can.: $400.00

BEDOUIN

Designer: Alastair MacIntosh
Type: Weight – Domed
Issued: 1999 in a limited edition of 350
Status: Fully subscribed
Series: Limited – Modern Design
O.I.P.: U.K. £99.00
U.S. $295.00

U.K.: £100.00
U.S.: $200.00
Can.: $260.00

BLAST OFF

Designer: Philip Chaplain
Type: Weight – Domed
Issued: 1999 in a limited edition of 750
Status: Closed at No. 291
Series: Limited – Modern Design
O.I.P.: U.K. £75.00
U.S. $225.00
U.K.: £ 75.00
U.S.: $150.00
Can.: $200.00

BLUE ANEMONE

Designer: Helen MacDonald
Type: Weight – Spherical
Issued: 1999
Status: Active
Series: Unlimited – Floral Charms
O.I.P.: U.K. £35.00
U.S. $82.50
U.K.: £39.95
U.S.: $85.00
Can.: –

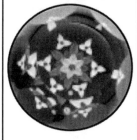

BLUE RHAPSODY

Designer: Rosette Fleming
Type: Weight – Spherical
Issued: 1999 in a limited edition of 50
Status: Closed at No. 42
Series: Whitefriars Collection
O.I.P.: U.K. £145.00
U.S. $450.00
U.K.: £150.00
U.S.: $300.00
Can.: $400.00

BREAKOUT

Designer: Alastair MacIntosh
Type: Weight – Domed, multifaceted/ pyramidal
Issued: 1999 in a limited edition of 150
Status: Closed at No. 60
Series: Limited – Modern Design
O.I.P.: U.K. £225.00
U.S. $695.00
U.K.: £225.00
U.S.: $450.00
Can.: $575.00

BRILLIANCE

Designer: Colin Terris
Type: Weight – Spherical
Issued: 1999 in a limited edition of 750
Status: Closed at No. 389
Series: Limited – Modern Design
O.I.P.: U.K. £75.00
U.S. $225.00
U.K.: £ 75.00
U.S.: $150.00
Can.: $200.00

BURGUNDY QUARTET

Designer: Rosette Fleming
Type: Weight – Spherical
Issued: 1999 in a limited edition of 50
Status: Fully subscribed
Series: Whitefriars Collection
O.I.P.: U.K. £99.00
U.S. $325.00
U.K.: £100.00
U.S.: $200.00
Can.: $260.00

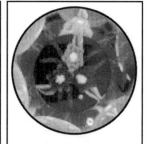

BURGUNDY TREFOIL

Designer: Rosette Fleming
Type: Weight – Spherical
Issued: 1999 in a limited edition of 50
Status: Closed at No. 25
Series: Traditional Collection Nature Study
O.I.P.: U.K. £295.00
U.S. $895.00
U.K.: £300.00
U.S.: $600.00
Can.: $775.00

CAPITAL CELEBRATION EDINBURGH

Designer: W. Bain
Type: Weight – Spherical, engraved
Issued: 1999
Status: Closed
Series: Millennium Collection
O.I.P.: U.K. £37.00
U.S. $110.00
U.K.: £ 40.00
U.S.: $ 80.00
Can.: $100.00

CARTOUCHE

Designer:	Helen MacDonald
Type:	Weight – Spherical
Issued:	1999 in a limited edition of 650
Status:	Closed at No. 160
O.I.P.:	U.K. £80.00
	U.S. $235.00
U.K.:	£ 80.00
U.S.:	$160.00
Can.:	$210.00

CASCADIA

Designer:	Helen MacDonald
Type:	Weight – Domed
Issued:	1999 in a limited edition of 650
Status:	Fully subscribed
Series:	Limited – Modern Design
O.I.P.:	U.K. £85.00
	U.S. $265.00
U.K.:	£ 85.00
U.S.:	$170.00
Can.:	$225.00

CEILIDH

Designer:	Helen MacDonald
Type:	Weight – Spherical
Issued:	1999
Status:	Closed
Series:	Unlimited – Scottish Inspirations
O.I.P.:	U.K. £50.00
	U.S. $120.00
U.K.:	£ 50.00
U.S.:	$100.00
Can.:	$130.00

CELEBRATION NUMERALS COBALT 21

Designer:	Helen MacDonald
Type:	Weight – Spherical
Issued:	1999
Status:	Closed
Series:	Unlimited – Modern Design
O.I.P.:	U.K. £38.00
	U.S. $92.50
U.K.:	£ 40.00
U.S.:	$ 80.00
Can.:	$100.00

CELEBRATION NUMERALS COBALT 25

Designer:	Helen MacDonald
Type:	Weight – Spherical
Issued:	1999
Status:	Closed
Series:	Unlimited – Modern Design
O.I.P.:	U.K. £38.00
	U.S. $92.50
U.K.:	£ 40.00
U.S.:	$ 80.00
Can.:	$100.00

CELEBRATION NUMERALS EMERALD 60

Designer:	Helen MacDonald
Type:	Weight – Spherical
Issued:	1999
Status:	Closed
Series:	Unlimited – Modern Design
O.I.P.:	U.K. £38.00
	U.S. $92.50
U.K.:	£ 40.00
U.S.:	$ 80.00
Can.:	$100.00

CELEBRATION NUMERALS EMERALD 75

Designer:	Helen MacDonald
Type:	Weight – Spherical
Issued:	1999
Status:	Closed
Series:	Unlimited – Modern Design
O.I.P.:	U.K. £38.00
	U.S. $92.50
U.K.:	£ 40.00
U.S.:	$ 80.00
Can.:	$100.00

CELEBRATION NUMERALS GOLD 50

Designer:	Helen MacDonald
Type:	Weight – Spherical
Issued:	1999
Status:	Closed
Series:	Unlimited – Modern Design
O.I.P.:	U.K. £38.00
	U.S. $92.50
U.K.:	£ 40.00
U.S.:	$ 80.00
Can.:	$100.00

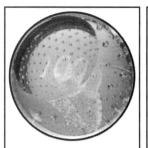

CELEBRATION NUMERALS GOLD 100

Designer: Helen MacDonald
Type: Weight – Spherical
Issued: 1999
Status: Closed
Series: Unlimited – Modern Design
O.I.P.: U.K. £38.00
U.S. $92.50

U.K.: £ 40.00
U.S.: $ 80.00
Can.: $100.00

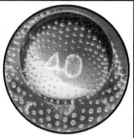

CELEBRATION NUMERALS HEATHER 40

Designer: Helen MacDonald
Type: Weight – Spherical
Issued: 1999
Status: Closed
Series: Unlimited – Modern Design
O.I.P.: U.K. £38.00
U.S. $92.50

U.K.: £ 40.00
U.S.: $ 80.00
Can.: $100.00

CELEBRATION NUMERALS HEATHER 65

Designer: Helen MacDonald
Type: Weight – Spherical
Issued: 1999
Status: Closed
Series: Unlimited – Modern Design
O.I.P.: U.K. £38.00
U.S. $92.50

U.K.: £ 40.00
U.S.: $ 80.00
Can.: $100.00

CELEBRATION NUMERALS KINGFISHER 18

Designer: Helen MacDonald
Type: Weight – Spherical
Issued: 1999
Status: Closed
Series: Unlimited – Modern Design
O.I.P.: U.K. £38.00
U.S. $92.50

U.K.: £ 40.00
U.S.: $ 80.00
Can.: $100.00

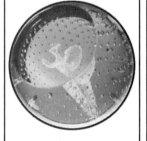

CELEBRATION NUMERALS KINGFISHER 30

Designer: Helen MacDonald
Type: Weight – Spherical
Issued: 1999
Status: Closed
Series: Unlimited – Modern Design
O.I.P.: U.K. £38.00
U.S. $92.50

U.K.: £ 40.00
U.S.: $ 80.00
Can.: $100.00

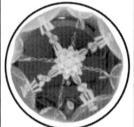

CELTIC CELEBRATION

Designer: Rosette Fleming
Type: Weight – Spherical
Issued: 1999 in a limited edition of 50
Status: Closed at No. 20
Series: Traditional Collection Nature Study
O.I.P.: U.K. £295.00
U.S. $895.00

U.K.: £300.00
U.S.: $600.00
Can.: $775.00

CHANELLE

Designer: Franco Toffolo
Type: Weight – Spherical
Size: Magnum
Issued: 1999 in a limited edition of 50
Status: Closed at No. 25
O.I.P.: U.K. £600.00
U.S. $1,800.00

U.K.: £ 600.00
U.S.: $1,200.00
Can.: $1,550.00

CHEVRONS

Designer: Stuart Cumming
Type: Weight – Spherical
Colour: 1. Blue
2. Green
3. Pink
Issued: 1999
Status: Closed
Series: Unlimited – Modern Design
O.I.P.: U.K. £25.00
U.S. $79.50

U.K.: £25.00
U.S.: $50.00
Can.: $65.00

CITRON

Designer: Philip Chaplain
Type: Weight – Domed
Issued: 1999 in a limited
edition of 150
Status: Closed at No. 62
Series: Collectable Eggs –
Limited
O.I.P.: U.K. £125.00
U.S. $385.00

U.K.: £125.00
U.S.: $250.00
Can.: $325.00

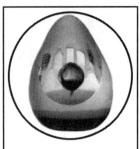

CITY LIMITS

Designer: Alastair MacIntosh
Type: Weight – Domed
Issued: 1999 in a limited
edition of 125
Status: Closed at No. 71
Series: Limited – Modern
Design
O.I.P.: U.K. £250.00
U.S. $775.00

U.K.: £250.00
U.S.: $500.00
Can.: $650.00

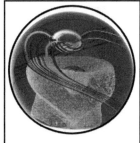

CLOSED CIRCUIT

Designer: Alastair MacIntosh
Type: Weight – Spherical
Size: Magnum
Issued: 1999 in a limited
edition of 750
Status: Closed at No. 182
O.I.P.: U.K. £55.00
U.S. $165.00

U.K.: £250.00
U.S.: $500.00
Can.: $650.00

CORAL CITY

Designer: Colin Terris
Type: Weight – Spherical,
engraved
Size: Magnum
Issued: 1999 in a limited
edition of 250
Status: Closed at No. 148
Series: Limited – Modern
Design
O.I.P.: U.K. £150.00
U.S. $475.00

U.K.: £150.00
U.S.: $300.00
Can.: $400.00

CORAL FANTASY '99

Designer: Colin Terris
Type: Weight – Spherical
Size: Magnum
Colour: Blue coral, yellow,
white and green
Issued: 1999 in a limited
edition of 75
Status: Fully subscribed
Series: Limited – Modern
Design
O.I.P.: U.K. £275.00
U.S. $975.00

U.K.: £275.00
U.S.: $550.00
Can.: $725.00

Note: This paperweight was
introduced in the U.S. in 1996.

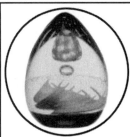

CORAL FRONDS

Designer: Philip Chaplain
Type: Weight – Domed
Issued: 1999 in a limited
edition of 750
Status: Closed at No. 435
Series: Limited – Modern
Design
O.I.P.: U.S.£70.00
U.S. $225.00

U.K.: £ 70.00
U.S.: $140.00
Can.: $180.00

CORNFLOWER
Style Two

Designer: Helen MacDonald
Type: Weight – Spherical
Issued: 1999
Status: Closed
Series: Unlimited – Modern
Design
O.I.P.: U.K. £35.00
U.S. $82.50

U.K.: £35.00
U.S.: $70.00
Can.: $90.00

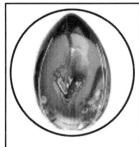

CROCUS
Style Two

Designer: Colin Terris
Type: Weight – Domed
Issued: 1999
Status: Closed
Series: Collectable Eggs –
Unlimited
O.I.P.: U.K. £49.00
U.S. $165.00

U.K.: £ 50.00
U.S.: $100.00
Can.: $130.00

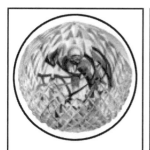

CROWN JEWEL
Designer: Colin Terris
Type: Weight – Spherical
Issued: 1999 in a limited edition of 50
Status: Closed at No. 42
Series: Limited – Modern Design
O.I.P.: U.K. £350.00
U.S. $995.00

U.K.: £350.00
U.S.: $700.00
Can.: $900.00

DAFFODIL
Designer: Colin Terris
Type: Weight – Domed
Issued: 1999
Status: Closed
Series: Collectable Eggs – Unlimited
O.I.P.: U.K. £49.00
U.S. $165.00

U.K.: £ 50.00
U.S.: $100.00
Can.: $130.00

DAISIES and TRELLIS
Designer: Allan Scott
Type: Weight – Spherical
Issued: 1999 in a limited edition of 50
Status: Fully subscribed
Series: Whitefriars Collection
O.I.P.: U.K. £120.00
U.S. $375.00

U.K.: £125.00
U.S.: $250.00
Can.: $325.00

DASH
Designer: Alastair MacIntosh
Type: Weight – Teardrop
Issued: 1999
Status: Closed
Series: Unlimited – Modern Design
O.I.P.: U.K. £30.00
U.S. $79.50

U.K.: £30.00
U.S.: $60.00
Can.: $80.00

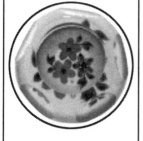

DAWN BOUQUET
Designer: Melanie Stuart
Type: Weight – Spherical
Issued: 1999 in a limited edition of 50
Status: Closed at No. 35
Series: Whitefriars Collection
O.I.P.: U.K. £125.00
U.S. $385.00

U.K.: £125.00
U.S.: $250.00
Can.: $325.00

DELILAH
Designer: Alastair MacIntosh
Type: Weight – Spherical
Issued: 1999 in a limited edition of 500
Status: Closed at No. 189
Series: Alastair MacIntosh Collection
O.I.P.: U.K. £90.00
U.S. $285.00

U.K.: £ 90.00
U.S.: $180.00
Can.: $235.00

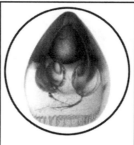

DESPERADO '99
Designer: Philip Chaplain
Type: Weight – Domed
Colour: Burgundy, violet and blue
Issued: 1999 in a limited edition of 250
Status: Closed at No. 245
Series: Limited – Modern Design
O.I.P.: U.K. £85.00
U.S. $275.00

U.K.: £ 85.00
U.S.: $170.00
Can.: $225.00

Note: Introduced in the U.S. in 1997.

DEWDROP ORCHID
Designer: Helen MacDonald
Type: Weight – Spherical
Colour: 1. Cobalt
2. Heather
3. Kingfisher
Issued: 1999
Status: Closed
Series: Unlimited – Modern Design
O.I.P.: U.K. £50.00
U.S. $135.00

U.K.: £ 50.00
U.S.: $100.00
Can.: $130.00

DIAMOND REFLECTIONS

Designer:	Rosette Fleming
Type:	Weight – Spherical
Issued:	1999 in a limited edition of 50
Status:	Fully subscribed
Series:	Whitefriars Collection
O.I.P.:	U.K. £120.00
	U.S. $395.00
U.K.:	£125.00
U.S.:	$250.00
Can.:	$325.00

DICHRO DAZZLE

Designer:	Unknown
Type:	Weight – Spherical
Issued:	1999 in a limited edition of 650
Status:	Fully subscribed
Series:	Limited – Millennium Collection II
O.I.P.:	£60.00
U.K.:	£ 85.00
U.S.:	$170.00
Can.:	$225.00

DIZZY LIZZY

Designer:	Alastair MacIntosh
Type:	Weight – Spherical
Issued:	1999 in a limited edition of 750
Status:	Closed at No. 454
Series:	Alastair MacIntosh Collection
O.I.P.:	U.K. £55.00
	U.S. $175.00
U.K.:	£ 55.00
U.S.:	$110.00
Can.:	$145.00

DOUBLE MAGNUM '99

Designer:	Franco Toffolo
Type:	Weight – Spherical
Size:	Double magnum
Issued:	1999 in a limited edition of 100
Status:	Closed at No. 47
Series:	Limited – Modern Design
O.I.P.:	U.K. £350.00
	U.S. $1075.00
U.K.:	£350.00
U.S.:	$700.00
Can.:	$900.00

DREAM WORLD

Designer:	Caithness Design Studios
Type:	Weight – Spherical
Issued:	1999
Status:	Closed
Series:	Collectors' Event
O.I.P.:	U.S. $95.00
U.K.:	£ 50.00
U.S.:	$100.00
Can.:	$130.00

Note: Dream World was the Event piece for 1999.

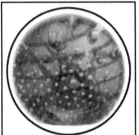

DUSKY MAIDEN

Designer:	Philip Chaplain
Type:	Weight – Spherical
Issued:	1999 in a limited edition of 750
Status:	Closed at No. 355
Series:	Limited – Modern Design
O.I.P.:	U.K. £75.00
	U.S. $225.00
U.K.:	£ 75.00
U.S.:	$150.00
Can.:	$200.00

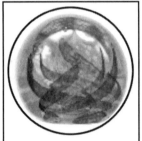

ELECTRIC SOUP

Designer:	Colin Terris
Type:	Weight – Spherical
Issued:	1999 in a limited edition of 650
Status:	Closed at No. 339
Series:	Limited – Modern Design
O.I.P.:	U.K. £80.00
	U.S. $250.00
U.K.:	£ 80.00
U.S.:	$160.00
Can.:	$210.00

EVANGELINE '99

Designer:	Colin Terris
Type:	Weight – Domed
Issued:	1999 in a limited edition of 250
Status:	Fully subscribed
Series:	Limited – Modern Design
O.I.P.:	U.K. £75.00
	U.S. $250.00
U.K.:	£ 75.00
U.S.:	$150.00
Can.:	$200.00

Note: This paperweight was introduced in the U.S. in 1997

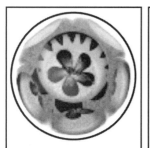

EVENING FLIGHT

Designer:	Colin Terris
Type:	Weight – Spherical
Issued:	1999 in a limited edition of 30
Status:	Fully subscribed
Series:	Limited – Modern Design
O.I.P.:	U.K. £450.00
	U.S. $1375.00
U.K.:	£ 450.00
U.S.:	$ 900.00
Can.:	$1,150.00

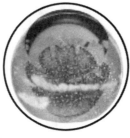

FAIRY LIGHTS '99

Designer:	Colin Terris
Type:	Weight – Spherical
Colour:	Blue, red and silver
Issued:	1999 in a limited edition of 250
Status:	Closed at No. 229
Series:	Limited – Modern Design
O.I.P.:	U.K. £75.00
	U.S. $225.00
U.K.:	£ 75.00
U.S.:	$150.00
Can.:	$200.00

Note: This paperweight was introduced in the U.S. in 1996.

FAR FRONTIERS

Designer:	Colin Terris
Type:	Weight – Domed
Issued:	1999 in a limited edition of 500
Status:	Closed at No. 266
Series:	Limited – Modern Design
O.I.P.:	U.K. £90.00
	U.S. $295.00
U.K.:	£ 90.00
U.S.:	$180.00
Can.:	$235.00

FESTIVITY

Designer:	Colin Terris
Type:	Weight – Domed
Issued:	1999 in a limited edition of 750
Status:	Closed at No. 682
O.I.P.:	U.K. £60.00
	U.S. $175.00
U.K.:	£ 90.00
U.S.:	$180.00
Can.:	$235.00

FLAMBÉ

Designer:	Alastair MacIntosh
Type:	Weight – Domed
Issued:	1999 in a limited edition of 350
Status:	Closed at No. 223
Series:	Limited – Modern Design
O.I.P.:	U.K. £99.00
	U.S. $295.00
U.K.:	£100.00
U.S.:	$200.00
Can.:	$260.00

FLORAL SPLENDOUR

Designer:	Melanie Stuart
Type:	Weight – Spherical
Issued:	1999 in a limited edition of 50
Status:	Fully subscribed
Series:	Whitefriars Collection
O.I.P.:	U.K. £120.00
	U.S. $350.00
U.K.:	£125.00
U.S.:	$250.00
Can.:	$325.00

FOUNTAIN OF DESIRE

Designer:	Colin Terris
Type:	Weight – Spherical
Issued:	1999 in a limited edition of 75
Status:	Closed at No. 42
Series:	Limited – Modern Design
O.I.P.:	U.K. £250.00
	U.S. $775.00
U.K.:	£250.00
U.S.:	$500.00
Can.:	$650.00

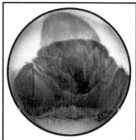

FRAGRANT ROSE

Designer:	Colin Terris
Type:	Weight – Spherical
Issued:	1999 in a limited edition of 650
Status:	Closed at No. 239
Series:	Colin Terris Rose Collection
O.I.P.:	U.K. £80.00
	U.S. $250.00
U.K.:	£ 80.00
U.S.:	$160.00
Can.:	$210.00

FROZEN IN TIME

Designer: Philip Chaplain
Type: Weight – Spherical
Issued: 1999 in a limited edition of 50
Status: Closed at No. 45
Series: Premier Stockist/ Premier Dealer Paperweight Collection
O.I.P.: £295.00

U.K.: £300.00
U.S.: $600.00
Can.: $775.00

GLOWING EMBERS

Designer: Alastair MacIntosh
Type: Weight – Spherical
Issued: 1999 in a limited edition of 150
Status: Closed at No. 50
O.I.P.: U.K. £195.00
U.S. $575.00

U.K.: £100.00
U.S.: $200.00
Can.: $260.00

GOLDEN GLORY

Designer: Rosette Fleming
Type: Weight – Spherical
Issued: 1999 in a limited edition of 50
Status: Closed at No. 27
Series: Whitefriars Collection
O.I.P.: U.K. £99.00
U.S. $325.00

U.K.: £100.00
U.S.: $200.00
Can.: $260.00

GOLDEN ROSE

Designer: Colin Terris
Type: Weight – Spherical
Issued: 1999 in a limited edition of 75
Status: Closed at No. 55
Series: Colin Terris Rose Collection
O.I.P.: U.K. £275.00
U.S. $825.00

U.K.: £275.00
U.S.: $550.00
Can.: $725.00

GOTHIC SPLENDOUR

Designer: Helen MacDonald
Type: Weight – Teardrop
Issued: 1999 in a limited edition of 100
Status: Closed at No. 60
Series: Premier Stockist/ Premier Dealer Paperweight Collection
O.I.P.: £225.00

U.K.: £225.00
U.S.: $450.00
Can.: $600.00

GREENMANTLE

Designer: Helen MacDonald
Type: Weight – Domed
Issued: 1999 in a limited edition of 350
Status: Closed at No. 159
Series: Limited – Modern Design
O.I.P.: U.K. £99.00
U.S. $295.00

U.K.: £100.00
U.S.: $200.00
Can.: $260.00

HARVEST FESTIVAL

Designer: Rosette Fleming
Type: Weight – Spherical, facets
Issued: 1999 in a limited edition of 50
Status: Closed at No. 23
Series: Traditional Collection Nature Study
O.I.P.: U.K. £295.00
U.S. $895.00

U.K.: £300.00
U.S.: $600.00
Can.: $775.00

IMPULSE '99
Style Two

Designer: Alastair MacIntosh
Type: Weight – Low Dome
Issued: 1999 in a limited edition of 750
Status: Closed at No. 453
Series: Limited – Modern Design
O.I.P.: U.K. £49.00
U.S. $150.00

U.K.: £ 50.00
U.S.: $100.00
Can.: $130.00

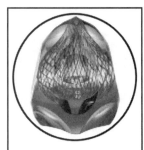

INTERNET
Designer: Alastair MacIntosh
Type: Weight – Domed, facets
Issued: 1999 in a limited edition of 50
Status: Closed at No. 43
Series: Limited – Modern Design
O.I.P.: U.K. £295.00
U.S. $895.00
U.K.: £300.00
U.S.: $600.00
Can.: $775.00

INTREPID
Designer: Alastair MacIntosh
Type: Weight – Spherical, facets
Issued: 1999 in a limited edition of 50
Status: Closed at No. 44
Series: Premier Stockist/ Premier Dealer Paperweight Collection
O.I.P.: £325.00
U.K.: £325.00
U.S.: $650.00
Can.: $850.00

ISLAND DREAM
Designer: Rosette Fleming
Type: Weight – Spherical
Issued: 1999 in a limited edition of 75
Status: Closed at No. 34
Series: Traditional Collection Nature Study
O.I.P.: U.K. £275.00
U.S. $825.00
U.K.: £275.00
U.S.: $550.00
Can.: $725.00

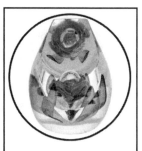

JACOBEAN ROSE
Designer: Colin Terris
Type: Weight – Domed
Issued: 1999 in a limited edition of 350
Status: Closed at No. 256
Series: Colin Terris Rose Collection
O.I.P.: U.K. £99.00
U.S. $325.00
U.K.: £100.00
U.S.: $200.00
Can.: $260.00

KALEIDOSCOPE '99
Designer: Colin Terris
Type: Weight – Spherical
Colour: Blue, pink, white and gold
Issued: 1999 in a limited edition of 650
Status: Closed at No. 178
Series: Limited – Modern Design
O.I.P.: U.K. £85.00
U.S. $265.00
U.K.: £ 85.00
U.S.: $170.00
Can.: $225.00

KATARINA
Designer: Colin Terris
Type: Weight – Domed, facets
Issued: 1999 in a limited edition of 100
Status: Closed at No. 46
Series: Collectable Eggs – Limited
O.I.P.: U.K. £175.00
U.S. $550.00
U.K.: £175.00
U.S.: $350.00
Can.: $450.00

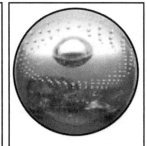

LANDING ZONE
Designer: Colin Terris
Type: Weight – Spherical
Issued: 1999 in a limited edition of 650
Status: Closed at No. 526
Series: Limited – Modern Design
O.I.P.: U.K. £75.00
U.S. $250.00
U.K.: £ 75.00
U.S.: $150.00
Can.: $200.00

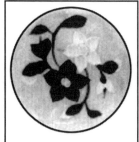

LATTICINO POSY
Designer: Allan Scott
Type: Weight – Spherical
Issued: 1999 in a limited edition of 50
Status: Fully subscribed
Series: Whitefriars Collection
O.I.P.: U.K. £120.00
U.S. $395.00
U.K.: £125.00
U.S.: $250.00
Can.: $325.00

LISTEN

Designer:	Helen MacDonald
Type:	Weight – Spherical, facets
Issued:	1999 in a limited edition of 350
Status:	Closed at No. 122
O.I.P.:	U.K. £99.00
	U.S. $295.00
U.K.:	£125.00
U.S.:	$250.00
Can.:	$325.00

LONDON TIME

Designer:	W. Bain
Type:	Weight – Spherical, engraved
Issued:	1999
Status:	Closed
Series:	Millennium Collection, Unlimited
O.I.P.:	£37.00
U.K.:	£ 40.00
U.S.:	$ 80.00
Can.:	$100.00

LOVE TOKEN

Designer:	Rosette Fleming
Type:	Weight – Spherical
Issued:	1999 in a limited edition of 75
Status:	Closed at No. 41
Series:	Traditional Collection Nature Study
O.I.P.:	U.K. £275.00
	U.S. $825.00
U.K.:	£275.00
U.S.:	$550.00
Can.:	$725.00

LUNAR ROSE

Designer:	Colin Terris
Type:	Weight – Spherical
Size:	Medium
Issued:	1999 in a limited edition of 750
Status:	Closed at No. 194
Series:	Colin Terris Rose Collection
O.I.P.:	U.K. £55.00
	U.S. $175.00
U.K.:	£ 55.00
U.S.:	$110.00
Can.:	$145.00

MAGIC CASTLE

Designer:	Alastair MacIntosh
Type:	Weight – Pyramidal, multifaceted
Issued:	1999 in a limited edition of 200
Status:	Closed at No. 91
Series:	Alastair MacIntosh Collection
O.I.P.:	U.K. £195.00
	U.S. $595.00
U.K.:	£200.00
U.S.:	$400.00
Can.:	$525.00

MAGIC MOMENT

Designer:	Colin Terris
Type:	Weight – Spherical
Issued:	1999 in a limited edition of 50
Status:	Closed at No. 44
Series:	Limited – Modern Design
O.I.P.:	U.K. £350.00
	U.S. $995.00
U.K.:	£350.00
U.S.:	$700.00
Can.:	$900.00

MAN O' WAR

Designer:	Colin Terris
Type:	Weight – Spherical
Issued:	1999 in a limited edition of 750
Status:	Closed at No. 355
O.I.P.:	U.K. £65.00
	U.S. $225.00
U.K.:	£350.00
U.S.:	$700.00
Can.:	$900.00

METROPOLIS '99

Designer:	Philip Chaplain
Type:	Weight – Domed
Colour:	Blue and purple
Issued:	1999 in a limited edition of 250
Status:	Fully subscribed
Series:	Limited – Modern Design
O.I.P.:	U.K. £80.00
	U.S. $275.00
U.K.:	£ 80.00
U.S.:	$160.00
Can.:	$210.00

Note: This paperweight was introduced in the U.S. in 1997.

MIDNIGHT MYSTERY

Designer: Colin Terris
Type: Weight – Spherical
Issued: 1999 in a limited edition of 75
Status: Fully subscribed
Series: Premier Stockist/ Dealer Paperweight Collection
O.I.P.: U.K. £250.00
U.S. $775.00

U.K.: £250.00
U.S.: $500.00
Can.: $650.00

MILLENNIUM 2000

Designer: Helen MacDonald
Type: Weight – Spherical
Colour: 1. Cobalt
2. Heather
3. Emerald
4. Gold
5. Kingfisher
Issued: 1999
Status: Closed
Series: Millennium Collection, Unlimited
O.I.P.: U.K. £40.00
U.S. $130.00

U.K.: £ 40.00
U.S.: $ 80.00
Can.: $100.00

MILLENNIUM AWAKENING

Designer: Helen MacDonald
Type: Weight – Spherical
Issued: 1999 in a limited edition of 750
Status: Closed at No. 546
Series: Millennium Collection
O.I.P.: U.K. £70.00
U.S. $225.00

U.K.: £ 70.00
U.S.: $140.00
Can.: $180.00

MILLENNIUM BLOSSOM

Designer: Helen MacDonald
Type: Weight – Teardrop
Issued: 1999 in a limited edition of 250
Status: Closed at No. 184
Series: Millennium Collection
O.I.P.: U.K. £140.00
U.S. $450.00

U.K.: £140.00
U.S.: $280.00
Can.: $360.00

MILLENNIUM CARNIVAL

Designer: Colin Terris
Type: Weight – Spherical
Size: Magnum
Cane: 2000
Issued: 1999
Status: Closed
Series: Millennium Collection, Unlimited
O.I.P.: U.K. £60.00
U.S. $195.00

U.K.: £ 60.00
U.S.: $120.00
Can.: $155.00

MILLENNIUM COUNTDOWN

Designer: Colin Terris
Type: Weight – Spherical
Issued: 1999 in a limited edition of 750
Status: Closed at No. 726
Series: Millennium Collection
O.I.P.: U.K. £55.00
U.S. $175.00

U.K.: £ 55.00
U.S.: $110.00
Can.: $145.00

MILLENNIUM CROSS

Designer: Colin Terris
Type: Weight – Domed
Issued: 1999 in a limited edition of 150
Status: Fully subscribed
Series: Millennium Collection II
O.I.P.: £120.00

U.K.: £ 55.00
U.S.: $110.00
Can.: $145.00

MILLENNIUM DANCER

Designer: Colin Terris
Type: Weight – Spherical
Issued: 1999 in a limited edition of 650
Status: Fully subscribed
Series: Millennium Collection
O.I.P.: £60.00

U.K.: £ 60.00
U.S.: $120.00
Can.: $155.00

MILLENNIUM DOVES

Designer: Helen MacDonald
Type: Weight – Spherical
Size: Medium
Issued: 1999
Status: Closed
Series: Millennium
           Collection, Unlimited
O.I.P.:   U.K. £27.00
           U.S. $87.50
U.K.:   £30.00
U.S.: $60.00
Can.: $80.00

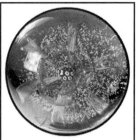

MILLENNIUM FANTASY

Designer: Colin Terris
Type: Weight – Spherical
Cane: 2000
Issued: 1999 in a limited
           edition of 500
Status: Closed
Series: Millennium
           Collection
O.I.P.:   U.K. £90.00
           U.S. $295.00
U.K.:   £ 90.00
U.S.: $180.00
Can.: $235.00

MILLENNIUM FIESTA

Designer: Colin Terris
Type: Weight – Domed
Issued: 1999 in a limited
           edition of 650
Status: Fully subscribed
Series: Millennium
           Collection
O.I.P.:   U.K. £75.00
           U.S. $450.00
U.K.:   £ 75.00
U.S.: $150.00
Can.: $200.00

MILLENNIUM GLOBE

Designer: Colin Terris
Type: Weight – Spherical
Colour: 1. Blue
           2. Red
Issued: 1999
Status: Closed
Series: Millennium
           Collection, Unlimited
O.I.P.:   U.K. £45.00
           U.S. $145.00
U.K.:   £ 45.00
U.S.: $ 90.00
Can.: $115.00

MILLENNIUM GLORY

Designer: Helen MacDonald
Type: Weight – Spherical
Issued: 1999 in a limited
           edition of 500
Status: Closed at No. 398
Series: Millennium
           Collection II
O.I.P.:   U.K. £85.00
           U.S. $265.00
U.K.:   £ 45.00
U.S.: $ 90.00
Can.: $115.00

MILLENNIUM JEWEL

Designer: Colin Terris
Type: Weight – Domed,
           multifaceted
Issued: 1999 in a limited
           edition of 100
Status: Fully subscribed
Series: Millennium
           Collection
O.I.P.:   U.K. £200.00
           U.S. $650.00
U.K.:   £200.00
U.S.: $400.00
Can.: $525.00

MILLENNIUM KATHERINE WHEEL

Designer: Colin Terris
Type: Weight – Domed
Cane: Whitefriars
Issued: 1999 in a limited
           edition of 150
Status: Fully subscribed
Series: Millennium
           Collection II
O.I.P.:   U.K. £200.00
U.K.:   £200.00
U.S.: $400.00
Can.: $525.00

MILLENNIUM PEBBLE

Designer: Colin Terris
Type: Weight – Sculptural
Size: Miniature
Issued: 1999
Status: Closed
Series: Millennium
           Collection, Unlimited
O.I.P.:   U.K.£12.50
           U.S. $39.50
U.K.:   £15.00
U.S.: $30.00
Can.: $40.00

Photograph not
available
at press time

Photograph not
available
at press time

MILLENNIUM RENAISSANCE

Designer:	Colin Terris
Type:	Weight – Domed
Issued:	1999 in a limited edition of 75
Status:	Fully subscribed
Series:	Millennium Collection
O.I.P.:	Unknown
U.K.:	Price not
U.S.:	available at
Can.:	press time

MILLENNIUM SANDS OF TIME

Designer:	Colin Terris
Type:	Weight – Hourglass
Issued:	1999 in a limited edition of 200
Status:	Fully subscribed
Series:	Millennium Collection
O.I.P.:	U.K.£99.00
	U.S. $295.00
U.K.:	£100.00
U.S.:	$200.00
Can.:	$260.00

MILLENNIUM SNOWFLAKE

Designer:	Colin Terris
Type:	Weight – Spherical
Cane:	Whitefriars
Issued:	1999 in a limited edition of 500
Status:	Closed at No. 492
Series:	Millennium Collection II
O.I.P.:	U.K.£95.00
	U.S. $310.00
U.K.:	£ 95.00
U.S.:	$190.00
Can.:	$250.00

MILLENNIUM STARBURST

Designer:	Colin Terris
Type:	Weight – Domed
Issued:	1999 in a limited edition of 650
Status:	Closed at No. 529
Series:	Millennium Collection
O.I.P.:	U.K. £75.00
	U.S. $240.00
U.K.:	£ 45.00
U.S.:	$ 90.00
Can.:	$120.00

MILLENNIUM TEDDY

Designer:	W. Bain
Type:	Weight – Spherical
Size:	Medium
Colour:	1. Blue
	2. Pink
Issued:	1999
Status:	Closed
Series:	Millennium Collection, Unlimited
O.I.P.:	U.K. £27.00
	U.S. $87.50
U.K.:	£30.00
U.S.:	$60.00
Can.:	$80.00

MILLENNIUM VISION

Designer:	Colin Terris
Type:	Weight – Spherical, with black glass foot
Issued:	1999 in a limited edition of 1,668
Status:	Fully subscribed
Series:	Collectors' Society
O.I.P.:	U.K. £85.00
	U.S. $225.00
U.K.:	£ 85.00
U.S.:	$170.00
Can.:	$225.00

MILLENNIUM VOYAGER

Designer:	Colin Terris
Type:	Weight – Spherical
Size:	Magnum
Issued:	1999 in a limited edition of 250
Status:	Fully subscribed
Series:	Millennium Collection
O.I.P.:	U.K. £150.00
	U.S. $475.00
U.K.:	£150.00
U.S.:	$300.00
Can.:	$400.00

NEMO'S KINGDOM

Designer:	Philip Chaplain
Type:	Weight – Domed
Issued:	1999 in a limited edition of 500
Status:	Closed at No. 340
Series:	Limited – Modern Design
O.I.P.:	U.K. £90.00
	U.S. $295.00
U.K.:	£ 90.00
U.S.:	$180.00
Can.:	$235.00

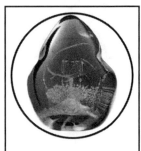

NORDIC CASTLE
Designer: Colin Terris
Type: Weight – Sculptural
Issued: 1999 in a limited edition of 350
Status: Closed at No. 190
Series: Limited – Modern Design
O.I.P.: U.K. £99.00
U.S. $295.00

U.K.: £100.00
U.S.: $200.00
Can.: $260.00

ON REFLECTION
Designer: Helen MacDonald
Type: Weight – Domed
Issued: 1999 in a limited edition of 150
Status: Closed at No. 60
O.I.P.: U.K. £215.00
U.S. $625.00

U.K.: £100.00
U.S.: $200.00
Can.: $260.00

ONE FINE DAY
Designer: Philip Chaplain
Type: Weight – Domed
Issued: 1999 in a limited edition of 100
Status: Closed at No. 46
Series: Limited – Modern Design
O.I.P.: U.K. £325.00
U.S. $875.00

U.K.: £325.00
U.S.: $650.00
Can.: $850.00

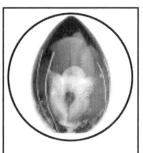

ORCHID
Style Two
Designer: Colin Terris
Type: Weight – Domed
Issued: 1999
Status: Closed
Series: Collectable Eggs – Unlimited
O.I.P.: U.K. £49.00
U.S. $165.00

U.K.: £ 50.00
U.S.: $100.00
Can.: $130.00

ORIENTAL DREAM
Designer: Helen MacDonald
Type: Weight – Teardrop
Issued: 1999 in a limited edition of 125
Status: Closed at No. 78
Series: Limited – Modern Design
O.I.P.: U.K. £285.00
U.S. $875.00

U.K.: £285.00
U.S.: $575.00
Can.: $750.00

OVER THE HILLS
Designer: Alastair MacIntosh
Type: Weight – Spherical
Size: Magnum
Issued: 1999 in a limited edition of 250
Status: Closed at No. 86
Series: Alastair MacIntosh Collection
O.I.P.: U.K. £175.00
U.S. $550.00

U.K.: £175.00
U.S.: $350.00
Can.: $450.00

OZONE
Designer: Alastair MacIntosh
Type: Weight – Spherical
Colour: 1. Amethyst
2. Cobalt
3. Kingfisher
Issued: 1999
Status: Closed
Series: Unlimited – Modern Design
O.I.P.: U.K. £30.00
U.S. $95.00

U.K.: £30.00
U.S.: $60.00
Can.: $80.00

PEEPING TOM
Designer: Helen MacDonald
Type: Weight – Domed
Issued: 1999 in a limited edition of 100
Status: Closed at No. 79
Series: Limited – Modern Design
O.I.P.: U.K. £325.00
U.S. $895.00

U.K.: £325.00
U.S.: $650.00
Can.: $850.00

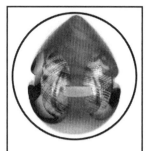

PERPLEXITY
Designer: Alastair MacIntosh
Type: Weight – Domed
Issued: 1999 in a limited edition of 50
Status: Closed at No. 47
Series: Alastair MacIntosh Collection
O.I.P.: U.K. £275.00
U.S. $865.00
U.K.: £275.00
U.S.: $550.00
Can.: $725.00

PINK DAHLIA
Designer: Helen MacDonald
Type: Weight – Spherical
Issued: 1999
Status: Closed
Series: Unlimited – Modern Design
O.I.P.: U.K. £35.00
U.S. $82.00
U.K.: £275.00
U.S.: $550.00
Can.: $725.00

POLYNESIAN PARADISE
Designer: Helen MacDonald
Type: Weight – Spherical
Size: Magnum
Issued: 1999 in a limited edition of 30
Status: Fully subscribed
Series: Limited – Modern Design
O.I.P.: U.K. £650.00
U.S. $1995.00
U.K.: £ 650.00
U.S.: $1,300.00
Can.: $1,700.00

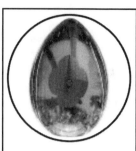

POPPY
Designer: Colin Terris
Type: Weight – Domed
Issued: 1999
Status: Closed
Series: Collectable Eggs – Unlimited
O.I.P.: U.K. £49.00
U.S. $165.00
U.K.: £ 50.00
U.S.: $100.00
Can.: $130.00

POWER SOURCE
Designer: Margot Thomson
Type: Weight – Domed
Issued: 1999 in a limited edition of 500
Status: Closed at No. 164
O.I.P.: U.K. £85.00
U.S. $250.00
U.K.: £ 85.00
U.S.: $170.00
Can.: $225.00

PROPULSION
Designer: Alastair MacIntosh
Type: Weight – Triple faceted
Issued: 1999 in a limited edition of 350
Status: Closed at No. 42
Series: Alastair MacIntosh Collection
O.I.P.: U.K. £99.00
U.S. $310.00
U.K.: £100.00
U.S.: $200.00
Can.: $260.00

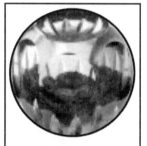

RADIANT ROSE
Designer: Colin Terris
Type: Weight – Spherical
Issued: 1999 in a limited edition of 75
Status: Closed at No. 44
Series: Colin Terris Rose Collection
O.I.P.: U.K. £250.00
U.S. $775.00
U.K.: £250.00
U.S.: $500.00
Can.: $650.00

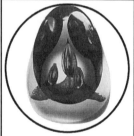

RED ALERT
Designer: Alastair MacIntosh
Type: Weight – Domed
Issued: 1999 in a limited edition of 250
Status: Closed at No. 91
O.I.P.: U.K. £150.00
U.S. $425.00
U.K.: £150.00
U.S.: $300.00
Can.: $400.00

RED CARNATION
Style One

Designer:	Helen MacDonald
Type:	Weight – Spherical
Issued:	1999
Status:	Closed
Series:	Unlimited – Modern Design
O.I.P.:	U.K. £35.00
	U.S. $82.50
U.K.:	£250.00
U.S.:	$500.00
Can.:	$650.00

RED POPPY

Designer:	Helen MacDonald
Type:	Weight – Spherical
Issued:	1999
Status:	Closed
Series:	Floral Charms, Unlimited
O.I.P.:	U.K. £35.00
	U.S. $82.50
U.K.:	£ 40.00
U.S.:	$ 80.00
Can.:	$100.00

SALTIRE

Designer:	Helen MacDonald
Type:	Weight – Spherical
Issued:	1999
Status:	Closed
Series:	Unlimited – Modern Design
O.I.P.:	U.K. £50.00
	U.S. $120.00
U.K.:	£250.00
U.S.:	$500.00
Can.:	$650.00

SARGASSO

Designer:	Philip Chaplain
Type:	Weight – Domed
Issued:	1999 in a limited edition of 500
Status:	Closed at No. 154
O.I.P.:	U.K. £85.00
	U.S. $250.00
U.K.:	£250.00
U.S.:	$500.00
Can.:	$650.00

SHAMAN

Designer:	Colin Terris
Type:	Weight – Spherical
Issued:	1999 in a limited edition of 650
Status:	Closed at No. 231
Series:	Limited – Modern Design
O.I.P.:	U.K. £85.00
	U.S. $265.00
U.K.:	£ 85.00
U.S.:	$170.00
Can.:	$225.00

SHEER INDULGENCE '99

Designer:	Colin Terris
Type:	Weight – Spherical
Colour:	Ruby and violet
Issued:	1999 in a limited edition of 75
Status:	Fully subscribed
Series:	Limited – Modern Design
O.I.P.:	U.K. £250.00
	U.S. $795.00
U.K.:	£250.00
U.S.:	$500.00
Can.:	$650.00

Note: This paperweight was introduced in the U.S. in 1996.

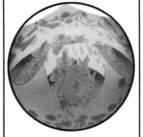

SILVER LACE

Designer:	Helen MacDonald
Type:	Weight – Spherical, Facets
Issued:	1999 in a limited edition of 150
Status:	Closed at No. 52
O.I.P.:	U.K. £195.00
	U.S. $575.00
U.K.:	£ 85.00
U.S.:	$170.00
Can.:	$225.00

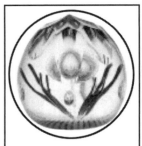

SILVER ORB

Designer:	Philip Chaplain
Type:	Weight – Spherical
Issued:	1999 in a limited edition of 75
Status:	Fully subscribed
Series:	Limited – Modern Design
O.I.P.:	U.K. £250.00
	U.S. $795.00
U.K.:	£250.00
U.S.:	$500.00
Can.:	$650.00

Note: This paperweight was introduced in the U.S. in 1996.

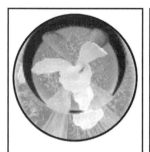

SNOWFIRE ORCHID '99

Designer: Helen MacDonald
Type: Weight – Spherical
Colour: White, green, blue
Issued: 1999 in a limited
edition of 500
Status: Fully subscribed
Series: Limited – Modern
Design
O.I.P.: U.K. £95.00
U.S. $295.00

U.K.: £ 95.00
U.S.: $190.00
Can.: $250.00

Note: This paperweight was
introduced in the U.S.
in 1996.

SOLEMNITY

Designer: Alastair MacIntosh
Type: Weight – Domed
Issued: 1999 in a limited
edition of 75
Status: Closed at No. 45
Series: Alastair MacIntosh
Collection
O.I.P.: U.K. £250.00
U.S. $785.00

U.K.: £250.00
U.S.: $500.00
Can.: $650.00

SPINDRIFT '99

Designer: Colin Terris
Stuart Cumming
Type: Weight – Spherical
Issued: 1999 in a limited
edition of 1,000
Status: Fully subscribed
Series: Limited – Modern
Design
O.I.P.: U.K. £40.00
U.S. $140.00

U.K.: £ 40.00
U.S.: $ 80.00
Can.: $100.00

SPRING MELODY
Style Two

Designer: Helen MacDonald
Type: Weight – Drawn
teardrop
Issued: 1999 in a limited
edition of 250
Status: Closed at No. 109
Series: Limited – Modern
Design
O.I.P.: U.K. £150.00
U.S. $425.00

U.K.: £150.00
U.S.: $300.00
Can.: $400.00

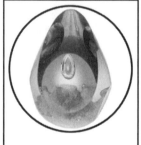

STATUS QUO

Designer: Alastair MacIntosh
Type: Weight – Domed
Issued: 1999 in a limited
edition of 100
Status: Closed at No. 74
Series: Premier Stockist/
Premier Dealer
Paperweight
Collection
O.I.P.: U.K. £225.00
U.S. $675.00

U.K.: £225.00
U.S.: $450.00
Can.: $600.00

STRAWBERRY SURPRISE

Designer: Alastair MacIntosh
Type: Weight – Spherical
Issued: 1999 in a limited
edition of 750
Status: Closed at No. 87
Series: Limited – Modern
Design
O.I.P.: U.K. £65.00
U.S. $195.00

U.K.: £ 65.00
U.S.: $130.00
Can.: $170.00

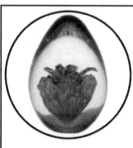

SUMATRA

Designer: Philip Chaplain
Type: Weight – Domed
Issued: 1999 in a limited
edition of 250
Status: Closed at No. 93
Series: Collectable Eggs –
Limited
O.I.P.: U.K. £99.00
U.S. $310.00

U.K.: £100.00
U.S.: $200.00
Can.: $260.00

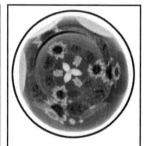

SUNFLOWER CELEBRATION

Designer: Rosette Fleming
Type: Weight – Spherical,
facets
Issued: 1999 in a limited
edition of 50
Status: Closed at No. 23
Series: Whitefriars Collection
O.I.P.: U.K. £145.00
U.S. $450.00

U.K.: £150.00
U.S.: $300.00
Can.: $400.00

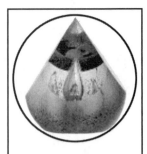

SWEET SURRENDER
Designer: Helen MacDonald
Type: Weight – Pyramid, facets
Issued: 1999 in a limited edition of 150
Status: Closed at No. 92
Series: Limited – Modern Design
O.I.P.: U.K. £195.00
U.S. $595.00

U.K.: £200.00
U.S.: $400.00
Can.: $525.00

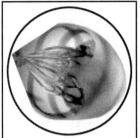

TIME MACHINE
Designer: Helen MacDonald
Type: Weight – Sculptural, ovoid
Issued: 1999 in a limited edition of 150
Status: Closed at No. 102
Series: Limited – Modern Design
O.I.P.: U.K. £225.00
U.S. $695.00

U.K.: £225.00
U.S.: $450.00
Can.: $600.00

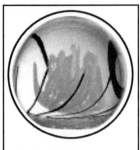

TOUCH OF FROST
Designer: Philip Chaplain
Type: Weight – Spherical
Issued: 1999 in a limited edition of 750
Status: Closed at No. 239
Series: Limited – Modern Design
O.I.P.: U.K. £75.00
U.S. $210.00

U.K.: £ 75.00
U.S.: $150.00
Can.: $200.00

TOURNAMENT
Designer: Colin Terris
Type: Weight – Domed
Issued: 1999 in a limited edition of 125
Status: Closed at No. 87
Series: Limited – Modern Design
O.I.P.: U.K. £250.00
U.S. $775.00

U.K.: £250.00
U.S.: $500.00
Can.: $650.00

TOWARDS THE MILLENNIUM
Designer: Colin Terris
Type: Weight – Domed
Issued: 1999 in a limited edition of 350
Status: Closed at No. 320
Series: Millennium Collection II
O.I.P.: U.K. £95.00
U.S. $295.00

U.K.: £250.00
U.S.: $500.00
Can.: $650.00

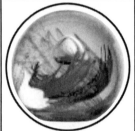

TRIBAL DANCE
Designer: Colin Terris
Type: Weight – Spherical
Issued: 1999 in a limited edition of 750
Status: Closed at No. 369
Series: Limited – Modern Design
O.I.P.: U.K. £70.00
U.S. $225.00

U.K.: £ 70.00
U.S.: $140.00
Can.: $200.00

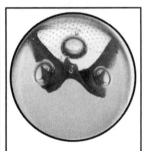

TRIPLE CROWN
Designer: Alastair MacIntosh
Type: Weight – Spherical
Colour: 1. Amethyst
2. Cobalt
3. Kingfisher
Issued: 1999
Status: Closed
Series: Unlimited - Modern Design
O.I.P.: U.K. £22.50
U.S. $54.50

U.K.: £225.00
U.S.: $450.00
Can.: $575.00

TROPICAL DELIGHT '99
Designer: Colin Terris
Type: Weight – Spherical
Colour: Blue, green, red
Issued: 1999 in a limited edition of 75
Status: Fully subscribed
Series: Limited – Modern Design
O.I.P.: U.K. £250.00
U.S. $795.50

U.K.: £250.00
U.S.: $500.00
Can.: $650.00

Note: This paperweight was introduced in the U.S. in 1996.

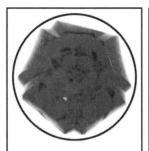

TRUE ROMANCE
Designer: Allan Scott
Type: Weight – Spherical,
         faceted
Issued: 1999 in a limited
         edition of 50
Status: Closed at No. 28
Series: Traditional Collection
         Nature Study
O.I.P.: U.K. £295.00
         U.S. $895.00

U.K.:   £300.00
U.S.: $600.00
Can.: $775.00

TURKISH DELIGHT
Designer: Colin Terris
Type: Weight – Domed
Issued: 1999 in a limited
         edition of 50
Status: Fully subscribed
Series: Limited – Modern
         Design
O.I.P.: U.K. £350.00
         U.S. $895.00

U.K.:   £350.00
U.S.: $700.00
Can.: $900.00

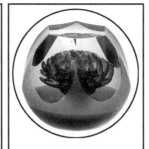

TWILIGHT ROSE
Designer: Colin Terris
Type: Weight – Spherical
Issued: 1999 in a limited
         edition of 75
Status: Closed at No. 44
Series: Colin Terris Rose
         Collection
O.I.P.: U.K. £250.00
         U.S. $775.00

U.K.:   £250.00
U.S.: $500.00
Can.: $650.00

TWO OF A KIND
Designer: Rosette Fleming
Type: Weight – Spherical
Issued: 1999 in a limited
         edition of 50
Status: Closed at No. 20
Series: Whitefriars Collection
O.I.P.: U.K. £155.00
         U.S. $475.00

U.K.:   £150.00
U.S.: $300.00
Can.: $400.00

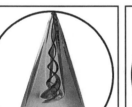

UNITY
Designer: Helen MacDonald
Type: Weight – Drawn
         teardrop
Issued: 1999 in a limited
         edition of 250
Status: Fully subscribed
Series: Unknown
O.I.P.: U.K. £150.00
         U.S. $425.00

U.K.:   £150.00
U.S.: $300.00
Can.: $400.00

VELOCITY
Designer: Helen MacDonald
Type: Weight – Faceted
Issued: 1999 in a limited
         edition of 250
Status: Closed at No. 47
Series: Unknown
O.I.P.: U.K. £150.00
         U.S. $425.00

U.K.:   £150.00
U.S.: $300.00
Can.: $400.00

VICTORIAN BLOSSOM
Designer: Rosette Fleming
Type: Weight – Spherical
Issued: 1999 in a limited
         edition of 50
Status: Fully subscribed
Series: Whitefriars Collection
O.I.P.: U.K. £99.00
         U.S. $325.00

U.K.:   £100.00
U.S.: $200.00
Can.: $260.00

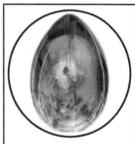

VIOLET
Designer: Colin Terris
Type: Weight – Domed
Issued: 1999
Status: Closed
Series: Collectable Eggs –
         Unlimited
O.I.P.: U.K. £49.00
         U.S. $165.00

U.K.:   £ 50.00
U.S.: $100.00
Can.: $130.00

WHITE ASTER
Designer:	Helen MacDonald
Type:	Weight – Spherical
Issued:	1999
Status:	Closed
Series:	Unlimited – Modern Design
O.I.P.:	U.K. £35.00
	U.S. $82.50
U.K.:	£35.00
U.S.:	$70.00
Can.:	$90.00

WHITE ROSE
Style Two
Designer:	Helen MacDonald
Type:	Weight – Spherical
Issued:	1999
Status:	Closed
Series:	Floral Charms – Unlimited
O.I.P.:	U.K. £35.00
	U.S. $82.50
U.K.:	£ 40.00
U.S.:	$ 80.00
Can.:	$100.00

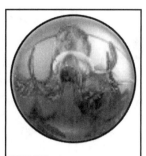

WISDOM
Designer:	Philip Chaplain
Type:	Weight – Spherical
Issued:	1999 in a limited edition of 750
Status:	Closed at No. 299
Series:	Limited – Modern Design
O.I.P.:	U.K. £75.00
	U.S. $225.00
U.K.:	£ 75.00
U.S.:	$150.00
Can.:	$200.00

WISPS
Designer:	Alastair MacIntosh
Type:	Weight – Spherical
Colour:	1. Blue
	2. Gold
	3. Green
	4. Pink
	5. Turquoise
Issued:	1999
Status:	Closed
Series:	Unlimited – Modern Design
O.I.P.:	U.K. £12.00
	U.S. $29.50
U.K.:	£15.00
U.S.:	$30.00
Can.:	$40.00

YELLOW CARNATION
Designer:	Helen MacDonald
Type:	Weight – Spherical
Issued:	1999
Status:	Closed
Series:	Floral Charms – Unlimited
O.I.P.:	U.K. £35.00
	U.S. $82.50
U.K.:	£ 40.00
U.S.:	$ 80.00
Can.:	$100.00

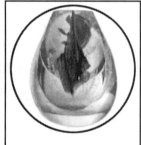

ZANZIBAR
Designer:	Alan Scrimgeour
Type:	Weight – Domed
Issued:	1999 in a limited edition of 350
Status:	Closed at No. 309
Series:	Limited – Modern Design
O.I.P.:	U.K. £99.00
	U.S. $295.00
U.K.:	£100.00
U.S.:	$200.00
Can.:	$260.00

ISSUES OF 2000

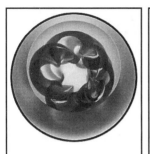

ALTERNATION
Designer: Alastair MacIntosh
Type: Weight – Spherical
Issued: 2000 in a limited
           edition of 750
Status: Closed at No. 282
Series: Limited editions
O.I.P.:   U.K. £75.00
           U.S. $230.00

U.K.:   £ 75.00
U.S.: $150.00
Can.: $200.00

ANGELINA
Designer: Alastair MacIntosh
Type: Weight – Domed
Issued: 2000 in a limited
           edition of 650
Status: Closed at No. 478
Series: Limited editions
O.I.P.:   U.K. £80.00
           U.S. $250.00

U.K.:   £ 80.00
U.S.: $160.00
Can.: $210.00

APRIL – DAFFODIL
Designer: Helen MacDonald
Type: Weight – Spherical
Issued: 2000
Status: Closed
Series: The Floral Year –
           Unlimited
O.I.P.:   U.K. £60.00
           U.S. $147.50

U.K.:   £ 60.00
U.S.: $120.00
Can.: $160.00

AUGUST – CARNATION
Designer: Helen MacDonald
Type: Weight – Cone
Issued: 2000
Status: Closed
Series: The Floral Year –
           Unlimited
O.I.P.:   U.K. £60.00
           U.S. $147.50

U.K.:   £ 60.00
U.S.: $120.00
Can.: $160.00

AUTUMN ILLUSIONS – MAPLE
Designer: Helen MacDonald
Type: Weight – Pyramidal
Issued: 2000 in a limited
           edition of 650
Status: Fully subscribed
Series: Limited Designs
O.I.P.:   U.K. £85.00
           U.S. $250.00

U.K.:   £ 85.00
U.S.: $170.00
Can.: $225.00

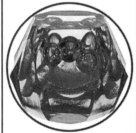

BALLOON RACE
Designer: Alastair MacIntosh
Type: Weight – Facetted
Issued: 2000 in a limited
           edition of 75
Status: Closed at No. 51
Series: Limited editions
O.I.P.:   U.K. £275.00
           U.S. $825.00

U.K.:   £275.00
U.S.: $550.00
Can.: $725.00

BETHLEHEM
Designer: Helen MacDonald
Type: Weight – Spherical
Issued: 2000 in a limited
           edition of 75
Status: Fully subscribed
Series: Helen MacDonald
           Collection
O.I.P.:   U.K. £225.00
           U.S. $695.00

U.K.:   £225.00
U.S.: $450.00
Can.: $575.00

BLUE LOTUS
Designer: Helen MacDonald
Type: Weight – Spherical,
           faceted
Issued: 2000 in a limited
           edition of 150
Status: Closed at No. 122
Series: Helen MacDonald
           Collection
O.I.P.:   U.K. £200.00
           U.S. $595.00

U.K.:   £200.00
U.S.: $400.00
Can.: $525.00

CARESS
Designer: Alastair MacIntosh
Type: Weight – Domed
Issued: 2000
Status: Closed
Series: Unlimited – Modern Design
O.I.P.: U.K. £30.00
U.S. $75.00

U.K.: £30.00
U.S.: $60.00
Can.: $80.00

CATACLYSM
Designer: Alastair MacIntosh
Type: Weight – Spherical
Issued: 2000 in a limited edition of 750
Status: Closed at No. 695
Series: Limited editions
O.I.P.: U.K. £65.00
U.S. $195.00

U.K.: £ 65.00
U.S.: $130.00
Can.: $170.00

CENTENARY YEAR CELEBRATION
Designer: Colin Terris
Type: Weight – Spherical
Issued: 2000 in a limited edition of 500
Status: Closed
Series: HM Queen Elizabeth The Queen Mother Centenary Collection
O.I.P.: U.K. £45.00

U.K.: £ 45.00
U.S.: $ 90.00
Can.: $120.00

CHERISH
Designer: Helen MacDonald
Type: Weight – Spherical, faceted
Issued: 2000 in a limited edition of 250
Status: Closed at No. 183
Series: l imited editions
O.I.P.: U.K. £150.00
U.S. $450.00

U.K.: £150.00
U.S.: $300.00
Can.: $400.00

COSMIC FOUNTAIN
Designer: Helen MacDonald
Type: Weight – Spherical
Issued: 2000
Status: Closed
Series: Unlimited – Modern Design
O.I.P.: U.K. £33.00
U.S. $82.50

U.K.: £35.00
U.S.: $70.00
Can.: $90.00

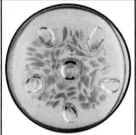

CRYSTAL CAROUSEL
Designer: Colin Terris
Type: Weight – Low Dome
Colour: 1. Blue
2. Pink
Issued: 2000
Status: Closed
Series: Unlimited – Modern Design
O.I.P.: U.K. £30.00
U.S. $75.00

U.K.: £30.00
U.S.: $60.00
Can.: $80.00

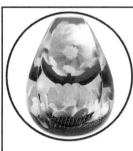

DAISY DAISY
Designer: Helen MacDonald
Type: Weight – Domed
Issued: 2000 in a limited edition of 350
Status: Fully subscribed
Series: Helen MacDonald Collection
O.I.P.: U.K. £95.00
U.S. $295.00

U.K.: £ 95.00
U.S.: $190.00
Can.: $250.00

DECEMBER – CHRISTMAS ROSE
Designer: Helen MacDonald
Type: Weight – Spherical
Issued: 2000
Status: Closed
Series: The Floral Year – Unlimited
O.I.P.: U.K. £60.00
U.S. $147.50

U.K.: £ 60.00
U.S.: $120.00
Can.: $160.00

DOUBLE STARBURST

Designer: Colin Terris
Type: Weight – Domed
Issued: 2000 in a limited
edition of 150
Status: Fully subscribed
Series: Limited editions
O.I.P.: U.K. £175.00
U.S. $525.00

U.K.: £175.00
U.S.: $350.00
Can.: $450.00

DREAM LOVERS

Designer: Helen MacDonald
Type: Weight – Spherical
Issued: 2000 in a limited
edition of 75
Status: Fully subscribed
Series: Limited Designs
O.I.P.: U.K. £250.00
U.S. $750.00

U.K.: £250.00
U.S.: $500.00
Can.: $650.00

ELIZABETH OF GLAMIS

Designer: Colin Terris
Type: Weight – Spherical
Issued: 2000
Status: Closed
Series: Unlimited – Modern
Design
O.I.P.: U.K. £35.00

U.K.: £35.00
U.S.: $70.00
Can.: $90.00

EMERALD ROULETTE

Designer: Colin Terris
Type: Weight – Spherical
Issued: 2000 in a limited
edition of 750
Status: Closed at No. 214
Series: Limited – Modern
Design
O.I.P.: U.K. £75.00
U.S. $225.00

U.K.: £ 75.00
U.S.: $150.00
Can.: $200.00

FEBRUARY – CROCUS

Designer: Helen MacDonald
Type: Weight – Spherical
Issued: 2000
Status: Closed
Series: The Floral Year –
Unlimited
O.I.P.: U.K. £60.00
U.S. $147.50

U.K.: £ 60.00
U.S.: $120.00
Can.: $160.00

FESTIVE REFLECTIONS

Designer: Helen MacDonald
Type: Weight – Domed
Issued: 2000 in a limited
edition of 350
Status: Closed at No. 341
Series: Festive Collection
O.I.P.: U.K. £125.00
U.S. $375.00

U.K.: £125.00
U.S.: $250.00
Can.: $325.00

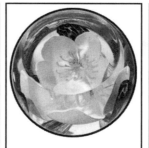

FESTIVE ROSE

Designer: Helen MacDonald
Type: Weight – Spherical
Issued: 2000 in a limited
edition of 750
Status: Closed at No. 610
Series: Festive Collection
O.I.P.: U.K. £80.00
U.S. $245.00

U.K.: £ 80.00
U.S.: $160.00
Can.: $210.00

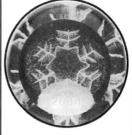

FESTIVE SNOWFLAKE 2000

Designer: Colin Terris
Type: Weight – Spherical
Issued: 2000
Status: Closed
Series: Festive Collection
O.I.P.: U.K. £39.00
U.S. $95.00

U.K.: £ 40.00
U.S.: $ 80.00
Can.: $100.00

FLORAL CELEBRATION

Designer:	Franco Toffolo
Type:	Weight – Magnum, faceted
Issued:	2000 in a limited edition of 25
Status:	Fully subscribed
Series:	HM Queen Elizabeth The Queen Mother Centenary Collection
O.I.P.:	U.K. £475.00
U.K.:	£ 475.00
U.S.:	$ 950.00
Can.:	$1,250.00

GRAVITATION

Designer:	Alastair MacIntosh
Type:	Weight – Spherical
Issued:	2000 in a limited edition of 750
Status:	Closed at No. 663
Series:	Unknown
O.I.P.:	U.K. £70.00 U.S. $225.00
U.K.:	£ 70.00
U.S.:	$140.00
Can.:	$180.00

GREETINGS EARTHLINGS

Designer:	Colin Terris
Type:	Weight – Spherical
Issued:	2000 in a limited edition of 750
Status:	Closed at No. 450
Series:	Unknown
O.I.P.:	U.K. £80.00 U.S. $250.00
U.K.:	£ 80.00
U.S.:	$160.00
Can.:	$210.00

HAWAIIAN HARMONY

Designer:	Helen MacDonald
Type:	Weight – Spherical
Size:	Magnum
Issued:	2000 in a limited edition of 30
Status:	Closed at No. 26
Series:	Helen MacDonald Collection
O.I.P.:	U.K. £500.00 U.S. $1,500.00
U.K.:	£ 500.00
U.S.:	$1,000.00
Can.:	$1,300.00

HOME COMING

Designer:	Alastair MacIntosh
Type:	Weight – Domed
Issued:	2000 in a limited edition of 350
Status:	Fully subscribed
Series:	Pictorial
O.I.P.:	U.K. £125.00 U.S. $375.00
U.K.:	£125.00
U.S.:	$250.00
Can.:	$325.00

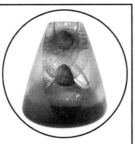

ICE BOUND

Designer:	Alastair MacIntosh
Type:	Weight – Domed
Issued:	2000 in a limited edition of 500
Status:	Closed at No. 326
Series:	Limited editions
O.I.P.:	U.K. £95.00 U.S. $295.00
U.K.:	£ 95.00
U.S.:	$180.00
Can.:	$235.00

ICE CASCADE

Designer:	Colin Terris
Type:	Weight – Spherical
Issued:	2000
Status:	Closed
Series:	Unlimited – Modern Design
O.I.P.:	U.K. £35.00 U.S. $87.50
U.K.:	£35.00
U.S.:	$70.00
Can.:	$90.00

JANUARY – SNOWDROP

Designer:	Helen MacDonald
Type:	Weight – Spherical
Issued:	2000
Status:	Closed
Series:	The Floral Year – Unlimited
O.I.P.:	U.K. £60.00 U.S. $147.50
U.K.:	£ 60.00
U.S.:	$120.00
Can.:	$155.00

JULY – PANSY
Designer: Helen MacDonald
Type: Weight – Spherical
Issued: 2000
Status: Closed
Series: The Floral Year – Unlimited
O.I.P.: U.K. £60.00
U.S. $147.50

U.K.: £ 60.00
U.S.: $120.00
Can.: $155.00

JUNE – ROSE
Designer: Helen MacDonald
Type: Weight – Spherical
Issued: 2000
Status: Closed
Series: The Floral Year – Unlimited
O.I.P.: U.K. £60.00
U.S. $147.50

U.K.: £ 60.00
U.S.: $120.00
Can.: $155.00

KRISHNA
Designer: Helen MacDonald
Type: Weight – Teardrop on black base
Issued: 2000 in a limited edition of 50
Status: Closed at No. 36
Series: Helen MacDonald Collection
O.I.P.: U.K. £600.00
U.S. $1,850.00

U.K.: £ 60.00
U.S.: $120.00
Can.: $155.00

LATTICINO CROWN
Designer: Colin Terris
Type: Weight – Spherical
Issued: 2000 in a limited edition of 200
Status: Fully subscribed
Series: HM Queen Elizabeth The Queen Mother Centenary Collection
O.I.P.: U.K. £99.00

U.K.: £100.00
U.S.: $200.00
Can.: $260.00

LIBERTÉ
Designer: Helen MacDonald
Type: Weight – Domed
Issued: 2000 in a limited edition of 150
Status: Closed at No. 82
Series: Limited – Modern Design
O.I.P.: U.K. £195.00
U.S. $595.00

U.K.: £200.00
U.S.: $400.00
Can.: $525.00

LOCOMOTION
Designer: Helen MacDonald
Type: Weight – Spherical
Issued: 2000 in a limited edition of 750
Status: Closed at No. 281
Series: Limited editions
O.I.P.: U.K. £60.00
U.S. $185.00

U.K.: £ 60.00
U.S.: $120.00
Can.: $155.00

MARCH – PRIMROSE
Designer: Helen MacDonald
Type: Weight – Spherical
Issued: 2000
Status: Closed
Series: The Floral Year – Unlimited
O.I.P.: U.K. £60.00
U.S. $147.50

U.K.: £ 60.00
U.S.: $120.00
Can.: $155.00

MAY – LILY OF THE VALLEY
Designer: Helen MacDonald
Type: Weight – Spherical
Issued: 2000
Status: Closed
Series: The Floral Year – Unlimited
O.I.P.: U.K. £60.00
U.S. $147.50

U.K.: £ 60.00
U.S.: $120.00
Can.: $155.00

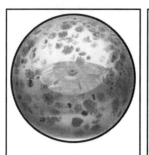

MILLEFIORI POOL

Designer: Colin Terris
Type: Weight – Spherical
Issued: 2000 in a limited
edition of 750
Status: Fully subscribed
Series: Monet Revisited
O.I.P.: U.K. £55.00
U.S. $175.00

U.K.: £ 55.00
U.S.: $110.00
Can.: $145.00

MILLENNIUM CAROUSEL

Designer: Colin Terris
Type: Weight – Domed
Issued: 2000
Status: Closed at No. 1,490
Series: Collectors' Society
Members 2000
O.I.P.: U.K. £95.00
U.S. $250.00

U.K.: £ 95.00
U.S.: $190.00
Can.: $250.00

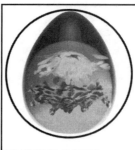

MILLENNIUM FANFARE

Designer: Caithness Design
Studios
Type: Weight – Domed
Issued: 2000
Status: Closed
Series: Collectors' Society
O.I.P.: U.K. £35.00
U.S. $95.00

U.K.: £ 95.00
U.S.: $190.00
Can.: $250.00

Note: Available at paperweight
promotions only.

MILLENNIUM MINIATURE

Designer: Caithness Design
Studios
Type: Low Dome
Issued: 2000
Status: Closed
Series: Collectors' Society
O.I.P.: Unknown

U.K.: £ 35.00
U.S.: $ 70.00
Can.: $100.00

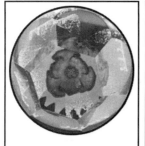

MILLENNIUM SPLENDOUR

Designer: Colin Terris
Type: Weight – Spherical
Issued: 2000 in a limited
edition of 75
Status: Fully subscribed
Series: Limited editions
O.I.P.: U.K. £250.00
U.S. $750.00

U.K.: £250.00
U.S.: $500.00
Can.: $650.00

MOODY BLUE

Designer: Helen MacDonald
Type: Weight – Teardrop
Issued: 2000 in a limited
edition of 250
Status: Closed at No. 156
Series: Helen MacDonald
Collection
O.I.P.: U.K. £150.00
U.S. $450.00

U.K.: £150.00
U.S.: $300.00
Can.: $400.00

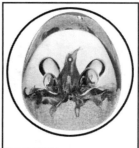

MOONBEAM
First Version

Designer: Colin Terris
Type: Weight – Domed
Colour: 1. Blue
2. Green
3. Pink
Issued: 2000
Status: Closed
Series: Unlimited – Modern
Design
O.I.P.: U.K. £20.00
U.S. $49.50

U.K.: £20.00
U.S.: $40.00
Can.: $50.00

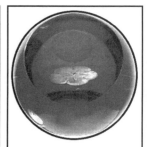

MOONLIGHT LILY

Designer: Colin Terris
Type: Weight – Spherical
Issued: 2000 in a limited
edition of 250
Status: Closed at No. 158
Series: Monet Revisited
O.I.P.: U.K. £150.00
U.S. $450.00

U.K.: £150.00
U.S.: $300.00
Can.: $400.00

MYSTIC TEMPLE
Designer: Colin Terris
Type: Weight – Drawn
teardrop
Issued: 2000 in a limited
edition of 250
Status: Closed at No. 227
Series: Limited editions
O.I.P.: U.K. £135.00
U.S. $425.00

U.K.: £135.00
U.S.: $270.00
Can.: $350.00

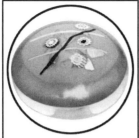

NOUGHTS and CROSSES
Designer: Colin Terris
Type: Weight – Low Dome
Colour: 1. Ebony black
2. Emerald green
3. Jaffa orange
4. Powder blue
5. Purple heather
6. Soft white
Issued: 2000
Status: Closed
Series: Unlimited – Modern
Design
O.I.P.: U.K. £19.50
U.S. $52.50

U.K.: £20.00
U.S.: $40.00
Can.: $50.00

NOVEMBER – VIOLET
Designer: Helen MacDonald
Type: Weight – Spherical
Issued: 2000
Status: Closed
Series: The Floral Year –
Unlimited
O.I.P.: U.K. £60.00
U.S. $147.50

U.K.: £ 60.00
U.S.: $120.00
Can.: $155.00

OBJET D'ART
Designer: Alastair MacIntosh
Type: Weight – Domed
Issued: 2000
Status: Closed
Series: Unlimited – Modern
Design
O.I.P.: U.K. £33.00
U.S. $82.50

U.K.: £35.00
U.S.: $70.00
Can.: $90.00

OCTOBER – ANEMONE
Designer: Helen MacDonald
Type: Weight – Spherical
Issued: 2000
Status: Closed
Series: The Floral Year –
Unlimited
O.I.P.: U.K. £60.00
U.S. $147.50

U.K.: £ 60.00
U.S.: $120.00
Can.: $155.00

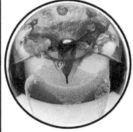

PARACHUTE
Designer: Alastair MacIntosh
Type: Weight – Spherical
Issued: 2000
Status: Closed
Series: Unlimited – Modern
Design
O.I.P.: U.K. £35.00
U.S. $87.50

U.K.: £39.95
U.S.: $90.00
Can.: –

PERSIAN PALACE
Designer: Helen MacDonald
Type: Weight – Teardrop,
faceted with base
Issued: 2000 in a limited
edition of 75
Status: Closed at No. 73
Series: Limited editions
O.I.P.: U.K. £295.00
U.S. $895.00

U.K.: £300.00
U.S.: $600.00
Can.: $775.00

PRIVATE VIEW
Designer: Colin Terris
Type: Weight – Domed
Issued: 2000 in a limited
edition of 500
Status: Closed at No. 179
Series: Limited editions
O.I.P.: U.K. £90.00
U.S. $275.00

U.K.: £ 90.00
U.S.: $180.00
Can.: $235.00

PROMISE

Designer: Helen MacDonald
Type: Weight – Domed, faceted
Issued: 2000 in a limited edition of 100
Status: Fully subscribed
Series: Limited Designs
O.I.P.: U.K. £225.00
        U.S. $675.00

U.K.: £225.00
U.S.: $450.00
Can.: $575.00

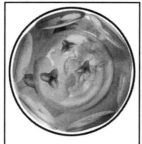

RAINBOW POOL

Designer: Colin Terris
Type: Weight – Spherical, facets
Issued: 2000 in a limited edition of 250
Status: Closed at No. 149
Series: Monet Revisited
O.I.P.: U.K. £160.00
        U.S. $495.00

U.K.: £175.00
U.S.: $350.00
Can.: $450.00

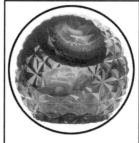

ROSE BASKET

Designer: Colin Terris
Type: Weight – Spherical, facets
Issued: 2000 in a limited edition of 100
Status: Fully subscribed
Series: HM Queen Elizabeth The Queen Mother Centenary Collection
O.I.P.: U.K. £185.00

U.K.: £185.00
U.S.: $370.00
Can.: $475.00

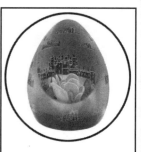

ROSE TAPESTRY

Designer: Colin Terris
Type: Weight – Domed
Issued: 2000 in a limited edition of 100
Status: Fully subscribed
Series: HM Queen Elizabeth The Queen Mother Centenary Collection
O.I.P.: U.K. £185.00

U.K.: £185.00
U.S.: $370.00
Can.: $475.00

ROYAL TRIBUTE

Designer: Colin Terris
Type: Weight – Spherical, facets
Issued: 2000 in a limited edition of 100
Status: Fully subscribed
Series: HM Queen Elizabeth The Queen Mother Centenary Collection
O.I.P.: U.K. £150.00

U.K.: £150.00
U.S.: $300.00
Can.: $400.00

SCARLET FANDANGO

Designer: Colin Terris
Type: Weight – Spherical
Issued: 2000 in a limited edition of 750
Status: Closed at No. 273
Series: Abstract Limited Editions
O.I.P.: U.K. £80.00
        U.S. $245.00

U.K.: £ 80.00
U.S.: $160.00
Can.: $210.00

SEPTEMBER – DAISY

Designer: Helen MacDonald
Type: Weight – Spherical
Issued: 2000
Status: Closed
Series: The Floral Year – Unlimited
O.I.P.: U.K. £60.00
        U.S. $147.50

U.K.: £ 60.00
U.S.: $120.00
Can.: $155.00

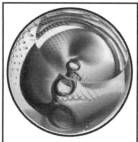

SLIPSTREAM

Designer: Helen MacDonald
Type: Weight – Spherical
Issued: 2000
Status: Closed
Series: Unlimited – Modern Design
O.I.P.: U.K. £35.00
        U.S. $87.50

U.K.: £35.00
U.S.: $70.00
Can.: $90.00

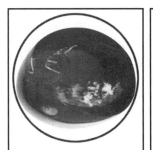

SOLAR WIND

Designer:	Alastair MacIntosh
Type:	Weight – Low Dome
Issued:	2000 in a limited edition of 350
Status:	Closed at No. 142
Series:	Limited editions
O.I.P.:	U.K. £130.00
	U.S. $395.00
U.K.:	£125.00
U.S.:	$250.00
Can.:	$325.00

SPACE TULIP

Designer:	Alastair MacIntosh
Type:	Weight – Domed
Issued:	2000 in a limited edition of 350
Status:	Closed at No. 215
Series:	Limited editions
O.I.P.:	U.K. £125.00
	U.S. $375.00
U.K.:	£125.00
U.S.:	$250.00
Can.:	$325.00

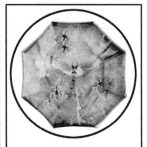

SUMMER FLIGHT

Designer:	Colin Terris
Type:	Weight – Facated Octagon
Issued:	2000 in a limited edition of 100
Status:	Closed at No. 96
Series:	Monet Revisited
O.I.P.:	U.K. £300.00
	U.S. $895.00
U.K.:	£300.00
U.S.:	$600.00
Can.:	$775.00

SUNSET POOL

Designer:	Colin Terris
Type:	Weight – Spherical
Issued:	2000 in a limited edition of 250
Status:	Closed at No. 155
Series:	Monet Revisited
O.I.P.:	U.K. £150.00
	U.S. $450.00
U.K.:	£150.00
U.S.:	$300.00
Can.:	$400.00

SWORD IN THE STONE

Designer:	Philip Chaplain
Type:	Weight – Domed
Issued:	2000 in a limited edition of 150
Status:	Closed at No. 150
Series:	Limited Designs
O.I.P.:	U.K. £195.00
	U.S. $575.00
U.K.:	£200.00
U.S.:	$400.00
Can.:	$525.00

TEDDY

Designer:	Helen MacDonald
Type:	Weight – Spherical
Issued:	2000
Status:	Closed
Series:	Unlimited – Modern Design
O.I.P.:	U.K. £30.00
	U.S. $75.00
U.K.:	£30.00
U.S.:	$60.00
Can.:	$80.00

TROPICAL RAIN

Designer:	Colin Terris
Type:	Weight – Domed
Issued:	2000
Status:	Closed
Series:	Unlimited – Modern Design
O.I.P.:	U.K. £30.00
	U.S. $75.00
U.K.:	£30.00
U.S.:	$60.00
Can.:	$80.00

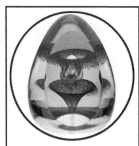

TRUE COLOURS

Designer:	Alastair MacIntosh
Type:	Weight – Domed
Issued:	2000 in a limited edition of 250
Status:	Closed at No. 562
Series:	Limited Designs
O.I.P.:	U.K. £150.00
	U.S. $225.00
U.K.:	£150.00
U.S.:	$300.00
Can.:	$400.00

TWILIGHT POOL
Designer: Colin Terris
Type: Weight – Spherical
Issued: 2000 in a limited edition of 350
Status: Closed at No. 135
Series: Monet Revisited
O.I.P.: U.K. £105.00
U.S. $325.00

U.K.: £100.00
U.S.: $200.00
Can.: $260.00

WATERCOLOURS
Designer: Colin Terris
Type: Weight – Spherical
Issued: 2000
Status: Closed
Series: Unlimited – Modern Design
O.I.P.: U.K. £30.00
U.S. $75.00

U.K.: £30.00
U.S.: $60.00
Can.: $80.00

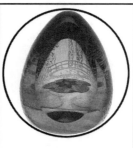

WATERLILY REFLECTION
Designer: Colin Terris
Type: Weight – Domed
Issued: 2000 in a limited edition of 150
Status: Fully subscribed
Series: Monet Revisited
O.I.P.: U.K. £200.00
U.S. $595.00

U.K.: £200.00
U.S.: $400.00
Can.: $525.00

WHEEL OF FORTUNE
Designer: Helen MacDonald
Type: Weight – Spherical
Colour: 1. Blue
2. Green
3. Red
Issued: 2000
Status: Closed
Series: Unlimited – Modern Design
O.I.P.: U.K. £30.00
U.S. $75.00

U.K.: £30.00
U.S.: $60.00
Can.: $80.00

WHITE TORNADO
Designer: Helen MacDonald
Type: Weight – Spherical
Issued: 2000 in a limited edition of 650
Status: Closed at No. 319
Series: Limited editions
O.I.P.: U.K. £80.00
U.S. $250.00

U.K.: £ 80.00
U.S.: $160.00
Can.: $210.00

WISE OWL
Designer: Alastair MacIntosh
Type: Weight – Spherical
Size: 1. Large
2. Medium
3. Small
Issued: 2000
Status: Active
Series: Graduations

	Large	Medium	Small
U.K.:	£ 49.00	44.00	34.00
U.S.:	$110.00	100.00	75.00
Can.:	–	–	–

WITH LOVE
Style One
Designer: Helen MacDonald
Type: Weight – Spherical
Size: Medium
Issued: 2000
Status: Active
Series: Medium and miniatures
O.I.P.: U.K. £35.00
U.S. $87.50

U.K.: £39.95
U.S.: $90.00
Can.: –

ISSUES OF 2001

AFFECTION
Designer: Helen MacDonald
Type: Weight – Teardrop
Size: Medium
Colour: 1. Blue
2. Red
Issued: 2001
Status: Closed
Series: Medium and Miniatures
O.I.P.: U.K. £35.00
U.S. $79.50

U.K.: £35.00
U.S.: $70.00
Can.: $90.00

ALBA (SCOTLAND)
Designer: Helen MacDonald
Type: Weight – Spherical
Issued: 2001
Status: Closed
Series: National Emblems
O.I.P.: U.K. £49.00
U.S. $110.00

U.K.: £ 50.00
U.S.: $100.00
Can.: $130.00

ASTRAL CELEBRATION
Designer: Colin Terris
Type: Weight – Sculptural
Issued: 2001 in a limited edition of 500
Status: Closed at No. 256
Series: 40th Anniversary Celebration
O.I.P.: U.K. £120.00
U.S. $325.00

U.K.: £125.00
U.S.: $250.00
Can.: $325.00

ASTRONAUT
Designer: Alastair MacIntosh
Type: Weight – Spherical, on base
Issued: 2001 in a limited edition of 75
Status: Fully subscribed
Series: Space 2001
O.I.P.: U.K. £380.00
U.S. $1,075.00

U.K.: £375.00
U.S.: $750.00
Can.: $975.00

**AUTUMN GOLD
(Four Seasons)**
Designer: Colin Terris
Type: Weight – Spherical
Issued: 2001
Status: Closed
Series: Four Seasons Impressionist Collection
O.I.P.: U.K. £49.00
U.S. $110.00

U.K.: £ 50.00
U.S.: $100.00
Can.: $130.00

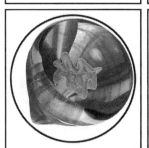

AUTUMN ILLUSIONS – OAK
Designer: Helen MacDonald
Type: Weight – Cone
Issued: 2001 in a limited edition of 650
Status: Active
Series: Limited Designs
O.I.P.: U.K. £85.00
U.S. $250.00

U.K.: £ 89.00
U.S.: $250.00
Can.: –

AZTEC SPIRES
Designer: Alastair MacIntosh
Type: Weight – Domed
Issued: 2001 in a limited edition of 500
Status: Closed at No. 105
Series: Premier Stockist/ Premier Dealer Paperweight Collection
O.I.P.: U.K. £110.00
U.S. $300.00

U.K.: £110.00
U.S.: $220.00
Can.: $285.00

BABES IN THE WOOD
Designer: Helen MacDonald
Type: Weight – Spherical
Issued: 2001 in a limited edition of 500
Status: Closed
Series: Once Upon A Time
O.I.P.: U.K. £79.00
U.S. $225.00

U.K.: £ 80.00
U.S.: $160.00
Can.: $210.00

BAPTISM
Designer: Helen MacDonald
Type: Weight – Spherical
Issued: 2001 in a limited edition of 75
Status: Fully subscribed
Series: Biblical
O.I.P.: U.K. £225.00
U.S. $650.00

U.K.: £225.00
U.S.: $450.00
Can.: $600.00

BEAUTY AND THE BEAST
Designer: Helen MacDonald
Type: Weight – Domed
Issued: 2001 in a limited edition of 500
Status: Closed
Series: Once Upon A Time
O.I.P.: U.K. £115.00
U.S. $325.00

U.K.: £125.00
U.S.: $250.00
Can.: $325.00

BLUEBELL BALLET
Designer: Allan Scott
Type: Weight – Spherical, facets
Issued: 2001 in a limited edition of 50
Status: Fully subscribed
Series: Limited editions
O.I.P.: U.K. £170.00
U.S. $475.00

U.K.: £170.00
U.S.: $340.00
Can.: $450.00

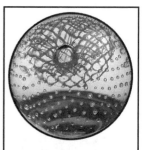

BLUSHES
Designer: Helen MacDonald
Type: Weight – Spherical
Issued: 2001
Status: Closed
Series: Unknown
O.I.P.: U.K. £29.00
U.S. $65.00

U.K.: £30.00
U.S.: $60.00
Can.: $80.00

BRIDAL WALTZ
Designer: Helen MacDonald
Type: Weight – Domed
Issued: 2001
Status: Active
Series: Gift Occasions
O.I.P.: U.K. £65.00
U.S. $140.00

U.K.: £ 69.00
U.S.: $150.00
Can.: –

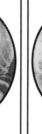

BUNDLE OF JOY 2001 (Boy)
Designer: Alastair MacIntosh
Type: Weight – Spherical
Colour: Blue
Issued: 2001
Status: Closed
Series: New Baby
O.I.P.: U.K. £29.00
U.S. $65.00

U.K.: £30.00
U.S.: $60.00
Can.: $80.00

BUNDLE OF JOY 2001 (Girl)
Designer: Alastair MacIntosh
Type: Weight – Spherical
Colour: Pink
Issued: 2001
Status: Closed
Series: New Baby
O.I.P.: U.K. £29.00
U.S. $65.00

U.K.: £30.00
U.S.: $60.00
Can.: $80.00

BURNING AMBITION
Designer: Helen MacDonald
Type: Weight – Spherical
Size: Standard
Issued: 2001
Status: Closed
Series: Unlimited – Modern Design
O.I.P.: U.K. £55.00
U.S. $125.00

U.K.: £ 55.00
U.S.: $110.00
Can.: $145.00

BURNING PASSION PERFUME BOTTLE

Designer: Helen MacDonald
Type: Perfume Bottle
Issued: 2001
Status: Closed at No. 204
Series: Prestige Perfume Bottles
O.I.P.: U.K. £159.00
U.S. $450.00

U.K.: £160.00
U.S.: $320.00
Can.: $420.00

CAIRNGORM

Designer: Alastair MacIntosh
Type: Weight – Domed
Issued: 2001
Status: Active
Series: Medium and Miniature
O.I.P.: U.K. £34.00
U.S. $75.00

U.K.: £39.95
U.S.: $80.00
Can.: –

CATALYST

Designer: Alastair MacIntosh
Type: Weight – Spherical
Issued: 2001
Status: Closed
Series: Unlimited – Modern Design
O.I.P.: U.K. £35.00
U.S. $195.00

U.K.: £ 40.00
U.S.: $ 80.00
Can.: $100.00

CELTIC CONNECTION

Designer: Alastair MacIntosh
Type: Weight – Domed
Issued: 2001 in a limited edition of 350
Status: Closed at No. 143
Series: Scottish Inspirations
O.I.P.: U.K. £140.00
U.S. $395.00

U.K.: £150.00
U.S.: $300.00
Can.: $400.00

CELTIC SYMBOL

Designer: Alastair MacIntosh
Type: Weight – Spherical
Issued: 2001 in a limited edition of 500
Status: Closed
Series: Scottish Inspirations
O.I.P.: U.K. £99.00
U.S. $275.00

U.K.: £100.00
U.S.: $200.00
Can.: $260.00

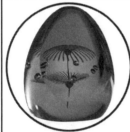

CLOSE HARMONY

Designer: Helen MacDonald
Type: Weight – Domed
Issued: 2001 in a limited edition of 500
Status: Fully subscribed
Series: Abstract Limited Editions
O.I.P.: U.K. £79.00
U.S. $225.00

U.K.: £ 80.00
U.S.: $160.00
Can.: $210.00

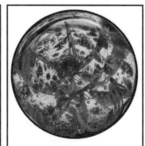

CORAL FLOWER

Designer: Sarah Peterson
Type: Weight – Spherical
Issued: 2001
Status: Closed
Series: Unlimited
O.I.P.: U.K. £46.00
U.S. $110.00

U.K.: £ 45.00
U.S.: $ 90.00
Can.: $120.00

COUNTRY GARDEN

Designer: Allan Scott
Type: Weight – Spherical
Issued: 2001 in a limited edition of 100
Status: Fully subscribed
Series: Whitefriars Collection
O.I.P.: U.K. £180.00
U.S. $495.00

U.K.: £180.00
U.S.: $360.00
Can.: $470.00

CRYSTAL CHANDELIER
Designer: Colin Terris
Type: Weight – Teardrop
Issued: 2001 in a limited
         edition of 200
Status: Fully subscribed
Series: 40th Anniversary
         Celebration
O.I.P.: U.K. £190.00
         U.S. $525.00

U.K.:   £200.00
U.S.: $400.00
Can.: $525.00

CRYSTAL CLEAR
Designer: Sarah Peterson
Type: Weight – Spherical
Issued: 2001
Status: Closed
Series: Unlimited – Modern
         Design
O.I.P.: U.K. £49.00
         U.S. $110.00

U.K.:   £ 50.00
U.S.: $100.00
Can.: $130.00

CRYSTAL DREAMS
Designer: Colin Terris
Type: Weight – Teardrop
Issued: 2001
Status: Closed
Series: Unlimited – Modern
         Design
O.I.P.: U.K. £55.00
         U.S. $125.00

U.K.:   £ 50.00
U.S.: $100.00
Can.: $130.00

CYMRU (WALES)
Designer: Helen MacDonald
Type: Weight – Spherical
Issued: 2001
Status: Closed
Series: National Emblems
O.I.P.: U.K. £49.00
         U.S. $110.00

U.K.:   £ 50.00
U.S.: $100.00
Can.: $130.00

DAISY DUET
Designer: Allan Scott
Type: Weight – Spherical,
         facets
Issued: 2001 in a limited
         edition of 50
Status: Fully subscribed
Series: Unknown
O.I.P.: U.K. £180.00
         U.S. $495.00

U.K.:   £200.00
U.S.: $400.00
Can.: $525.00

DÉJÀ VU
Designer: Alastair MacIntosh
Type: Weight – Domed
Issued: 2001
Status: Active
Series: Unlimited – Modern
         Design
O.I.P.: U.K. £29.95
         U.S. $65.00

U.K.:   £29.95
U.S.: $65.00
Can.:   –

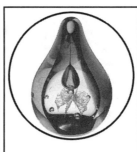

DIGNITY
Designer: Helen MacDonald
Type: Weight – Teardrop
Issued: 2001 - 2001
Status: Closed at No. 1,165
Series   Collectors' Society
         Annual Weight
O.I.P.: U.K. £95.00
         U.S. $235.00

U.K.:   £ 95.00
U.S.: $190.00
Can.: $250.00

EIREANN (IRELAND)
Designer: Helen MacDonald
Type: Weight – Spherical
Issued: 2001
Status: Closed
Series: National Emblems
O.I.P.: U.K. £49.00
         U.S. $110.00

U.K.:   £ 50.00
U.S.: $100.00
Can.: $130.00

ENGLAND
Designer: Helen MacDonald
Type: Weight – Spherical
Issued: 2001
Status: Closed
Series: National Emblems
O.I.P.: U.K. £49.00
U.S. $110.00

U.K.: £ 50.00
U.S.: $100.00
Can.: $130.00

FAIR JULIET
Designer: Alastair MacIntosh
Type: Weight – Spherical
Issued: 2001 in a limited edition of 500
Status: Closed at No. 139
Series: Paperweight Lovers
O.I.P.: U.K. £125.00
U.S. $350.00

U.K.: £125.00
U.S.: $250.00
Can.: $325.00

FALLING LEAVES
Designer: Helen MacDonald
Type: Weight – Domed
Issued: 2001
Status: Closed
Series: The Mountain Range
O.I.P.: U.K. £29.00
U.S. $65.00

U.K.: £30.00
U.S.: $60.00
Can.: $80.00

FESTIVE KISSES
Designer: Helen MacDonald
Type: Weight – Domed
Issued: 2001
Status: Closed
Series: Festive Collection
O.I.P.: U.K. £69.00
U.S. $155.00

U.K.: £ 70.00
U.S.: $140.00
Can.: $180.00

FESTIVE SNOWFLAKE 2001
Designer: Colin Terris
Type: Weight – Spherical
Issued: 2001-2001
Status: Closed
Series: Festive Collection
O.I.P.: U.K. £39.00
U.S. $95.00

U.K.: £ 40.00
U.S.: $ 80.00
Can.: $100.00

FIREWORK ORCHID
Designer: Colin Terris
Type: Weight – Spherical
Issued: 2001 in a limited edition of 500
Status: Fully subscribed
Series: Floral Limited Editions
O.I.P.: U.K. £95.00
U.S. $275.00

U.K.: £100.00
U.S.: $200.00
Can.: $260.00

FORCE TEN
Designer: Alastair MacIntosh
Type: Weight – Spherical
Issued: 2001
Status: Active
Series: Unlimited – Modern Design
O.I.P.: U.K. £31.00
U.S. $69.50

U.K.: £34.95
U.S.: $75.00
Can.: –

FOUNTAIN OF YOUTH
Designer: Helen MacDonald
Type: Weight – Domed
Issued: 2001
Status: Active
Series: Unlimited – Modern Design
O.I.P.: U.K. £65.00
U.S. $150.00

U.K.: £ 65.00
U.S.: $150.00
Can.: –

FROSTY'S NIGHT OUT
Designer: Helen MacDonald
Type: Weight – Spherical
Issued: 2001 in a limited
        edition of 100
Status: Fully subscribed
Series: Frosted Christmas
O.I.P.: U.K. £290.00
        U.S. $825.00

U.K.: £300.00
U.S.: $600.00
Can.: $775.00

GARDEN FUCHSIAS
Designer: Allan Scott
Type: Weight – Spherical
Issued: 2001 in a limited
        edition of 100
Status: Fully subscribed
Series: Whitefriars
        Collection
O.I.P.: U.K. £180.00
        U.S. $495.00

U.K.: £180.00
U.S.: $360.00
Can.: $470.00

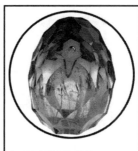

GLASS SLIPPER, THE
Designer: Helen MacDonald
Type: Weight – Domed,
        facets
Size: Magnum
Issued: 2001 in a limited
        edition of 100
Status: Closed
Series: Once Upon A Time
O.I.P.: U.K. £290.00
        U.S. $825.00

U.K.: £300.00
U.S.: $600.00
Can.: $775.00

GOLD
Style Two
Designer: Alastair MacIntosh
Type: Weight – Spherical
Colour: Gold
Issued: 2001 in a limited
        edition of 500
Status: Active
Series: We Three Kings
O.I.P.: U.K. £100.00
        U.S. $275.00

U.K.: £110.00
U.S.: $275.00
Can.: –

GOLDEN ANGEL
Designer: Helen MacDonald
Type: Weight – Spherical
Issued: 2001
Status: Closed
Series: Festive Collection
O.I.P.: U.K. £43.00
        U.S. $99.50

U.K.: £ 45.00
U.S.: $ 90.00
Can.: $120.00

GOLDEN CROWN
Designer: Helen MacDonald
Type: Weight – Spherical
Issued: 2001
Status: Closed
Series: Festive Collection
O.I.P.: U.K. £43.00
        U.S. $99.50

U.K.: £ 45.00
U.S.: $ 90.00
Can.: $120.00

GOLDEN GALAXY
Designer: Colin Terris
Type: Weight – Spherical
Issued: 2001 in a limited
        edition of 350
Status: Closed at No. 192
Series: 40th Anniversary
        Celebration
O.I.P.: U.K. £140.00
        U.S. $395.00

U.K.: £150.00
U.S.: $300.00
Can.: $400.00

GOLDEN JUBILEE
Style One
Designer: Colin Terris
Type: Weight – Spherical
Size: Magnum
Issued: 2001 in a limited
        edition of 200
Status: Closed at No. 116
Series: Golden Jubilee
O.I.P.: U.K. £199.00
        U.S. $575.00

U.K.: £200.00
U.S.: $400.00
Can.: $525.00

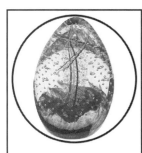

GOLDEN JUBILEE CAROUSEL
Designer: Colin Terris
Type: Weight – Domed
Issued: 2001
Status: Closed
Series: Golden Jubilee
O.I.P.: U.K. £39.00
U.S. $87.50

U.K.: £ 40.00
U.S.: $ 80.00
Can.: $100.00

GOLDEN JUBILEE CELEBRATION
Designer: Colin Terris
Type: Weight – Spherical
Issued: 2001
Status: Closed
Series: Golden Jubilee
O.I.P.: U.K. £59.00
U.S. $150.00

U.K.: £ 60.00
U.S.: $120.00
Can.: $155.00

GOLDEN JUBILEE CROWN
Designer: Colin Terris
Type: Weight – Spherical, facets
Issued: 2001 in a limited edition of 200
Status: Closed at No. 92
Series: Golden Jubilee
O.I.P.: U.K. £235.00
U.S. $725.00

U.K.: £250.00
U.S.: $500.00
Can.: $650.00

GOLDEN JUBILEE CROWN BASKET
Designer: Colin Terris
Type: Weight – Sculptural
Issued: 2001 in a limited edition of 100
Status: Closed at No. 91
Series: Golden Jubilee
O.I.P.: U.K. £275.00
U.S. $775.00

U.K.: £275.00
U.S.: $550.00
Can.: $725.00

GOLDEN JUBILEE GOLD CROWN
Designer: Colin Terris
Type: Weight – Spherical
Size: Medium
Issued: 2001 in a limited edition of 500
Status: Fully subscribed
Series: Golden Jubilee
O.I.P.: U.K. £75.00
U.S. $235.00

U.K.: £ 75.00
U.S.: $150.00
Can.: $200.00

GOLDEN JUBILEE MAJESTY
Designer: Frances Toffolo
Type: Centre Piece
Issued: 2001 in a limited edition of 30
Status: Fully subscribed
Series: Golden Jubilee
O.I.P.: U.K. £535.00
U.S. $1500.00

U.K.: £ 550.00
U.S.: $1,100.00
Can.: $1,425.00

GOLDEN JUBILEE MILLEFIORI CROWN
Designer: Colin Terris
Type: Weight – Spherical
Issued: 2001 in a limited edition of 350
Status: Closed at No. 124
Series: Golden Jubilee
O.I.P.: U.K. £175.00
U.S. $535.00

U.K.: £175.00
U.S.: $350.00
Can.: $450.00

GOLDEN JUBILEE MILLEFIORI ROYAL CYPHER
Designer: Colin Terris
Type: Weight – Spherical
Issued: 2001 in a limited edition of 200
Status: Closed at No. 172
Series: Golden Jubilee
O.I.P.: U.K. £195.00
U.S. $595.00

U.K.: £200.00
U.S.: $400.00
Can.: $525.00

GOLDEN JUBILEE MOONBEAM

Designer: Colin Terris
Type: Weight – Domed
Issued: 2001
Status: Closed
Series: Golden Jubilee
O.I.P.: U.K. £20.00
U.S. $49.50

U.K.: £20.00
U.S.: $40.00
Can.: $50.00

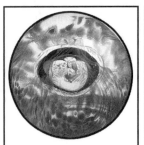

GOLDEN JUBILEE MOONCRYSTAL

Designer: Colin Terris
Type: Weight – Spherical
Issued: 2001
Status: Closed
Series: Golden Jubilee
O.I.P.: U.K. £13.00
U.S. $37.50

U.K.: £15.00
U.S.: $30.00
Can.: $40.00

GOLDEN JUBILEE QUEEN ELIZABETH ROSE

Designer: Colin Terris
Type: Weight – Spherical
Issued: 2001
Status: Closed
Series: Golden Jubilee
O.I.P.: U.K. £36.00
U.S. $82.50

U.K.: £35.00
U.S.: $70.00
Can.: $90.00

GOLDEN JUBILEE REFLECTIONS

Designer: Colin Terris
Type: Weight – Teardrop
Issued: 2001 in a limited
edition of 200
Status: Closed at No. 111
Series: Golden Jubilee
O.I.P.: U.K. £195.00
U.S. $550.00

U.K.: £200.00
U.S.: $400.00
Can.: $525.00

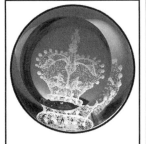

GOLDEN JUBILEE REGAL CROWN

Designer: Colin Terris
Type: Weight – Spherical
Issued: 2001 in a limited
edition of 500
Status: Closed at No. 226
Series: Golden Jubilee
O.I.P.: U.K. £79.00
U.S. $225.00

U.K.: £ 80.00
U.S.: $160.00
Can.: $210.00

GOLDEN JUBILEE REGAL REFLECTIONS

Designer: Colin Terris
Type: Weight – Domed
Issued: 2001 in a limited
edition of 500
Status: Fully subscribed
Series: Golden Jubilee
O.I.P.: U.K. £85.00
U.S. $250.00

U.K.: £ 85.00
U.S.: $170.00
Can.: $225.00

GOLDEN JUBILEE ROSE

Designer: Colin Terris
Type: Weight – Spherical
Issued: 2001 in a limited
edition of 350
Status: Closed at No. 249
Series: Golden Jubilee
O.I.P.: U.K. £175.00
U.S. $495.00

U.K.: £175.00
U.S.: $350.00
Can.: $450.00

GOLDEN JUBILEE ROYAL ARMS

Designer: Colin Terris
Type: Weight – Spherical
Issued: 2001
Status: Closed
Series: Golden Jubilee
O.I.P.: U.K. £50.00
U.S. $115.00

U.K.: £ 50.00
U.S.: $100.00
Can.: $130.00

GOLDEN JUBILEE ROYAL CYPHER

Designer: Colin Terris
Type: Weight – Domed
Issued: 2001
Status: Closed
Series: Golden Jubilee
O.I.P.: U.K. £50.00
U.S. $115.00

U.K.: £ 50.00
U.S.: $100.00
Can.: $130.00

GOLDEN JUBILEE TAPESTRY

Designer: Colin Terris
Type: Weight – Domed
Issued: 2001 in a limited edition of 200
Status: Closed at No. 166
Series: Golden Jubilee
O.I.P.: U.K. £220.00
U.S. $625.00

U.K.: £225.00
U.S.: $450.00
Can.: $600.00

GOLDEN JUBILEE TRIBUTE

Designer: Colin Terris
Type: Weight – Low Dome
Issued: 2001 in a limited edition of 500
Status: Fully subscribed
Series: Golden Jubilee
O.I.P.: U.K. £99.00
U.S. $295.00

U.K.: £100.00
U.S.: $200.00
Can.: $260.00

GOLDEN STAR

Designer: Helen MacDonald
Type: Weight – Spherical
Issued: 2001
Status: Closed
Series: Unlimited
O.I.P.: U.K. £43.00
U.S. $99.50

U.K.: £ 45.00
U.S.: $ 90.00
Can.: $120.00

GOLDEN SUNFLOWER

Designer: Helen MacDonald
Type: Weight – Sculptural, facets
Issued: 2001 in a limited edition of 200
Status: Closed at No. 149
Series: Van Gogh Inspirations
O.I.P.: U.K. £195.00
U.S. $550.00

U.K.: £200.00
U.S.: $400.00
Can.: $525.00

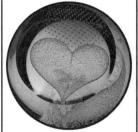

HEART OF GOLD

Designer: Helen MacDonald
Type: Weight – Spherical
Issued: 2001
Status: Active
Series: Loved Ones
O.I.P.: U.K. £39.00
U.S. $87.50

U.K.: £39.95
U.S.: $90.00
Can.: –

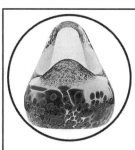

HEATHER HILLS

Designer: Helen MacDonald
Type: Weight – Domed
Issued: 2001
Status: Closed
Series: The Mountain Range
O.I.P.: U.K. £29.00
U.S. $65.00

U.K.: £30.00
U.S.: $60.00
Can.: $80.00

HIGHLAND DANCE

Designer: Helen MacDonald
Type: Weight – Spherical
Issued: 2001
Status: Closed
Series: Scottish Inspirations
O.I.P.: U.K. £49.00
U.S. $110.00

U.K.: £ 50.00
U.S.: $100.00
Can.: $130.00

HOLLY
Style Two
Designer: Helen MacDonald
Type: Weight – Spherical
Issued: 2001
Status: Closed
Series: Festive Collection
O.I.P.: U.K. £59.00
U.S. $135.00

U.K.: £ 60.00
U.S.: $120.00
Can.: $155.00

HOT! HOT! HOT!
Designer: Helen MacDonald
Type: Weight – Spherical
Issued: 2001
Status: Active
Series: Loved Ones
O.I.P.: U.K. £58.00
U.S. $125.00

U.K.: £ 59.00
U.S.: $125.00
Can.: –

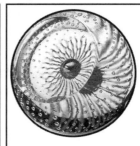

I SPY
Designer: Helen MacDonald
Type: Weight – Spherical
Issued: 2001
Status: Closed
Series: Unlimited – Modern
Design
O.I.P.: U.K. £28.00
U.S. $99.50

U.K.: £30.00
U.S.: $60.00
Can.: $80.00

IRIS, THE
Style Three
Designer: Helen MacDonald
Type: Weight – Domed
Issued: 2001 in a limited
edition of 100
Status: Fully subscribed
Series: Van Gogh
Inspirations
O.I.P.: U.K. £295.00
U.S. $795.00

U.K.: £300.00
U.S.: $600.00
Can.: $775.00

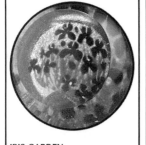

IRIS GARDEN
Designer: Helen MacDonald
Type: Weight – Spherical
Issued: 2001 in a limited
edition of 500
Status: Closed
Series: Van Gogh
Inspirations
O.I.P.: U.K. £95.00
U.S. $275.00

U.K.: £ 95.00
U.S.: $190.00
Can.: $250.00

JUBILATION
Designer: Colin Terris
Type: Weight – Sculptural
Size: Magnum
Issued: 2001
Status: Unknown
Series: 40th Anniversary
Celebration
O.I.P.: Unknown

U.K.: £100.00
U.S.: $200.00
Can.: $260.00

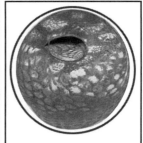

LACEMAKER
Designer: Alastair MacIntosh
Type: Weight – Spherical
Issued: 2001
Status: Closed
Series: Collectors' Society
Complimentary
Weight

U.K.: £100.00
U.S.: $200.00
Can.: $260.00

LAND OF OZ, THE
Designer: Helen MacDonald
Type: Weight – Domed
Issued: 2001 in a limited
edition of 500
Status: Closed
Series: Once Upon A Time
O.I.P.: U.K. £125.00
U.S. $365.00

U.K.: £125.00
U.S.: $250.00
Can.: $325.00

LAST TANGO, THE

Designer: Helen MacDonald
Type: Weight – Domed
Issued: 2001 in a limited edition of 100
Status: Fully subscribed
Series: Dance
O.I.P.: U.K. £280.00
U.S. $795.00

U.K.: £280.00
U.S.: $560.00
Can.: $725.00

LATE SUMMER SUNFLOWER

Designer: Helen MacDonald
Type: Weight – Domed
Issued: 2001 in a limited edition of 350
Status: Closed at No. 226
Series: Van Gogh Inspirations
O.I.P.: U.K. £150.00
U.S. $425.00

U.K.: £150.00
U.S.: $300.00
Can.: $400.00

LITTLE RED RIDING HOOD

Designer: Helen MacDonald
Type: Weight – Domed
Issued: 2001 in a limited edition of 200
Status: Closed
Series: Once Upon A Time
O.I.P.: U.K. £200.00
U.S. $575.00

U.K.: £200.00
U.S.: $400.00
Can.: $525.00

LOCAL HERO

Designer: Alastair MacIntosh
Type: Weight – Spherical
Issued: 2001 in a limited edition of 500
Status: Closed at No. 285
Series: Abstract Limited Editions
O.I.P.: U.K. £87.00
U.S. $235.00

U.K.: £ 90.00
U.S.: $180.00
Can.: $235.00

LOVE HEARTS

Designer: Helen MacDonald
Type: Weight – Spherical
Issued: 2001
Status: Active
Series: Loved Ones
O.I.P.: U.K. £39.00
U.S. $87.50

U.K.: £39.95
U.S.: $90.00
Can.: –

LUNAR ENIGMA

Designer: Alastair MacIntosh
Type: Weight – Domed
Issued: 2001 in a limited edition of 500
Status: Closed at No. 157
Series: Space 2001
O.I.P.: U.K. £110.00
U.S. $300.00

U.K.: £110.00
U.S.: $220.00
Can.: $285.00

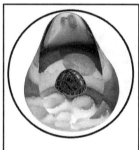

LUNAR QUEST

Designer: Alastair MacIntosh
Type: Weight – Domed
Issued: 2001 in a limited edition of 350
Status: Closed at No. 162
Series: Space 2001
O.I.P.: U.K. £170.00
U.S. $475.00

U.K.: £175.00
U.S.: $350.00
Can.: $450.00

MARBLE

Designer: Unknown
Type: Weight – Domed
Colour: 1. Ivory
2. Jet
Issued: 2001
Status: Closed
Series: Collectable Eggs – Limited
O.I.P.: U.K. £35.00
U.S. $79.50

U.K.: £35.00
U.S.: $70.00
Can.: $90.00

MEADOW FLOWERS
Designer: Helen MacDonald
Type: Weight – Domed
Issued: 2001
Status: Closed
Series: The Mountain Range
O.I.P.: U.K. £29.00
U.S. $65.00

U.K.: £30.00
U.S.: $60.00
Can.: $80.00

MILLEFIORI FLOWER
Designer: Colin Terris
Type: Weight – Spherical
Issued: 2001
Status: Closed
Series: Medium and Miniature
O.I.P.: U.K. £45.00
U.S. $99.50

U.K.: £ 45.00
U.S.: $ 90.00
Can.: $115.00

MIRROR IMAGE
Designer: Colin Terris
Type: Weight – Domed
Issued: 2001 in a limited edition of 350
Status: Closed at No. 304
Series: 40th Anniversary Celebration
O.I.P.: U.K. £150.00
U.S. $425.00

U.K.: £150.00
U.S.: $300.00
Can.: $400.00

NOSTRADAMUS
Designer: Colin Terris
Type: Weight – Spherical
Size: Magnum
Issued: 2001 in a limited edition of 100
Status: Fully subscribed
Series: 40th Anniversary Celebration
O.I.P.: U.K. £290.00
U.S. $795.00

U.K.: £300.00
U.S.: $600.00
Can.: $775.00

ONE STARRY NIGHT
Designer: Helen MacDonald
Type: Weight – Spherical
Issued: 2001 in a limited edition of 500
Status: Fully subscribed
Series: Van Gogh Inspirations
O.I.P.: U.K. £85.00
U.S. $245.00

U.K.: £ 85.00
U.S.: $170.00
Can.: $225.00

PEACE TO THE WORLD
Designer: Helen MacDonald
Type: Weight – Teardrop
Issued: 2001 in a limited edition of 500
Status: Fully subscribed
Series: Pictorial
O.I.P.: U.K. £90.00
U.S. $250.00

U.K.: £ 90.00
U.S.: $180.00
Can.: $235.00

PLANET PEPPERMINT
Designer: Colin Terris
Type: Weight – Spherical
Issued: 2001 in a limited edition of 500
Status: Closed at No. 439
Series: Abstract – Limited Editions
O.I.P.: U.K. £79.00
U.S. $225.00

U.K.: £ 80.00
U.S.: $160.00
Can.: $210.00

PRIMARY COLOURS
Designer: Helen MacDonald
Type: Weight – Spherical
Issued: 2001
Status: Closed
Series: Unlimited – Modern Design
O.I.P.: U.K. £34.00
U.S. $75.00

U.K.: £35.00
U.S.: $70.00
Can.: $90.00

PRINCESS and THE PEA
Designer: Helen MacDonald
Type: Weight – Spherical
Issued: 2001 in a limited edition of 350
Status: Closed
Series: Once Upon A Time
O.I.P.: U.K. £145.00
U.S. $395.00

U.K.: £145.00
U.S.: $290.00
Can.: $375.00

RAIN DANCE
Designer: Alastair MacIntosh
Type: Weight – Domed
Issued: 2001
Status: Active
Series: Unlimited – Modern Design
O.I.P.: U.K. £32.00
U.S. $72.50

U.K.: £39.95
U.S.: $80.00
Can.: –

RAINBOW GEM
Designer: Helen MacDonald
Type: Weight – Spherical
Colour: 1. Blue
2. Red
Issued: 2001
Status: Closed
Series: Unknown
O.I.P.: U.K. £25.00
U.S. $58.50

U.K.: £25.00
U.S.: $50.00
Can.: $65.00

RED BARON
Designer: Alastair MacIntosh
Type: Weight – Spherical
Issued: 2001 in a limited edition of 500
Status: Closed
Series: Pictorial
O.I.P.: U.K. £75.00
U.S. $225.00

U.K.: £ 75.00
U.S.: $150.00
Can.: $200.00

RED SHIFT
Designer: Alastair MacIntosh
Type: Weight – Spherical
Issued: 2001 in a limited edition of 500
Status: Closed at No. 118
Series: Space 2001
O.I.P.: U.K. £125.00
U.S. $350.00

U.K.: £125.00
U.S.: $250.00
Can.: $325.00

RETURN TO EARTH
Designer: Alastair MacIntosh
Type: Weight – Spherical
Issued: 2001 in a limited edition of 500
Status: Fully subscribed
Series: Space 2001
O.I.P.: U.K. £75.00
U.S. $215.00

U.K.: £ 75.00
U.S.: $150.00
Can.: $200.00

RHYTHM
Designer: Caithness Design Studios
Type: Weight – Domed
Issued: 2001
Status: Closed
Series: Collectors' Society
O.I.P.: U.K. £35.00
U.S. $79.50

U.K.: £35.00
U.S.: $70.00
Can.: $90.00

Note: This Paperweight is an event piece.

RINGED PLANET
Designer: Alastair MacIntosh
Type: Weight – Spherical
Size: Magnum
Issued: 2001 in a limited edition of 200
Status: Closed at No. 133
Series: Space 2001
O.I.P.: U.K. £225.00
U.S. $625.00

U.K.: £225.00
U.S.: $450.00
Can.: $575.00

RIPPLES

Designer: Alastair MacIntosh
Type: Weight – Spherical
Issued: 2001
Status: Closed
Series: Unlimited – Modern Design
O.I.P.: U.K. £32.00
U.S. $72.50

U.K.: £35.00
U.S.: $70.00
Can.: $90.00

ROMEO

Designer: Alastair MacIntosh
Type: Weight – Spherical
Issued: 2001 in a limited edition of 500
Status: Closed at No. 149
Series: Paperweight Lovers
O.I.P.: U.K. £125.00
U.S. $350.00

U.K.: £125.00
U.S.: $250.00
Can.: $325.00

SAFE HEAVEN

Designer: Colin Terris
Type: Weight – Spherical
Issued: 2001 in a limited edition of 500
Status: Closed at No. 444
Series: Limited – Modern Design
O.I.P.: U.K. £89.00
U.S. $250.00

U.K.: £ 90.00
U.S.: $180.00
Can.: $235.00

SHIMMER

Designer: Colin Terris
Type: Weight – Spherical
Size: Miniature
Colour: 1. Gold
2. Green
3. Pink
4. Purple
Issued: 2001
Status: Closed
Series: Medium and Miniature
O.I.P.: U.K. £18.50
U.S. $42.50

U.K.: £20.00
U.S.: $40.00
Can.: $50.00

SHORELINE

Designer: Gordon Hendry
Type: Weight – Domed
Colour: 1. Sea Grass
2. Sky Blue
3. Warm Sand
Issued: 2001
Status: Closed
Series: Artglass
O.I.P.: U.K. £43.00
U.S. $96.50

U.K.: £ 45.00
U.S.: $ 90.00
Can.: $115.00

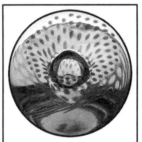

SILKSCREEN

Designer: Alastair MacIntosh
Type: Weight – Spherical
Issued: 2001
Status: Closed
Series: Unlimited – Modern Design
O.I.P.: U.K. £38.00
U.S. $87.50

U.K.: £ 40.00
U.S.: $ 80.00
Can.: $100.00

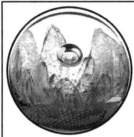

SIREN

Designer: Helen MacDonald
Type: Weight – Spherical
Size: Magnum
Issued: 2001 in a limited edition of 350
Status: Closed
Series: Limited – Modern Design
O.I.P.: U.K. £155.00
U.S. $435.00

U.K.: £155.00
U.S.: $310.00
Can.: $400.00

SNOW FALL

Designer: Helen MacDonald
Type: Weight – Domed
Issued: 2001
Status: Closed
Series: The Mountain Range
O.I.P.: U.K. £29.00
U.S. $65.00

U.K.: £30.00
U.S.: $60.00
Can.: $80.00

SNOWDROP SYMPHONY
Designer: Allan Scott
Type: Weight – Spherical, facets
Issued: 2001 in a limited edition of 50
Status: Fully subscribed
Series: Whitefriars
O.I.P.:   U.K. £160.00
        U.S. $450.00

U.K.:   £175.00
U.S.: $350.00
Can.: $450.00

SPRING SYMPHONY
Designer: Colin Terris
Type: Weight – Spherical
Issued: 2001
Status: Closed
Series: Four Seasons Impressionist Collection
O.I.P.:   U.K. £49.00
        U.S. $110.00

U.K.:   £ 50.00
U.S.: $100.00
Can.: $130.00

STRAWBERRY TEAS
Designer: Linda Campbell
Type: Weight – Spherical
Issued: 2001 in a limited edition of 100
Status: Fully subscribed
Series: Whitefriars Collection
O.I.P.:   U.K. £180.00
        U.S. $495.00

U.K.:   £180.00
U.S.: $360.00
Can.: $470.00

SUBMERSION
Designer: Helen MacDonald
Type: Weight – Spherical
Issued: 2001
Status: Closed
Series: Annual – Unlimited
O.I.P.:   U.K. £39.00
        U.S. $87.50

U.K.:   £ 40.00
U.S.: $ 80.00
Can.: $100.00

SUMMER DAY
Designer: Colin Terris
Type: Weight – Spherical
Issued: 2001
Status: Closed
Series: Four Seasons Impressionist Collection
O.I.P.:   U.K. £49.00
        U.S. $110.00

U.K.:   £ 50.00
U.S.: $100.00
Can.: $130.00

TEXAS TREASURE
Designer: Alastair MacIntosh
Type: Weight – Spherical
Issued: 2001 in a limited edition of 500
Status: Closed
Series: Floral Inspired
O.I.P.:   U.K. £95.00
        U.S. $275.00

U.K.:   £ 95.00
U.S.: $190.00
Can.: $250.00

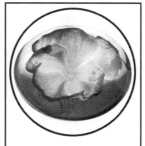

THOUGHTFULNESS
Designer: Helen MacDonald
Type: Weight – Low Dome
Issued: 2001-2001
Status: Closed at No. 669
Series: Collectors' Society Annual Weight
O.I.P.:   U.K. £95.00
        U.S. $235.00

U.K.:   £ 95.00
U.S.: $190.00
Can.: $250.00

TITANIC
Designer: Alastair MacIntosh
Type: Weight – Domed
Issued: 2001 in a limited edition of 500
Status: Closed
Series: Pictorial
O.I.P.:   U.K. £119.00
        U.S. $350.00

U.K.:   £125.00
U.S.: $250.00
Can.: $325.00

TO INFINITY and BEYOND
Designer: Helen MacDonald
Type: Weight – Domed
Issued: 2001 in a limited
           edition of 500
Status: Closed
Series: Space 2001
O.I.P.:   U.K. £119.00
           U.S. $350.00

U.K.:   £125.00
U.S.: $250.00
Can.: $325.00

VINCENT'S CHAIR
Designer: Helen MacDonald
Type: Weight – Spherical
Issued: 2001 in a limited
           edition of 350
Status: Closed at No. 120
Series: Van Gogh
           Inspirations
O.I.P.:   U.K. £145.00
           U.S. $425.00

U.K.:   £150.00
U.S.: $300.00
Can.: $400.00

WEDDING DAY
Designer: Helen MacDonald
Type: Weight – Spherical
Issued: 2001
Status: Active
Series: Weddings and
           Anniversaries
O.I.P.:   U.K. £29.95
           U.S. $65.00

U.K.:   £29.95
U.S.: $65.00
Can.:   –

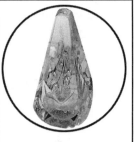

WINTER SCENE
Designer: Colin Terris
Type: Weight – Spherical
Issued: 2001
Status: Closed
Series: Four Seasons
           Impressionist
           Collection
O.I.P.:   U.K. £49.00
           U.S. $110.00

U.K.:   £ 50.00
U.S.: $100.00
Can.: $130.00

WINTER WONDERLAND
Designer: Colin Terris
Type: Weight – Domed
Issued: 2001 in a limited
           edition of 350
Status: Closed at No. 222
Series: 40th Anniversary
           Celebration
O.I.P.:   U.K. £160.00
           U.S. $450.00

U.K.:   £160.00
U.S.: $320.00
Can.: $420.00

ISSUES OF 2002

ALWAYS
Designer: Helen MacDonald
Type: Weight – Spherical
Issued: 2002
Status: Active
Series: Mini Gems
O.I.P.: U.K. £14.95
U.S. $25.00

U.K.: £14.95
U.S.: $35.00
Can.: –

AMAZING GRACE
Designer: Helen MacDonald
Type: Weight – Domed, facets
Issued: 2002 in a limited edition of 250
Status: Fully subscribed
Series: Floral Inspired
O.I.P.: U.K. £195.00
U.S. $375.00

U.K.: £200.00
U.S.: $400.00
Can.: $525.00

ANOTHER WORLD
Designer: Sarah Peterson
Type: Weight – Domed
Size: Magnum
Issued: 2002 in a limited edition of 200
Status: Closed
O.I.P.: U.K. £86.70
U.S. $425.00

U.K.: £200.00
U.S.: $400.00
Can.: $525.00

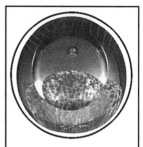

ARCTIC TWILIGHT
Designer: Colin Terris
Type: Weight – Spherical
Issued: 2002
Status: Closed
Series: The Colin Terris Classic Collection
O.I.P.: U.K. £55.00
U.S. $125.00

U.K.: £ 55.00
U.S.: $110.00
Can.: $145.00

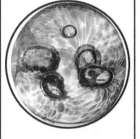

AURA
Designer: Helen MacDonald
Type: Weight – Spherical
Issued: 2002
Status: Active
Series: Unlimited – Modern Design
O.I.P.: U.K. £29.00
U.S. $55.00

U.K.: £29.95
U.S.: $60.00
Can.: –

AUTUMN ILLUSIONS – BEECH
Designer: Helen MacDonald
Type: Weight – Cone
Issued: 2002 in a limited edition of 650
Status: Active
Series: Limited Designs
O.I.P.: U.K. £85.00
U.S. $250.00

U.K.: £ 89.00
U.S.: $250.00
Can.: –

BLAZE
Designer: Alastair MacIntosh
Type: Weight – Spherical
Issued: 2002
Status: Closed
Series: Unlimited – Modern Design
O.I.P.: U.K. £24.00
U.S. $42.50

U.K.: £25.00
U.S.: $50.00
Can.: $65.00

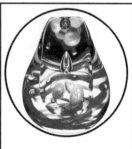

BLUE TEMPEST
Designer: Helen MacDonald
Type: Weight – Domed
Issued: 2002 in a limited edition of 500
Status: Fully subscribed
Series: Abstract
O.I.P.: U.K. £95.00
U.S. $175.00

U.K.: £ 95.00
U.S.: $190.00
Can.: $250.00

BUNDLE OF JOY 2002
(Boy)
Designer: Alastair MacIntosh
Type: Weight – Spherical
Colour: Blue
Issued: 2002
Status: Closed
Series: Unlimited – Modern
Design
O.I.P.: U.K. £29.00
U.S. $49.50

U.K.: £30.00
U.S.: $60.00
Can.: $80.00

BUNDLE OF JOY 2002
(Girl)
Designer: Alastair MacIntosh
Type: Weight – Spherical
Colour: Pink
Issued: 2002
Status: Closed
Series: Unlimited – Modern
Design
O.I.P.: U.K. £29.00
U.S. $49.50

U.K.: £30.00
U.S.: $60.00
Can.: $80.00

BUTTERCUP
Designer: Helen MacDonald
Type: Weight – Spherical
Issued: 2002
Status: Closed
Series: Unlimited – Modern
Design
O.I.P.: U.K. £22.00
U.S. $42.50

U.K.: £25.00
U.S.: $50.00
Can.: $65.00

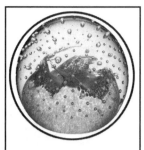

CAULDRON
Designer: Innes Burns
Type: Weight – Spherical
Colour: 1. Lilac
2. Pastel Blue
Issued: 2002
Status: Active
Series: Unlimited – Modern
Design
O.I.P.: U.K. £31.00
U.S. $87.50

U.K.: £34.95
U.S.: $87.50
Can.: –

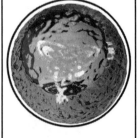

CELTIC CHARM
Designer: Helen MacDonald
Type: Weight – Spherical
Colour: 1. Cobalt Blue
2. Green
3. Heather
Issued: 2002
Status: Closed
Series: Celtic Charms
O.I.P.: U.K. £29.50
U.S. $45.00

U.K.: £30.00
U.S.: $60.00
Can.: $80.00

CHANCE ENCOUNTER
Designer: Colin Terris
Willie Bain
Type: Weight – Domed
Issued: 2002 in a limited
edition of 500
Status: Fully subscribed
Series: Aquamarina
Collection
O.I.P.: U.K. £75.00
U.S. $145.00

U.K.: £ 75.00
U.S.: $150.00
Can.: $200.00

CLIFF TOP
Designer: Allan Scott
Type: Weight – Spherical,
facets
Issued: 2002 in a limited
edition of 100
Status: Active
Series: Whitefriars Collection
O.I.P.: U.K. £180.00
U.S. $395.00

U.K.: £180.00
U.S.: $395.00
Can.: –

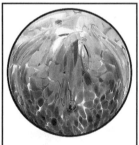

COMPANIONS
Designer: Helen MacDonald
Type: Weight – Spherical
Size: Miniature
Colour: 1. Blue
2. Green
3. Pink
Issued: 2002
Status: Closed
Series: Medium and
miniature
O.I.P.: U.K. £17.00
U.S. $32.50

U.K.: £20.00
U.S.: $40.00
Can.: $50.00

CONGRATULATIONS
Style Three
Designer: Helen MacDonald
Type: Weight – Spherical
Issued: 2002
Status: Active
Series: Mini Gems
O.I.P.: U.K. £14.95
U.S. $25.00

U.K.: £14.95
U.S.: $35.00
Can.: –

CONGRATULATIONS – 21ST
Designer: Helen MacDonald
Type: Weight – Spherical
Issued: 2002
Status: Active
Series: Mini Gems
O.I.P.: U.K. £14.95
U.S. $25.00

U.K.: £14.95
U.S.: $35.00
Can.: –

CONGRATULATIONS – 40TH
Designer: Helen MacDonald
Type: Weight – Spherical
Issued: 2002
Status: Active
Series: Mini Gems
O.I.P.: U.K. £14.95
U.S. $25.00

U.K.: £14.95
U.S.: $35.00
Can.: –

CONGRATULATIONS – 50TH
Designer: Helen MacDonald
Type: Weight – Spherical
Issued: 2002
Status: Active
Series: Mini Gems
O.I.P.: U.K. £14.95
U.S. $25.00

U.K.: £14.95
U.S.: $35.00
Can.: –

CORAL DREAM
Designer: Colin Terris
Type: Weight – Spherical
Issued: 2002 in a limited
edition of 500
Status: Closed at No. 309
Series: The Colin Terris
Classic Collection
O.I.P.: U.K. £110.00
U.S. $210.00

U.K.: £110.00
U.S.: $220.00
Can.: $285.00

COSMIC CROWN
Designer: Alastair MacIntosh
Type: Weight – Spherical
Issued: 2002
Status: Closed
Series: Unlimited – Modern
Design
O.I.P.: U.K. £35.00
U.S. $65.00

U.K.: £35.00
U.S.: $70.00
Can.: $90.00

COURT JESTER
Designer: Colin Terris
Type: Weight – Domed
Issued: 2002 in a limited
edition of 500
Status: Closed at No. 327
Series: The Colin Terris
Classic Collection
O.I.P.: U.K. £95.00
U.S. $175.00

U.K.: £ 95.00
U.S.: $190.00
Can.: $250.00

DAISY
Designer: Helen MacDonald
Type: Weight – Spherical
Issued: 2002
Status: Closed
Series: Unlimited – Modern
Design
O.I.P.: U.K. £22.00
U.S. $42.50

U.K.: £25.00
U.S.: $50.00
Can.: $65.00

DANCING SEAHORSE

Designer: Colin Terris and
Willie Bain
Type: Weight – Domed
Issued: 2002
Status: Active
Series: Aquamarina
Collection
O.I.P.: U.K. £55.00
U.S. $110.00

U.K.: £ 69.00
U.S.: $145.00
Can.: –

DEWDROP PERFUME BOTTLE

Designer: Alastair MacIntosh
Type: Perfume Bottle
Issued: 2002 in a limited
edition of 250
Status: Closed at No. 101
Series: HM Queen Elizabeth
The Queen Mother
Tribute
O.I.P.: U.K. £280.00
U.S. $575.00

U.K.: £280.00
U.S.: $560.00
Can.: $725.00

DOLPHIN DUET

Designer: Colin Terris and
Willie Bain
Type: Weight – Low Dome
Issued: 2002 in a limited
edition of 500
Status: Fully subscribed
Series: Aquamarina
Collection
O.I.P.: U.K. £85.00
U.S. $175.00

U.K.: £ 85.00
U.S.: $175.00
Can.: $225.00

EAGLE IN FLIGHT

Designer: Alastair MacIntosh
and Willie Bain
Type: Weight – Spherical
Issued: 2002
Status: Active
Series: Americana
O.I.P.: U.K. $95.00

U.K.: –
U.S.: $95.00
Can.: –

ELIZABETH OF GLAMIS ROSE

Designer: Alastair MacIntosh
Type: Weight – Spherical
Issued: 2002 in a limited
edition of 500
Status: Closed at No. 141
Series: HM Queen Elizabeth
The Queen Mother
Tribute
O.I.P.: U.K. £110.00
U.S. $210.00

U.K.: £110.00
U.S.: $220.00
Can.: $285.00

EVE

Designer: Alastair MacIntosh
Type: Weight – Spherical
Issued: 2002 in a limited
edition of 500
Status: Closed
Series: Pictorial
O.I.P.: U.K. £85.00
U.S. $175.00

U.K.: £ 85.00
U.S.: $170.00
Can.: $225.00

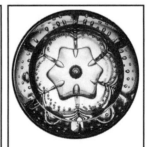

FATAL ATTRACTION

Designer: Sarah Peterson
Type: Weight – Spherical
Issued: 2002
Status: Closed
Series: Unlimited – Modern
Design
O.I.P.: U.K. £56.00
U.S. $125.00

U.K.: £ 60.00
U.S.: $120.00
Can.: $155.00

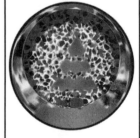

FESTIVE CHRISTMAS TREE

Designer: Helen MacDonald
Type: Weight – Spherical
Issued: 2002
Status: Closed
Series: Festive Collection
O.I.P.: U.K. £29.00
U.S. $52.50

U.K.: £30.00
U.S.: $60.00
Can.: $80.00

FESTIVE SNOWFLAKE 2002
Designer: Colin Terris
Type: Weight – Spherical
Issued: 2002
Status: Closed
Series: Festive Collection
O.I.P.: U.K. £39.00
U.S. $95.00

U.K.: £ 40.00
U.S.: $ 80.00
Can.: $100.00

FESTIVE SNOWMAN
Designer: Helen MacDonald
Type: Weight – Spherical
Issued: 2002
Status: Closed
Series: Festive Collection
O.I.P.: U.K. £29.00
U.S. $52.50

U.K.: £30.00
U.S.: $60.00
Can.: $80.00

FIREWORK FESTIVAL
Designer: Colin Terris
Type: Weight –
Hexagonal column
Issued: 2002 in a limited
edition of 350
Status: Closed at No. 203
Series: The Colin Terris
Classic Collection
O.I.P.: U.K. £160.00
U.S. $325.00

U.K.: £160.00
U.S.: $320.00
Can.: $420.00

FLORAL DANCE
Designer: Colin Terris
Type: Weight – Domed
Colour: 1. Amethyst
2. Pink
Issued: 2002
Status: Active
Series: Unlimited – Modern
Design
O.I.P.: U.K. £39.00
U.S. $79.50

U.K.: £45.00
U.S.: $85.00
Can.: –

FLORAL VISION
Designer: Colin Terris
Type: Weight – Spherical
Issued: 2002 in a limited
edition of 250
Status: Closed at No. 160
Series: The Colin Terris
Classic Collection
O.I.P.: U.K. £190.00
U.S. $325.00

U.K.: £200.00
U.S.: $400.00
Can.: $525.00

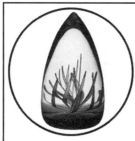

FOREST FLAME
Designer: Alastair MacIntosh
Type: Weight – Domed
Issued: 2002 in a limited
edition of 500
Status: Closed at No. 125
Series: Premier Stockist
Collection
O.I.P.: U.K. £125.00
U.S. $500.00

U.K.: £125.00
U.S.: $250.00
Can.: $325.00

FRANKINCENSE
Designer: Alastair MacIntosh
Type: Weight – Spherical
Issued: 2002 in a limited
edition of 500
Status: Active
Series: We Three Kings
O.I.P.: U.K. £100.00
U.S. $275.00

U.K.: £110.00
U.S.: $275.00
Can.: –

GALAXY
Designer: Alastair MacIntosh
Type: Weight – Spherical
Issued: 2002 in a limited
edition of 500
Status: Active
Series: Space
O.I.P.: U.K. £150.00
U.S. $300.00

U.K.: £150.00
U.S.: $325.00
Can.: –

GOLDEN RENAISSANCE

Designer: Colin Terris
Type: Weight – Spherical
Issued: 2002 in a limited
edition of 500
Status: Closed at No. 127
Series: The Colin Terris
Classic Collection
O.I.P.: U.K. £105.00
U.S. $200.00

U.K.: £100.00
U.S.: $200.00
Can.: $260.00

GONE FISHING

Designer: Helen MacDonald
Type: Weight – Spherical
Issued: 2002
Status: Active
Series: Unlimited – Modern
Design
O.I.P.: U.K. £45.00
U.S. $80.00

U.K.: £49.00
U.S.: $90.00
Can.: –

GOOD LUCK

Designer: Helen MacDonald
Type: Weight – Spherical
Issued: 2002
Status: Active
Series: Mini Gems
O.I.P.: U.K. £14.95
U.S. $25.00

U.K.: £14.95
U.S.: $35.00
Can.: –

HAPPY ANNIVERSARY

Designer: Helen MacDonald
Type: Weight – Spherical
Issued: 2002
Status: Active
Series: Mini Gems
O.I.P.: U.K. £14.95
U.S. $25.00

U.K.: £14.95
U.S.: $35.00
Can.: –

HAPPY BIRTHDAY

Designer: Helen MacDonald
Type: Weight – Spherical
Issued: 2002
Status: Active
Series: Mini Gems
O.I.P.: U.K. £14.95
U.S. $25.00

U.K.: £14.95
U.S.: $35.00
Can.: –

HEY YOU, GET OFF MY CLOUD

Designer: Helen MacDonald
Type: Weight – Spherical
Issued: 2002 in a limited
edition of 100
Status: Active
Series: Frosted Christmas
O.I.P.: U.K. £290.00
U.S. $775.00

U.K.: £290.00
U.S.: $775.00
Can.: –

JIVE TIME

Designer: Helen MacDonald
Type: Weight – Domed
Issued: 2002 in a limited
edition of 200
Status: Active
Series: Dance
O.I.P.: U.K. £260.00
U.S. $595.00

U.K.: £260.00
U.S.: $595.00
Can.: –

JOURNEY

Designer: Helen MacDonald
Type: Weight – Spherical
Colour: 1. Aqua
2. Blue
3. Green
4. Red
Issued: 2002
Status: Active
Series: Unlimited
O.I.P.: U.K. £24.95
U.S. $49.50

U.K.: £24.95
U.S.: $55.00
Can.: –

KING CANUTE
Designer: Alastair MacIntosh
Type: Weight – Domed
Issued: 2002 in a limited edition of 350
Status: Closed
Series: Abstract limited editions
O.I.P.: U.K. £175.00
U.S. $325.00
U.K.: £175.00
U.S.: $350.00
Can.: $450.00

MARK ANTHONY
Designer: Alastair MacIntosh
Type: Weight – Pyramidal, facets
Issued: 2002 in a limited edition of 500
Status: Closed
Series: Paperweight Lovers
O.I.P.: U.K. £125.00
U.S. $250.00
U.K.: £125.00
U.S.: $250.00
Can.: $325.00

MARTIAN SKYLINE
Designer: Colin Terris
Type: Weight – Spherical
Issued: 2002 in a limited edition of 500
Status: Closed at No. 268
Series: The Colin Terris Classic Collection
O.I.P.: U.K. £115.00
U.S. $265.00
U.K.: £115.00
U.S.: $230.00
Can.: $300.00

MERRIMENT
Designer: Helen MacDonald
Type: Weight – Spherical
Issued: 2002
Status: Closed
Series: Unlimited – Modern Design
O.I.P.: U.K. £49.00
U.S. $90.00
U.K.: £ 50.00
U.S.: $100.00
Can.: $130.00

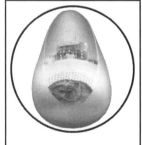

MEY TAPESTRY
Designer: Alastair MacIntosh Willie Bain
Type: Weight – Domed
Issued: 2002 in a limited edition of 250
Status: Closed at No. 119
Series: HM Queen Elizabeth The Queen Mother Tribute
O.I.P.: U.K. £195.00
U.S. $375.00
U.K.: £200.00
U.S.: $400.00
Can.: $525.00

MIRRORED GARDEN
Designer: Franco Toffolo
Type: Weight – Cone (??)
Issued: 2002 in a limited edition of 100
Status: Fully subscribed
Series: Unknown
O.I.P.: U.K. £250.00
U.S. $500.00
U.K.: £250.00
U.S.: $450.00
Can.: $575.00

MOONDANCE
Designer: Colin Terris
Type: Weight – Domed
Issued: 2002-2002
Status: Closed at No. 978
Series: Collectors' Society Annual Weight
O.I.P.: U.K. £95.00
U.S. $235.00
U.K.: £ 95.00
U.S.: $190.00
Can.: $250.00

MOONFLOWER ECHOES
Designer: Colin Terris
Type: Weight – Domed
Issued: 2002
Status: Closed
Series: The Colin Terris Classic Collection
O.I.P.: U.K. £37.00
U.S. $82.50
U.K.: £ 40.00
U.S.: $ 80.00
Can.: $100.00

MOONFLOWER SERENADE

Designer: Colin Terris
Type: Weight – Spherical
Issued: 2002
Status: Closed
Series: The Colin Terris
Classic Collection
O.I.P.: U.K. £37.00
U.S. $82.50

U.K.: £ 40.00
U.S.: $ 80.00
Can.: $100.00

MOROCCAN NIGHTS

Designer: Helen MacDonald
Type: Weight – Domed
Issued: 2002 in a limited
edition of 500
Status: Fully subscribed
Series: Limited – Modern
Design
O.I.P.: U.K. £110.00
U.S. $225.00

U.K.: £110.00
U.S.: $220.00
Can.: $285.00

MOTHER

Designer: Helen MacDonald
Type: Weight – Spherical
Issued: 2002
Status: Active
Series: Mini Gems
O.I.P.: U.K. £14.95
U.S. $25.00

U.K.: £14.95
U.S.: $35.00
Can.: –

MOULIN ROUGE

Designer: Helen MacDonald
Type: Weight – Spherical
Issued: 2002
Status: Active
Series: Unlimited – Modern
Design
O.I.P.: U.K. £35.00
U.S. $65.00

U.K.: £39.95
U.S.: $75.00
Can.: –

OCEAN MYSTERY

Designer: Alastair MacIntosh
Type: Weight – Spherical
Issued: 2002
Status: Closed
Series: Unlimited – Modern
Design
O.I.P.: U.K. £35.00
U.S. $72.50

U.K.: £35.00
U.S.: $70.00
Can.: $90.00

OCEAN RENDEZVOUS

Designer: Colin Terris
Willie Bain
Type: Weight – Spherical
Issued: 2002
Status: Active
Series: Aquamarina
Collection
O.I.P.: U.K. £49.00
U.S. $110.00

U.K.: £ 65.00
U.S.: $140.00
Can.: –

ON THE WINGS OF A DOVE

Designer: Helen MacDonald
Type: Weight – Spherical
Issued: 2002
Status: Active
Series: Unlimited – Modern
Design
O.I.P.: U.K. £39.00
U.S. $72.50

U.K.: £39.95
U.S.: $80.00
Can.: –

ONLY A ROSE

Designer: Helen MacDonald
Type: Weight – Spherical
Issued: 2002
Status: Closed
Series: Unlimited – Modern
Design
O.I.P.: U.K. £29.00
U.S. $55.00

U.K.: £30.00
U.S.: $60.00
Can.: $80.00

OPUS 2002
Designer: Colin Terris
Type: Weight – Spherical, facets
Issued: 2002 in a limited edition of 250
Status: Closed at No. 197
Series: The Colin Terris Classic Collection
O.I.P.: U.K. £250.00
U.S. $495.00

U.K.: £250.00
U.S.: $500.00
Can.: $650.00

PAGODA ORCHID
Designer: Colin Terris
Type: Weight – Domed, facets
Issued: 2002 in a limited edition of 250
Status: Closed at No. 165
Series: The Colin Terris Classic Collection
O.I.P.: U.K. £250.00
U.S. $525.00

U.K.: £250.00
U.S.: $500.00
Can.: $650.00

PERPETUA
Designer: Caithness Design Studios
Type: Weight – Teardrop
Issued: 2002
Status: Closed
Series: Collectors' Society
O.I.P.: U.K. £35.00
U.S. $72.50

U.K.: £35.00
U.S.: $70.00
Can.: $90.00

Note: This is an event piece.

PLAYTIME
Designer: Helen MacDonald
Type: Weight – Spherical
Issued: 2002
Status: Closed
Series: Unlimited – Modern Design
O.I.P.: U.K.£45.00
U.S. $80.00

U.K.: £ 45.00
U.S.: $ 90.00
Can.: $115.00

PRIMA BALLERINA
Style One
Designer: Colin Terris
Type: Weight – Spherical
Colour: 1. Apple Green
2. Sugar Plum
Issued: 2002
Status: Closed
Series: The Colin Terris Classic Collection
O.I.P.: U.K. £39.00
U.S. $69.50

U.K.: £40.00
U.S.: $70.00
Can.: $90.00

PUNTING ON THE RIVER
Designer: Allan Scott
Type: Weight – Spherical, facets
Issued: 2002 in a limited edition of 100
Status: Closed
Series: Whitefriars Collection
O.I.P.: U.K. £180.00
U.S. $395.00

U.K.: £180.00
U.S.: $360.00
Can.: $475.00

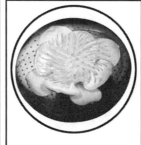

PURITY OF HEART
Designer: Helen MacDonald
Type: Weight – Low Dome
Issued: 2002 - 2002
Status: Closed at No. 712
Series: Collectors' Society Annual Weight
O.I.P.: U.K. £95.00
U.S. $200.00

U.K.: £ 95.00
U.S.: $190.00
Can.: $250.00

QUEEN CLEOPATRA
Designer: Alastair MacIntosh
Type: Weight – Pebble, facets
Issued: 2002 in a limited edition of 500
Status: Closed
Series: Paperweight Lovers
O.I.P.: U.K. £125.00
U.S. $250.00

U.K.: £125.00
U.S.: $250.00
Can.: $325.00

QUEEN MOTHER'S ARMS

Designer: Alastair MacIntosh
Willie Bain
Type: Weight – Spherical
Issued: 2002
Status: Closed
Series: HM Queen Elizabeth
The Queen Mother
Tribute
O.I.P.: U.K. £45.00
U.S. $82.50

U.K.: £ 45.00
U.S.: $ 90.00
Can.: $120.00

QUINTET

Designer: Colin Terris
Type: Weight – Spherical
Issued: 2002
Status: Closed
Series: The Colin Terris
Classic Collection
O.I.P.: U.K. £45.00
U.S. $82.50

U.K.: £ 45.00
U.S.: $ 90.00
Can.: $120.00

RAINDROP

Designer: Helen MacDonald
Type: Weight – Teardrop
Size: Miniature
Issued: 2002
Status: Closed
Series: Collectors' Society
Complimentary
Paperweight 2002

U.K.: £30.00
U.S.: $60.00
Can.: $80.00

REMEMBRANCE POPPY

Designer: Helen MacDonald
Alastair MacIntosh
Type: Weight – Spherical
Issued: 2002
Status: Closed
Series: HM Queen Elizabeth
The Queen Mother
Tribute
O.I.P.: U.K. £40.00
U.S. $85.00

U.K.: £ 40.00
U.S.: $ 80.00
Can.: $100.00

REMEMBRANCE WHITE ROSE

Designer: Alastair MacIntosh
Type: Weight – Spherical
Issued: 2002
Status: Closed
Series: HM Queen Elizabeth
The Queen Mother
Tribute
O.I.P.: U.K. £40.00
U.S. $85.00

U.K.: £ 40.00
U.S.: $ 80.00
Can.: $100.00

ROBIN HOOD

Designer: Alastair MacIntosh
Type: Weight – Domed
Issued: 2002 in a limited
edition of 500
Status: Active
Series: British Myths
and Legends
O.I.P.: U.K. £150.00
U.S. $300.00

U.K.: £150.00
U.S.: $325.00
Can.: –

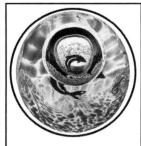

ROLLING SURF DOLPHIN

Designer: Helen MacDonald
Type: Weight – Spherical
Issued: 2002
Status: Active
Series: Unlimited – Modern
Design
O.I.P.: U.K. £41.00
U.S. $82.50

U.K.: £45.00
U.S.: $85.00
Can.: –

ROLLING SURF LIGHTHOUSE

Designer: Helen MacDonald
Type: Weight – Spherical
Issued: 2002
Status: Active
Series: Unlimited – Modern
Design
O.I.P.: U.K. £41.00
U.S. $82.50

U.K.: £45.00
U.S.: $85.00
Can.: –

ROLLING SURF YACHT
Designer: Helen MacDonald
Type: Weight – Spherical
Issued: 2002
Status: Active
Series: Unlimited – Modern Design
O.I.P.: U.K. £41.00
U.S. $82.50
U.K.: £45.00
U.S.: $85.00
Can.: –

ROSE DEWDROPS
Designer: Alastair MacIntosh
Type: Weight – Domed
Issued: 2002
Status: Closed
Series: HM Queen Elizabeth The Queen Mother Tribute
O.I.P.: U.K. £55.00
U.S. $125.00
U.K.: £ 55.00
U.S.: $110.00
Can.: $145.00

SAND DUNES
Designer: Allan Scott
Type: Weight – Spherical, facets
Issued: 2002 in a limited edition of 100
Status: Closed
Series: Whitefriars Collection
O.I.P.: U.K. £180.00
U.S. $395.00
U.K.: £180.00
U.S.: $360.00
Can.: $470.00

SEA VIEW
Designer: Colin Terris
Willie Bain
Type: Spherical
Issued: 2002
Status: Active
Series: Aquamarina Collection
O.I.P.: Unknown
U.K.: £ 55.00
U.S.: $120.00
Can.: –

SELENE
Designer: Alastair MacIntosh
Type: Weight – Spherical
Issued: 2002 in a limited edition of 500
Status: Closed
Series: Floral Inspired
O.I.P.: U.K. £98.00
U.S. $210.00
U.K.: £100.00
U.S.: $200.00
Can.: $260.00

SENTIMENTS: THANK YOU
Designer: Helen MacDonald
Type: Weight – Spherical
Issued: 2002
Status: Closed
Series: Unlimited – Modern Design
O.I.P.: U.K. £29.00
U.S. $47.50
U.K.: £30.00
U.S.: $60.00
Can.: $80.00

SENTIMENTS: THINKING OF YOU
Designer: Helen MacDonald
Type: Weight – Spherical
Issued: 2002
Status: Closed
Series: Unlimited – Modern Design
O.I.P.: U.K. £29.00
U.S. $47.50
U.K.: £30.00
U.S.: $60.00
Can.: $80.00

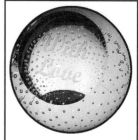

SENTIMENTS: WITH LOVE
Designer: Helen MacDonald
Type: Weight – Spherical
Issued: 2002
Status: Closed
Series: Unlimited – Modern Design
O.I.P.: U.K. £29.00
U.S. $47.50
U.K.: £30.00
U.S.: $60.00
Can.: $80.00

SHINGLE BEACH
Designer: Allan Scott
Type: Weight – Spherical, facets
Issued: 2002 in a limited edition of 100
Status: Active
Series: Whitefriars Collection
O.I.P.: U.K. £180.00
U.S. $395.00

U.K.: £180.00
U.S.: $395.00
Can.: –

SILKIE
Designer: Alastair MacIntosh
Type: Weight – Spherical
Colour: 1. Aqua
2. Pink
Issued: 2002
Status: Closed
Series: Unlimited – Modern Design
O.I.P.: U.K. £25.00
U.S. $50.00

U.K.: £25.00
U.S.: $50.00
Can.: $65.00

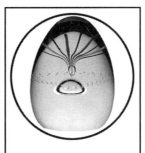

SUPERHERO
Designer: Alastair MacIntosh
Type: Weight – Domed
Issued: 2002 in a limited edition of 500
Status: Closed
Series: Abstract
O.I.P.: U.K. £75.00
U.S. $150.00

U.K.: £ 75.00
U.S.: $150.00
Can.: $195.00

SUSPENSE
Designer: Alastair MacIntosh
Type: Weight – Spherical
Issued: 2002
Status: Closed
Series: Unlimited – Modern Design
O.I.P.: U.K. £35.00
U.S. $65.00

U.K.: £35.00
U.S.: $70.00
Can.: $90.00

SWANS BY THE RIVERBANK
Designer: Allan Scott
Type: Weight – Spherical, facets
Issued: 2002 in a limited edition of 100
Status: Closed
Series: Whitefriars Collection
O.I.P.: U.K. £210.00
U.S. $450.00

U.K.: £210.00
U.S.: $420.00
Can.: $550.00

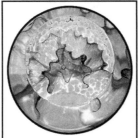

SWEETPEA LILAC
Designer: Helen MacDonald
Type: Weight – Spherical
Issued: 2002
Status: Closed
Series: Unlimited – Modern Design
O.I.P.: U.K. £39.00
U.S. $75.50

U.K.: £ 40.00
U.S.: $ 80.00
Can.: $100.00

TRANSMISSION
Designer: Helen MacDonald
Type: Weight – Spherical
Issued: 2002 in a limited edition of 500
Status: Closed
Series: Space 2002
O.I.P.: U.K. £75.00
U.S. $150.00

U.K.: £ 75.00
U.S.: $150.00
Can.: $200.00

ULTRA COOL
Designer: Sarah Peterson
Type: Weight – Domed
Issued: 2002
Status: Active
Series: Unlimited – Modern Design
O.I.P.: U.K. £34.00
U.S. $69.50

U.K.: £39.95
U.S.: $80.00
Can.: –

ULTRA HOT
Designer: Sarah Peterson
Type: Weight – Domed
Issued: 2002
Status: Active
Series: Unlimited – Modern
 Design
O.I.P.: U.K. £34.00
 U.S. $69.50

U.K.: £39.95
U.S.: $80.00
Can.: –

VAN GOGH STARRY NIGHT
Designer: Helen MacDonald
Type: Weight – Spherical
Issued: 2002
Status: Active
Series: Museum Collection
O.I.P.: U.S. $125.00

U.K.: –
U.S.: $125.00
Can.: –

VAN GOGH SUNFLOWER
Designer: Helen MacDonald
Type: Weight – Spherical
Issued: 2002
Status: Active
Series: Museum Collection
O.I.P.: U.S. $125.00

U.K.: –
U.S.: $125.00
Can.: –

VILLAGE POND
Designer: Allan Scott
Type: Weight – Spherical
Issued: 2002 in a limited
 edition of 100
Status: Fully subscribed
Series: Whitefriars Collection
O.I.P.: U.K. £210.00
 U.S. $450.00

U.K.: £225.00
U.S.: $450.00
Can.: $575.00

WALKING ON WATER
Designer: Helen MacDonald
Type: Weight – Spherical
Issued: 2002 in a limited
 edition of 200
Status: Active
Series: Biblical
O.I.P.: U.K. £215.00
 U.S. $495.00

U.K.: £220.00
U.S.: $495.00
Can.: –

WATER BABIES
Designer: Helen MacDonald
Type: Weight – Spherical
Issued: 2002-2002
Status: Closed
Series: Caithness Annual
 Paperweight
O.I.P.: U.K. £39.00
 U.S. $82.50

U.K.: £ 40.00
U.S.: $ 80.00
Can.: $100.00

WAVE CONTROL
Designer: Sarah Peterson
Type: Weight – Spherical
Size: Standard
Issued: 2002
Status: Closed
Series: Unlimited edition
O.I.P.: U.K. £36.00
 U.S. $62.50

U.K.: £35.00
U.S.: $70.00
Can.: $90.00

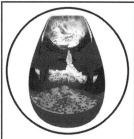

WHITE HEAT
Designer: Alastair MacIntosh
Type: Weight – Domed
Issued: 2002 in a limited
 edition of 500
Status: Closed
Series: Abstract
O.I.P.: U.K. £95.00
 U.S. $200.00

U.K.: £ 95.00
U.S.: $190.00
Can.: $250.00

WITH LOVE
Style Two

Designer: Helen MacDonald
Type: Weight – Spherical
Issued: 2002
Status: Active
Series: Mini Gems
O.I.P.:   U.K. £14.95
              U.S. $25.00

U.K.:   £14.95
U.S.: $35.00
Can.:   –

ISSUES OF 2003

ACOUSTICS BLUE
Designer: Helen MacDonald
Type: Weight – Spherical
Issued: 2003
Status: Active
Series: Unlimited – Modern Design
O.I.P.: U.K. £95.00
U.S. $175.00

U.K.: £ 95.00
U.S.: $200.00
Can.: –

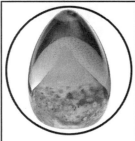

ALPINE PEAK
Designer: Helen MacDonald
Type: Weight – Domed
Issued: 2003
Status: Active
Series: Natural Environments
O.I.P.: U.K. £39.00
U.S. $85.00

U.K.: £39.95
U.S.: $85.00
Can.: –

AUTUMN
Style Three
Designer: Alastair MacIntosh
Type: Weight – Spherical
Issued: 2003
Status: Active
Series: Pastures New
O.I.P.: U.K. £39.00
U.S. $80.00

U.K.: £39.00
U.S.: $80.00
Can.: –

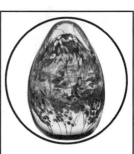

BABYLON
Designer: Helen MacDonald
Type: Weight – Domed
Issued: 2003 in a limited edition of 500
Status: Active
Series: Pictorial
O.I.P.: U.K. £85.00
U.S. $175.00

U.K.: £ 85.00
U.S.: $180.00
Can.: –

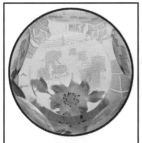

BEE KEEPING
Designer: Allan Scott
Type: Weight – Spherical, facets
Issued: 2003 in a limited edition of 100
Status: Active
Series: Countryside Crafts
O.I.P.: U.K. £225.00
U.S. $500.00

U.K.: £225.00
U.S.: $500.00
Can.: –

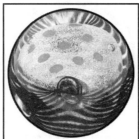

BETWEEN THE LINES
Designer: Sarah Peterson
Type: Weight – Spherical
Issued: 2003
Status: Active
Series: Unlimited – Modern Design
O.I.P.: U.K. £39.95
U.S. $85.00

U.K.: £39.95
U.S.: $85.00
Can.: –

BLACK HOLE
Designer: Alastair MacIntosh
Type: Weight – Spherical
Issued: 2003 in a limited edition of 500
Status: Active
Series: Space
O.I.P.: U.K. £110.00
U.S. $225.00

U.K.: £110.00
U.S.: $235.00
Can.: –

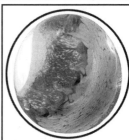

BREAKERS DAWN
Designer: Alastair MacIntosh
Type: Weight – Spherical
Issued: 2003
Status: Active
Series: Unlimited – Modern Design
O.I.P.: U.K. £35.00
U.S. $75.00

U.K.: £39.95
U.S.: $80.00
Can.: –

BREAKERS DUSK

Designer: Alastair MacIntosh
Type: Weight – Spherical
Issued: 2003
Status: Active
Series: Unlimited – Modern Design
O.I.P.: U.K. £35.00
U.S. $75.00
U.K.: £39.95
U.S.: $80.00
Can.: –

BUGS – BUTTERFLY

Designer: Helen MacDonald
Type: Weight – Spherical
Issued: 2003
Status: Closed
Series: Unlimited – Modern Design
O.I.P.: U.K. £35.00
U.S. $70.00
U.K.: £35.00
U.S.: $70.00
Can.: $90.00

CORAL PARADISE

Designer: Helen MacDonald
Type: Weight – Domed
Issued: 2003 in a limited edition of 500
Status: Active
Series: Natural Environments
O.I.P.: U.K. £120.00
U.S. $250.00
U.K.: £120.00
U.S.: $250.00
Can.: –

CORONATION COACH
Style One

Designer: Alastair MacIntosh
Type: Weight – Domed
Issued: 2003 in a limited edition of 500
Status: Closed
Series: Coronation Celebration
O.I.P.: U.K. £120.00
U.S. $250.00
U.K.: £120.00
U.S.: $250.00
Can.: $325.00

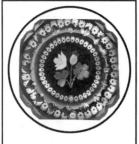

CORONATION FOUR NATIONS

Designer: Alastair MacIntosh
Type: Weight – Square
Issued: 2003 in a limited edition of 250
Status: Closed
Series: Coronation Celebration
O.I.P.: U.K. £199.00
U.S. $400.00
U.K.: £200.00
U.S.: $400.00
Can.: $525.00

CORONATION PERFUME BOTTLE

Designer: Alastair MacIntosh
Type: Perfume Bottle
Issued: 2003 in a limited edition of 100
Status: Closed
Series: Coronation Celebration
O.I.P.: U.K. £280.00
U.S. $575.00
U.K.: £280.00
U.S.: $575.00
Can.: $725.00

CORONATION PROCESSION

Designer: Alastair MacIntosh
Type: Weight – Spherical?
Issued: 2003
Status: Closed
Series: Coronation Celebration
O.I.P.: U.K. £45.00
U.S. $95.00
U.K.: £ 45.00
U.S.: $ 90.00
Can.: $115.00

CORONATION TUDOR ROSE

Designer: Alastair MacIntosh
Type: Weight – Spherical
Issued: 2003 in a limited edition of 500
Status: Closed
Series: Coronation Celebration
O.I.P.: U.K. £80.00
U.S. $195.00
U.K.: £ 80.00
U.S.: $175.00
Can.: $225.00

COUNTDOWN
Designer: Alastair MacIntosh
Type: Weight – Cone
Issued: 2003 in a limited edition of 500
Status: Active
Series: Space
O.I.P.: U.K. £120.00
U.S. $275.00

U.K.: £120.00
U.S.: $275.00
Can.: –

DAVID AND GOLIATH
Designer: Helen MacDonald
Type: Weight – Spherical
Issued: 2003 in a limited edition of 200
Status: Active
Series: Biblical
O.I.P.: U.K. £195.00
U.S. $425.00

U.K.: £195.00
U.S.: $425.00
Can.: –

DESERT DREAMS
Designer: Helen MacDonald
Type: Weight – Domed
Issued: 2003 in a limited edition of 500
Status: Active
Series: Natural Environments
O.I.P.: U.K. £120.00
U.S. $250.00

U.K.: £120.00
U.S.: $250.00
Can.: –

DIMPLES
Designer: Alastair MacIntosh
Type: Weight – Spherical
Issued: 2003
Status: Active
Series: Unlimited – Modern Design
O.I.P.: U.K. £39.95
U.S. $85.00

U.K.: £39.95
U.S.: $85.00
Can.: –

DISTRACTION
Designer: Sarah Peterson
Type: Weight – Domed
Colour: 1. Spots
2. Stripes
Issued: 2003
Status: Active
Series: Unlimited – Modern Design
O.I.P.: U.K. £45.00
U.S. $95.00

U.K.: £45.00
U.S.: $95.00
Can.: –

DOLPHIN LIASON
Designer: Colin Terris and Willie Bain
Type: Weight – Domed
Issued: 2003 in a limited edition of 500
Status: Active
Series: Aquamarina
O.I.P.: U.K. £75.00
U.S. $150.00

U.K.: £ 75.00
U.S.: $160.00
Can.: –

DRYSTONE WALLING
Designer: Allan Scott
Type: Weight – Spherical, facets
Issued: 2003 in a limited edition of 100
Status: Active
Series: Countryside Crafts
O.I.P.: U.K. £225.00
U.S. $500.00

U.K.: £225.00
U.S.: $500.00
Can.: –

EUREKA
Designer: Alastair MacIntosh
Type: Weight – Spherical
Issued: 2003
Status: Active
Series: Unlimited – Modern Design
O.I.P.: U.K. £49.95
U.S. $100.00

U.K.: £ 49.95
U.S.: $100.00
Can.: –

EXOTICA

Designer: Helen MacDonald
Type: Weight – Domed, facets
Issued: 2003 in a limited edition of 100
Status: Fully subscribed
Series: Floral Inspired
O.I.P.: U.K. £250.00
U.S. $550.00

U.K.: £250.00
U.S.: $550.00
Can.: $700.00

FESTIVE BEAUTY

Designer: Helen MacDonald
Type: Weight – Low Dome
Issued: 2003 in a limited edition of 500
Status: Active
Series: Festive Collection
O.I.P.: U.K. £120.00
U.S. $245.00

U.K.: £120.00
U.S.: $250.00
Can.: –

FIREBRAND

Designer: Alastair MacIntosh
Type: Weight – Spherical
Issued: 2003 in a limited edition of 500
Status: Active
Series: Abstract
O.I.P.: U.K. £105.00
U.S. $225.00

U.K.: £105.00
U.S.: $225.00
Can.: –

FLAMENCO PASSIONS

Designer: Helen MacDonald
Type: Weight – Domed
Issued: 2003 in a limited edition of 250
Status: Closed
Series: Dance
O.I.P.: U.K. £260.00
U.S. $550.00

U.K.: £260.00
U.S.: $525.00
Can.: $675.00

GERANIUM
Style Two

Designer: Helen MacDonald
Type: Weight – Spherical
Issued: 2003
Status: Active
Series: Blue and White Treasures
O.I.P.: U.K. £45.00
U.S. $95.00

U.K.: £45.00
U.S.: $95.00
Can.: –

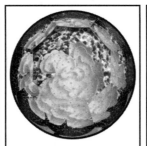

GLOBAL BEAUTY

Designer: Helen MacDonald
Type: Weight – Spherical
Issued: 2003 in a limited edition of 500
Status: Active
Series: Floral Inspired
O.I.P.: U.K. £120.00
U.S. $250.00

U.K.: £120.00
U.S.: $260.00
Can.: –

GOLDEN CORONET

Designer: Helen MacDonald
Type: Weight – Spherical
Issued: 2003 in a limited edition of 500
Status: Active
Series: Abstract
O.I.P.: U.K. £85.00
U.S. $185.00

U.K.: £ 85.00
U.S.: $185.00
Can.: –

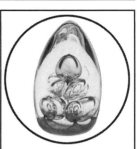

HIGH JINKS

Designer: Alastair MacIntosh
Type: Weight – Domed
Issued: 2003 in a limited edition of 500
Status: Closed
Series: Abstract
O.I.P.: U.K. £99.00
U.S. $225.00

U.K.: £100.00
U.S.: $200.00
Can.: $260.00

ISADORA

Designer: Alastair MacIntosh
Type: Weight – Spherical
Issued: 2003
Status: Active
Series: Unlimited – Modern
 Design
O.I.P.: U.K. £49.00
 U.S. $95.00

U.K.: £ 49.00
U.S.: $100.00
Can.: –

JAPANESE IKEBANA

Designer: Linda Campbell
Type: Weight – Spherical
Issued: 2003 in a limited
 edition of 100
Status: Closed
Series: Japanese Inspired
O.I.P.: U.K. £225.00
 U.S. $500.00

U.K.: £225.00
U.S.: $450.00
Can.: $575.00

JAPANESE TEA CEREMONY

Designer: Linda Campbell
Type: Weight – Spherical
Issued: 2003 in a limited
 edition of 100
Status: Closed
Series: Japanese Inspired
O.I.P.: U.K. £225.00
 U.S. $500.00

U.K.: £225.00
U.S.: $450.00
Can.: $575.00

JAPANESE WHITE CRANE

Designer: Linda Campbell
Type: Weight – Spherical
Issued: 2003 in a limited
 edition of 100
Status: Closed
Series: Japanese Inspired
O.I.P.: U.K. £225.00
 U.S. $500.00

U.K.: £225.00
U.S.: $450.00
Can.: $575.00

LUCKY CLOVER

Designer: Helen MacDonald
Type: Weight – Spherical
Issued: 2003 in a limited
 edition of 500
Status: Active
Series: Floral Inspired
O.I.P.: U.K. £75.00
 U.S. $160.00

U.K.: £ 75.00
U.S.: $165.00
Can.: –

LUSCIOUS LASHES

Designer: Helen MacDonald
Type: Weight – Spherical
Colour: 1. Black and white
 2. Blue and red
Issued: 2003
Status: Active
Series: Unlimited – Modern
 Design
O.I.P.: U.K. £39.00
 U.S. $90.00

U.K.: £44.00
U.S.: $95.00
Can.: –

MIDNIGHT MOUNTAIN

Designer: Sarah Peterson
Type: Weight – Spherical
Issued: 2003
Status: Active
Series: Fantasy Island
O.I.P.: U.K. £150.00
 U.S. $300.00

U.K.: £150.00
U.S.: $325.00
Can.: –

MIDNIGHT RAPTURE

Designer: Alastair MacIntosh
Type: Weight – Domed
Issued: 2003 in a limited
 edition of 250
Status: Active
Series: Floral Inspired
O.I.P.: U.K. £225.00
 U.S. $475.00

U.K.: £225.00
U.S.: $475.00
Can.: –

MOONBEAM
Second Version
Designer: Colin Terris
Type: Weight – Domed
Colour: 1. Lilac
            2. Yellow
Issued: 2003
Status: Active
Series: Unlimited
O.I.P.:   U.K. £20.00
            U.S. $50.00

U.K.:   £22.00
U.S.: $50.00
Can.:   –

MORNING SUNSHINE
Designer: Helen MacDonald
Type: Weight – Teardrop
Issued: 2003 in a limited
            edition of 500
Status: Active
Series: Dawn to Dusk
O.I.P.:   U.K. £125.00
            U.S. $275.00

U.K.:   £125.00
U.S.: $300.00
Can.:   –

MORNING SUNSHINE
PERFUME BOTTLE
Designer: Helen MacDonald
Type: Perfume Bottle
Issued: 2003 in a limited
            edition of 500
Status: Active
Series: Dawn to Dusk
O.I.P.:   U.K. £195.00
            U.S. $400.00

U.K.:   £195.00
U.S.: $475.00
Can.:   –

MYRRH
Designer: Alastair MacIntosh
Type: Spherical
Issued: 2003 in a limited
            edition of 500
Status: Active
Series: We Three Kings
O.I.P.:   U.K. £100.00
            U.S. $275.00

U.K.:   £110.00
U.S.: $275.00
Can.:   –

NETTED
Designer: Helen MacDonald
Type: Weight – Spherical
Issued: 2003 - 2003
Status: Closed
Series: Annual Unlimited
O.I.P.:   U.K. £55.00
            U.S. $125.00

U.K.:   £ 55.00
U.S.: $125.00
Can.: $160.00

NOW, WHERE IS RUDOLPH?
Designer: Helen MacDonald
Type: Weight – Spherical
Issued: 2003 in a limited
            edition of 100
Status: Closed
Series: Frosted Christmas
O.I.P.:   U.K. £290.00
            U.S. $775.00

U.K.:   £300.00
U.S.: $600.00
Can.: $750.00

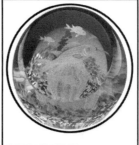

OCEAN FANTASY
Designer: Colin Terris
            Willie Bain
Type: Weight – Spherical
Issued: 2003
Status: Active
Series: Aquamarina
O.I.P.:   U.K. £65.00
            U.S. $130.00

U.K.:   £ 69.00
U.S.: $150.00
Can.:   –

OCEAN RACER
Designer: Alastair MacIntosh
Type: Weight – Spherical
Issued: 2003
Status: Active
Series: Unlimited – Modern
            Design
O.I.P.:   U.K. £55.00
            U.S. $110.00

U.K.:   £ 59.00
U.S.: $125.00
Can.:   –

ORIENTAL PEONY
Designer: Helen MacDonald
Type: Weight – Domed
Issued: 2003 in a limited
edition of 250
Status: Active
Series: Blue and White
Treasure
O.I.P.: U.K. £265.00
U.S. $550.00

U.K.: £265.00
U.S.: $550.00
Can.: –

PAISLEY TWISTS
Designer: Helen MacDonald
Type: Weight – Teardrop
Colour: 1. Amethyst
2. Aquamarine
3. Emerald
4. Sapphire
5. Topaz
Issued: 2003
Status: Active
O.I.P.: U.K. £45.00
U.S. $95.00

U.K.: £ 45.00
U.S.: $100.00
Can.: –

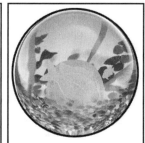

PEACEFUL WATERS
Designer: Colin Terris
Willie Bain
Type: Weight – Spherical
Issued: 2003
Status: Active
Series: Aquamarina
O.I.P.: U.K. £60.00
U.S. $125.00

U.K.: £ 65.00
U.S.: $140.00
Can.: –

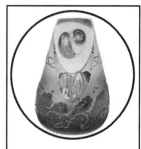

PERFECT STORM
Designer: Helen MacDonald
Type: Weight – Domed
Issued: 2003 in a limited
edition of 100
Status: Active
Series: Abstract
O.I.P.: U.K. £350.00
U.S. $750.00

U.K.: £350.00
U.S.: $750.00
Can.: –

PIATTO AZZURRO
Designer: Helen MacDonald
Type: Weight – Spherical
Issued: 2003 in a limited
edition of 250
Status: Active
Series: Blue and White
Treasures
O.I.P.: U.K. £225.00
U.S. $475.00

U.K.: £225.00
U.S.: $475.00
Can.: –

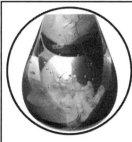

POLAR ICE FLOW
Designer: Helen MacDonald
Type: Weight – Domed
Issued: 2003 in a limited
edition of 500
Status: Active
Series: Natural
Environments
O.I.P.: U.K. £120.00
U.S. $250.00

U.K.: £120.00
U.S.: $250.00
Can.: –

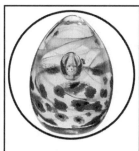

POPPY MEADOW
Designer: Helen MacDonald
Type: Weight – Domed
Issued: 2003
Status: Active
Series: Natural
Environments
O.I.P.: U.K. £39.00
U.S. $80.00

U.K.: £39.95
U.S.: $85.00
Can.: –

PRECIOUS JEWEL – ORCHID
Designer: Helen MacDonald
Type: Weight – Sculptured
facets
Issued: 2003 in a limited
edition of 250
Status: Fully subscribed
Series: Floral Inspired
O.I.P.: U.K. £199.00
U.S. $450.00

U.K.: £200.00
U.S.: $400.00
Can.: $525.00

PRIDE and BEAUTY

Designer:	Helen MacDonald
Type:	Weight – Low Dome
Issued:	2003-2003
Status:	Closed
Series:	Collectors' Society Annual Piece
O.I.P.:	U.K. £99.00
	U.S. $200.00
U.K.:	£100.00
U.S.:	$200.00
Can.:	$260.00

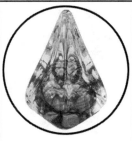

PYRAMID TWISTS

Designer:	Helen MacDonald
Type:	Weight – Teardrop
Colour:	1. Black
	2. Blue
	3. Green
	4. Pink
	5. Red
Issued:	2003
Status:	Active
Series:	Unlimited – Modern Design
O.I.P.:	U.K. £19.95
	U.S. $40.00
U.K.:	£19.95
U.S.:	$45.00
Can.:	–

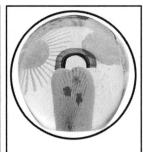

RAINBOW MEADOW

Designer:	Sarah Peterson
Type:	Weight – Spherical
Issued:	2003
Status:	Active
Series:	Fantasy Island
O.I.P.:	U.K. £150.00
	U.S. $300.00
U.K.:	£150.00
U.S.:	$325.00
Can.:	–

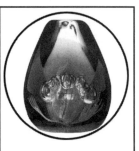

RAINFOREST

Designer:	Helen MacDonald
Type:	Weight – Domed
Issued:	2003 in a limited edition of 500
Status:	Active
Series:	Natural Environments
O.I.P.:	U.K. £120.00
	U.S. $250.00
U.K.:	£120.00
U.S.:	$250.00
Can.:	–

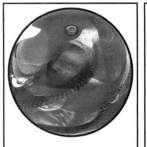

RIBBON DANCER

Designer:	Alastair MacIntosh
Type:	Weight – Spherical
Issued:	2003
Status:	Active
Series:	Unlimited – Modern Design
O.I.P.:	U.K. £39.00
	U.S. $95.00
U.K.:	£45.00
U.S.:	$95.00
Can.:	–

ROBERT THE BRUCE

Designer:	Helen MacDonald
Type:	Weight – Domed
Issued:	2003 in a limited edition of 500
Status:	Active
Series:	British Myths and Legends
O.I.P.:	U.K. £150.00
	U.S. $325.00
U.K.:	£150.00
U.S.:	$325.00
Can.:	–

ROX

Designer:	Alastair MacIntosh
Type:	Weight – Pebble
Colour:	1. Amethyst, black and white
	2. Amethyst, green and green
	3. Clear, green and green
	4. Clear, pink and blue
	5. Clear, red and blue
	6. Clear, yellow and blue
Issued:	2003
Status:	Active
Series:	Unlimited – Modern Design
O.I.P.:	U.K. £14.95
	U.S. $35.00
U.K.:	£14.95
U.S.:	$35.00
Can.:	–

SAILING AWAY
Designer: Helen MacDonald
Type: Weight – Spherical
Issued: 2003
Status: Active
Series: Blue and White Treasures
O.I.P.: U.K. £45.00
U.S. $95.00

U.K.: £45.00
U.S.: $95.00
Can.: –

SAILING BY
Designer: Sarah Peterson
Type: Weight – Spherical
Issued: 2003
Status: Active
Series: Fantasy Island
O.I.P.: U.K. £150.00
U.S. $300.00

U.K.: £150.00
U.S.: $325.00
Can.: –

SEEDS OF TIME
Designer: Sarah Peterson
Type: Weight – Spherical
Issued: 2003
Status: Active
Series: Unlimited – Modern Design
O.I.P.: U.K. £45.00
U.S. $100.00

U.K.: £ 49.00
U.S.: $110.00
Can.: –

SHOOTING STAR
Designer: Alastair MacIntosh
Type: Weight – Domed
Issued: 2003-2003
Status: Closed
Series: Collectors' Society Annual Weight
O.I.P.: U.K. £120.00
U.S. $250.00

U.K.: £120.00
U.S.: $250.00
Can.: $300.00

SPRING
Style Three
Designer: Alastair MacIntosh
Type: Weight – Spherical
Issued: 2003
Status: Active
Series: Pastures New
O.I.P.: U.K. £39.00
U.S. $80.00

U.K.: £39.00
U.S.: $80.00
Can.: –

SUMMER
Style Three
Designer: Alastair MacIntosh
Type: Weight – Spherical
Issued: 2003
Status: Active
Series: Pastures New
O.I.P.: U.K. £39.00
U.S. $80.00

U.K.: £39.00
U.S.: $80.00
Can.: –

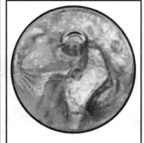

SUMMER HAZE
Designer: Sarah Peterson
Type: Weight – Spherical
Issued: 2003 - 2003
Status: Closed
Series: Collectors' Society Complimentary Weight

U.K.: £30.00
U.S.: $60.00
Can.: $80.00

SWEET MAGIC
Designer: Alastair MacIntosh
Type: Weight – Domed, faceted
Issued: 2003 in a limited edition of 100
Status: Active
Series: Floral Inspired
O.I.P.: U.K. £275.00
U.S. $575.00

U.K.: £275.00
U.S.: $575.00
Can.: –

TANTALISE
Designer: Helen MacDonald
Type: Weight – Domed
Issued: 2003 in a limited edition of 250
Status: Active
Series: Floral Inspired
O.I.P.: U.K. £175.00
U.S. $375.00

U.K.: £175.00
U.S.: $375.00
Can.: –

THATCHING
Designer: Allan Scott
Type: Weight – Spherical, facets
Issued: 2003 in a limited edition of 100
Status: Closed
Series: Countryside Crafts
O.I.P.: U.K. £225.00
U.S. $500.00

U.K.: £225.00
U.S.: $450.00
Can.: $575.00

TRANQUIL OASIS
Designer: Caithness Design Studios
Type: Weight – Domed
Issued: 2003
Status: Closed
Series: Collectors' Society Event Weight
O.I.P.: U.K. £55.00
U.S. $125.00

U.K.: £ 55.00
U.S.: $125.00
Can.: $165.00

TRANSYLVANIA
Designer: Helen MacDonald
Type: Domed
Issued: 2003 in a limited edition of 250
Status: Active
Series: Pictorial
O.I.P.: £195.00

U.K.: £195.00
U.S.: $425.00
Can.: –

UNDYING LOVE
Designer: Helen MacDonald
Type: Spherical
Issued: 2003
Status: Active
Series: Blue and White Treasures
O.I.P.: U.K. £45.00
U.S. $95.00

U.K.: £45.00
U.S.: $95.00
Can.: –

WILLOW
Designer: Helen MacDonald
Type: Domed
Issued: 2003 in a limited edition of 100
Status: Active
Series: Blue and White Treasures
O.I.P.: U.K. £485.00
U.S. $1,000.00

U.K.: £ 485.00
U.S.: $1,000.00
Can.: –

WINTER
Style Three
Designer: Alastair MacIntosh
Type: Weight – Spherical
Issued: 2003
Status: Active
Series: Pastures New
O.I.P.: U.K. £39.00
U.S. $80.00

U.K.: £39.00
U.S.: $80.00
Can.: –

LIMITED EDITIONS

Wildcard

Silver Orb

Emerald Roulette

Landing Zone

Ice Dance

Eurythmic

Elegance

Safe Haven

Exotica

LIMITED EDITIONS

Crescendo

Indian Summer

Strawberry Surprise

Snow Dance

Cauldron Aqua

40 Fathoms

Soothsayer

Myriad
(Style One)

Etheria

LIMITED EDITIONS

Moroccan Nights

Stardust

Siren
(Magnum)

Amber Gambler

Creation

White Heat

Babylon

Covenant

Dream Flower

Liberté

LIMITED EDITIONS

Dream Weaver

Lucky Clover

Precious Jewel (Rose)

Red Alert

Scarlet Fandango

Hydrofoil

Close Harmony

Symphony

Spindrift

MODERN DESIGNS UNLIMITED

Splashdown

Vibrance

Diabolo

Daydreams

Scimitar

Extravaganza (Black)

Force Ten

Burning Ambition

Seeds of Time

MODERN DESIGNS UNLIMITED

Parachute

Silkscreen

Wavecrest

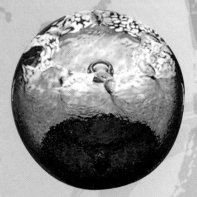

Blue Splash

Inner Circle

Fountain of Youth

Cupcake

Flower of Scotland

Cosmic Fountain

MODERN DESIGNS UNLIMITED

Primary Colours

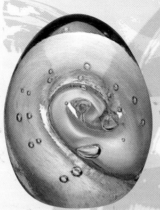

Cinderella

Cascade
(Style Two)

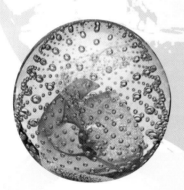

Pink Champagne

Watercolours

Floral Dance (Pink)

Whirlpool

Déjà Vu

Desert Spring

MODERN DESIGNS UNLIMITED

Space Station Zebra
(Annual Unlimited Edition 2004)

Ascension

Escapade

Quicksilver

Object D'Art

Vortice (Red)

Luscious Lashes (Blue & Red)

Starwatch (Yellow)

Ruffles

ISSUES OF 2004

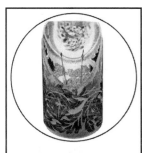

ACANTHUS

Designer: Helen MacDonald
Type: Weight – Cylindrical
Colour: Greens and yellow
Issued: 2004 in a limited edition of 170
Status: Active
Series: William Morris
O.I.P.: U.K. £150.00
U.S. $350.00

U.K.: £150.00
U.S.: $350.00
Can.: –

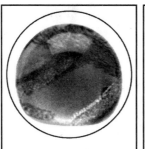

ALLEGRO

Designer: Caithness Design Studios
Type: Weight – Dome
Size: Standard
Colour: 1. Berry
2. Lilac
3. Pearl
Issued: 2004
Status: Active
Series: Art glass
O.I.P.: U.K. £21.95
U.S. $50.00

U.K.: £21.95
U.S.: $50.00
Can.: –

AMBROSIA

Designer: Caithness Design Studios
Type: Weight – Spherical
Issued: 2004
Status: Active
Series: Events 2004
O.I.P.: U.K. £45.00
U.S. $110.00

U.K.: £ 45.00
U.S.: $110.00
Can.: –

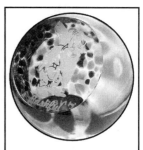

BASHFUL™

Designer: Helen MacDonald
Type: Weight – Spherical
Size: Miniature
Issued: 2004
Status: Active
Series: Snow White and the Seven Dwarfs
O.I.P.: U.K. £21.00
U.S. $40.00

U.K.: £21.00
U.S.: $40.00
Can.: –

BELLADONNA

Designer: Allan Scott
Type: Weight – spherical
Issued: 2004 in a limited edition of 100
Status: Active
Series: Whitefriars Collection
O.I.P.: U.K. £195.00
U.S. $475.00

U.K.: £195.00
U.S.: $475.00
Can.: –

BEYOND THE STARS

Designer: Sarah Peterson
Type: Weight – domed
Issued: 2004 in a limited edition of 500
Status: Active
Series: Space
O.I.P.: U.K. £120.00
U.S. $300.00

U.K.: £120.00
U.S.: $300.00
Can.: –

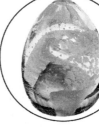

BLESSINGS

Designer: Helen MacDonald
Type: Weight – Domed
Colour: 1. Aqua
2. Blue
3. Gold
4. Green
5. Pink
6. White
Issued: 2004
Status: Active
Series: Miniatures
O.I.P.: U.K. £14.95
U.S. $35.00

U.K.: £14.95
U.S.: $35.00
Can.: –

BLUE BLOSSOM

Designer: Helen MacDonald
Type: Weight – Spherical, facets
Issued: 2004 in a limited edition of 170
Status: Active
Series: William Morris
O.I.P.: U.K. £130.00
U.S. $300.00

U.K.: £130.00
U.S.: $300.00
Can.: –

BORNEO

Designer: Helen MacDonald
Type: Weight – Domed
Issued: 2004 in a limited
edition of 250
Status: Active
Series: Floral Garden
O.I.P.: U.K. £225.00
U.S. $550.00

U.K.: £225.00
U.S.: $550.00
Can.: –

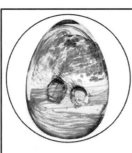

BRAIN WAVES AMBER

Designer: Helen MacDonald
Type: Weight – Domed
Size: Standard
Issued: 2004
Status: Active
Series: Unlimited
O.I.P.: U.K. £34.95
U.S. $75.00

U.K.: £34.95
U.S.: $75.00
Can.: –

BUTTERFLIES
Style Three
Designer: Gordon Hendry
Type: Weight – Domed
Size: Standard
Issued: 2004
Status: Active
Series: Images
O.I.P.: U.K. £42.00
U.S. $90.00

U.K.: £42.00
U.S.: $90.00
Can.: –

CASTLE IN THE SKY

Designer: Helen MacDonald
Type: Weight – Tall Dome
Issued: 2004 in a limited
edition of 500
Status: Active
Series: Snow White and the
Seven Dwarfs
O.I.P.: U.K. £125.00
U.S. $250.00

U.K.: £125.00
U.S.: $250.00
Can.: –

CATS

Designer: Gordon Hendry
Type: Weight – Domed
Size: Standard
Issued: 2004
Status: Active
Series: Images
O.I.P.: U.K. £42.00
U.S. $90.00

U.K.: £42.00
U.S.: $90.00
Can.: –

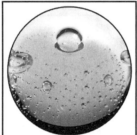

CIRCLE OF FRIENDS –
AMETHYST
Designer: Helen MacDonald
Type: Weight – Spherical
Issued: 2004 - 2004
Status: Active
Series: Annual Unlimited
Edition
O.I.P.: U.K. £34.95
U.S. $75.00

U.K.: £34.95
U.S.: $75.00
Can.: –

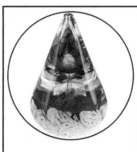

COMMANDING THE WAVES

Designer: Helen MacDonald
Type: Weight – Domed,
facets
Issued: 2004 in a limited
edition of 500
Status: Active
Series: Fantasia
O.I.P.: U.K. £79.00
U.S. $150.00

U.K.: £ 79.00
U.S.: $150.00
Can.: –

COOL BLUE

Designer: Helen MacDonald
Type: Weight – Spherical
Issued: 2004 in a limited
edition of 500
Status: Active
Series: Floral Garden
O.I.P.: U.K. £85.00
U.S. $200.00

U.K.: £ 85.00
U.S.: $200.00
Can.: –

CUPCAKE
Designer: Helen MacDonald
Type: Weight – Spherical
Issued: 2004
Status: Active
Series: Unlimited - Standard
O.I.P.: U.K. £39.95
U.S. $85.00

U.K.: £39.95
U.S.: $85.00
Can.: –

CURIOUS CATS
Designer: Helen MacDonald
Type: Weight – Spherical
Size: Standard
Issued: 2004
Status: Active
Series: Creatures Great and Small
O.I.P.: U.K. £37.50
U.S. $85.00

U.K.: £37.50
U.S.: $85.00
Can.: –

DELIVERER
Designer: Helen MacDonald
Type: Weight – Domed
Issued: 2004 in a limited edition of 250
Status: Active
Series: Abstract
O.I.P.: U.K. £125.00
U.S. $300.00

U.K.: £125.00
U.S.: $300.00
Can.: –

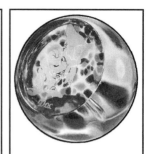

DOC™
Designer: Helen MacDonald
Type: Weight – Spherical
Size: Miniature
Issued: 2004
Status: Active
Series: Snow White and the Seven Dwarfs
O.I.P.: U.K. £21.00
U.S. $40.00

U.K.: £21.00
U.S.: $40.00
Can.: –

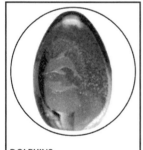

DOLPHINS
Designer: Gordon Hendry
Type: Weight – Dome
Size: Standard
Issued: 2004
Status: Active
Series: Images
O.I.P.: U.K. £42.00
U.S. $90.00

U.K.: £42.00
U.S.: $90.00
Can.: –

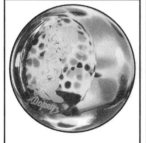

DOPEY™
Designer: Helen MacDonald
Type: Weight – Spherical
Size: Miniature
Issued: 2004
Status: Active
Series: Snow White and the Seven Dwarfs
O.I.P.: U.K. £21.00
U.S. $40.00

U.K.: £21.00
U.S.: $40.00
Can.: –

DWARFS' COTTAGE™, THE
Designer: Helen MacDonald
Type: Weight – Spherical
Size: Standard
Issued: 2004
Status: Active
Series: Snow White and the Seven Dwarfs
O.I.P.: U.K. £60.00
U.S. $125.00

U.K.: £ 60.00
U.S.: $125.00
Can.: –

EARTH
Style Four
Designer: Linda Campbell
Type: Weight – Square Lampwork
Issued: 2004 in a limited edition of 100
Status: Active
Series: Tian De Ren
O.I.P.: U.K. £225.00
U.S. $550.00

U.K.: £225.00
U.S.: $550.00
Can.: –

Note: Contains a Caithness Glass signature cane.

ENCHANTED APPLE
Designer: Helen MacDonald
Type: Weight – Spherical
Size: Standard
Issued: 2004
Status: Active
Series: Snow White and
          the Seven Dwarfs
O.I.P.:   U.K. £85.00
          U.S. $175.00

U.K.:   £ 85.00
U.S.: $175.00
Can.:   –

FLAMENCO
Style Two
Designer: Caithness Design
          Studios
Type: Weight – Dome
Size: Medium
Colour: 1. Dawn
          2. Dusk
          3. Rainbow
Issued: 2004
Status: Active
Series: Artglass
O.I.P.:   U.K. £24.95
          U.S. $50.00

U.K.:   £24.95
U.S.: $50.00
Can.:   –

FLAMING BEAUTY
Designer: Helen MacDonald
Type: Weight – Spherical
Issued: 2004 in a limited
          edition of 500
Status: Active
Series: Floral Garden
O.I.P.:   U.K. £85.00
          U.S. $200.00

U.K.:   £ 85.00
U.S.: $200.00
Can.:   –

FLORAL AWAKENING
Designer: Helen MacDonald
Type: Weight – Spherical
Size: Magnum
Issued: 2004 in a limited
          edition of 350
Status: Active
Series: Fantasia Floral Ballet
O.I.P.:   U.K. £229.00
          U.S. $475.00

U.K.:   £229.00
U.S.: $475.00
Can.:   –

FLORAL BALLET DANCER
Designer: Helen MacDonald
Type: Weight – Low
          Dome
Issued: 2004
Status: Active
Series: Fantasia Floral Ballet
O.I.P.:   U.K. £50.00
          U.S. $85.00

U.K.:   £50.00
U.S.: $85.00
Can.:   –

FLORAL DREAM
Designer: Helen MacDonald
Type: Weight – Spherical
Size: Magnum
Issued: 2004 in a limited
          edition of 100
Status: Active
Series: Blue and White
          Treasures
O.I.P.:   U.K. £375.00
          U.S. $900.00

U.K.:   £375.00
U.S.: $900.00
Can.:   –

FLORAL MIST PERFUME
BOTTLE
Designer: Sarah Peterson
Type: Perfume Bottle
Issued: 2004
Status: Active
Series: Unknown
O.I.P.:   U.K. £39.95
          U.S. $100.00

U.K.:   £ 39.95
U.S.: $100.00
Can.:   –

FORTUNE
Designer: Helen MacDonald
Type: Weight – domed
Size: Miniature
Issued: 2004
Status: Active
Series: Collectors' Society
          Complimentary
          Weight
U.K.:   –
U.S.:   –
Can.:   –

**GALILEO'S THERMOMETER
60 DEGREES**
Designer: Helen MacDonald
Type: Weight – Domed
Issued: 2004-2004
Status: Active
Series: Annual Unlimited
Edition
O.I.P.: U.K. £49.00
U.S. $120.00

U.K.: £ 49.00
U.S.: $120.00
Can.: –

Note: Inspired by Galilei's
thermometer from the
17th century. Number
one of three.

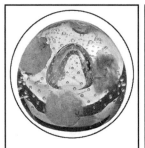

GENTLE TOUCH
Designer: Helen MacDonald
Type: Weight – Domed
Size: Magnum
Issued: 2004 in a limited
edition of 500
Status: Active
Series: Floral Garden
O.I.P.: U.K. £95.00
U.S. $225.00

U.K.: £ 95.00
U.S.: $225.00
Can.: –

GOLDEN FANCY
Designer: Sarah Peterson
Type: Weight – Spherical
Issued: 2004 in a limited
edition of 250
Status: Active
Series: Floral Garden
O.I.P.: U.K. £130.00
U.S. $300.00

U.K.: £130.00
U.S.: $300.00
Can.: –

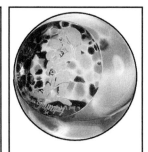

GRUMPY™
Designer: Helen MacDonald
Type: Weight – Spherical
Size: Miniature
Issued: 2004
Status: Active
Series: Snow White and
the Seven Dwarfs
O.I.P.: U.K. £21.00
U.S. $40.00

U.K.: £21.00
U.S.: $40.00
Can.: –

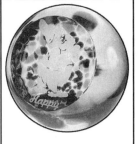

HAPPY™
Designer: Helen MacDonald
Type: Weight – Spherical
Size: Miniature
Issued: 2004
Status: Active
Series: Snow White and
the Seven Dwarfs
O.I.P.: U.K. £21.00
U.S. $40.00

U.K.: £21.00
U.S.: $40.00
Can.: –

HEAVEN
Designer: Linda Campbell
Type: Weight – Square,
lampwork
Issued: 2004 in a limited
edition of 100
Status: Active
Series: Tian De Ren
O.I.P.: U.K. £225.00
U.S. $550.00

U.K.: £225.00
U.S.: $550.00
Can.: –

Note: Contains a Caithness
Glass signature cane.

HELLEBORE
Designer: Allan Scott
Type: Weight – Spherical
Issued: 2004 in a limited
edition of 100
Status: Active
Series: Whitefriars Collection
O.I.P.: U.K. £195.00
U.S. $475.00

U.K.: £195.00
U.S.: $475.00
Can.: –

HERITAGE
Designer: Helen MacDonald
Type: Weight – Domed
Issued: 2004 in a limited
edition of 250
Status: Active
Series: Dance
O.I.P.: U.K. £150.00
U.S. $350.00

U.K.: £150.00
U.S.: $350.00
Can.: –

HIGHLAND DANCER
Designer: Helen MacDonald
Type: Weight – Domed
Issued: 2004 in a limited
edition of 250
Status: Active
Series: Dance
O.I.P.: U.K. £195.00
U.S. $475.00

U.K.: £195.00
U.S.: $475.00
Can.: –

HUMANITY
Designer: Linda Campbell
Type: Weight – Square,
lampwork
Issued: 2004 in a limited
edition of 100
Status: Active
Series: Tian De Ren
O.I.P.: U.K. £225.00
U.S. $550.00

U.K.: £225.00
U.S.: $550.00
Can.: –

Note: Contains a Caithness
Glass signature cane.

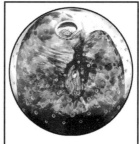

INDULGENCE
Designer: Helen MacDonald
Type: Weight – Spherical
Issued: 2004
Status: Active
Series: Unlimited – Standard
O.I.P.: U.K. £29.95
U.S. $65.00

U.K.: £29.95
U.S.: $65.00
Can.: –

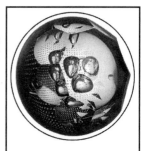

INTO THE LIGHT
Designer: Sarah Peterson
Type: Weight – Spherical,
facets
Size: Magnum
Issued: 2004-2004
Status: Active
Series: Collectors' Society
Annual Weight
O.I.P.: U.K. £120.00
U.S. $285.00

U.K.: £120.00
U.S.: $285.00
Can.: –

LAZY AFTERNOON
Designer: Helen MacDonald
Type: Weight – Tear Drop
Issued: 2003 in a limited
edition of 500
Status: Active
Series: Dawn to Dusk
O.I.P.: U.K. £125.00
U.S. $300.00

U.K.: £125.00
U.S.: $300.00
Can.: –

**LAZY AFTERNOON
PERFUME BOTTLE**
Designer: Helen MacDonald
Type: Perfume Bottle
Issued: 2004 in a limited
edition of 500
Status: Active
Series: Dawn to Dusk
O.I.P.: U.K. £195.00
U.S. $475.00

U.K.: £195.00
U.S.: $475.00
Can.: –

**MAGIC MIRROR ON THE
WALL™**
Designer: Helen MacDonald
Type: Weight – Domed
Issued: 2004 in a limited
edition of 750
Status: Active
Series: Snow White and
the Seven Dwarfs
O.I.P.: U.K. £140.00
U.S. $275.00

U.K.: £140.00
U.S.: $275.00
Can.: –

MOON WAVES
Designer: Sarah Peterson
Type: Weight – Spherical
Size: Magnum
Issued: 2004 in a limited
edition of 500
Status: Active
Series: Space
O.I.P.: U.K. £99.00
U.S. $250.00

U.K.: £ 99.00
U.S.: $250.00
Can.: –

OLEANDER
Designer: Allan Scott
Type: Weight – Spherical
Issued: 2004 in a limited edition of 100
Status: Active
Series: Whitefriars Collection
O.I.P.: U.K. £195.00
U.S. $475.00
U.K.: £195.00
U.S.: $475.00
Can.: –

ORBITAL JOURNEY
Designer: Helen MacDonald
Type: Weight – Spherical
Issued: 2004 in a limited edition of 500
Status: Active
Series: Space
O.I.P.: U.K. £75.00
U.S. $180.00
U.K.: £ 75.00
U.S.: $180.00
Can.: –

ORCHIDS
Style Three
Designer: Gordon Hendry
Type: Weight – Domed
Size: Standard
Issued: 2004
Status: Active
Series: Images
O.I.P.: U.K. £42.00
U.S. $90.00
U.K.: £42.00
U.S.: $90.00
Can.: –

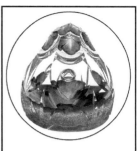

PANSY PASSION
Designer: Helen MacDonald
Type: Weight – Domed, facets
Issued: 2004 in a limited edition of 250
Status: Active
Series: Floral Garden
O.I.P.: U.K. £130.00
U.S. $300.00
U.K.: £130.00
U.S.: $300.00
Can.: –

PAPAVER
Designer: Allan Scott
Type: Weight – Spherical
Issued: 2004 in a limited edition of 100
Status: Active
Series: Whitefriars Collection
O.I.P.: U.K. £195.00
U.S. $475.00
U.K.: £195.00
U.S.: $475.00
Can.: –

PEACEFUL PARADISE
Designer: Helen MacDonald
Type: Weight – Domed
Size: Magnum
Issued: 2004 in a limited edition of 250
Status: Active
Series: Abstract
O.I.P.: U.K. £175.00
U.S. $425.00
U.K.: £175.00
U.S.: $425.00
Can.: –

POLAR PLAYTIME
Designer: Helen MacDonald
Type: Weight – Spherical
Size: Standard
Issued: 2004
Status: Active
Series: Creatures Great and Small
O.I.P.: U.K. £37.50
U.S. $85.00
U.K.: £37.50
U.S.: $85.00
Can.: –

POTREADORA
Designer: Helen MacDonald
Type: Weight – Domed
Issued: 2004 in a limited edition of 500
Status: Active
Series: Abstract
O.I.P.: U.K. £75.00
U.S. $180.00
U.K.: £ 75.00
U.S.: $180.00
Can.: –

PRECIOUS JEWEL – ROSE
Designer: Helen MacDonald
Type: Weight – Domed
Issued: 2004 in a limited edition of 250
Status: Active
Series: Floral Garden
O.I.P.: U.K. £199.00
U.S. $475.00

U.K.: £199.00
U.S.: $475.00
Can.: –

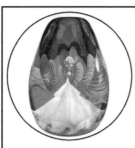

PRIMA BALLERINA
Style Two
Designer: Helen MacDonald
Type: Weight – Domed
Issued: 2004 in a limited edition of 500
Status: Active
Series: Fantasia Floral Ballet
O.I.P.: U.K. £149.00
U.S. $300.00

U.K.: £149.00
U.S.: $300.00
Can.: –

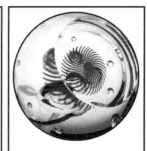

RED CAROUSEL
Designer: Sarah Peterson
Type: Weight – spherical
Issued: 2004 in a limited edition of 500
Status: Active
Series: Abstract
O.I.P.: U.K. £75.00
U.S. $175.00

U.K.: £ 75.00
U.S.: $175.00
Can.: –

RED ROSE
Style Four
Designer: Helen MacDonald
Type: Weight – Domed
Issued: 2004 in a limited edition of 170
Status: Active
Series: William Morris
O.I.P.: U.K. £165.00
U.S. $400.00

U.K.: £165.00
U.S.: $400.00
Can.: –

RENNIE'S GLASGOW ROSE
Designer: Sarah Peterson
Type: Weight – Spherical
Issued: 2004
Size: Medium
Status: Active
Series: Rennie MacIntosh Collection
O.I.P.: U.K. £32.00
U.S. $75.00

U.K.: £32.00
U.S.: $75.00
Can.: –

RENNIE'S ROSE
Designer: Sarah Peterson
Type: Weight – Domed
Issued: 2004
Status: Active
Series: Rennie MacIntosh Collection
O.I.P.: U.K. £55.00
U.S. $130.00

U.K.: £ 55.00
U.S.: $130.00
Can.: –

RENNIE'S WINDOW
Designer: Sarah Peterson
Type: Weight – Spherical
Issued: 2004
Status: Active
Series: Rennie Macintosh Collection
O.I.P.: U.K. £59.00
U.S. $140.00

U.K.: £ 59.00
U.S.: $140.00
Can.: –

ROSES
Designer: Gordon Hendry
Type: Weight – Domed
Size: Standard
Issued: 2004
Status: Active
Series: Images
O.I.P.: U.K. £42.00
U.S. $90.00

U.K.: £42.00
U.S.: $90.00
Can.: –

SAND DANCERS

Designer: Sarah Peterson
Type: Weight – Tear Drop
Issued: 2004
Status: Active
Series: Unlimited Standard
O.I.P.: U.K. £39.95
U.S. $85.00

U.K.: £39.95
U.S.: $85.00
Can.: –

SCARLET TWISTER

Designer: Helen MacDonald
Type: Weight – Domed
Issued: 2004
Status: Active
Series: Unlimited Standard
O.I.P.: U.K. £39.95
U.S. $85.00

U.K.: £39.95
U.S.: $85.00
Can.: –

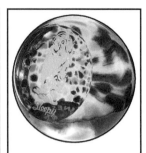

SHINING THROUGH

Designer: Linda Campbell
Type: Weight – Spherical
Lampwork
Issued: 2004 in a limited
edition of 200
Status: Active
Series: Whitefriars Collection
O.I.P.: U.K. £150.00
U.S. $350.00

U.K.: £150.00
U.S.: $350.00
Can.: –

SLEEPY™

Designer: Helen MacDonald
Type: Weight – Spherical
Size: Miniature
Issued: 2004
Status: Active
Series: Snow White and
the Seven Dwarfs
O.I.P.: U.K. £21.00
U.S. $40.00

U.K.: £21.00
U.S.: $40.00
Can.: –

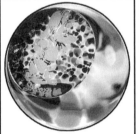

SNEEZY™

Designer: Helen MacDonald
Type: Weight – Spherical
Size: Miniature
Issued: 2004
Status: Active
Series: Snow White and
the Seven Dwarfs
O.I.P.: U.K. £21.00
U.S. $40.00

U.K.: £21.00
U.S.: $40.00
Can.: –

SOARING EAGLES

Designer: Helen MacDonald
Type: Weight – Spherical
Size: Standard
Issued: 2004
Status: Active
Series: Creatures Great
and Small
O.I.P.: U.K. £37.50
U.S. $85.00

U.K.: £37.50
U.S.: $85.00
Can.: –

SOLO PERFORMANCE

Designer: Helen MacDonald
Type: Weight –
Cylindrical
Issued: 2004 in a limited
edition of 500
Status: Active
Series: Abstract
O.I.P.: U.K. £99.00
U.S. $235.00

U.K.: £ 99.00
U.S.: $235.00
Can.: –

SPACE STATION ZEBRA

Designer: Sarah Peterson
Type: Weight – Domed
Issued: 2004
Status: Active
Series: Annual Unlimited
Edition
O.I.P.: U.K. £45.00
U.S. $100.00

U.K.: £ 45.00
U.S.: $100.00
Can.: –

SPIRAL HARMONY

Designer: Gordon Hendry
Type: Weight – Domed
Issued: 2004 in a limited
edition of 500
Status: Active
Series: Abstract
O.I.P.: U.K. £75.00
U.S. $180.00

U.K.: £ 75.00
U.S.: $180.00
Can.: –

SPIRAL RHYTHM

Designer: Gordon Hendry
Type: Weight – Domed
Issued: 2004 in a limited
edition of 500
Status: Active
Series: Abstract
O.I.P.: U.K. £75.00
U.S. $180.00

U.K.: £ 75.00
U.S.: $180.00
Can.: –

SPIRAL TEMPO

Designer: Gordon Hendry
Type: Weight – Domed
Issued: 2004 in a limited
edition of 500
Status: Active
Series: Abstract
O.I.P.: U.K. £75.00
U.S. $180.00

U.K.: £ 75.00
U.S.: $180.00
Can.: –

SWEET COLUMBINE

Designer: Helen MacDonald
Type: Weight – Spherical
Issued: 2004 - 2004
Status: Active
Series: Collectors' Society
O.I.P.: U.K. £99.00
U.S. $235.00

U.K.: £ 99.00
U.S.: $235.00
Can.: –

TROPICAL WONDER

Designer: Helen MacDonald
Type: Weight – Spherical
Issued: 2004 in a limited
edition of 500
Status: Active
Series: Floral Garden
O.I.P.: U.K. £85.00
U.S. $200.00

U.K.: £ 85.00
U.S.: $200.00
Can.: –

TRUMPET CALL

Designer: Helen MacDonald
Type: Weight – Spherical
Size: Standard
Issued: 2004
Status: Active
Series: Creatures Great
and Small
O.I.P.: U.K. £37.50
U.S. $85.00

U.K.: £37.50
U.S.: $85.00
Can.: –

TWEED

Designer: Helen MacDonald
Type: Weight – Spherical
Issued: 2004
Status: Active
Series: Annual Unlimited
Edition
O.I.P.: U.K. £39.95
U.S. $85.00

U.K.: £39.95
U.S.: $85.00
Can.: –

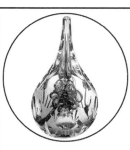

UP, UP AND AWAY

Designer: Helen MacDonald
Type: Weight – Tear Drop
Drawn
Issued: 2004 in a limited
edition of 250
Status: Active
Series: Abstract
O.I.P.: U.K. £195.00
U.S. $475.00

U.K.: £195.00
U.S.: $475.00
Can.: –

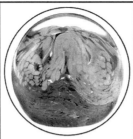

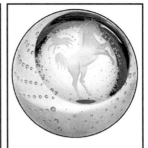

WEB SPINNERS

Designer:	Sarah Peterson
Type:	Weight – Spherical
Issued:	2004 in a limited edition of 500
Status:	Active
Series:	Abstract
O.I.P.:	U.K. £75.00
	U.S. $175.00
U.K.:	£ 75.00
U.S.:	$175.00
Can.:	–

WELL WISHER

Designer:	Helen MacDonald
Type:	Weight – Spherical
Issued:	2004
Status:	Active
Series:	Unlimited Standard
O.I.P.:	U.K. £29.95
	U.S. $65.00
U.K.:	£29.95
U.S.:	$65.00
Can.:	–

WILD HORSES

Designer:	Helen MacDonald
Type:	Weight – Spherical
Size:	Standard
Issued:	2004
Status:	Active
Series:	Creatures Great and Small
O.I.P.:	U.K. £37.50
	U.S. $85.00
U.K.:	£37.50
U.S.:	$85.00
Can.:	–

WISE OLD OWLS

Designer:	Helen MacDonald
Type:	Weight – Spherical
Size:	Standard
Issued:	2004
Status:	Active
Series:	Creatures Great and Small
O.I.P.:	U.K. £37.50
	U.S. $85.00
U.K.:	£37.50
U.S.:	$85.00
Can.:	–

Pagoda Orchid

COMMISSIONED WEIGHTS

ANTHONY JACKSON CHINA AND GLASSWARE BLACKBURN, U.K.

ROCKET, THE

Designer:	Caithness Engraving Studios
Type:	Weight – Spherical, engraved
Issued:	1980 in a limited edition of 1,000
Status:	Closed at No. 250
O.I.P.:	£57.60
U.K.:	£ 75.00
U.S.:	$150.00
Can.:	$200.00

ANTIQUES LIFESTYLE MAGAZINE

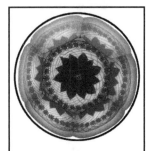

PURPLE CLEMATIS

Designer:	Colin Terris
Type:	Weight – Spherical
Issued:	2000 in a limited edition of 100
Status:	Closed at No. 57
O.I.P.:	U.K. £100.00
	U.S. $175.00
U.K.:	£100.00
U.S.:	$200.00
Can.:	$250.00

ART INSTITUTE OF CHICAGO
CHICAGO, U.S.

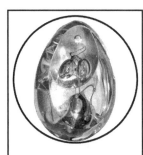   

FESTIVAL OF COLOUR
Designer: Colin Terris
Type: Weight – Domed
Issued: 1999 in a limited
edition of 75
Status: Fully subscribed
O.I.P.: U.S. $275.00

U.K.: £150.00
U.S.: $275.00
Can.: $350.00

ORCHID
Style Three
Designer: Allan Scott
Type: Weight – Spherical
Issued: 1991 in a limited
edition of 150
Status: Fully subscribed
O.I.P.: U.S. $595.00

U.K.: £300.00
U.S.: $600.00
Can.: $800.00

TRANQUIL FLIGHT
Designer: Colin Terris
Type: Weight – Spherical
Issued: 1998 in a limited
edition of 75
Status: Fully subscribed
O.I.P.: U.S. $310.00

U.K.: £150.00
U.S.: $300.00
Can.: $400.00

WATERLILY IMPRESSIONS
Designer: Colin Terris
Type: Weight – Spherical
Issued: 1994 in a limited
edition of 250
Status: Fully subscribed
O.I.P.: U.S. $295.00

U.K.: £150.00
U.S.: $300.00
Can.: $400.00

ARTS WEST UNIQUE GIFTS
(SEATTLE)

SEATTLE SKYLINE
COMMEMORATING THE
MILLENNIUM YEAR
Designer: Unknown
Type: Spherical
Issued: 2000
Status: Closed
O.I.P.: $115.00

U.K.: £ 55.00
U.S.: $115.00
Can.: $150.00

ATLANTIC BRIDGE

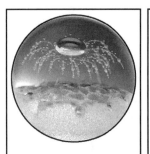

ALIEN ENCOUNTER
Designer: Helen MacDonald
Type: Weight –
Issued: 2000 in a limited
          edition of 500
Status: Closed at No. 21
O.I.P.:   U.S. $120.00

U.K.:   £100.00
U.S.: $200.00
Can.: $250.00

BURNING DESIRE
Designer: Helen MacDonald
Type: Weight – Domed
Issued: 2000 in a limited
          edition of 350
Status: Closed at No. 79
O.I.P.:   U.S. $145.00

U.K.:   £ 95.00
U.S.: $175.00
Can.: $225.00

DEEP SECRET
Designer: Alastair MacIntosh
Type: Weight – Spherical
Issued: 2001 in a limited
          edition of 500
Status: Closed at No. 17
O.I.P.:   U.S. $125.00

U.K.:   £100.00
U.S.: $200.00
Can.: $250.00

DOUBLE TAKE
Designer: Alastair MacIntosh
Type: Weight – Teardrop
Issued: 2001 in a limited
          edition of 350
Status: Closed at No. 49
O.I.P.:   U.S. $145.00

U.K.:   £100.00
U.S.: $200.00
Can.: $250.00

GALE FORCE
Designer: Helen MacDonald
Type: Weight – Spherical
Issued: 2000 in a limited
          edition of 750
Status: Closed at No. 47
O.I.P.:   U.S. $90.00

U.K.:   £100.00
U.S.: $200.00
Can.: $250.00

GIANT STEP
Designer: Alastair MacIntosh
Type: Weight – Spherical
Issued: 2001 in a limited
          edition of 350
Status: Closed at 16
O.I.P.:   U.S. $145.00

U.K.:   £100.00
U.S.: $200.00
Can.: $250.00

MAGICAL ROUNDABOUT
Designer: Helen MacDonald
Type: Weight – Teardrop
Issued: 1997 in a limited
          edition of 750
Status: Closed at No. 24
O.I.P.:   U.S. $140.00

U.K.:   £100.00
U.S.: $200.00
Can.: $250.00

ARTISTIC TREASURES
RICHMOND, U.K.

SOLAR FLOWER
Designer: Colin Terris
Type: Weight – Spherical
Issued: 1995 in a limited
          edition of 100
Status: Closed
O.I.P.:   £175.00

U.K.:   £175.00
U.S.: $350.00
Can.: $450.00

ASHBOURNE HOUSE
ASHBOURNE, U.K.

AMBIENCE
Designer: Colin Terris
Type: Weight – Spherical
Issued: 1996 in a limited
          edition of 75
Status: Closed
O.I.P.:   £115.00

U.K.:   £250.00
U.S.: $500.00
Can.: $650.00

CANDLELIGHT
Designer: Margot Thomson
Type: Weight – Domed
Issued: 1995 in a limited
          edition of 75
Status: Closed
O.I.P.:   £95.00

U.K.:   £250.00
U.S.: $500.00
Can.: $650.00

BERGSTROM-MAHLER MUSEUM
NEENAH, U.S.

MECCA

Designer: Colin Terris
Type: Weight – Spherical
Issued: 1989 in a limited
           edition of 100
Status: Fully subscribed
O.I.P.:   U.S. $195.00

U.K.:   £150.00
U.S.: $300.00
Can.: $400.00

Note: This weight was
        commissioned to
        celebrate the 1989 PCA
        Convention held in Nina,
        Wisconsin in 1980.
        (Paperweight Collectors
        Association)

MECCA MILLENNIUM

Designer: Colin Terris
Type: Weight – Domed
Issued: 1999 in a limited
           edition of 100
Status: Fully subscribed
O.I.P.:   U.S. $395.00

U.K.:   £200.00
U.S.: $400.00
Can.: $525.00

Photograph not
available
at press time

STAR OF WONDER

Designer: Colin Terris
Type: Weight – Unknown
Issued: 2001 in a limited
           edition of 75
Status: Fully subscribed
O.I.P.:   U.S. $100.00

U.K.:   £ 50.00
U.S.: $100.00
Can.: $128.00

BROOKS and BENTLEY

FOOTPRINTS
Designer: Gordon Hendry
Type: Weight – Domed
Issued: 2001 unlimited
Status: Closed
O.I.P.:   U.K. £88.00

U.K.:   £ 90.00
U.S.: $175.00
Can.: $225.00

QUEEN ELIZABETH II GOLDEN JUBILEE
Designer: Colin Terris
Type: Weight – Domed
Issued: 2001 in a limited
           edition of 950
Status: Closed at No. 25
O.I.P.:   U.K. £299.00

U.K.:   £300.00
U.S.: $600.00
Can.: $775.00

TUTANKHAMUN
Style One
Designer: Willie Bain
Type: Weight – Spherical
Issued: 2000 unlimited
Status: Closed
O.I.P.:   U.K. £45.00

U.K.:   £ 45.00
U.S.: $ 90.00
Can.: $125.00

C. D. PEACOCK
(CHICAGO)

**CHICAGO SKYLINE
COMMEMORATING THE
MILLENNIUM YEAR**

Designer: Unknown
Type: Spherical
Issued: 2000
Status: Closed
O.I.P.: $115.00

U.K.:   £ 55.00
U.S.: $115.00
Can.: $150.00

CASHS OF IRELAND

ANGEL FISH
Style Two
Designer: Willie Bain
Type: Weight – Spherical
Issued: 2002 Unlimited
Status: Closed
O.I.P.: Unknown

U.K.: Not
U.S.: Available
Can.:

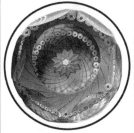

CHRISTMAS POINSETTIA 2000
Designer: Alastair MacIntosh
Type: Weight – Spherical, facets
Issued: 2000 in a limited edition of 150
Status: Fully subscribed
O.I.P.: U.S. $229.00

U.K.: £125.00
U.S.: $250.00
Can.: $325.00

DANCING DAFFODILS
Designer: Helen MacDonald
Type: Weight – Spherical
Issued: 2001 Unlimited
Status: Closed
O.I.P.: U.S. $89.00

U.K.: £ 50.00
U.S.: $100.00
Can.: $125.00

DANCING SHAMROCK
Designer: Helen MacDonald
Type: Weight – Spherical
Issued: 2000 Unlimited
Status: Closed
O.I.P.: U.S. $59.00

U.K.: £30.00
U.S.: $60.00
Can.: $80.00

FORGET ME NOT
Designer: Allan Scott
Type: Weight – Spherical
Size: Miniature
Issued: 1994
Status: Closed
O.I.P.: U.S. $49.00

U.K.: £25.00
U.S.: $50.00
Can.: $65.00

FUCHSIAS
Style Two
Designer: Margot Thomson
Type: Weight – Spherical
Issued: 1990 in a limited edition of 250
Status: Closed
O.I.P.: U.S. $169.00

U.K.: £ 85.00
U.S.: $175.00
Can.: $225.00

HOLLY and BELLS
Designer: Allan Scott
Type: Weight – Spherical
Issued: 1991 in a limited edition of 150
Status: Closed
O.I.P.: U.S. $159.00

U.K.: £ 85.00
U.S.: $175.00
Can.: $225.00

IRISH BOUQUET
Designer: Colin Terris
Type: Weight – Spherical
Issued: 1999 in a limited edition of 150
Status: Closed
O.I.P.: U.S. $189.00

U.K.: £100.00
U.S.: $200.00
Can.: $250.00

CASHS OF IRELAND (cont.)

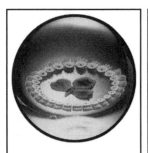

IRISH SHAMROCK

Designer: Allan Scott
Type: Weight – Spherical
Issued: 1997
Status: Closed
O.I.P.: U.S. $39.00

U.K.: £25.00
U.S.: $40.00
Can.: $55.00

IRISH WILD FLOWER

Designer: Allan Scott
Type: Weight – Spherical
Issued: 1998 in a limited
edition of 500
Status: Closed
O.I.P.: U.S. $159.00

U.K.: £ 85.00
U.S.: $160.00
Can.: $200.00

IRISH WILD FLOWERS

Designer: Allan Scott
Type: Weight – Spherical
Issued: 1997 in a limited
edition of 500
Status: Closed
O.I.P.: U.S. $139.00

U.K.: £ 75.00
U.S.: $140.00
Can.: $175.00

MINIATURE HEART
Style Three

Designer: Allan Scott
Type: Weight – Spherical
Issued: 1991
Status: Closed
O.I.P.: U.S. $59.00

U.K.: £ 40.00
U.S.: $ 75.00
Can.: $100.00

NATIVITY
Style Two

Designer: Helen MacDonald
Type: Weight – Unknown
Issued: 2003 Unlimited
Status: Closed
O.I.P.: Unknown

U.K.: Not
U.S.: Available
Can.:

PINK ENTWINED HEARTS

Designer: Alastair MacIntosh
Type: Weight – Spherical
Issued: 2002 Unlimited
Status: Closed
O.I.P.: Unknown

U.K.: Not
U.S.: Available
Can.:

RED CARNATION
Style Two

Designer: Alastair MacIntosh
Type: Weight – Unknown
Issued: 2002 Unlimited
Status: Closed
O.I.P.: Unknown

U.K.: Not
U.S.: Available
Can.:

SHAMROCK SNOWMAN

Designer: Gordon Henry
Type: Weight – Spherical
Issued: 2002 Unlimited
Status: Closed
O.I.P.: Unknown

U.K.: Not
U.S.: Available
Can.:

THE COCA-COLA COMPANY
ATLANTA, U.S.

ALWAYS...!
Designer: Helen MacDonald
Type: Weight – Spherical
Issued: 1998 in a limited edition of 750
Status: Closed
O.I.P.: U.S. $195.00

U.K.: £100.00
U.S.: $200.00
Can.: $275.00

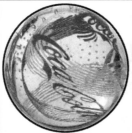

BUBBLES 'N STRIPES
Designer: Helen MacDonald
Type: Weight – Spherical
Issued: 1998 in a limited edition of 750
Status: Closed
O.I.P.: U.S. $150.00

U.K.: £ 75.00
U.S.: $150.00
Can.: $200.00

COOL CAP
Designer: Helen MacDonald
Type: Weight – Bottlecap
Issued: 1998 in a limited edition of 1,000
Status: Closed
O.I.P.: U.S. $95.00

U.K.: £ 50.00
U.S.: $100.00
Can.: $125.00

EFFERVESCENT RIBBONS
Designer: Helen MacDonald
Type: Weight – Spherical
Issued: 1998 in a limited edition of 1,000
Status: Closed
O.I.P.: U.S. $89.50

U.K.: £ 45.00
U.S.: $ 90.00
Can.: $125.00

FOUNTAIN MEMORIES
Designer: Helen MacDonald
Type: Weight – Tumbler style
Issued: 1998 in a limited edition of 750
Status: Closed
O.I.P.: U.S. $185.00

U.K.: £100.00
U.S.: $200.00
Can.: $275.00

ICE COLD
Designer: Helen MacDonald
Type: Weight – Spherical
Issued: 1998 in a limited edition of 100
Status: Closed
O.I.P.: U.S. $725.00

U.K.: £350.00
U.S.: $725.00
Can.: $950.00

INNER SPACE
Designer: Helen MacDonald
Type: Weight – Spherical
Issued: 1998 in a limited edition of 750
Status: Closed
O.I.P.: U.S. $165.00

U.K.: £ 85.00
U.S.: $165.00
Can.: $200.00

LIFE'S A BEAR...N-ICE!
Designer: Allan Scott
Type: Weight – Spherical
Issued: 1998 in a limited edition of 50
Status: Closed
O.I.P.: U.S. $895.00

U.K.: £ 450.00
U.S.: $ 900.00
Can.: $1,200.00

THE COCA-COLA COMPANY
ATLANTA, U.S. (Cont.)

REAL THING
Designer: Helen MacDonald
Type: Weight – Spherical
Issued: 1998 in a limited
edition of 1,000
Status: Closed
O.I.P.: U.S. $115.00

U.K.: £ 65.00
U.S.: $125.00
Can.: $150.00

RIBBONS MEMORIES
Designer: Helen MacDonald
Type: Weight – Spherical
Issued: 1998 in a limited
edition of 1,000
Status: Closed
O.I.P.: U.S. $99.50

U.K.: £ 50.00
U.S.: $100.00
Can.: $125.00

Note: The Coca-Cola weights
are issued in the U.S.
only.

RIBBONS WINDOW
Designer: Helen MacDonald
Type: Weight – Spherical
Issued: 1998 in a limited
edition of 1,000
Status: Closed
O.I.P.: U.S. $115.00

U.K.: £ 65.00
U.S.: $125.00
Can.: $150.00

COMPTON & WOODHOUSE

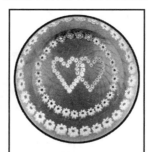

LUCKENBOOTH 2000
Designer: Caithness Design
Studios
Type: Weight – Spherical
Issued: 2000 in a limited
edition of 2000
Status: Unknown
O.I.P.: £85.00

U.K.: £ 85.00
U.S.: $175.00
Can.: $225.00

DAVID SANDBACH
LLANDUDNO, U.K.

BALLET

Designer:	Unknown
Type:	Weight – Spherical
Issued:	Unknown
Status:	Closed
Series:	Unknown
O.I.P.:	Unknown
U.K.:	Not
U.S.:	Available
Can.:	

OPERA

Designer:	Unknown
Type:	Weight – Sphercial
Issued:	Unknown
Status:	Closed
Series:	Unknown
O.I.P.:	Unknown
U.K.:	Not
U.S.:	Available
Can.:	

THEATRE

Designer:	Unknown
Type:	Weight – Spherical
Issued:	Unknown
Status:	Closed
Series:	Unknown
O.I.P.:	Unknown
U.K.:	Not
US.:	Available
Can.:	

WELSH DRAGON

Designer:	Caithness Engraving Studios
Type:	Weight – Spherical, engraved
Issued:	1981 in a limited edition of 100
Status:	Fully subscribed
Series:	Royal Wedding Collection
O.I.P.:	£36.00
U.K.:	£ 75.00
U.S.:	$150.00
Can.:	$200.00

Note: This paperweight was issued to commemorate the wedding of Prince Charles and Lady Diana Spencer.

DOULTON DIRECT

ADVENTURE BEGINS, THE
Designer: Willie Bain
Type: Weight – Spherical
Issued: 2001 in a limited
           edition of 750
Status: Unknown
O.I.P.:   £49.98

U.K.:   £ 50.00
U.S.: $100.00
Can.: $125.00

DANCING IN THE SNOW
Designer: Willie Bain
Type: Weight – Spherical
Issued: 2001 in a limited
           edition of 750
Status: Unknown
O.I.P.:   £49.98

U.K.:   £ 50.00
U.S.: $100.00
Can.: $125.00

GOLDEN JUBILEE
Style Two
Designer: Willie Bain
Type: Weight – Spherical
Issued: 2001 in a limited
           edition of 500
Status: Unknown
O.I.P.:   £49.98

U.K.:   £ 50.00
U.S.: $100.00
Can.: $125.00

THANK YOU SNOWMAN
Designer: Willie Bain
Type: Weight – Spherical
Issued: 2002 in a limited
           edition of 750
Status: Unknown
O.I.P.:   £49.98

U.K.:   £ 50.00
U.S.: $100.00
Can.: $125.00

WALKING IN THE AIR
Designer: Willie Bain
Type: Weight – Spherical
Issued: 2000 in a limited
           edition of 750
Status: Unknown
O.I.P.:   £49.98

U.K.:   £ 50.00
U.S.: $100.00
Can.: $125.00

GOVIER'S OF SIDMOUTH
SIDMOUTH, U.K.

UNICORN, DAWN

Designer: Colin Terris
Type: Weight – Domed
Issued: 1999 in a limited
          edition of 50
Status: Closed
O.I.P.:   £295.00

U.K.:   £300.00
U.S.: $600.00
Can.: $775.00

UNICORN, DUSK

Designer: Colin Terris
Type: Weight – Domed
Issued: 1999 in a limited
          edition of 50
Status: Closed
O.I.P.:   £295.00

U.K.:   £300.00
U.S.: $600.00
Can.: $775.00

UNICORN, TWILIGHT

Designer: Colin Terris
Type: Weight – Domed
Issued: 1999 in a limited
          edition of 50
Status: Closed
O.I.P.:   £295.00

U.K.:   £300.00
U.S.: $600.00
Can.: $775.00

GUMP'S
SAN FRANCISCO, U.S.

ENTWINED HEARTS

Designer: Colin Terris
Type: Weight – Spherical
Issued: 1993
Status: Closed
O.I.P.:   U.S. $175.00

U.K.:   £ 85.00
U.S.: $175.00
Can.: $225.00

HEART and FLOWERS

Designer: Colin Terris
Type: Weight – Spherical
Issued: 1997 in a limited
          edition of 250
Status: Closed
O.I.P.:   U.S. $120.00

U.K.:   £ 65.00
U.S.: $125.00
Can.: $150.00

HEART OF HEARTS

Designer: Colin Terris
Type: Weight – Spherical
Issued: 1996
Status: Closed
O.I.P.:   U.S. $190.00

U.K.:   £100.00
U.S.: $200.00
Can.: $250.00

TWIN HEARTS

Designer: Colin Terris
Type: Weight – Spherical
Issued: 1991
Status: Closed
O.I.P.:   U.S. $175.00

U.K.:   £ 85.00
U.S.: $175.00
Can.: $225.00

WHITE FUGUE
Style One

Designer: Colin Terris
Type: Weight – Spherical
Issued: 1983 in a limited
          edition of 500
Status: Fully subscribed
O.I.P.:   U.S. $225.00

U.K.:   £125.00
U.S.: $225.00
Can.: $300.00

Note: For White Fugue, Style
One, see page 55.

HADLEIGH CHINA & CRYSTAL
ABINGDON, U.K.

LUNAR SEAL

Designer:	Helen MacDonald
Type:	Weight – Domed
Issued:	1992 in a limited edition of 100
Status:	Closed
O.I.P.:	£200.00
U.K.:	£250.00
U.S.:	$500.00
Can.:	$650.00

HISTORIC SCOTLAND
EDINBURGH, U.K.

HONOURS

Designer: Helen MacDonald
Type: Weight – Spherical
Issued: 1996
Status: Closed
O.I.P.:   £26.00

U.K.:   £30.00
U.S.: $60.00
Can.: $80.00

Note: The designs of weights HS-001, 002 and 003 are based on the Honours of Scotland (the Scottish crown jewels).

HONOURS, FLEUR-DE-LYS

Designer: Helen MacDonald
Type: Weight – Spherical
Issued: 1996 in a limited
          edition of 750
Status: Closed
O.I.P.:   £65.00

U.K.:   £ 65.00
U.S.: $125.00
Can.: $150.00

HONOURS, ORB

Designer: Helen MacDonald
Type: Weight – Domed
Issued: 1996 in a limited
          edition of 50
Status: Closed
O.I.P.:   £225.00

U.K.:   £300.00
U.S.: $600.00
Can.: $775.00

IN THE SPIRIT MAIL ORDER HANOVER, PENNSYLVANIA, U.S.

ICHTHUS

Designer: Helen MacDonald
Type: Weight – Spherical
Issued: 1998
Status: Closed
O.I.P.: U.S. $98.00

U.K.: £ 50.00
U.S.: $100.00
Can.: $125.00

KING EDWARD VII HOSPITAL FOR OFFICERS

KING EDWARD VII HOSPITAL FOR OFFICERS

Designer: Unknown
Type: Weight – Spherical
Issued: 1999
Status: Closed
O.I.P.: £37.50

U.K.: £ 40.00
U.S.: $ 80.00
Can.: $100.00

LADS PORCELAIN AND GLASS TORONTO, CANADA

KING TUTENKHAMUN

Designer: Jennie Robertson
Type: Weight – Spherical, engraved
Issued: 1979 in a limited edition of 250
Status: Closed at No. 120
O.I.P.: Can. $150.00

U.K.: £ 65.00
U.S.: $125.00
Can.: $150.00

L. H. SELMAN LTD.
SANTA CRUZ, U.S.

BURGUNDY BOUQUET
Designer: Colin Terris
         Allan Scott
Type: Weight – Spherical
Issued: 1998 in a limited
         edition of 50
Status: Closed
O.I.P.: U.S. $465.00

U.K.:   £250.00
U.S.: $475.00
Can.: $625.00

FLYING PEGASUS
Designer: Colin Terris
Type: Weight – Spherical
Issued: 1997 in a limited
         edition of 500
Status: Closed
O.I.P.: U.S. $115.00

U.K.:   £ 65.00
U.S.: $125.00
Can.: $150.00

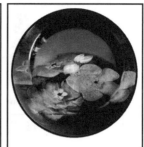

GARDEN POOL and DRAGONFLY
Designer: Colin Terris
Type: Weight – Spherical
Issued: 1995 in a limited
         edition of 50
Status: Fully subscribed
O.I.P.: U.S. $450.00

U.K.:   £300.00
U.S.: $550.00
Can.: $725.00

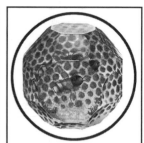

HONEY BEE
Style Two
Designer: Colin Terris
Type: Weight – Spherical
Issued: 1996 in a limited
         edition of 25
Status: Fully subscribed
O.I.P.: U.S. $260.00

U.K.:   £175.00
U.S.: $350.00
Can.: $475.00

MODESTY
Designer: Helen MacDonald
Type: Weight – Spherical
Issued: 1999 in a limited
         edition of 50
Status: Closed
O.I.P.: U.S. $395.00

U.K.:   £200.00
U.S.: $400.00
Can.: $525.00

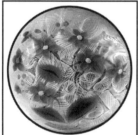

ONE TRUE LOVE
Designer: Helen MacDonald
Type: Weight – Spherical
Issued: 1999 in a limited
         edition of 50
Status: Closed
O.I.P.: U.S. $395.00

U.K.:   £200.00
U.S.: $400.00
Can.: $525.00

SANTA'S TREE
Designer: William Manson
Type: Weight – Spherical
Issued: 1997 in a limited
         edition of 150
Status: Closed
O.I.P.: U.S. $315.00

U.K.:   £175.00
U.S.: $325.00
Can.: $425.00

SILVER UNICORN
Designer: Colin Terris
Type: Weight – Spherical
Issued: 1997 in a limited
         edition of 500
Status: Closed
O.I.P.: U.S. $115.00

U.K.:   £ 65.00
U.S.: $125.00
Can.: $150.00

L. H. SELMAN LTD.
SANTA CRUZ, U.S. (cont.)

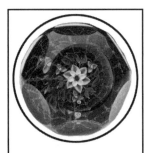

SPIDER'S WEB
Designer:	Colin Terris and Allan Scott
Type:	Weight – Spherical
Issued:	1998 in a limited edition of 50
Status:	Closed
O.I.P.:	U.S. $465.00
U.K.:	£250.00
U.S.:	$475.00
Can.:	$600.00

TEARDROP PETUNIA
Designer:	Colin Terris
Type:	Weight – Teardrop
Issued:	1998 in a limited edition of 250
Status:	Closed
O.I.P.:	U.S. $85.00
U.K.:	£ 45.00
U.S.:	$ 85.00
Can.:	$100.00

UNICORN DANCE
Designer:	Colin Terris and William Manson
Type:	Weight – Spherical
Issued:	1997 in a limited edition of 150
Status:	Closed
O.I.P.:	U.S. $315.00
U.K.:	£175.00
U.S.:	$325.00
Can.:	$425.00

LENOX U.S.A.

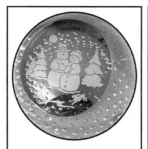

Photograph not
available
at press time

COLD NIGHTS, WARM HEARTS
Designer: Willie Bain
Type: Weight – Spherical
Issued: 2002 in a limited
          edition of 150
Status: Fully subscribed
O.I.P.:   U.S. $95.00

U.K.:   £ 50.00
U.S.: $100.00
Can.: $125.00

DOLPHIN LIGHT
Designer: Willie Bain
Type: Weight –
Issued: 2000 in a limited
          edition of 300
Status: Fully subscribed
O.I.P.:   U.S. $95.00

U.K.:   £ 50.00
U.S.: $100.00
Can.: $125.00

Photograph not
available
at press time

DOLPHIN TALL
Designer: Willie Bain
Type: Weight – Domed
Issued: 2002 unlimited
Status: Closed
O.I.P.:   U.S. $95.00

U.K.:   £ 50.00
U.S.: $100.00
Can.: $125.00

ENCHANTED EVENING
Designer: Willie Bain
Type: Weight –
Issued: 2001 in a limited
          edition of 300
Status: Fully subscribed
O.I.P.:   U.S. $95.00

U.K.:   £ 50.00
U.S.: $100.00
Can.: $125.00

SNOWFLAKE
Designer: Gordon Hendry
Type: Weight – Spherical
Issued: 2002 in a limited
          edition of 300
Status: Fully subscribed
O.I.P.:   U.S. $95.00

U.K.:   £ 50.00
U.S.: $100.00
Can.: $125.00

PAST TIMES

QUEEN MOTHER'S CENTENARY

Designer:	Colin Terris
Type:	Weight – Spherical
Issued:	2000 unlimited
Status:	Closed
O.I.P.:	£45.00
U.K.:	£ 45.00
U.S.:	$ 90.00
Can.:	$110.00

QUEEN MOTHER'S CENTENARY ROSE

Designer:	Colin Terris
Type:	Weight – Spherical
Issued:	2000 Unlimited
Status:	Closed
O.I.P.:	£39.99
U.K.:	£ 40.00
U.S.:	$ 80.00
Can.:	$100.00

PETER DYER
SOUTHSEA, U.K.

MARY ROSE

Designer:	Helen MacDonald
Type:	Weight – Spherical, engraved
Issued:	1982 in a limited edition of 100
Status:	Fully subscribed
O.I.P.:	£75.00
U.K.:	£100.00
U.S.:	$200.00
Can.:	$250.00

SILVER JUBILEE FLEET REVIEW

Designer:	Peter Dyer and Colin Terris
Type:	Weight – Spherical
Issued:	1977 in a limited edition of 100
Status:	Fully subscribed
Series:	HM Queen Elizabeth II Silver Jubilee Collection
O.I.P.:	£75.00
U.K.:	£175.00
U.S.:	$350.00
Can.:	$450.00

Note: This paperweight was issued to commemorate the 25th anniversary of the coronation of Queen Elizabeth II.

PETER JONES CHINA
WAKEFIELD, U.K.

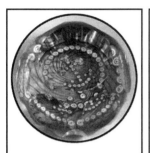

ANCHOR
Designer: Colin Terris
Type: Weight – Spherical
Issued: 1996 in a limited edition of 75
Status: Active
O.I.P.: £150.00

U.K.: £150.00
U.S.: $300.00
Can.: $400.00

Note: Commissioned to celebrate the 75th birthday of the Duke of Edinburgh.

ARK ROYAL
Designer: Caithness Engraving Studios
Type: Weight – Spherical, engraved
Issued: 1980 in a limited edition of 500
Status: Closed at No. 263
O.I.P.: £35.00

U.K.: £ 85.00
U.S.: $165.00
Can.: $200.00

BATTLE OF BRITAIN
Style Two
Designer: Colin Terris
Type: Weight – Spherical
Issued: 1990 in a limited edition of 2,000
Status: Closed
O.I.P.: £29.50

U.K.: £30.00
U.S.: $60.00
Can.: $80.00

Note: This paperweight was commissioned to commemorate the 50th anniversary of the Battle of Britain.

BIG BEN MILLENNIUM
Designer: Colin Terris
Type: Weight – Domed, prestige
Issued: 1999 in a limited edition of 200
Status: Closed
O.I.P.: £120.00

U.K.: £125.00
U.S.: $250.00
Can.: $325.00

BLUE ZANFIRICO GOLDEN JUBILEE
Designer: Alastair MacIntosh
Type: Weight – Low Dome, facets
Issued: 2002 in a limited edition of 100
Status: Closed at No. 93
O.I.P.: £175.00

U.K.: £175.00
U.S.: $350.00
Can.: $450.00

Note: Issued to commemorate the 50th Anniversary of the Coronation of HRH Queen Elizabeth II.

CASTLE OF MEY
Style Two
Designer: Colin Terris
Type: Weight – Domed
Issued: 2000 in a limited edition of 100
Status: Closed at No. 34
O.I.P.: £235.00

U.K.: £235.00
U.S.: $450.00
Can.: $575.00

Note: Issued to celebrate the Centenary of H.M. the Queen Mother.

CHANNEL TUNNEL, THE
Designer: Margot Thomson
Type: Weight – Spherical
Issued: 1994 in a limited edition of 500
Status: Closed
O.I.P.: £69.95

U.K.: £ 70.00
U.S.: $125.00
Can.: $175.00

Note: This paperweight was commissioned to commemorate the opening of the Channel Tunnel on May 6, 1994.

CHRISTOPHER COLUMBUS –
500TH ANNIVERSARY
Designer: Colin Terris
Type: Weight – Spherical
Issued: 1992 in a limited edition of 500
Status: Closed
O.I.P.: £49.95

U.K.: £ 50.00
U.S.: $100.00
Can.: $125.00

Note: Commemorating the 500th anniversary of Christopher Columbus's voyage of discovery.

PETER JONES CHINA
WAKEFIELD, U.K. (cont.)

CHURCHILL 60TH ANNIVERSARY
Designer: Willie Bain
Type: Weight – Spherical
Issued: 2000 in a limited edition of 100
Status: Closed at No. 52
O.I.P.: £49.95

U.K.: £ 50.00
U.S.: $100.00
Can.: $125.00

CONCORDE
Designer: Colin Terris
Type: Weight – Spherical
Issued: 1994 in a limited edition of 250
Status: Closed
O.I.P.: £39.95

U.K.: £ 40.00
U.S.: $ 80.00
Can.: $100.00

Note: This paperweight was commissioned to commemorate the 25th anniversary of the Concorde's first flight.

CONCORDE TRIBUTE
Designer: Colin Terris
Type: Weight – Spherical
Issued: 2001 in a limited edition of 200
Status: Fully subscribed
O.I.P.: £89.95

U.K.: £ 90.00
U.S.: $175.00
Can.: $225.00

CORONATION ANNIVERSARY PRESTIGE PERFUME BOTTLE
Designer: Helen MacDonald
Type: Perfume Bottle
Issued: 2002 in a limited edition of 50
Status: Closed
O.I.P.: £325.00

U.K.: £325.00
U.S.: $600.00
Can.: $775.00

CORONATION COACH
Style Two
Designer: Willie Bain
Type: Weight – Spherical
Issued: 2002 unlimited
Status: Closed
O.I.P.: £49.95

U.K.: £ 50.00
U.S.: $100.00
Can.: $125.00

Note: Issued to commemorate the 50th anniversary of the Coronation of HRH Queen Elizabeth II.

CROWN, ORB and SCEPTRE PRESTIGE CORONATION
Designer: Helen MacDonald
Type: Weight – Low Dome, facets
Issued: 2002 in a limited edition of 200
Status: Closed
O.I.P.: £150.00

U.K.: £150.00
U.S.: $300.00
Can.: $400.00

Note: Issued to commemorate the 50th anniversary of the Coronation of HRH Queen Elizabeth II.

D-DAY LANDINGS
Designer: Alastair MacIntosh
Type: Weight – Spherical
Issued: 1994 in a limited edition of 750
Status: Closed
O.I.P.: £59.95

U.K.: £ 60.00
U.S.: $120.00
Can.: $150.00

Note: This paperweight was commissioned to commemorate the 50th anniversary of D-Day.

EDINBURGH CASTLE
Designer: Colin Terris
Type: Weight – Spherical
Issued: 1996 in a limited edition of 250
Status: Closed
O.I.P.: £45.00

U.K.: £ 50.00
U.S.: $100.00
Can.: $125.00

Note: Commissioned to celebrate the 75th birthday of the Duke of Edinburgh.

PETER JONES CHINA
WAKEFIELD, U.K. (cont.)

ELIZABETH OF GLAMIS PERFUME BOTTLE

Designer:	Colin Terris
Type:	Perfume bottle
Issued:	1995 in a limited edition of 95
Status:	Closed
O.I.P.:	£245.00
U.K.:	£250.00
U.S.:	$500.00
Can.:	$650.00

Note: This perfume bottle was commissioned to commemorate the Queen Mother's 95th birthday.

END OF AN ERA

Designer:	Colin Terris
Type:	Weight – Spherical
Issued:	1997 in a limited edition of 500
Status:	Closed
O.I.P.:	£49.95
U.K.:	£ 50.00
U.S.:	$100.00
Can.:	$125.00

Note: This paperweight was issued to commemorate the handover of Hong Kong to China on June 30, 1997.

FAREWELL BRITANNIA

Designer:	Colin Terris
Type:	Weight – Spherical
Issued:	1997 in a limited edition of 350
Status:	Closed
O.I.P.:	£49.95
U.K.:	£ 50.00
U.S.:	$100.00
Can.:	$125.00

Note: This paperweight was issued to commemorate the decommissioning of the Royal Yacht Britannia on December 11, 1997.

40TH ANNIVERSARY OF QUEEN ELIZABETH II ACCESSION

Designer:	Colin Terris
Type:	Weight – Spherical, engraved
Issued:	1992 in a limited edition of 2,000
Status:	Closed
O.I.P.:	£35.00
U.K.:	£ 35.00
U.S.:	$ 70.00
Can.:	$100.00

40TH ANNIVERSARY QUEEN ELIZABETH II CORONATION – COBALT BASE

Designer:	Colin Terris
Type:	Weight – Spherical, engraved
Issued:	1993 in a limited edition of 250
Status:	Closed
O.I.P.:	£95.00
U.K.:	£100.00
U.S.:	$200.00
Can.:	$250.00

40TH ANNIVERSARY QUEEN ELIZABETH II CORONATION – RUBY BASE

Designer:	Colin Terris
Type:	Weight – Spherical, engraved
Issued:	1993 in a limited edition of 2,000
Status:	Closed
O.I.P.:	£39.95
U.K.:	£ 40.00
U.S.:	$ 75.00
Can.:	$100.00

40TH ANNIVERSARY QUEEN ELIZABETH II CORONATION – RUBY OVERLAY

Designer:	Colin Terris
Type:	Weight – Spherical, facets
Issued:	1993 in a limited edition of 40
Status:	Closed
O.I.P.:	£295.00
U.K.:	£300.00
U.S.:	$600.00
Can.:	$775.00

GLAMIS CASTLE

Designer:	Colin Terris
Type:	Weight – Domed
Issued:	2000 in a limited edition of 100
Status:	Closed at No. 33
O.I.P.:	£235.00
U.K.:	£250.00
U.S.:	$500.00
Can.:	$650.00

Note: Issued to commemorate the 100th birthday of HM the Queen Mother.

PETER JONES CHINA
WAKEFIELD, U.K. (cont.)

GOLDEN JUBILEE SPLENDOUR

Designer: Alastair MacIntosh
Type: Weight – Spherical
Issued: 2002 in a limited
          edition of 200
Status: Closed at No. 51
O.I.P.:   £49.95

U.K.:   £ 50.00
U.S.: $100.00
Can.: $125.00

HMQM COAT OF ARMS

Designer: Colin Terris
Type: Weight – Spherical,
          engraved
Issued: 1995 in a limited
          edition of 500
Status: Closed
O.I.P.:   £45.00

U.K.:   £ 45.00
U.S.: $ 90.00
Can.: $125.00

Note: This paperweight was
          commissioned to
          commemorate the Queen
          Mother's 95th birthday.

HMQM FAVOURITE FLOWERS

Designer: Colin Terris
Type: Weight – Spherical
Issued: 1995 in a limited
          edition of 95
Status: Closed
O.I.P.:   £195.00

U.K.:   £200.00
U.S.: $400.00
Can.: $500.00

Note: This paperweight was
          commissioned to
          commemorate the Queen
          Mother's 95th birthday.

HMQM 75TH TRIBUTE

Designer: Allan Scott
Type: Weight – Spherical
Issued: 1998 in a limited
          edition of 75
Status: Closed
O.I.P.:   £195.00

U.K.:   £200.00
U.S.: $400.00
Can.: $525.00

Note: This weight and the
          following two were issued
          to commemorate the
          Queen Mother's 75 years
          of service to the United
          Kingdom.

HMQM 75TH TRIBUTE PERFUME BOTTLE

Designer: Colin Terris
Type: Perfume Bottle
Issued: 1998 in a limited
          edition of 50
Status: Closed
O.I.P.:   £220.00

U.K.:   £225.00
U.S.: $450.00
Can.: $575.00

HMQM 75TH TRIBUTE – GLAMIS ROSE

Designer: Colin Terris
Type: Weight – Spherical
Issued: 1998 in a limited
          edition of 250
Status: Closed
O.I.P.:   £79.95

U.K.:   £ 80.00
U.S.: $150.00
Can.: $200.00

HRH PRINCE OF WALES 50TH BIRTHDAY, First Edition

Designer: Allan Scott
Type: Weight – Spherical
Issued: 1998 in a limited
          edition of 50
Status: Closed
O.I.P.:   £150.00

U.K.:   £150.00
U.S.: $300.00
Can.: $425.00

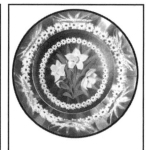

HRH PRINCE OF WALES 50TH BIRTHDAY, Second Edition

Designer: Allan Scott
Type: Weight – Spherical
Issued: 1998 in a limited
          edition of 50
Status: Closed
O.I.P.:   £150.00

U.K.:   £150.00
U.S.: $300.00
Can.: $425.00

PETER JONES CHINA
WAKEFIELD, U.K. (cont.)

MILLENNIUM CELEBRATION
Designer: Colin Terris
Type: Weight – Spherical
Issued: 1999 in a limited edition of 250
Status: Closed
O.I.P.: £85.00

U.K.: £ 85.00
U.S.: $125.00
Can.: $150.00

MILLENNIUM FLAME
Designer: Colin Terris
Type: Weight – Domed, dichroic
Issued: 1999 in a limited edition of 100
Status: Closed
O.I.P.: £75.00

U.K.: £ 75.00
U.S.: $150.00
Can.: $200.00

MOON LANDING
Designer: Colin Terris
Type: Weight – Spherical
Issued: 1994 in a limited edition of 250
Status: Closed
O.I.P.: £75.00

U.K.: £ 75.00
U.S.: $150.00
Can.: $200.00

Note: This paperweight was commissioned to commemorate the 25th anniversary of man's first landing on the moon.

PEACE IN EUROPE
Designer: Colin Terris
Type: Weight – Spherical, engraved
Issued: 1995 in a limited edition of 500
Status: Closed
O.I.P.: £49.95

U.K.: £ 50.00
U.S.: $100.00
Can.: $125.00

Note: Commissioned to commemorate the 50th anniversary of VE Day (May 8, 1945).

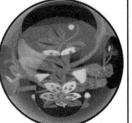

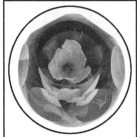

PINK ORCHID
Designer: William Manson
Type: Weight – Spherical, facets
Issued: 1997 in a limited edition of 150
Status: Closed
Series: Tropical Orchids
O.I.P.: £195.00/set

U.K.: £100.00
U.S.: $200.00
Can.: $250.00

Note: This weight forms a set of two with Yellow Orchid, see page 356.

PRINCE WILLIAM 18TH BIRTHDAY
Designer: Colin Terris
Type: Weight – Spherical
Issued: 2000 in a limited edition of 250
Status: Closed
O.I.P.: £49.95

U.K.: £ 50.00
U.S.: $100.00
Can.: $125.00

PRINCE WILLIAM 18TH BIRTHDAY PRESTIGE
Designer: Colin Terris
Type: Weight – Spherical
Issued: 2000 in a limited edition of 100
Status: Closed
O.I.P.: £99.95

U.K.: £100.00
U.S.: $200.00
Can.: $250.00

PRINCESS MARGARET PRESTIGE
Designer: Colin Terris
Type: Weight – Spherical, facets
Issued: 2000 in a limited edition of 50
Status: Closed at No. 22
O.I.P.: £125.00

U.K.: £150.00
U.S.: $300.00
Can.: $400.00

PETER JONES CHINA
WAKEFIELD, U.K. (cont.)

PRINCESS MARGARET'S 70TH BIRTHDAY
Designer: Colin Terris
Type: Weight – Spherical
Issued: 2000 in a limited edition of 200
Status: Closed at No. 22
O.I.P.: £49.95

U.K.: £ 50.00
U.S.: $100.00
Can.: $125.00

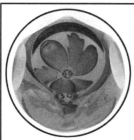

PRINCESS ROYAL PRESTIGE
Designer: Colin Terris
Type: Weight – Spherical, facets
Issued: 2000 in a limited edition of 50
Status: Closed at No. 16
O.I.P.: £125.00

U.K.: £125.00
U.S.: $250.00
Can.: $325.00

Note: Issued to commemorate the 50th birthday of the Princess Royal.

PRINCESS ROYAL'S 50TH BIRTHDAY
Designer: Willie Bain
Type: Weight – Spherical
Issued: 2000 in a limited edition of 200
Status: Closed
O.I.P.: £49.95

U.K.: £ 50.00
U.S.: $100.00
Can.: $125.00

Note: Issued to commemorate the 50th birthday of the Princess Royal.

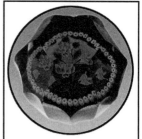

QUEEN ELIZABETH ROSE
Designer: Colin Terris
Type: Weight – Spherical
Issued: 1996 in a limited edition of 100
Status: Closed
O.I.P.: £225.00

U.K.: £225.00
U.S.: $450.00
Can.: $575.00

Note: Issued to commemorate the 70th birthday of Queen Elizabeth II.

QUEEN ELIZABETH ROSE PERFUME BOTTLE
Designer: Colin Terris
Type: Perfume bottle
Issued: 1996 in a limited edition of 70
Status: Closed
O.I.P.: £245.00

U.K.: £250.00
U.S.: $500.00
Can.: $650.00

Note: Issued to commemorate the 70th birthday of Queen Elizabeth II.

QE II VISIT TO RUSSIA
Designer: Colin Terris
Type: Weight – Spherical
Issued: 1994 in a limited edition of 250
Status: Closed
O.I.P.: £49.95

U.K.: £ 50.00
U.S.: $100.00
Can.: $125.00

QUEEN VICTORIA DIAMOND JUBILEE CENTENARY
Designer: Colin Terris
Type: Weight – Spherical
Issued: 1997 in a limited edition of 250
Status: Closed
O.I.P.: £49.95

U.K.: £ 50.00
U.S.: $100.00
Can.: $125.00

QUEEN'S CROWN GOLDEN JUBILEE PRESTIGE PERFUME BOTTLE
Designer: Colin Terris
Type: Perfume Bottle
Issued: 2002 in a limited edition of 100
Status: Closed at No. 38
O.I.P.: £295.00

U.K.: £300.00
U.S.: $600.00
Can.: $800.00

PETER JONES CHINA
WAKEFIELD, U.K. (cont.)

QUEEN'S GOLDEN JUBILEE CONGRATULATIONS

Designer: Willie Bain
Type: Weight – Spherical
Issued: 2002 in a limited edition of 250
Status: Fully subscribed
O.I.P.: £49.95

U.K.: £ 50.00
U.S.: $100.00
Can.: $125.00

QUEEN'S GOLDEN JUBILEE STARLIGHT

Designer: Alastair MacIntosh
Type: Weight – Spherical, facets
Issued: 2002 in a limited edition of 100
Status: Closed at No. 39
O.I.P.: £195.00

U.K.: £200.00
U.S.: $400.00
Can.: $525.00

RED ARROWS
Style Two

Designer: Alastair MacIntosh
Type: Weight – Spherical
Issued: 1992 in a limited edition of 2,000
Status: Closed
O.I.P.: £39.95

U.K.: £ 40.00
U.S.: $ 70.00
Can.: $100.00

ROYAL CYPHER

Designer: Caithness Engraving Studios
Type: Weight – Spherical, engraved
Issued: 1981 in a limited edition of 500
Status: Closed at No. 200
Series: Royal Wedding Collection
O.I.P.: £50.00

U.K.: £ 75.00
U.S.: $150.00
Can.: $200.00

ROYAL WEDDING FLORAL BOUQUET

Designer: Melanie Stuart
Type: Weight – Spherical
Canes: E and S (Edward and Sophie)
Issued: 1999 in a limited edition of 100
Status: Closed
O.I.P.: £195.00

U.K.: £350.00
U.S.: $700.00
Can.: $900.00

ROYAL WEDDING ORCHID BOUQUET

Designer: Allan Scott
Type: Weight – Spherical
Issued: 1997 in a limited edition of 50
Status: Closed
O.I.P.: £225.00

U.K.: £225.00
U.S.: $450.00
Can.: $575.00

Note: This weight and the two previous celebrate the golden wedding anniversary of Queen Elizabeth II and Prince Philip.

ROYAL WEDDING ORCHID BOUQUET PERFUME BOTTLE

Designer: Allan Scott
Type: Perfume bottle
Issued: 1997 in a limited edition of 50
Status: Closed
O.I.P.: £250.00

U.K.: £250.00
U.S.: $500.00
Can.: $650.00

ROYAL WEDDING PRESTIGE PERFUME BOTTLE

Designer: Allan Scott
Type: Perfume Bottle
Canes: E and S (Edward and Sophie)
Issued: 1999 in a limited edition of 50
Status: Closed
O.I.P.: £250.00

U.K.: £250.00
U.S.: $500.00
Can.: $650.00

Note: Commissioned to celebrate the wedding of Prince Edward and Sophie Rhys-Jones.

PETER JONES CHINA
WAKEFIELD, U.K. (cont.)

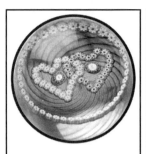

ROYAL WEDDING LUCKENBOOTH

Designer: Colin Terris
Type: Weight – Spherical
Canes: E and S (Edward and Sophie)
Issued: 1999 in a limited edition of 200
Status: Closed
O.I.P.: £75.00

U.K.: £ 75.00
U.S.: $150.00
Can.: $200.00

75TH ANNIVERSARY OF ROYAL AIR FORCE

Designer: Colin Terris
Type: Weight – Spherical
Issued: 1993 in a limited edition of 1,000
Status: Closed
O.I.P.: £45.00

U.K.: £ 45.00
U.S.: $ 90.00
Can.: $125.00

25TH ANNIVERSARY OF INVESTITURE OF PRINCE OF WALES

Designer: Colin Terris
Type: Weight – Spherical
Issued: 1994 in a limited edition of 500
Status: Closed
O.I.P.: £39.95

U.K.: £ 40.00
U.S.: $ 75.00
Can.: $100.00

25TH ANNIVERSARY OF INVESTITURE OF PRINCE OF WALES – PRESTIGE EDITION

Designer: Colin Terris
Type: Weight – Spherical
Issued: 1994 in a limited edition of 100
Status: Closed
O.I.P.: £195.00

U.K.: £200.00
U.S.: $400.00
Can.: $525.00

30TH ANNIVERSARY CONCORDE

Designer: Colin Terris
Type: Weight – Spherical
Issued: Limited edition of 500
Status: Closed
O.I.P.: £45.00

U.K.: £ 45.00
U.S.: $ 90.00
Can.: $125.00

Note: Issued to commemorate the 30th anniversary of Concorde.

30TH ANNIVERSARY CONCORDE, PRESTIGE

Designer: Colin Terris
Type: Weight – Spherical
Issued: Limited edition of 100
Status: Closed
O.I.P.: £95.00

U.K.: £ 95.00
U.S.: $200.00
Can.: $275.00

Note: Issued to commemorate the 39th anniversary of Concorde.

30TH ANNIVERSARY OF MOON LANDING

Designer: Colin Terris
Type: Weight – Spherical
Issued: Limited edition of 300
Status: Closed
O.I.P.: £45.00

U.K.: £ 45.00
U.S.: $ 90.00
Can.: $125.00

30TH ANNIVERSARY OF MOON LANDING, PRESTIGE

Designer: Colin Terris
Type: Weight – Spherical
Issued: Limited edition of 100
Status: Closed
O.I.P.: £125.00

U.K.: £125.00
U.S.: $250.00
Can.: $325.00

PETER JONES CHINA
WAKEFIELD, U.K. (cont.)

30TH ANNIVERSARY OF MOON LANDING, MAGNUM

Designer: Colin Terris
Type: Weight – Spherical
Issued: Limited edition of 30
Status: Closed
O.I.P.: £250.00

U.K.: £250.00
U.S.: $500.00
Can.: $650.00

TOTAL ECLIPSE

Designer: Colin Terris
Type: Weight – Spherical
Issued: Limited edition of 500
Status: Closed
O.I.P.: £45.00

U.K.: £ 45.00
U.S.: $ 90.00
Can.: $125.00

TOTAL ECLIPSE, PRESTIGE

Designer: Colin Terris
Type: Weight – Spherical
Issued: Limited edition of 200
Status: Closed
O.I.P.: £95.00

U.K.: £ 95.00
U.S.: $200.00
Can.: $250.00

TUTANKHAMUN
Style Two

Designer: Colin Terris
Type: Weight – Spherical
Issued: 1997 in a limited edition of 250
Status: Closed
O.I.P.: £49.95

U.K.: £ 50.00
U.S.: $100.00
Can.: $125.00

Note: This paperweight was commissioned to commemorate the 75th anniversary of the discovery of King Tutankhamun's tomb.

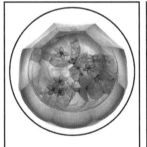

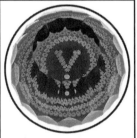

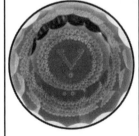

TWILIGHT FLIGHT

Designer: Colin Terris
Type: Weight – Low dome, facets
Issued: Unknown in a limited edition of 50
Status: Closed at No. 31
O.I.P.: £330.00

U.K.: £350.00
U.S.: $700.00
Can.: $900.00

VICTORY

Designer: Colin Terris
Type: Weight – Spherical, facets
Cane: E (Europe)
Issued: 1995 in a limited edition of 100
Status: Closed
O.I.P.: £175.00

U.K.: £175.00
U.S.: $350.00
Can.: $450.00

Note: Issued to commemorate the 50th anniversary of VE Day (May 8, 1945).

VICTORY IN JAPAN

Designer: Colin Terris
Type: Weight – Spherical, facets
Cane: J (Japan)
Issued: 1995 in a limited edition of 100
Status: Closed
O.I.P.: £175.00

U.K.: £175.00
U.S.: $350.00
Can.: $450.00

Note: Issued to commemorate the 50th anniversary of the victory in Japan.

WESTMINSTER ABBEY

Designer: Colin Terris
Type: Weight – Spherical, engraved
Issued: 1997 in a limited edition of 250
Status: Closed
O.I.P.: £45.00

U.K.: £ 45.00
U.S.: $ 90.00
Can.: $125.00

PETER JONES CHINA
WAKEFIELD, U.K. (cont.)

WINDSOR CASTLE GOLDEN JUBILEE CELEBRATION

Designer: Alastair MacIntosh
Type: Weight – Domed
Issued: 2002 in a limited
           edition of 100
Status: Closed at No. 26
O.I.P.:   £235.00

U.K.:   £250.00
U.S.: $500.00
Can.: $650.00

WORLD PEACE

Designer: Colin Terris
Type: Weight – Spherical
Issued: 1995 in a limited
           edition of 250
Status: Closed
O.I.P.:   £95.00

U.K.:   £100.00
U.S.: $200.00
Can.: $250.00

Note: Issued to commemorate
      the 50th anniversary of
      VJ Day (August 15,
      1945).

YEAR OF THE VIKING

Designer: Gordon Hendry
Type: Weight – Spherical,
           engraved
Issued: 1980 in a limited
           edition of 500
Status: Closed at No. 325
O.I.P.:   £39.95

U.K.:   £ 75.00
U.S.: $150.00
Can.: $200.00

YELLOW ORCHID

Designer: William Manson
Type: Weight – Spherical
Issued: 1997 in a limited
           edition of 150
Status: Closed
Series: Tropical Orchids
O.I.P.:   £195.00/set

U.K.:   £100.00
U.S.: $200.00
Can.: $250.00

Note: This weight forms a set
      of two with Pink Orchid,
      see page 351.

YURI GAGARIN

Designer: Alastair MacIntosh
Type: Weight – Spherical
Issued: 2001 in a limited
           edition of 100
Status: Closed at No. 30
O.I.P.:   £99.00

U.K.:   £100.00
U.S.: $200.00
Can.: $250.00

ROYAL ALBERT

RUBY CELEBRATION

Designer: Caithness Design
Studios
Type: Weight – Spherical
Issued: 2002 unlimited
Status: Closed
O.I.P.: £54.99

U.K.: £ 55.00
U.S.: $100.00
Can.: $125.00

ROYAL MINT EXCLUSIVES

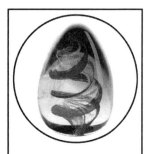

DNA

Designer: Alastair MacIntosh
Type: Weight – Domed
Issued: 2003 in a limited
edition of 250
Status: Fully subscribed
O.I.P.: £95.00

U.K.: £100.00
U.S.: $200.00
Can.: $250.00

FLEUR
Style Two

Designer: Colin Terris
Type: Weight – Spherical
Issued: 2001 in a limited
edition of 1,970
Status: Active
O.I.P.: £34.50

U.K.: £ 35.00
U.S.: $ 70.00
Can.: $100.00

FLOWER IN THE RAIN
Style Three

Designer: Colin Terris
Type: Weight – Spherical
Issued: 2001 in a limited
edition of 1,970
Status: Active
O.I.P.: £34.50

U.K.: £ 35.00
U.S.: $ 70.00
Can.: $100.00

JUBILEE CELEBRATION

Designer: Colin Terris
Type: Weight – Spherical
Issued: 2001 in a limited
edition of 250
Status: Fully subscribed
O.I.P.: £169.00

U.K.: £170.00
U.S.: $350.00
Can.: $450.00

JUBILEE ROSE
Style Two

Designer: Colin Terris
Type: Weight –
Issued: 2001 in a limited
edition of 2002
Status: Active
O.I.P.: £75.00

U.K.: £ 75.00
U.S.: $150.00
Can.: $200.00

MOONFLOWER
Second Variation

Designer: Colin Terris
Type: Weight – Low Dome
Issued: 2001 in a limited
edition of 1,970
Status: Active
O.I.P.: £34.50

U.K.: £ 35.00
U.S.: $ 70.00
Can.: $100.00

MYRIAD
Style Two

Designer: Colin Terris
Type: Weight – Spherical
Issued: 2001 in a limited
edition of 1,970
Status: Active
O.I.P.: £34.50

U.K.: £ 35.00
U.S.: $ 70.00
Can.: $100.00

QUEEN MOTHER CENTENARY

Designer: Caithness Design
Studios
Type: Weight – Low Dome
Issued: 2000 in a limited
edition of 250
Status: Fully subscribed
O.I.P.: £89.95

U.K.: £ 90.00
U.S.: $175.00
Can.: $225.00

ROYAL MINT EXCLUSIVES (cont.)

 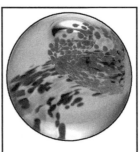

SENTINEL **Style Two**	**WHIRLWIND** **Style Two**
Designer: Colin Terris	Designer: Colin Terris
Type: Weight – Spherical	Type: Weight – Spherical

Issued: 2001 in a limited
           edition of 1,970
	Issued: 2001 in a limited
	           edition of 1,970

Status: Active	Status: Active
O.I.P.: £34.50	O.I.P.: £34.50
U.K.: £ 35.00	U.K.: £ 35.00
U.S.: $ 70.00	U.S.: $ 70.00
Can.: $100.00	Can.: $100.00

ROYAL SOCIETY FOR THE PROTECTION OF BIRDS
SANDY, U.K.

PEREGRINE FALCON

Designer:	Caithness Engraving Studios
Type:	Weight – Spherical, engraved
Issued:	1978 in a limited edition of 200
Status:	Fully subscribed
O.I.P.:	£66.00
U.K.:	£150.00
U.S.:	$300.00
Can.:	$400.00

PUFFIN
Style Two

Designer:	Helen MacDonald
Type:	Weight – Spherical, engraved
Issued:	1979 in a limited edition of 250
Status:	Closed at No. 195
O.I.P.:	£75.00
U.K.:	£100.00
U.S.:	$200.00
Can.:	$250.00

S.C.M. CHEMICALS

TOMORROW

Designer: Unknown
Type: Spherical
Issued: Unknown in a limited
          edition of 750
Status: Closed
O.I.P.:   Unknown

U.K.:   Not
U.S.:   Available
Can.:

SCHERING AGRICULTURAL

Photograph not
available
at press time

SCHERING

Designer: Unknown
Type: Weight – Unknown
Issued: 1987
Status: Closed
Series: Unknown
O.I.P.:   Unknown

U.K.:   Not
U.S.:   Available
Can.:

SCOTSMAN NEWSPAPERS
EDINBURGH, U.K.

NORTH SEA
Designer: Colin Terris
Type: Weight – Spherical
Issued: 1976 in a limited
          edition of 1,000
Status: Fully subscribed
O.I.P.:   £20.00

U.K.:   £125.00
U.S.: $250.00
Can.: $325.00

SMITHSONIAN INSTITUTION
WASHINGTON, D.C., U.S.

HALLEY'S COMET
Style Two
Designer: Colin Terris
Type: Weight – Spherical
Issued: 1985 in a limited
          edition of 500
Status: Fully subscribed
          U.K.$90.00

U.K.:   £100.00
U.S.: $200.00
Can.: $250.00

Note: This paperweight was
       issued to commemorate
       the appearance of the
       comet.

SPILLERS

"PURRFECT"

Designer: Unknown
Type: Low Dome
Issued: 1991 in a limited
          edition of 750
Status: Closed
O.I.P.:   Unknown

U.K.:   Not
U.S.:   Available
Can.:

TOUCH OF CLASS
JACKSON, U.S.

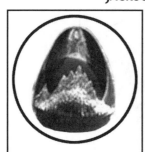

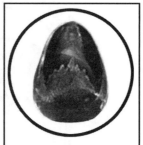

GRAND TETONS SUMMER

Designer:	Alastair MacIntosh
Type:	Weight – Domed
Issued:	1997 in a limited edition of 250
Status:	Closed
O.I.P.:	U.S. $275.00
U.K.:	£135.00
U.S.:	$275.00
Can.:	$375.00

GRAND TETONS WINTER

Designer:	Alastair MacIntosh
Type:	Weight – Domed
Issued:	1997 in a limited edition of 250
Status:	Closed
O.I.P.:	U.S. $275.00
U.K.:	£135.00
U.S.:	$275.00
Can.:	$375.00

U.S. EXCLUSIVE WEIGHTS

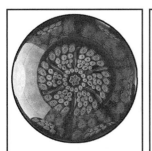

ALEXANDRA
Designer: Colin Terris
Type: Weight – Spherical
Issued: 1986 in a limited edition of 350
Status: Closed at No. 56
O.I.P.: U.S. $300.00

U.K.: £150.00
U.S.: $300.00
Can.: $400.00

BLUE ANGELS
Designer: Alastair MacIntosh
Type: Weight – Teardrop
Issued: 1990 in a limited edition of 750
Status: Closed
O.I.P.: U.S. $190.00

U.K.: £100.00
U.S.: $200.00
Can.: $250.00

CAPE HATTERAS
Designer: Philip Chaplain
Type: Weight – Domed
Issued: 1998 in a limited edition of 200
Status: Closed
O.I.P.: U.S. $350.00

U.K.: £175.00
U.S.: $350.00
Can.: $450.00

CHAI
Designer: Helen MacDonald
Type: Weight – Spherical
Colour: 1. Blue
2. Gold
Issued: 2000
Status: Closed
Series: Judaica Collection
O.I.P.: U.S. $95.00

U.K.: £ 50.00
U.S.: $100.00
Can.: $125.00

DESERT STORM
Designer: Colin Terris
Type: Weight – Spherical
Issued: 1991 in a limited edition of 500
Status: Closed
O.I.P.: U.S. $235.00

U.K.: £125.00
U.S.: $250.00
Can.: $325.00

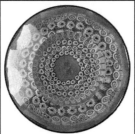

DRAGONFLY
Style Two
Designer: Colin Terris
Type: Weight – Spherical
Issued: 1986 in a limited edition of 350
Status: Closed at No. 66
O.I.P.: U.S. $250.00

U.K.: £150.00
U.S.: $300.00
Can.: $400.00

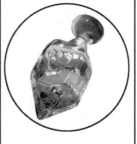

DREIDEL
Designer: Helen MacDonald
Type: Weight – Faceted, sculpture
Issued: 2000
Status: Closed
Series: Judaica Collection
O.I.P.: U.S. $225.00

U.K.: £125.00
U.S.: $225.00
Can.: $275.00

ELINOR
Designer: Colin Terris
Type: Weight – Spherical
Issued: 1986 in a limited edition of 350
Status: Closed at No. 80
O.I.P.: U.S. 250.00

U.K.: £225.00
U.S.: $450.00
Can.: $600.00

U.S. EXCLUSIVE WEIGHTS (cont.)

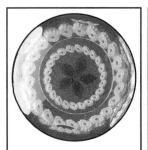

HOLLY
Style One

Designer: Colin Terris
Type: Weight – Spherical
Issued: 1986 in a limited
edition of 350
Status: Closed at No. 66
O.I.P.: U.S. $225.00

U.K.: £200.00
U.S.: $400.00
Can.: $525.00

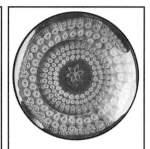

HUPPA
(Gold and Kingfisher)

Designer: Helen MacDonald
Type: Weight – Spherical
Colour: 1. Gold
2. Kingfisher
Issued: 2000 in a limited
edition of 250 (each)
Status: 1. Closed at No. 79
2. Closed at No. 63
Series: Judaica Collection
O.I.P.: U.S. $395.00

U.K.: £200.00
U.S.: $400.00
Can.: $525.00

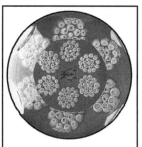

KATHERINE

Designer: Colin Terris
Type: Weight – Spherical
Issued: 1986 in a limited
edition of 350
Status: Closed at No. 54
O.I.P.: U.S. $250.00

U.K.: £225.00
U.S.: $450.00
Can.: $625.00

LADYBIRD
Style Two

Designer: Colin Terris
Type: Weight – Spherical
Issued: 1986 in a limited
edition of 350
Status: Closed at No. 71
O.I.P.: U.S. $295.00

U.K.: £250.00
U.S.: $525.00
Can.: $675.00

LIFE

Designer: Helen MacDonald
Type: Weight – Spherical
Issued: 2000 in a limited
edition of 750
Status: Closed at No. 154
Series: Judaica Collection
O.I.P.: U.S. $95.00

U.K.: £ 50.00
U.S.: $100.00
Can.: $125.00

MARDIS GRAS

Designer: Colin Terris
Type: Weight – Spherical
Issued: 2001
Status: Closed
Series: Unknown
O.I.P.: U.K. £49.00
U.S. $100.00

U.K.: £ 50.00
U.S.: $100.00
Can.: $130.00

MARIONETTE

Designer: Colin Terris and
William Manson
Type: Weight – Spherical
Issued: 1996 in a limited
edition of 50
Status: Closed
O.I.P.: U.S. $850.00

U.K.: £ 425.00
U.S.: $ 850.00
Can.: $1,100.00

MENORAH

Designer: Helen MacDonald
Type: Weight – Spherical
Colour: 1. Blue
2. Gold
Issued: 2000
Status: Closed
Series: Judaica Collection
O.I.P.: U.S. $95.00

U.K.: £ 50.00
U.S.: $100.00
Can.: $125.00

U.S. EXCLUSIVE WEIGHTS (cont.)

MILLENNIUM LIBERTY
Designer: Colin Terris
Type: Weight – Domed
Issued: 1999 in a limited
edition of 350
Status: Fully subscribed
Series: Millennium
Collection
O.I.P.: U.S. $295.00

U.K.: £150.00
U.S.: $300.00
Can.: $400.00

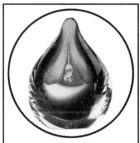

MISTLETOE
Style Two
Designer: Helen MacDonald
Type: Weight – Teardrop
Issued: 1996 in a limited
edition of 350
Status: Closed
O.I.P.: U.S. $350.00

U.K.: £175.00
U.S.: $350.00
Can.: $450.00

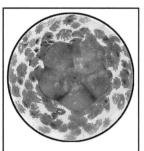

MONET WATERLILY
Designer: Helen MacDonald
Type: Weight – Spherical
Issued: 2002
Status: Active
Series: Museum Collection
O.I.P.: U.S. $125.00

U.K.: –
U.S.: $125.00
Can.: –

MOUNT RUSHMORE
Designer: Colin Terris
Type: Weight – Spherical
Issued: 1987 in a limited
edition of 500
Status: Fully subscribed
O.I.P.: U.S. $250.00

U.K.: £150.00
U.S.: $300.00
Can.: $400.00

Note: This paperweight was
commissioned to
celebrate the 50th
anniversary of the Mount
Rushmore Memorial.

Photograph not
available
at press time

PERCHED EAGLE
Designer: Alastair MacIntosh
Willie Bain
Type: Weight – Unknown
Issued: 2002
Status: Active
Series: Unknown
O.I.P.: Unknown

U.K.: Not
U.S.: Available
Can.:

PIT STOP
Designer: William Manson
Type: Weight – Spherical
Issued: 1996 in a limited
edition of 50
Status: Closed
O.I.P.: U.S. $850.00

U.K.: £ 425.00
U.S.: $ 850.00
Can.: $1,100.00

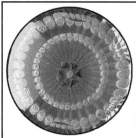

POINSETTIA
Style One
Designer: Colin Terris
Type: Weight – Spherical
Issued: 1986 in a limited
edition of 350
Status: Closed at No. 46
O.I.P.: U.S. $325.00

U.K.: £275.00
U.S.: $550.00
Can.: $700.00

PRIMA DONNA
Designer: Philip Chaplain
Type: Weight – Spherical
Issued: 1997 in a limited
edition of 250
Status: Closed
O.I.P.: U.S. $250.00

U.K.: £125.00
U.S.: $250.00
Can.: $325.00

U.S. EXCLUSIVE WEIGHTS (cont.)

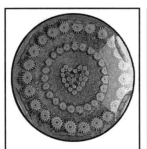

ROMANCE
Style One
Designer: Colin Terris
Type: Weight – Spherical
Issued: 1986 in a limited
            edition of 350
Status: Fully subscribed
O.I.P.:   U.S. $175.00

U.K.:   £150.00
U.S.: $300.00
Can.: $400.00

SHOAL MATES
Designer: Charlotte Judd
Type: Weight – Spherical
Issued: 1997
Status: Active
O.I.P.:   U.S. $100.00

U.K.:   £ 50.00
U.S.: $100.00
Can.: $125.00

STAR OF DAVID
First Version
Designer: Helen MacDonald
Type: Weight – Spherical
Issued: 2000
Status: Closed
Series: Judaica Collection
O.I.P.:   US $99.50

U.K.:   £ 50.00
U.S.: $100.00
Can.: $125.00

STAR OF DAVID
Second Version
Designer: Helen MacDonald
Type: Weight – Spherical
Size: Medium
Colour: 1. Blue
            2. Gold
Issued: 2000
Status: Closed
Series: Judaica Collection
O.I.P.:   U.S. $110.00

U.K.:   £ 65.00
U.S.: $125.00
Can.: $150.00

STAR REFLECTION
Designer: Helen MacDonald
Type: Weight – Domed
Colour: 1. Blue
            2. Gold
Issued: 2000 in a limited
            edition of 650
Status: Blue closed at No. 80
            Gold closed at No. 36
Series: Judaica Collection
O.I.P.:   U.S. $265.00

U.K.:   £135.00
U.S.: $265.00
Can.: $325.00

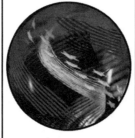

STARS and STRIPES
Designer: Helen MacDonald
Type: Weight – Spherical
Issued: 1997
Status: Active
O.I.P.:   U.S. $100.00

U.K.:   £ 50.00
U.S.: $100.00
Can.: $125.00

TABLETS
Designer: Helen MacDonald
Type: Weight Spherical
Colour: 1. Blue
            2. Gold
Issued: 2000
Status: Closed
Series: Judaica Collection
O.I.P.:   U.S. $95.00

U.K.:   £ 50.00
U.S.: $100.00
Can.: $125.00

TABLETS FROM THE MOUNT
Designer: Helen MacDonald
Type: Weight – Domed
Issued: 2000 in a limited
            edition of 250
Status: Closed at No. 80
Series: Judaica Collection
O.I.P.:   U.S. $365.00

U.K.:   £185.00
U.S.: $365.00
Can.: $500.00

U.S. EXCLUSIVE WEIGHTS (cont.)

 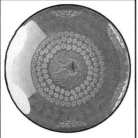  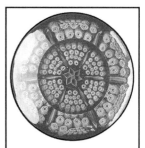

TORAH		**TROPICAL FISH**	
Designer:	Helen MacDonald	Designer:	Colin Terris
Type:	Weight – Spherical	Type:	Weight – Spherical
Colour:	1. Blue	Issued:	1986 in a limited
	2. Gold		edition of 350
Issued:	2000	Status:	Closed at No. 61
Status:	Closed	O.I.P.:	U.S. $300.00
Series:	Judaica Collection		
O.I.P.:	U.S. $95.00	U.K.:	£300.00
		U.S.:	$600.00
U.K.:	£ 50.00	Can.:	$775.00
U.S.:	$100.00		
Can.:	$125.00		

UNITED WE STAND		**VICTORIA**	
Designer:	Colin Terris	Designer:	Colin Terris
Type:	Weight – Spherical	Type:	Weight – Spherical
Issued:	2002	Issued:	1986 in a limited
Status:	Active		edition of 350
Series:	Closed	Status:	Closed at No. 60
O.I.P.:	U.S. 95.00	O.I.P.:	U.S. $295.00
U.K.:	£ 50.00	U.K.:	£300.00
U.S.:	$100.00	U.S.:	$600.00
Can.:	$125.00	Can.:	$775.00

YEAR OF THE CHILD NATIONAL CHARITY
SCOTTISH HEADQUARTERS, GLASGOW, U.K.

YEAR OF THE CHILD

Designer:	Caithness Engraving Studios
Type:	Weight – Spherical, engraved
Issued:	1980 in a limited edition of 250
Status:	Closed at No. 80
O.I.P.:	£30.00
U.K.:	£100.00
U.S.:	$200.00
Can.:	$250.00

ADDENDUM

CELEBRATION BLUE
Designer: Margot Thomson
Type: Weight – Spherical, Standard
Issued: c.1997
Status: Active
Series: Unlimited
O.I.P.: U.K. £39.95
U.S. $110.00

U.K.: £ 39.95
U.S.: $110.00
Can.: –

CELEBRATION GOLD - 50TH
Designer: Margot Thomson
Type: Weight – Spherical, Standard
Issued: c.1997
Status: Active
Series: Unlimited
O.I.P.: U.K. £39.95
U.S. $110.00

U.K.: £ 39.95
U.S.: $110.00
Can.: –

CELEBRATION RUBY - 40TH
Designer: Margot Thomson
Type: Weight – Spherical, Standard
Issued: c.1997
Status: Active
Series: Unlimited
O.I.P.: U.K. £39.95
U.S. $110.00

U.K.: £ 39.95
U.S.: $110.00
Can.: –

CELEBRATION SILVER - 25TH
Designer: Margot Thomson
Type: Weight – Spherical, Standard
Issued: c.1997
Status: Active
Series: Unlimited
O.I.P.: U.K. £39.95
U.S. $110.00

U.K.: £ 39.95
U.S.: $110.00
Can.: –

CELTIC MYTHS
Designer: Gordon Hendry
Type: Weight – Spherical
Colour: 1. Blue
2. Green
3. Heather
Issued: 2001
Status: Active
O.I.P.: U.K. £39.95
U.S. $90.00

U.K.: £39.95
U.S.: $90.00
Can.: –

GOLD (Executive)
Style One
Designer: Alastair MacIntosh
Type: Weight – Spherical
Issued: c.1998
Status: Closed
Series: Executive Collection
O.I.P.: Unknown

U.K.: Not
U.S.: Available
Can.:

BLUE (Executive)
Designer: Alastair MacIntosh
Type: Weight – Spherical
Issued: c. 1998
Status: Closed
Series: Executive Collection
O.I.P.: Unknown

U.K.: Not
U.S.: Available
Can.:

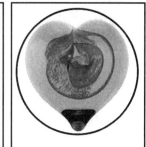

TRUE HEARTS
Designer: Helen MacDonald
Type: Weight – Sculptural
Colour: 1. Gold
2. Pearl
3. Pink
4. Rudy
Issued: 2002/03
Status: Active
O.I.P.: U.K. £19.95
U.S. $40.00

U.K.: £19.95
U.S.: $40.00
Can.: –

ADDENDUM (Cont.)

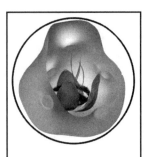

BULLSEYE BLUE

Designer: Sarah Peterson
Type: Weight – Standard
Issued: 2003
Status: Active
Series: Unlimited Cosmic Bubble
O.I.P.: U.K. £75.00
      U.S. $150.00

U.K.: £ 75.00
U.S.: $150.00
Can.: –

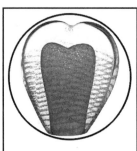

PASSION HEART

Designer: Sarah Peterson
Type: Weight –
Size: 1. Large
     2. Small
Issued: 2003
Status: Active
Series: Unlimited
O.I.P.: U.K. £29.95
      U.S. $65.00

U.K.: £29.95
U.S.: $65.00
Can.: –

SANDSTORM

Designer: Helen MacDonald
Type: Weight – Spherical, Standard
Issued: 2003
Status: Active
Series: Unlimited – Natural Environments
O.I.P.: U.K. £39.95
      U.S. $85.00

U.K.: £39.95
U.S.: $85.00
Can.: –

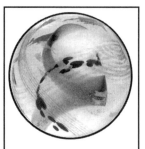

TROPICAL LAGOON

Designer: Helen MacDonald
Type: Weight –Spherical, Standard
Issued: 2003
Status: Active
Series: Unlimited edition – Natural Environments
O.I.P.: U.K. £39.95
      U.S. $85.00

U.K.: £39.95
U.S.: $85.00
Can.: –

MILLEFIORI FAIRY

Designer: Helen MacDonald
Type: Weight – Spherical
Issued: 2004
Status: Active
Series: Fantasia
O.I.P.: Unknown

U.K.: Prices not
U.S.: available
Can.: press time

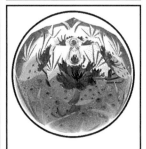

MOONLIT MEADOW

Designer: Helen MacDonald
Type: Weight – Spherical
Issued: 2004 in a limited edition of 100
Status: Active
O.I.P. Unknown

U.K.: Prices not
U.S.: available at
Can.: press time

ST. GEORGE AND THE DRAGON

Designer: Gordon Hendry
Type: Weight – Domed
Issued: 2004 in a limited edition of 400
Status: Active
O.I.P. Unknown

U.K.: Prices not
U.S.: available at
Can.: press time

SORCERER'S APPRENTICE
Style Two

Designer: Helen MacDonald
Type: Weight – Spherical Facetted
Size: Medium
Issued: 2004
Status: Active
Series: Unlimited – Fantasia
O.I.P.: U.K. £23.50
      U.S. $50.00

U.K.: £23.50
U.S.: $50.00
Can.: –

ALPHABETICAL INDEX

20,000 Leagues 64
25th Anniversary of Investiture of
   Prince of Wales 354
     Prestige Edition 354
30th Anniversary Concorde 354
   Prestige 354
30th Anniversary of Moon Landing 354
   Magnum 355
   Prestige 354
40 Fathoms 227
40th Anniversary of Queen
   Elizabeth II Accession 349
40th Anniversary Queen
   Elizabeth II Coronation
     Cobalt Base 349
     Ruby 349
     Ruby Overlay 349
5-4-3-2-1 144
75th Anniversary of Royal Air Force 354

A

Aberration 219
Abracadabra 213
Abseil 111
Abyss 188
Acanthus 311
Accord 155
Acoustics Blue 301
Acquiescence 203
Acrobat 86
Adagio 80
Admiration 202
Adoration 180
Adventure 91
Adventure Begins 336
Aegean Pearl 219
Aeronaut 240
Affection 271
Affinity 101
African Adventure 219
African Chameleon 181
Age of Chivalry 215
Air 8, 101
Aladdin 111
Alba (Scotland) 271
Alba Gold 240
Alba Kingfisher 240
Alchemist 219
Alchemy 111
Alexandra 365
Alien 16
Alien Encounter 326
All the Fun of the Fair 187

Allegro 311
Alley Cat 171
Allure 196
Alpha 82, 131
Alpine Glory 217
Alpine Peak 301
Alpine Pink 126
Alpine Summer 219
Alpine Winter 101
Alternation 261
Always 287
Always…! 333
Amazing Grace 287
Amazonia 212
Amber Gambler 240
Ambience 327
Ambrosia 311
Amethyst Bouquet 59
Amethyst Garland 219
Amethyst Lace 41
Amethyst Poppy 240
Amethyst Spray 83
Ammadora 203
Ammonite 91
Amore 168
Amoroso 219
Anastasia 219
Anchor 347
Andromeda 51
Anemone 68, 117
Angel Fish 20, 331
Angelina 261
Angler Dome 17
Another World 287
Anoushka 214
Antenna 51
Aperture 220
Apparition 210
Apple Blossom 65
April – Daffodil 261
April Perfume Flask 45
April Showers 240
Aquaflora 220
   Perfume Bottle 39
Aquamarina 220
Aquamarine 70
Aquarelle 67
Aquarium 218
Aquarius 111, 183
Aquila 20
Aquilegia 117
Arabesque 122
Arctic Awakening 163
Arctic Carnation 140

Arctic Crocus 220
Arctic Crystal 220
Arctic Night 24
Arctic Orchid 122
Arctic Tern 11
Arctic Twilight 287
Argo 131
Argon 122
Argosy 97
Aria 220
Ariel 6
Aries 25, 109, 183
Ark Royal 347
Art deco 240
Ascension 166
Aspiration 122
Asteroid 20
Astra Dance 220
Astral 75
Astral Celebration 271
Astral Navigator 215
Astronaut 271
Atlantis 27
August – Carnation 261
Auld Lang syne 202
Aura 287
Auricula 193
Aurora 91
Autumn 14, 192, 301
Autumn Bouquet 72
Autumn Breeze 90
Autumn Celebration
   Weight One 158
   Weight Two 158
Autumn Dream 153
Autumn Gold 207
Autumn Gold (Four Seasons) 271
Autumn Hedgerow 220
Autumn Illusions – Maple 261
Autumn Illusions – Oak 271
Autumn Illusions – Beech 287
Autumn Leaves 70
Aventurine 196
Azalea 163
Aztec 162
Aztec Rainflower 201
Aztec Spires 271
Azure Bouquet 163
Azurina 221

B

Babes In The Wood 271
Babylon 301

Badger 94
Bagatelle 107
Ballerina 140
Ballet 335
Balloon Race 261
Balloon Seller 81
Balmoral Inkwell 148
Bamboozled 194
Banshee 221
Baptism 272
Barrier Reef 127
Bashful 311
Battle of Britain 121, 347
Bauble, Bangle and Beads 31
Beauty and the Beast 272
Becalmed 122
Bed of Roses 48
Bedouin 240
Bee Keeping 301
Belladonna 311
Bethlehem 261
Between the Lines 301
Bewitched 108
Beyond the Stars 311
Bezique 115
   Perfume Bottle 116
Bianca Perfume Flask 45
Big Ben Millennium 347
Big Top 199
Biosphere 204
Birds of Paradise 154
Black and Gold 35
   Perfume Bottle 35
Black Gem 34
Black Headed Gull 17
Black Hole 301
Black Magic 162
Black Narcissus 111
Black Salamander 61
Blackberries and Ladybird 116
Blast Off 241
Blaze 287
Blessings 311
Blithe Spirit 92
Blossom 162
Blue 287
Blue (Executive) 371
Blue and Pink Posy 58
Blue and White Garland 85
Blue Anemone 241
Blue Angels 365
Blue Blossom 311
Blue Butterfly – Gold Flower 192
Blue Butterfly – Latticino Base 192

Blue Butterfly – Miniature 191
Blue Coral 54
Blue Floral Fountain 31
Blue Flower 58
Blue Ice 140
Blue Lagoon 175, 211
Blue Lotus 261
Blue Marlin 68
Blue Moon 221
Blue Octavia 56
Blue Petal Perfume Bottle 25
Blue Rhapsody 241
Blue Rose 35
   Perfume Bottle 35
Blue Sail 155
Blue Spiral 31
Blue Splash 147
Blue Spray 72
Blue Tempest 287
Blue Velvet 67
Blue Zanfirico 347
Bluebell Ballet 272
Bluebirds 56
Bluetits 150
Blush 74, 272
Bolero 59
Bonsai 101
Borneo 312
Bounteous 221
Bouquet and Ferns 58
Bouquet Perfume Bottle 66
Boyhood Memories 198
Brachiosaurus 221
Brain Waves Amber 312
Branching Out 216
Breakers Dawn 301
Breakers Dusk 302
Breakout 241
Bridal Waltz 272
Bright New Day 208
Brilliance 241
Brimstone 119
Britannia 98
Brocade Butterfly 93
Brushstrokes 177
Bubbles 'n Stripes 333
Buccaneer 221
Bugs – Butterfly 302
Bullseye Blue 372
Bullseye Millefiori 11
Bumblebee And Bluebells 174
Bundle of Joy 2001(Boy) 272
Bundle of Joy 2001(Girl) 272
Bundle of Joy 2002 (Boy) 288

Bundle of Joy 2002 (Girl) 288
Bunnies 221
Burgundy Bloom 208
Burgundy Bouquet 342
Burgundy Quartet 241
Burgundy Trefoil 241
Burning 326
Burning Ambition 272
Burning Bush 221
Burning Passion 273
Busy Bees 222
Buttercup 288
Buttercups 160
Buttercups and Butterfly 222
Buttercups and Daisies 145
Butterflies 73, 117, 312
Butterfly 11, 48, 134, 151
Butterfly – Latticino Base 182
Butterfly – Purple Flower 182
Butterfly – Yellow Flower 182
Butterfly and Bluebells 150
Butterfly and Flower 23, 28
Butterfly Bouquet 163
Butterfly Duet 84
Butterfly Garland 159
Butterfly Orchid 101
Byzantium 111

C

Cabaret 70
Cactus City 202
Cactus Reflection 210
Cairngorm 273
Caliph 97
Calypso 95
Camelia 73
Camelot 51
Camelot II 211
Camilla Perfume Bottle 77
Camomile 193
Cancer 183
Candida 78
Candlelight 327
Cantata 58
   Perfume Bottle 58
Cape Hatteras 365
Cape Primrose 174
Capital Celebration Edinburgh 241
Caprice 52
Capricorn 183
Captor 187
Caress 262
Caribbean Sunrise 171

Carnation	116, 158	Centenary Year Celebration	262	Closed Circuit	244
Perfume Bottle	158	Chai	365	Cobalt splendour	223
Carnival	66	Chameleon	89	Cobra	22, 27, 35
Carnival Cascade	210	Chance Encounter	288	Cockatoo	146
Carnival Silver	94	Chanelle	243	Cocoon	171
Cartouche	242	Channel Crossing	186	Cold Nights, Warm Hearts	344
Cascade	10, 198	Channel Tunnel	347	Colour Pool	223
Cascade Rainbow	11	Chantilly	56	Columbine	178
Cascadia	242	Chantilly Perfume Bottle	64	Comet	19
Cased Coral	5	Charisma	112	Commanding The Waves	312
Castaway	111	Charity	39	Communication	168
Castillion	131	Chartreuse	222	Companions	288
Castle Garden	207	Chasm	222	Compassion	215
Castle In The Sky	312	Checkers	188	Concentrix	223
Castle of Mey	184, 347	Checkpoints	135	Concorde	348
Castles In The Air	222	Cherish	262	Concorde Tribute	348
Cataclysm	262	Cherries	47, 146	Confetti Cascade	223
Catalyst	273	Cherry Blossom	165	Confusion	101
Catching Raindrops	171	Perfume Bottle	158	Congratulations	43, 147, 289
Caterpillar	146	Cherry Pie	208	21st	289
Caterpillar and Cherry Blossom	181	Chevrons	243	40th	289
Cats	312	Chicago Skyline	330	50th	289
Cauldron	288	Chiffon	63	Conquistador	195
Cauldron Aqua	49	Chorale	88	Contours	131
Cauldron Rainbow	177	Christmas Candle	61	Contrast	33
Cauldron Ruby	49	Christmas Decoration	87	Cool Blue	312
Cavalcade	111	Christmas Lantern	110	Cool Cap	333
Cavatina	222	Christmas Poinsettia 2000	331	Coquette	39
Cavern	127	Christmas Rose	29, 50, 157	Coral	5
Ceilidh	242	Christmas Star	87	Coral City	244
Celebration	42	Christmas Tree	50	Coral Dream	289
Celebration Blue	371	Christmas Weight	19	Coral Encounter	138
Celebration Gold - 50th	371	Christopher Columbus –		Coral Fantasy '99	244
Celebration Numerals		500th Anniversary	347	Coral Flower	273
Cobalt 21	242	Chrysalis	122	Coral Fronds	244
Cobalt 25	242	Chuckie Stane	211	Coral Garden	211
Emerald 60	242	Churchill 60th Anniversary	348	Coral Paradise	302
Emerald 75	242	Cinderella	106	Coral Reef	175
Gold 100	243	Cinnabar	222	Coral Voyager	122
Gold 50	242	Cinquefoil	164	Cordelia Perfume Flask	45
Heather 40	243	Circle of Friends – Amethyst	312	Cormorant	15
Heather 65	243	Citadel	59	Cornflower	187, 244
Kingfisher 18	243	Citron	244	Corona	140
Kingfisher 30	243	City Limits	244	Coronation Anniversary Prestige	
Ruby - 40th	371	Clairvoyant	122	Perfume Bottle	348
Silver - 25th	371	Clarion Call	112	Coronation Coach	302, 348
Celeste	70	Classical Moment	217	Coronation Four Nations	302
Celestial Crystal	149	Clematis	126, 147	Coronation Perfume Bottle	302
Celtic Celebration	243	Clematis and Trellis	223	Coronation Procession	302
Celtic Charm	288	Clematis Perfume Bottle	148	Coronation Silver Jubilee	24
Celtic Connection	273	Cleopatra	101	Coronation Tudor Rose	302
Celtic Knot	222	Cliff Top	288	Coronet	38
Celtic Myths	371	Clockwork	140	Corryvreckan Perfume Bottle	53
Celtic Symbol	273	Close Harmony	273	Cosmic Collision	196

Cosmic Crown	289	Daisy Chain	117	Dimples	303
Cosmic Fountain	262	Daisy Daisy	262	Dinner Party	140
Cosmic Rain	31	Daisy Duet	274	Discovery	123
Cosmic Vision	223	Damask	67	Distraction	303
Cosmos	119, 174	Damsel Fly	190	Divine Light	155
Perfume Bottle	174	Damson Floral Fountain	47	Diving Tern	15
Cottage Garden	223	Dancing Daffodils	331	Divinity	215
Countdown	303	Dancing In The Snow	336	Dizzy	130
Counterpoint	91	Dancing Seahorse	290	Dizzy Lizzy	246
Country Garden	273	Dancing Shamrock	331	DNA	358
Country Posy	223	Danielle Perfume Flask	45	Doc	313
Court Jester	289	Dark Island	54	Dog Rose	134
Covenant	172	Dark Secret	131	Dog Tooth Violet	180
Crab Apple	206	Dash	245	Dolphin	16, 57, 105
Creation	49	David and Goliath	303	Dolphin Duet	290
Crescendo	112	Dawn	26	Dolphin liason	303
Crescent Moon	140	Dawn Bouquet	245	Dolphin Light	344
Critical Mass	203	Dawn Chorus	116	Dolphin Tall	344
Crocodile	95	Day	189	Dolphinarium	217
Crocus	54, 244	Daydreams	106	Dolphins	313
Crossed Halberds	61	D-Day Landings	348	Domino	78
Crown	10, 42	Debut	168	Dopey	313
Crown Jewel	245	Debutante	198	Double Cross	141
Crown, Orb and Sceptre Prestige		December – Christmas Rose	262	Double Dragonfly	83
Coronation	348	Deep	144	Double Exposure	138
Crucible	128	Deep Endeavour	224	Double Helix	225
Crusader	91	Deep Sea Diver	198	Double Magnum 92	136
Crystal Carousel	262	Deep Secret	326	Double Magnum 93	141
Crystal Chandelier	274	Deity	224	Double Magnum 94	153
Crystal Clear	274	Déjà Vu	274	Double Magnum '95	170
Crystal Dreams	274	Delilah	245	Double Magnum '96	189
Crystal Voyager	224	Deliverer	313	Double Magnum 97	200
Cupcake	313	Delphinium	117	Double Magnum '98	225
Curio	45	Delphinium and Ladybird	182	Double Magnum '99	246
Perfume Bottle	45	Dervish	63	Double Magnum Amethyst	62
Curious Cats	313	Desert Dreams	303	Double Magnum Azure	107
Curling (Crossed Brooms)	78	Desert Orchid	112	Double Magnum Crimson	83
Curling (Female)	78	Desert Spring	137	Double Magnum Emerald	66
Curling (Male)	78	Desert Storm	365	Double Magnum Jade	119
Cyclamen	145	Desperado '99	245	Double Magnum Magenta	128
Cycloid	140	Destination Deimos	224	Double Magnum Ruby	53
Cyclone	91	Destination Mars	206	Double Magnum Sable	96
Cymru (Wales)	274	Devil's Advocate	188	Double Magnum Violet	74
		Devotion	224	Double Salamander	150
D		Dew Drops	194	Double Spiral	32
		Dewdrop Orchid	245	Double Starburst	263
Daffodil	245	Dewdrop Perfume Bottle	290	Double Take	326
Daffodil Spray	197	Diabolo	147	Double Vision	172
Dahlia	176, 179	Diamond Bouquet	207	Doves	146
Daisies and Trellis	245	Diamond Lily	224	Down on the Farm	205
Daisy	289	Diamond Reflections	246	Dragonfly	13, 98, 365
Daisy and Forget-Me-Not	224	Dichro Dazzle	246	Dragonfly – Blue Flower	176
Daisy and Ladybird	116	Dignity	274	Dragonfly – Latticino Base	176
Daisy Bouquet	224	Dilemma	56	Dragonfly – White Flower	176

Dragonfly and Flowers 47
Dragonfly and Snail 137
Dragonfly and waterlilies 127
Dragonfly Garland 116
Dream Flower 31
Dream Lovers 263
Dream Maker 169
Dream Weaver 201
Dreidel 365
Drifting By 206
Druid 154
Drystone Walling 303
Duck Pond 84
Duet
  Weight One 42
  Weight Two 42
Dunvegan Inkwell 148
Dusk 26
Dusky Maiden 246
Dwarfs' Cottage, The 313
Dynasty 112

E

Eagle Dome 17
Eagle Has Landed 167
Eagle In Flight 290
Earth 3, 8, 101, 313
Eastern Promise 171
Echo 128
Edelweiss 127
Edinburgh Castle 348
Effervescence 225
Effervescent Ribbons 333
Eggstravaganza 225
Egret 190
Eider Duck 17, 20
Eighty Eight 81
Eireann (Ireland) 274
El Dorado 23
Electric Soup 246
Elegance 37
Elfin Dance 112
Elinor 365
Elixir 108
Elizabeth I 52
Elizabeth of Glamis 263
Elizabeth of Glamis Perfume Bottle 349
Elizabeth of Glamis Rose 290
Elsinore 225
Embryo 30
Emerald 81
Emerald City 214
Emerald Dancers 208

Emerald Grotto 211
Emerald Poppy 225
Emerald Roulette 263
Emerald Spray 191
Emerald Vision 168
Enchanté Perfume Bottle 46
Enchanted Apple 314
Enchanted Castle 138
Enchanted Evening 344
Enchanted Forest 39
Enchantment 189
Encore 225
Encounter 76
End of an Era 349
Endearment 156
Energize 225
England 275
Enigma 43
Entwined Hearts 338
Equinox 90
Erica Perfume Flask 45
Escapade 166
Escape 128
Eterna 39
Eternal Flame 226
Eternal Love 217
Eternal Passion 226
Eternity 177
Etheria 89
Eureka 303
Eurythmic 149
Evangeline '99 246
Eve 290
Evening Flight 247
Evensong 63
Everest 149
Evergreen 59
Evolution 102
Exotica 304
Explorer 123
Extravaganza 199
Exuberance 141
Eye of the Storm 226

F

Faerie Dance 226
Fair Juliet 275
Fairy Land 172
Fairy Lights '99 247
Fairy Tale 161
Faith 38
Falling Leaves 275
Fandang 120, 172

Fanfare 108
Fantasia 37
Fantasy Orchid 141
Far Frontiers 247
Far Horizons 112
Far Pavilion 187
Farewell Britannia 349
Fascination 137
Fatal Attraction 290
Feathers 161
February – Crocus 263
Festival 152
Festival Of Colour 325
Festive Beauty 304
Festive Bouquet 105
Festive Christmas Tree 290
Festive Delight 207
Festive Kisses 275
Festive Of Colour 325
Festive Reflections 263
Festive Rose 263
Festive Snowflake 2000 263
Festive Snowflake 2001 275
Festive Snowflake 2002 291
Festive Snowman 291
Festive Window 226
Festivity 247
Field Study Butterfly 74
Fiesta 99
Finale 213
Finesse 170
Fiona 47
Fire 6, 46, 102
Fire birds 214
Fire Dance 8
Fire Flower 32
Fire Lizard 57
Fireball 51
Firebrand 304
Firecracker 89
Fireflame 154
Firefly 68
Firenze Flask 144
Firework Festival 291
Firework Fiesta 213
Firework Orchid 275
Fireworks 33
First Love 226
First Quarter 16
Fish 6
Flag Iris 127
Flambé 247
Flamboyance 226
Flame Nasturtium 193

Flamenco	33, 314	Fountain Memories	333	Glacier	141
Flamenco Passions	304	Fountain of Desire	247	Gladiators	204
Flaming Beauty	314	Fountain of Youth	275	Glamis Castle	349
Flamingo	205	Foursome	198	Glamis Rose	184
Flamingoes	116	Fragrance	47	Perfume Bottle	184
Fleur	82, 358	Fragrant Orchid	227	Glass Slipper, The	276
Fleur Rouge	206	Fragrant Rose	247	Glassmaker, The	41
Flight	81	Framboise	200	Global Beauty	304
Flight of Fancy	92	Frankincense	291	Globe Trotter	102
Flora	54	Free Fall	123	Glowing Embers	248
Floral Awakening	314	Free Spirit	54	Go-Between	141
Floral Ballet Dancer	314	Freedom	112	Gold	276
Floral Basket	58	Freeform	119	Gold (Executive)	371
Floral Carousel	226	Freesias	174	Gold Butterfly – Pink Flower	197
Floral Celebration	264	French Fancy	217	Gold Rose	182
Floral Dance	291	Fritillaria	173	Gold Rush	228
Floral Diamond	227	Frivolity	210	Gold Throat	35
Floral Dream	314	Frog	160	Golden Angel	276
Floral Garden	164	Frog and Ladybird	94	Golden Awakening	228
Floral Illusion	123	From the Flames	227	Golden Citadel	213
Floral Mist Perfume Bottle	314	Frost	45	Golden Coronet	304
Floral Pink	59	Frosty Morning	162	Golden Corsage	74
Floral Reflections	117	Frosty's Night Out	276	Golden Crown	276
Floral splendour	247	Frozen In Time	248	Golden Fancy	315
Floral Tribute	41	Fruit	207	Golden Galaxy	276
Floral Vision	291	Fuchsia	58, 148, 193	Golden Glory	248
Floral Whimsy	93	Fuchsia Inkwell	167	Golden Haven	108
Florette	68	Fuchsia Perfume Bottle	134, 148	Golden Jubilee	276, 336
Floriana	106	Fuchsias	117, 331	Golden Jubilee Carousel	277
Floribunda	227	Fugue	51	Golden Jubilee Celebration	277
Flourish	77	Fujiyama	212	Golden Jubilee Crown	277
Flower Crystal		Fulmar	9	Golden Jubilee Crown Basket	277
Black Orchids	62	Fusion	170	Golden Jubilee Golden Crown	277
Blue Pansies	62			Golden Jubilee Majesty	277
Pink Carnations	62	**G**		Golden Jubilee Millefiori Crown	277
Red Poppies	62			Golden Jubilee Millefiori Royal	
Flower in the Rain	10, 157, 358	Galactica	63	Cypher	277
Flower in the Snow	52	Galaxy	291	Golden Jubilee Moonbeam	278
Flower of Scotland	166	Gale Force	326	Golden Jubilee Mooncrystal	278
Flowerpot People		Galileo's Thermometer 60 Degrees	315	Golden Jubilee Queen Elizabeth	
Weight – One	227	Galleon	98	Rose	278
Weight – Two	227	Gannet	15	Golden Jubilee Reflections	278
Flutter By	77	Garden Fuchsias	276	Golden Jubilee Regal Crown	278
Flying Fish	70	Garden Pool and Dragonfly	342	Golden Jubilee Regal Reflections	278
Flying Pegasus	342	Garden Posy	227	Golden Jubilee Rose	278
Follow My Leader	190	Garland	42	Golden Jubilee Royal Arms	278
Footprints	329	Garland of Roses	48	Golden Jubilee Royal cypher	279
Force Ten	275	Gaucho	153	Golden Jubilee Splendour	350
Forcefield	170	Gazebo	38	Golden Jubilee Tapestry	279
Forest Flame	291	Gemini	71, 183	Golden Jubilee Tribute	279
Forget Me Not	331	Genesis	8	Golden Mitre	200
Fortune	314	Gentle Touch	315	Golden Rainbow	139
Fossil	160	Geranium	173, 304	Golden Renaissance	292
Fountain	147	Giant Step	326	Golden Rose	248

Golden Sanctuary	210	Heart	41, 42	Hot! Hot! Hot!		280
Golden Splendour	191	Hearts	73	HRH Prince of Wales 50th Birthday		350
Golden Star	279	Heather	47	Humanity		316
Golden Sunflower	279	Heather Bell	28	Humbug		141
Golden Sunrise	162	Heather Corsage	228	Humming Bird	25, 79, 150, 160	
Golf Dome	128	Heather Hills	279	Huppa		366
Golf		Heaven	315	Hyacinth Bouquet		228
(Female)	78	Hedgehog	84, 174	Hydrofoil		149
(Male)	78	Helium	113	Hydroponic		131
Golfer	128	Helix	71	Hypnosis		196
Golfing Dome	17	Hellebore	315			
Gone Fishing	292	Helter Skelter	51	**I**		
Good Luck	292	Henry VIII	29, 52			
Gothic Splendour	248	Heritage	315	I Saw Three Ships		43
Grace	56	Hermitage	201	I Spy		280
Grand Tetons Summer	364	Heron	205	Ice Blossom		27
Grand Tetons Winter	364	Hey You, Get Off My Cloud	292	Ice Bound		264
Grapes	146, 166	Hibernation	196	Ice Cascade		264
Gravitation	264	Hibiscus	164	Ice Cold		333
Greenmantle	248	Hickory Dickory Dock	201	Ice Dance		67
Greetings Earthlings	264	Hidden In Time	228	Ice Fairy		102
Grumpy	315	High Dive	141	Ice Flame		26
Guardian	113	High Flyer	123	Ice Fountain		27
Guardian Angel	163	High Jinks	304	Ice Forest		214
Guillemot	18	High Seas	109	Ice Petal Perfume Bottle		22
Gulf Stream	161	Highland Dance	279	Ice Princess		63
Gyro	59	Highland Dancer	316	Ichthus		341
		Highland Fling	54	Iguana		175
H		HM Queen Elizabeth II		Illusion		27
		70th Birthday Crown	199	Images		153
Hall of Mirrors	188	Crown Overlay	199	Impressions		132
Halley's Comet	66, 362	Rose	199	Imprint		203
Halloween	102	Rose Perfume Bottle	199	Impulse		76
Hallucination	213	HM Queen Mother 75th Tribute	350	Impulse '99		248
Hanging Basket	98	Coat of Arms	350	Inca Gold		189
Happy	315	Favourite Flowers	350	Incandescence		228
Happy Anniversary	292	Glamis Rose	350	Incantation		102
Happy Birthday	292	Perfume Bottle	350	Incognito		204
Harebells	145	HMS Kelly 40th Anniversary	44	Indian Summer		123
Harlequin Double	5, 156	Hobgoblin	86	Indigo		169
Harlequin Single	5, 156	Holly	280, 366	Indulgence		316
Harmonics	194, 209	Holly and Bells	331	Inferno		74
Harmony	46	Home Coming	264	Initial		41
Harvest Festival	248	Holly Wreath	29	Ink Bottle		5
Harvest Mouse	94	Homeward Bound	200	Inner Circle		161
Harvest Time	131	Honesty	51	Inner Sanctum		228
Hawaiian Harmony	264	Honey Bee	65, 342	Inner Space		333
Healer	155	Honeysuckle	134	Innocence		201
Heart	41, 42	Perfume Bottle	71	Innovation		139
Heart and Flowers	338	Honours	340	Interceptor		142
Heart Inkwell	167	Honours, Fleur-de-Lys	340	Interlude		113
Heart of Gold	279	Honours, Orb	340	Intermezzo		142
Heart of Hearts	338	Hope	39	Internet		249
Heart Perfume Bottle	139	Hosta	193	Into Focus		113

Into the Light	316
Intrepid	249
Intrigue	102
Intruder	19
Invincible	228
Ionian Voyager	212
Iris	77, 148, 280
Iris Bouquet	173
Iris Garden	280
Iris Perfume Bottle	148
Irish Bouquet	331
Irish Shamrock	332
Irish Wild Flower	332
Irish Wild Flowers	332
Isadora	305
Island Dream	249
Island Fantasy	142
Istanbul	132
It's Life Jim	200

J

Jack In The Box	173
Jacob's Ladder	129
Jacobean Rose	249
Jacuzzi	149
Jalal	229
Jamboree	90
January – Snowdrop	264
Japanese Ikebana	305
Japanese Tea Ceremony	305
Japanese White Crane	305
Jasmine	134
Jellyfish	6
Jester	38
Jive Time	292
Joseph	178
Journey	292
Journey of the Wise Men	23
Journey's End	52
Jubilation	280
Jubilee	70
Jubilee 94 Double Magnum	161
Jubilee Celebration	358
Jubilee Crown Bubble	18
Jubilee Floating Crown	18
Jubilee Millefiori Crown	19
Jubilee Moonflower	18
Jubilee Orchid	157
Jubilee Rose	76, 358
Juggler	186
Juliet	73
July – Pansy	265
Jumping for Joy	216

June – Rose	265
Jupiter	3, 81

K

Kaleidoscope	29
Kaleidoscope '97	215
Kaleidoscope '99	249
Katarina	249
Katherine	366
Katmandu	196
Khamsin	229
Killer Whale	175
King Canute	293
King Neptune	25
King Tutenkhamun	341
Kingdom of the Deep	195
Kingfisher	61, 205
Kismet	76
Kittiwake	20
Knossos	210
Krishna	265

L

L'Amour	162
Labyrinth	63
Lace	93
Lacemaker	280
Ladybird	23, 28, 151, 366
Ladybird and Butterfly	159
Lagoon	113
Lagoon Life	190
Land of Oz, The	280
Landing Zone	249
Laser	172
Last Tango, The	281
Late Summer Splendour	229
Late Summer Sunflower	281
Latticino	16
Latticino Crown	265
Latticino Posy	249
Lazy Afternoon	316
Perfume Bottle	316
Leo	184
Levitation	153
Liberté	265
Liberty	129
Libra	25, 184
Life	366
Life Force	60
Life's a Beach	203
Life's a Bear…N-Ice!	333

Lilac Pool	132
Lilac Time	64
Perfume Bottle	65
Lilies and Ladybird	127
Lilium	64, 176
Lily of the Valley	157
Lily Pond	162
Lily Pool	229
Limelight	119
Listen	250
Listener	91
Little Red Riding Hood	281
Live Wire	229
Lizard	134
Lobster	18
Local Hero	281
Locomotion	265
London Time	250
Loop The Loop	80
Lorikeet	164
Los Tres Amigos	203
Lost City	218
Lost World	229
Love Hearts	281
Love Token	250
Lovebirds	180
Luckenbooth	109
Luckenbooth 2000	334
Lucky Clover	305
Lullaby	108
Lunar Enigma	281
Lunar III	37
Lunar Orchid	142
Lunar Quest	281
Lunar Rose	250
Lunar Sea	339
Lunar Touchdown	167
Luscious Lashes	305

M

Madrigal	92
Maelstrom	92
Magenta	80
Magic Carpet	76
Magic Castle	250
Magic Circle	49
Magic Lantern	89
Magic Mirror on the Wall	316
Magic Moment	250
Magic Potion	202
Magic Roundabout	213
Magical Roundabout	326
Magnolia	157

Magnum Opus '88	99
Malaysian Melody	229
Mallow	180
Man O' War	250
Manta Ray	23, 28, 35
Manta Ray and Coral	57
Marble Paperweight	281
March – Primrose	265
Mardi-Gras	366
Mardis Grad	103
Marguerite	53, 175
Marigolds	173
Marine Fantasy	229
Mariner 2	60
Marionette	366
Mark Anthony	293
Marooned	21
Marquee	216
Marrakesh	86
Mars	2, 170
Martian Skyline	293
Mary Rose	346
Masquerade	195
Matador	142
May – Lily of the Valley	265
May Dance	7
May Dance Magenta	177
Mayfly and Flowers	68
Maypole	155
Maze	142
Mazourka	103
Meadow Flowers	282
Meadow Pool	198
Mecca	328
Mecca Millennium	328
Meconopsis	174
Meditation	132
Melody	156
Menorah	366
Mephistopheles	179
Mercator	103
Mercury	2, 90, 169
Mercury Bottle	90
Meridian	97
Merlin	113
Mermaid	20
Mermaid's Secret	180
Merriment	293
Merry Go Round	89
Merry Maker	90
Messenger	113
Metamorphosis	204
Meteor	33
Metropolis '99	250

Mey Tapestry	293
Michaelmas Daisy	77
Midas	38
Midnight	103
Midnight Bouquet	93
Midnight Mountain	305
Midnight Mystery	251
Midnight Orchids	151
Midnight Rapture	305
Midsummer	113
Milano Flask	144
Milky Way	123
Millefiori Fairy	372
Millefiori Flower	282
Millefiori Pool	266
Millefiori Reflections	16
Millennium 2000	251
Millennium Awakening	251
Millennium Blossom	251
Millennium Carnival	251
Millennium Carousel	266
Millennium Celebration	351
Millennium Countdown	251
Millennium Cross	251
Millennium Dancer	251
Millennium Doves	252
Millennium Fanfare	266
Millennium Fantasy	252
Millennium Fiesta	252
Millennium Flame	351
Millennium Globe	252
Millennium Glory	252
Millennium Jewel	252
Millennium Katherine Wheel	252
Millennium Liberty	367
Millennium Miniature	266
Millennium Pebble	252
Millennium Renaissance	253
Millennium Sands Of Time	253
Millennium Snowflake	253
Millennium Splendour	266
Millennium Starburst	253
Millennium Teddy	253
Millennium Vision	253
Millennium Voyager	253
Minaret	81
Miniature Angel	87
Miniature Butterfly	130
Miniature Butterfly and Orange Flower	165
Miniature Butterfly and Yellow Flower	165
Miniature Butterfly Perfume Bottle	136
Miniature Candle	99

Miniature Christmas Tree	87
Miniature Cornflower	107, 120
Miniature Daffodil	96
Miniature Dragonfly	84, 96
Miniature Dragonfly – Blue Base	176
Miniature Dragonfly – Gold Base	176
Miniature Festive Fare	100
Miniature Forget-Me-Not	84, 97, 120
Miniature Heart	84, 96, 120, 130, 332
Miniature Heart Perfume Bottle	136
Miniature Ladybird	96, 120
Miniature Mistletoe	99
Miniature Narcissus	84
Miniature Orchid	130
Miniature Pansy	130
Miniature Poinsettia	87, 100
Miniature Posy	107, 121
Miniature Rose	96, 121, 130
Miniature Rose Perfume Bottle	136
Miniature Scots Thistle	84
Miniature Shamrock	96
Miniature Snowman	87
Miniature Thistle	96, 121
Miniature Thistle Perfume Bottle	137
Minuet	80
Mirage	114
Mirror Image	282
Mirrored Garden	293
Mischief	119
Mission	123
Mission Apollo XI	167
Mistletoe	23, 367
Mistral	63
Mists of Time	98
Misty Lavender Mist	88
Misty Perfume Bottle	53
Misty Rose Mist	88
Modesty	342
Momentum	109
Monet Tribute	162
Monet Waterlily	367
Moody Blue	266
Moon	4
Moon Landing	351
Moon Mountains	142
Moon Orchid	69
Moon Waves	316
Moonbeam	266, 306
Mooncrystal	66, 209
Moondance	293
Moondrop	61
Moonflower	3, 358
Moonflower Carnival	216
Moonflower Celebration	103

Moonflower Echoes 293
Moonflower Green 194
Moonflower Magenta 136
Moonflower Rainbow 161
Moonflower Red 152
Moonflower Serenade 294
Moonlight 144
Moonlight Blossom 215
Moonlight Dancer 103
Moonlight Lily 266
   Perfume Bottle 144
Moonlit Meadow 372
Moonprobe 32
Moonrise 155
Moonscape 51
Moonwalk 217
Morello 230
   Perfume Bottle 230
Morning Dew 21
Morning Flight 230
Morning Glory 160
Morning Reflections 230
Morning Sunshine 306
   Perfume Bottle 306
Moroccan Nights 294
Mosaic 138
Moses 189
Mother 294
Moulin Rouge 294
Mount Rushmore 367
Mountains of Mars 56
Myriad 21, 358
Myriad Red 152
Myrrh 306
Mysteria 103
Mystic Island 132
Mystic Shrine 230
Mystic Temple 267
Mystique 27

N

Narcissus 134
Nasturtium 134
National Flowers 83
National Quartet
   One 230
   Two 230
   Three 230
   Four 231
Nativity 34, 332
Nature Study 94
Nautilus 56
Navigator 132

Nebula 86
Nectar 89
Nemesis 204
Nemo's Kingdom 253
Neon 95
Neptune 3
Neptune's Kingdom 71, 190
Nesting Bluebird 94
Netted 306
New Horizons 179
New World 114
Newt 105
Night 189
Night Flower 32
Night Owl 80
Night Venture 31
Night Vision 150
Nimbus 142
Nineteen Eighty-Four 60
Nirvana 114
Noah's Ark 186
Nocturne 46
Noel 87
Nomad 26
Nordic Castle 254
Nordic Glade 143
Norman Conquest 202
Norse Legend 200
North Sea 362
Northern Exposure 194
Nosegay 77
Nostradamus 282
Noughts And Crosses 267
Nova 40
November – Violet 267
Now, Where's Rudolph? 306
Nucleus 29

O

Oasis 104
Objet D'art 267
Obsession 138
Ocean Breeze 166
Ocean Duet 109
Ocean Encounter 190
Ocean Fantasy 306
Ocean Hunter 94
Ocean Mystery 294
Ocean Odyssey 150
Ocean Pearl 148
Ocean Racer 306
Ocean Rendezvous 294
Ocean Serenade 216

Ocean Spring 29
Ocean Treasure 76
Ocean Wave 143
Oceanic 187
Octavia 54
Octect 27
October – Anemone 267
Octopus 22, 28
Odyssey 85
Oleander 317
Omega 131
Omphalos 180
On Reflection 254
On The Wings of a Dove 294
Once Upon a Time 231
One Fine Day 254
One Starry Night 282
One True Love 342
Only A Rose 294
Opera 335
Opium Poppy 85
Optima 124
Optix 209
Opulence 231
Opus 2002 295
Opus 88 100
Oracle 81
Orange Butterfly 165
Oration 213
Orbit 3
Orbital journey 317
Orchid 191, 254, 325
Orchid Spray 173
Orchids 73, 118, 317
Organza 168
Oriental Dawn 172
Oriental Dream 254
Oriental Lily 231
Oriental Peony 307
Oriental Pool 231
Oriental Silk 147
Origin 132
Ornamental Pool 231
Osiris 186
Osprey 17
Otter 17
Out of the Blue 201
Over the Hills 254
Overseer 155
Ozone 254

P

Oachyrhnosaurus 231

Pagan Ritual	231	Petronella	104	Pretty In Pink		217
Pagoda	60	Petunias	232	Pride And Beauty		308
Pagoda Orchid	295	Phaedra	232	Prima ballerina		
Paintbox	124	Phantom	196	Style One		295
Painted Desert	132	Pharaoh	178	Syle Two		318
Paisley Twists	307	Pheasant	68	Prima Donna		367
Panache	114	Phoenix	108	Primary colours		282
Panda	40	Piatto Azzurro	307	Primroses		65, 135
Pansies	158	Pilgrimage	143	Primula		118
Pansy	65, 160, 182, 193	Pilot Fish	159	Prince William 18th Birthday		351
Pansy Latticino	232	Pink Anemone	187	Prestige		351
Pansy Passion	317	Pink Beauty	211	Princess		104
Pansy Perfume Bottle	173	Pink Blossom	191	Princess and the Pea		283
Papaver	317	Pink Butterfly – Blue Flower	192	Princess Margaret Prestige		351
Paper Chase	168	Pink Butterfly – Miniature	191	Princess Margaret's 70th Birthday		352
Parachute	267	Pink Champagne	86	Princess Royal Prestige		352
Parade	124	Pink Chiffon	154	Princess Royal's 50th Birthday		352
Paradise	171	Pink Confetti	232	Private View		267
Paradise Lost	232	Pink Dahlia	255	Promise		268
Paradox	232	Pink Entwined Hearts	332	Prophecy		133
Parallel Lines	152	Pink Orchid	351	Propulsion		255
Parasol	33	Pink Rhododendron	180	Protea		188
Parrot	98	Pink Rose	182	Pterosaurus		233
Partridge in a Pear Tree	54	Pinnacle	92	Puffin	15, 135, 360	
Pasque Flower	197	Pinpoint	188	Pulsar		143
Passion	154	Pirouette	36	Punting on the River		295
Passion Flower	214	Pisces	183	"Purrfect"		363
Passion Heart	372	Pit Stop	367	Purity		214
Pastel	72	Pixie	130	Purity of Heart		295
Pastorale	68	Planet Peppermint	282	Purple Butterfly – Latticino Base		197
Pathfinder	114	Planetarium	104	Purple Clematis		324
Patriot	232	Playful and Watchful	79	Pursuit		124
Peace in Europe	351	Playtime	295	Pyramid Twists		308
Peace to the World	282	Plough	19	Pyrotechnics		124
Peaceful Paradise	317	Pluto	4	Python		175
Peaceful Waters	307	Poinsettia	176, 367			
Peach Floral Fountain	37	Poinsettia Perfume Bottle	90	**Q**		
Peacock	106, 154	Polar Bear	17			
Pebble	61, 72	Polar Ice Flow	307	Queen Elizabeth II, Visit to Russia		352
Peeping Tom	254	Polar Playtime	317	Quadrille		76
Pegasus	21	Pole Star	149	Quartet Perfume Bottle		22
Penguins	109	Polka	40	Queen Cleopatra		295
Pentecost	204	Polynesian Paradise	255	Queen Elizabeth I		36
Perched Eagle	367	Pond Life	68	Queen Elizabeth Ii Golden Jubilee		329
Peregrine Falcon	360	Poppies	47, 118, 192	Queen Elizabeth Rose		352
Perfect Storm	307	Poppies Perfume Bottle	145	Perfume Bottle		352
Periwinkles	158, 232	Poppy	255	Queen Mother		36
Perpetua	295	Poppy Meadow	307	Queen Mother Centenary		358
Perplexity	255	Pot pourri	114	Queen Mother's Arms		296
Persephone	50	Potreadora	317	Queen Mother's Centenary		345
Persian Palace	267	Power Source	255	Queen mother's Centenary Rose		345
Peruvian Lilies	127	Precious Jewel – Orchid	307	Queen Victoria Diamond Jubilee		
Petal Perfume Bottle	19	Precious Jewel – Rose	318	Centenary		352
Petals	95	Prelude	114			

Queen's Crown Golden Jubilee
Prestige Perfume Bottle 352
Queen's Golden Jubilee 353
Queen's Golden Jubilee Starlight 353
Quest 114
Quicksilver 66
Quintessence 67
Quintessence Perfume Bottle 67
Quintet 296
Quorum 115

R

Radiance 115
Radiant Rose 255
Rain Dance 283
Rainbow Gem 283
Rainbow Meadow 308
Rainbow Pool 268
Raindrop 296
Rainforest 308
Raj 233
Rapture 195
Raspberries 137
Rattlesnake 74
Razzamatazz 136
Reactor 186
Ready Steady Go 89
Real Thing 334
Red Admiral 205
Red Alert 255
Red Arrows 104, 353
Red Baron 283
Red Butterfly – Miniature 183
Red Carnation 256, 332
Red Carousel 318
Red Poppy 256
Red Rose 74, 160, 178, 318
Red Rose Bouquet 233
Red Rose Perfume Bottle 178
Red Roses 151
Red Sea 213
Red Shift 283
Reflections 12
Refractor 233
Regal Iris 233
Regal Lily 145
Regatta 85
Regency Stripe 40
Reincarnation 210
Remembrance Poppy 296
Remembrance White Rose 296
Renaissance 71
Rendezvous 81

Rennie's Glasgow Rose 318
Rennie's Rose 318
Rennie's Window 318
Repose 90
Reticello Rose 233
Return To Earth 283
Revelation 124
Reverence 156
Reverie 82
Revival 233
Rhapsody 16
Rhododendron 173
Rhythm 283
Rhythm 'n Blues 209
Ribbon Dancer 308
Ribbons 107
Ribbons Memories 334
Ribbons Window 334
Richard III 55
Ring o' Roses 156
Ring of Fire 194
Ringed Planet 283
Rings of Roses 48
Ripples 284
Rites of Spring 233
River Dancers 186
Robert the Bruce 308
Robin 43
Robin and Kettle 55
Robin Hood 296
Rock Pool 206
Rock Rose 193
Rocket 324
Rolling Surf Dolphin 296
Rolling Surf Lighthous 296
Rolling Surf Yacht 297
Romance 177, 368
Romance Perfume Bottle 41
Romeo 284
Rona 48
Rose and Ladybird 98
Rose Basket 268
Rose Dewdrops 297
Rose Garden 48
Rose Garland 135
Rose Inkwell 167
Rose of Sharon 180
Rose Tapestry 268
Rosebud 28, 34
Roses 318
Rosette 78
Round the Twist 214
Rox 308
Royal Arms 36

Royal Birthday 36
Royal Birthday Bouquet 118
Royal Birthday Crown 49, 57
Royal Birthday glamis Rose 119
Royal Birthday Moonflower 49, 58
Royal Birthday Perfume Bottle 119
Royal Birthday Tribute 49. 57
Royal Blue 106
Royal Bouquet Perfume Bottle 75
Royal Cypher 353
Royal Flourish 105
Royal Golden Wedding 211
Royal Golden Wedding Bell 212
Royal Golden Wedding Crown 211
Royal Golden Wedding Perfume
Bottle 212
Royal Portrait 43
Royal Tribute 268
Royal Wedding 41, 52
Royal Wedding Anchor 75
Royal Wedding Floral Bouquet 353
Royal Wedding Heart 75
Royal Wedding Luckenbooth 354
Royal Wedding Millefiori Crown 44
Royal Wedding Monogram 75
Royal Wedding Moonflower 43
Royal Wedding Orchid Bouquet 353
Bouquet Perfume Bottle 353
Royal Wedding Prestige Perfume
Bottle 353
Royal Wedding Tribute 75
Royale 178
Ruby Celebration 357
Ruffles 136

S

Sacred Spirit 203
Safe Heaven 284
Saffron 61
Sagittarius 20, 184
Sailing Away 309
Sailing By 309
Saladin 204
Salamander 22, 28, 34
Salomé 190
Saltire 256
Samarkand Perfume Bottle 39
Sanctuary 32
Sand Dancers 319
Sand Devil 115
Sand Dunes 297
Sand Sprite 39
Sandflower 138

Sandstorm	372	Seeds of Time	309	Siren	284
Santa's Tree	342	Selene	297	Sirocco	129
Sapphire Star	93	Sensations	234	Skua	20
Saqqara	179	Sentiments: Thank You	297	Skyhigh	124
Saracen	177	Sentiments: Thinking Of You	297	Skyline	34
Sargasso	256	Sentiments: With Love	297	Sleepy	319
Satellite	32	Sentinel	13, 359	Slipstream	268
Saturn	2, 170	September – Daisy	268	Small World	172
Scarab	133	Serenade	153	Smoke Signal	143
Scarecrow	198	Serendipity	195	Snail And Blossom	181
Scarlet Bouquet	106	Serenity	63	Snake Basket	205
Scarlet Fandango	268	Sergeant Major	133	Sneezy	319
Scarlet Hibiscus	163	Serpent	135	Snow Crystal	44
Scarlet Pimpernel	85, 181	Serpentine	97	Snow Dance	179
Scarlet Pimpernel Perfume Bottle	181	Seventh Heaven	153	Snow Fall	284
Scarlet Twister	319	Shamal	82	Snow Orchid	235
Scheherazade	104	Shaman	256	Snow Trail	95
Schering	361	Shambalah	234	Snow Trail Blue	129
Scimitar	177	Shamrock Snowman	332	Snowdrop Symphony	285
Scorpio	184	Shangri-La	80	Snowdrops	83
Scorpion	127	Shark	77	snowfire Orchid '99	257
Scotia	234	She	212	Snowflake	344
Scots Thistle	118, 234	Sheer Indulgence '99	256	Snowflake Crown	43
Sculpture	8	Shepherds	29	Snowflake Orchid	124
Sculptured Pool	234	Shifting Sands	163	Snowflame	97
Sea Bed	128	Shimmer	284	Snowflower	22
Sea Crab	10	Shingle Beach	298	Snowman	164
Sea Crystal	143	Shining Through	319	Snowy Owl	188
Sea Dance	55	Ship's Wheel	40	Soaring Eagles	319
Sea Dance Blue	59	Shipwreck	6	Solace	82
Sea Dance Sable	109	Shoal Mates	368	Solar Flower	327
Sea Gem	177	Shockwave	234	Solar Wind	269
Sea Grass Perfume Bottle	22	Shooting Star	309	Solemnity	257
Sea Kelp	12	Shoreline	284	Solitaire	60
Sea Lace	25	Showtime	195	Solitude	235
Sea Lace Perfume Bottle	25	Siamese Fighting Fish	34	Solo Performance	319
Sea Nymphs	212	Sidewinder	159	Solstice	143
Sea Orchid	14	Siena Flask	169	Sonata	53
Sea Pearl	14	Silent Watcher	35	Sonata Perfume Bottle	53
Sea Pearls	234	Silken Strands	195	Songbird	166
Sea Shanty	199	Silkie	298	Soothsayer	178
Sea Spray	71	Silkscreen	284	Sorcerer	166
Sea Sprite	92	Silver Coral	157	Sorcerer's Apprentice	194, 372
Sea Urchin	6	Silver Jubilee Fleet Review	346	Sorrento Flask	169
Sea View	297	Silver Lace	256	Southern Exposure	201
Seabase	14	Silver Lizard	23	Space Beacon	12
Seaform	50	Silver Moonflower	157	Space Courier	50
Seahorse	73, 175	Silver Orb	256	Space Crystal	133
Seal	15, 34	Silver Orb '99	256	Space Encounter	186
Seals	117	Silver Rain	136	Space Flower	14
Seascape	164	Silver Unicorn	342	Space Frontier	86
Seattle Skyline	325	Silver Sentinel	26	Space Hibiscus	235
Secret Garden	108	Sing For Your Supper	187	Space Journey	104
Secret Garden '98	234	Sir Percival's Quest	235	Space Landing	133

Space Orchid	31	
Space Pearl	22	
Space Rose	10	
Space Shuttle	37	
Space Station Zebra	319	
Space Trail	50	
Space Traveller	31	
Space Tulip	269	
Space Vista	50	
Spaceport	34	
Sparkle	161	
Spectre	16	
Spectrum	60	
Spellbound	108	
Spellcaster	179	
Spider's Web	343	
Spin Off	129	
Spinaway	55	
Spindrift	21	
Spindrift '99	257	
Spinnaker	99	
Spinning Jenny	143	
Spinning Top	92	
Spinosaurus	159	
Spiral	4	
Spiral Harmony	320	
Spiral Rhythm	320	
Spiral Tempo	320	
Spirit Dancer	202	
Splash	125	
Splashdown	46	
Spoilt For Choice	217	
Spooky Hands	188	
Spread of Roses	48	
Spring	14, 191, 309	
Spring Botanical	207	
Spring Bouquet	72	
Spring Breeze	85	
Spring Breeze Perfume Bottle	92	
Spring Celebration		
Weight 1	145	
Weight 2	145	
Spring Crocus	196	
Spring Festival	235	
Spring Florette, Cobalt	235	
Spring Florette, Kingfisher	235	
Spring Flowers	118	
Spring Melody	125, 257	
Spring Posy	197	
Spring Sentinel	202	
Spring Symphony	285	
Springtime	37	
SS Politician	130	
St. George and the Dragon	372	

St. Paul's	43	
Star Beacon	60	
Star Conquest	154	
Star Crystal	235	
Star Flower	26	
Star of David	368	
Star of Roses	48	
Star of Wonder	328	
Star Orchid	133	
Star Pavilion	38	
Star Reflection	368	
Star Ship	71	
Starbase	4	
Starburst	49	
Stardust	8	
Stargazer	125	
Starlight	129	
Stars and Stripes	368	
Starstruck	236	
Starwatch	66	
Starwatch Silver	95	
Status Quo	257	
Steel Blue	129	
Stegosaurus	236	
Stella Maris	210	
Still Life	93	
Stingray	165	
Storm Watch	154	
Stormy Petrel	18	
Strange Brew	209	
Stratosphere	149	
Strawberry	135, 166	
Strawberry Fayre	86	
Strawberry Surprise	257	
Strawberry Teas	285	
Streamers	120	
Submariner	156	
Submersion	285	
Sugar Fruits	209	
Sumatra	257	
Summer	14, 192, 309	
Summer Blue	93	
Summer Bouquet	72	
Summer Breeze	115	
Summer Breeze Perfume Bottle	116	
Summer Celebration		
Weight One	151	
Weight Two	152	
Summer Day	285	
Summer Fair	236	
Summer Flight	269	
Summer Flowers	145	
Summer Garden	98	
Summer Glade	163	

Summer Haze	309	
Summer Lilies	216	
Summer Meadow Butterfly	65	
Summer Meadow Dragonfly	65	
Summer Pool	64	
Summer Posy	164, 191	
Summer Trilogy	146	
Summit	104	
Sun	4	
Sun Dance	16	
Sun Seekers	125	
Sunburst	150	
Sunflare	21	
Sunflower	5, 165	
Sunflower Celebration	257	
Sunflowers	236	
Sunny Days Perfume Bottle	236	
Sunset	33	
Sunset Duet	206	
Sunset Flight	181	
Sunset Orchid	138	
Sunset Pool	269	
Super Nova	125	
Superhero	298	
Supersonic	168	
Surveillance	133	
Suspense	298	
Swan	23, 29, 205	
Swan Flight	153	
Swan Lake	94	
Swan Vista	236	
Swans By The Riverbank	298	
Sweet Columbine	320	
Sweet Dreams	212	
Sweet Magic	309	
Sweet Pea	118	
Sweet Sensation Cobalt	208	
Sweet Sensation Kingfisher	208	
Sweet Surrender	258	
Sweet Violet	181	
Sweetheart	83	
Sweetpea Lilac	298	
Swish	216	
Sword Dance	125	
Sword In The Stone	269	
Symphony	52	
Symphony In Blue	236	

T

Tablets	368	
Tablets From The Mount	368	
Tadpoles	151	
Tailspin	125	

Tango	82	Touch of Frost	258	Turkish Delight	259
Tantalise	310	Touchdown	37	Turquoise Delight	237
Tapestry	125	Tournament	258	Turtle	175
Tarantella	200	Towards the Millennium	258	Tutankhamun	329, 355
Tartan Twirl	194	Traditional Pool	237	Tweed	320
Tartan Twist	147	Traditional Tribute	208	Twilight	33
Taurus	183	Trailblazer	115	Twilight Flight	355
Tawny Owl	105	Trampoline	126	Twilight Mystery	238
Teardrop Petunia	343	Tranquil Flight	325	Twilight Pool	270
Tears of Joy	237	Tranquil Oasis	310	Twilight Rose	259
Techno-Trip	237	Tranquil Pond	237	Twilight Zone	189
Teddy	269	Tranquil Pool	195	Twin Hearts	338
Teddy Bear	190	Tranquillity	60	Twirl	147
Telstar	64	Transatlantic	155	Twister	200
Tempest	87	Transmission	298	Two of a Kind	259
Temptation	202	Transylvania	310	Two Salmon	57
Tempus Fugit	215	Trapeze	120	Two's Company	178
Tennis		Treasure Trove	206	Tyrannosaurus	238
Female	79	Treble Chance	171	Tyrolean Summer	170
Male	79	Tree Lizard	137		
Terra Nova	46	Triad	26	**U**	
Terrarium	197	Tribal Dance	258		
Texas Treasure	285	tricolour	149	Ultra Cool	298
Thank You Snowman	336	Trillium	207	Ultra Hot	299
Thatching	310	Trilogy	76	Ultramarine	238
Theatre	335	Trinculo	203	Undying Love	310
Thistle	77, 135	Trinity	105	Unicorn Dance	343
Thistle and Rose	36	Trio		Unicorn, Dawn	337
Thistle Inkwell	167	Weight – One	15	Unicorn, Dusk	337
Thistledown	144	Weight – Two	15	Unicorn, Twilight	337
Thoughtfulness	285	Weight – Three	15	Unison	105
Three Gentians	199	Triple Crown	258	United We Stand	369
Three Tenors	179	Triple Fancy	106	Unity	259
Three Witches	56	Tristar	37	Up, Up and Away	320
Tidal Wave	95	Triton	64	Uranus	3
Tiger	40	Triumph	126	Utopia	126
Tiger Fish	106	Tropical Bouquet	197		
Tijuana	237	Tropical Delight '99	258	**V**	
Time Machine	258	Tropical Fantasy	171		
Time traveller	138	Tropical Fish	65, 369	Vagabond	80
Time Tunnel	237	Tropical Lagoon	372	Valentine Perfume Bottle	73
Time Warp	97	Tropical Parakeet	181	Valentino	238
Time Zone	32	Tropical Pool	133	Valhalla	85
Titania	193	Tropical Rain	269	Van Gogh Starry Night	299
Titanic	285	Tropical Vision	172	Van Gogh Sunflower	299
To Boldly Go...	237	Tropical Wonder	320	Veg	207
To Infinity and Beyond	286	Tropicana	6, 189	Veil Tail	25
Token of Love	206	Trout	57	Velocity	259
Tomorrow	361	Trout and Mayfly	57	Venus	2. 170
Topsy-Turvy	109	True Colours	269	Vermilion	46
Torah	369	True Hearts	371	Verona Flask	144
Torino Flask	169	True Romance	259	Vertigo	32
Total Eclipse	355	Trumpet Call	320	Vesuvius	97
Prestige	355	Tuna Fish	146	Vibrance	107

Victoria 369
Victorian Blossom 259
Victorian Bouquet 93
Victorian Memories 208
Victoriana 238
Victory 355
Victory In Europe 185
Victory In Japan 355
Vigil 80
Viking Flame 38
Village Pond 299
Vincent's Chair 286
Violet 259
Violetta 238
Virgo 184
Viridian 238
Virtue 64
Virtuoso 126
Vision 115
Visitation 204
Vivaldi 187
Vivat Regina 75
Vogue 168
Volcano 105
Vortex 12
Vortice 238

W

Walkabout 205
Walking in the Air 336
Walking on Water 299
Walls of Jericho 239
Wanderer 70
Wanderlust 126
Watchtower 169
Water 8, 102
Water Babies 299
Water Garden 239
Water Lilies 64
Watercolours 270
Waterhen 159
Waterlilies and Dragonfly 150
Waterlily 151
Waterlily Impressions 325
Waterlily Reflection 270

Wave Control 299
Wavecrest 167
Wavedancers 239
Weathervane 135
Web Spinners 321
Wedding Bell 42
Wedding Day 286
Well Wisher 321
Welsh Dragon 335
Westminster Abbey 355
Wheel of Fortune 270
Wheelspin 89
Whirlpool 216
Whirlwind 52, 359
Whirlygig 40
Whirlygig Amethyst 46
Whispers 61
White and Pink Spray 59
White Aster 260
White Butterfly – Yellow Flower 197
White Fugue 55, 338
White Heat 299
White Heather 83
White Horses 129
White Narcissus 201
White Rhino 40
White Rose 47, 260
White Tornado 270
Whizz 198
Wild Horses 321
Wild Orchids 192
Wild Pansy and Storksbill 146
Wild Rose Bouquet 128
Wildcard 186
Will o' the Wisp 85
Willow 310
Windchimes 126
Windfall 107
Windflower Ruby 67
Windsor Castle Golden Jubilee
  Celebration 356
Winter 14, 192, 310
Winter Bouquet 72
Winter Celebration – Snowdrops 137
Winter Celebration –Aconites 137

Winter Celebration
  Weight One 137
  Weight Two 137
Winter Flower 53
Winter Flowers 158
Winter Moon 33
Winter Palace 214
Winter Scene 286
Winter Wonderland 286
Wisdom 260
Wise Old Owls 321
Wise Owl 270
Wishing Well 179
Wisps Blue 260
With Love 270, 300
Wood Anemones 157
Wood Nymph 91
Wood Violet 215
Woodland Flowers 151
Woodland Glade 159
World Peace 356

Y

Yachting Dome 17
Year of the Child 370
Year of the Viking 356
Yellow Butterfly 165
Yellow Butterfly – Latticino Base 165
Yellow Butterfly – Miniature 182
Yellow Carnation 260
Yellow Orchid 356
Yellow Rose 160, 174
Yuletide 73
Yuri gagarin 356

Z

Zanzibar 260
Zebra Fish 159
Zenith Perfume Bottle 38
Zephyr 19
Zest 71
Zinnia 83
Zodiac 53
Zoom 115